MOSDOS PRESS
Literature

JADE

Mosdos Press
CLEVELAND, OHIO

MOSDOS PRESS Literature

EDITOR-IN-CHIEF
Judith Factor

EXECUTIVE EDITOR
Libby Spero

CREATIVE/ART DIRECTOR
Carla Martin

ART/GRAPHICS
Aviva Gross
Shoshana Howitt
Eva Martin

PROJECT MANAGER/COPY EDITOR
Laya Dewick

SENIOR EDITOR
Abigail Rozen

SENIOR WRITER
Esther Schwarz

ASSOCIATE EDITORS/WRITERS
Jill Brotman
Aidel Fishman
Etta Green
Selma Hellman
Susan Polster

TEXT AND CURRICULUM ADVISOR
Rabbi Ahron Dovid Goldberg

ISBN 0-9671009-0-9

ISBN 978-0-9671009-0-6 Student Edition

acknowledgments

We would like to gratefully acknowledge the following sources for their permission to reprint their copyrighted material:

Arcade Publishing "A Balmy Spring Wind" by Richard Wright. Copyright © 1959 by Richard Wright, published by Arcade Publishing, Inc., New York, N. Y.

The Barbara Hogenson Agency "The Night the Bed Fell" by James Thurber, from My Life and Hard Times. Copyright © 1933, 1961 James Thurber. Reprinted by arrangement with Rosemary A. Thurber and The Barbara Hogenson Agency.

Elizabeth Barnett "The Courage That My Mother Had" by Edna St. Vincent Millay. From Collected Poems, HarperCollins. Copyright © 1928, 1954, 1955, 1982 by Edna St. Vincent Millay and Norma Millay Ellis. All rights reserved. Reprinted by permission of Elizabeth Barnett, literary executor.

Bill Berger Associates, Inc. "The Dinner Party" by Mona Gardner. Copyright © 1942, 1970 by SATURDAY REVIEW, reprinted by permission of Bill Berger Associates, Inc.

Gwendolyn Brooks "Home" by Gwendolyn Brooks. Copyright © 1991 from "Maud Martha" (a novel) Third World Press, Chicago 1991.

John Ciardi "The River Is a Piece of Sky" by John Ciardi. Copyright © 1994 by the family of John Ciardi.

Don Congdon Associates, Inc. "The Third Level" by Jack Finney. Reprinted by permission of Don Congdon Associates, Inc. Copyright © 1950 by Crowell Collier; renewed 1977 by Jack Finney. "The Sound of Summer Running" by Ray Bradbury. Reprinted by permission of Don Congdon Associates, Inc. Copyright © 1956 by the Curtis Publishing Co., renewed 1984 by Ray Bradbury. Slightly edited.

Dell Publishing, a division of Random House "Look Back at the Sea" by Betsy Byars. From The Animal, The Vegetable and John D. Jones by Betsy Byars. Copyright © 1982 by Betsy Byars. Illustrations copyright © 1982 by Dell Publishing, a division of Random House. Used by permission of Random House Children's Books, a division of Random House, Inc.

Doubleday, a Division of Random House "Bamboo Grove" by Basho and "The New and The Old" by Shiki. From An Introduction To Haiku by Harold G. Henderson. Copyright © 1958 by Harold G. Henderson. "The Sloth" by Theodore Roethke. Copyright © 1950 from The Collected Poems of Theodore Roethke by Theodore Roethke. "Florence Nightingale" from Living Biographies of Famous Women by Henry Thomas and Dana Lee Thomas. Copyright © 1942, 1959 by Doubleday, a division of Bantam Doubleday Dell Publishing Group, Inc. Used by permission of Doubleday, a division of Random House, Inc. Slightly edited.

Harcourt Brace & Company "The Hummingbird That Lived Through Winter" by William Saroyan, from My Kind of Crazy, Wonderful People: Seventeen Stories and a Play. Copyright © 1944 and renewed 1972 by William Saroyan, reprinted by permission of Harcourt Brace & Company.

HarperCollins Publishers "Sarah Cynthia Sylvia Stout Would Not Take the Garbage Out" by Shel Silverstein. Copyright © 1974 by Evil Eye Music, Inc. "A Boy and a Man" by James Ramsey Ullman. Copyright © 1954 by James Ramsey Ullman. Used by permission of HarperCollins Publishers.

Harvard University Press "I'm Nobody! Who Are You?" by Emily Dickinson. Reprinted by permission of the publishers and the Trustees of Amherst College from The Poems of Emily Dickinson, Thomas H. Johnson, editor, Cambridge, Mass.: The Belknap Press of Harvard University Press. Copyright © 1951, 1955, 1979, 1983 by the President and Fellows of Harvard College.

Edward D. Hoch "Zoo" by Edward D. Hoch. Copyright © 1958 by King Size Publications; renewed 1986 by Edward D. Hoch. Reprinted by permission of the author.

Holiday House, Inc. "The Runner" by Jane and Paul Annixter. Copyright © 1956 by Jane and Paul Annixter. Reprinted by permission of Holiday House, Inc.

Henry Holt & Company, Inc. "The Road Not Taken" and "The Pasture" from The Poetry of Robert Frost, edited by Edward Connery Lathem. Copyright © 1944, 1958 by Robert Frost. Copyright © 1967 by Lesley Frost Ballantine. Copyright © 1916, 1930, 1939, © 1969 by Henry Holt & Company. Reprinted by permission of Henry Holt & Company, Inc.

Holt Rinehart and Winston "The Circuit" by Francisco Jiménez, from Adventures for Readers, Athena Edition. Copyright © 1996 by Holt Rinehart and Winston, reprinted by permission of the publisher.

International Creative Management, Inc. "Grandpa and the Statue" by Arthur Miller. Reprinted by permission of International Creative Management, Inc. Copyright © 1945 by Arthur Miller, copyright renewed.

Johnson Publishing Company, Inc. "My Journey Is Still Long" by Charles L. Sanders, Johnson Publishing Company, Inc. Full credit to Ebony Magazine. Slightly edited.

Alfred A. Knopf, Inc. "Pendulum" by John Updike, from The Carpentered Hen and Other Tame Creatures by John Updike. Copyright © 1982 by John Updike, reprinted by permission of Alfred A Knopf, Inc.

Liveright Publishing Corporation "in Just—" by E .E. Cummings. Copyright 1923, 1951 © 1991 by the Trustees for the E. E. Cummings Trust. Copyright © 1976 by George James Firmage, from COMPLETE POEMS: 1904-1962 by E. E. Cummings, edited by George J. Firmage. Reprinted by permission of Liveright Publishing Corporation.

William Morris Agency, Inc. "Roberto Clemente: A Bittersweet Memoir" by Jerry Izenberg. Copyright © 1976. Reprinted by permission of William Morris Agency, Inc. on behalf of the author. Slightly edited.

Miriam Morton "The Sparrow" by Ivan Turgenev, which first appeared in A Harvest of Russian Children's Literature, edited and with an Introduction by Miriam Morton, University of California Press, 1968.

Notre Dame Press From "Barrio Boy" by Ernesto Galarza. Copyright © 1971 by University of Notre Dame Press. Used by permission of the publisher. Slightly edited.

Harold Ober Associates, Inc. "Cat on the Go" by James Herriot. Copyright © as given by St. Martin's Press. "Cats" by Eleanor Farjeon. Copyright © 1957 by Eleanor Farjeon. "Stolen Day" by Sherwood Anderson. Copyright © 1941 by United Newspapers Magazine Corporation. Copyright renewed 1969 by Eleanor Copenhaver Anderson. Reprinted by permission of Harold Ober Associates, Inc.

Penguin Putnam Inc. "The Flower-Fed Buffaloes," from Going to the Stars by Vachel Lindsay. Copyright © 1926 by D. Appleton & Co., renewed 1954 by Elizabeth C. Lindsay. A Hawthorne Book. Used by permission of Dutton Children's Books, a division of Penguin Putnam Inc.

Malcolm Reiss "Kid at the Stick" by Mike Miller first appeared in the August 1957 issue of Redbook Magazine. Reprinted by permission of Malcolm Reiss.

Estate of Quentin Reynolds "A Secret For Two" by Quentin Reynolds. Copyright © 1936, Crowell-Collier Publishing Co. Reprinted by permission of the Estate of Quentin Reynolds. Slightly edited.

The Jesse Stuart Foundation "The Clearing" by Jesse Stuart originally published in Ladies Home Journal, August 1954. Reprinted by permission of the Jesse Stuart Foundation.

Scribner, a Division of Simon & Schuster "A Day's Wait" from Winner Take Nothing by Ernest Hemingway. Copyright © 1933 Charles Scribner's Sons. Copyright renewed © 1961 by Mary Hemingway. "Rattlesnake Hunt" from Cross Creek by Marjorie Kinnan Rawlings. Copyright © 1942 by Marjorie Kinnan Rawlings; copyright renewed © 1970 by Norton Baskin. "Abrahan Lincoln Walks at Midnight" from The Collected Poems of Vachel Lindsay. Copyright © 1925 by Macmillan Publishing Company. Reprinted with permission of Scribner, a Division of Simon & Schuster.

Simon & Schuster "Something Told the Wild Geese" by Rachel Field. Reprinted with the permission of Simon & Schuster. Copyright © 1934 by McMillan Publishing.

The Society of Authors "The Listeners" by Walter de la Mare. The Literary Trustees of Walter de la Mare and The Society of Authors. "Roadways" by John Masefield. The Society of Authors as the Literary Representative of the Estate of John Masefield.

TRO "This Land Is Your Land" words and music by Woody Guthrie TRO © Copyright 1956, 1958, 1970 Ludlow Music, Inc., New York, New York.

University of Massachusetts "Seagulls" reprinted from Robert Francis; Robert Francis Collected Poems, 1936-1976. (Amherst: University of Massachusetts, 1976) Copyright © 1944, 1976.

To ease readability, some selections in the public domain have been slightly abridged.

Note: We have expended much effort to contact all copyright holders to receive permission to reprint their works. We will correct any omissions brought to our attention in future editions.

index of authors & titles

MOSDOS PRESS
Literature

ANTHOLOGY SERIES

OPAL

RUBY

CORAL

PEARL

JADE

GOLD

Short Stories

Poetry

Nonfiction

Drama

The Novel

short stories

Fiction is imaginative literature—a story created and developed in the imagination of its author. It transports the readers beyond the limits of their own experience.

Short story writers must develop their plots quickly, capturing the reader's attention as soon as the story begins. Through the elements of plot, characterization, setting, and theme, the author can introduce the reader to new events, interesting people, and faraway places. The fiction you are about to read explores these basic literary elements through fantasy, humor, suspense, science fiction, and drama.

Short stories revolve around a central conflict. The conflict can be internal or external, between man and himself, man and man, man and society, or between man

and nature. As the plot unfolds, tension builds by adding suspense until the climax when the conflict is finally resolved.

Camel ride!

The short story unit of your anthology is divided into five parts. The first four groups explore each of the major literary elements of fiction. The last group combines all the components and helps the reader to understand how they all work together to create an overall effect.

Most readers enjoy short stories because they are a quick, entertaining way to visit new and interesting places (*"My Journey Is Still Long"*), meet different types of people (*The Strangers That Came to Town*), attend exciting events (*Barnum's First Circus*), and consider different points of view (*The Clearing*). Short stories are the brief afternoon trips that take us to a different place and then bring us speedily home again.

Cologne neighborhood

mini table of contents

Recognizing Plot

Defining Character

Exploring Setting

Understanding Theme

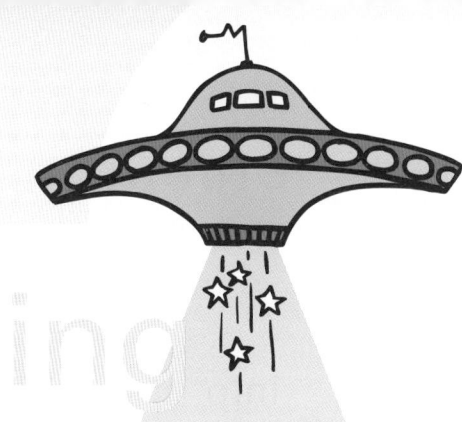

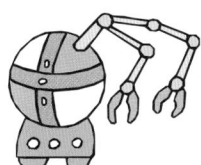

Pulling It All Together

Into • *Rikki-Tikki-Tavi*

"This is the story of the great war..." The reader expects to hear of a battle fought on foreign land between two powerful armies. The story continues, "fought single-handed, through the bathrooms of the big bungalow...," and the reader smiles. Rikki-tikki-tavi is not a threatening Roman warrior—he is a mongoose! This story is told in the traditional English style of talking animals and their "humans." But, man or mongoose, war is war, and defending one's home and family from an enemy requires courage and skill. Why does Rudyard Kipling use animals as characters with a blend of human and animal characteristics? Can you tell which are which? For example, does Nag wish to kill Rikki-tikki because the natural instinct of a cobra is to kill a mongoose, or is Nag "evil"? Perhaps there is no difference—or is there?

Focus

The plot of *Rikki-Tikki-Tavi* is simple. Characters are introduced, a conflict arises, a climax is reached, and a resolution follows. The struggle between good and evil is clear and well-defined. The conflict is easy to follow because it is an external conflict, a conflict between two characters, Nagaina and Rikki-tikki-tavi. The story is like a fable in some ways, not only because the characters are mostly animals, but also because the symbolism of the story is so much a part of the story itself. It is hard to know where the story leaves off and the symbolism begins. Nagaina, for example, is a cobra. She is also the symbol of evil in the story. But why is she evil? Are all snakes evil in Kipling's eyes, or has Kipling given Nagaina the traits of an evil human being?

About the Author

British author, **RUDYARD KIPLING**, was born in 1865 in Bombay, India. At the time, Bombay was a British colony. Kipling's parents sent him to England when he was only five years old. He was educated there and did not return to India until 1892. His experiences in India are reflected in many of his works. Kipling received the Nobel Prize for Literature in 1907. *Rikki-Tikki-Tavi* is an excerpt from *The Jungle Book*, which draws on Kipling's early memories of India. Kipling died in 1936.

Rikki Tikki Tavi

Rudyard Kipling

This is the story of the great war that Rikki-tikki-tavi fought single-handed, through the bathrooms of the big bungalow in Segowlee cantonment.[1] Darzee, the tailorbird, helped him, and Chuchundra,[2] the muskrat, who never comes out into the middle of the floor, but always creeps round by the wall, gave him advice; but Rikki-tikki did the real fighting.

He was a mongoose, rather like a little cat in his fur and his tail, but quite like a weasel in his head and his habits. His eyes and the end of his restless nose were pink; he could scratch himself anywhere he pleased, with any leg, front or back, that he chose to use; he could fluff up his tail till it looked like a bottle brush, and his war cry, as he scuttled through the long grass, was "*Rikk-tikk-tikki-tikki-tchk!*"

One day, a high summer flood washed him out of the burrow where he lived with his father and mother, and carried him, kicking and clucking, down a roadside ditch. He found a little wisp of grass floating there, and clung to it till he lost his senses. When he revived, he was lying in the hot sun on the middle of a garden path, very draggled indeed, and a small boy was saying: "Here's a dead mongoose. Let's have a funeral."

"No," said his mother; "let's take him in and dry him. Perhaps he isn't really dead."

They took him into the house, and a big man picked him up between his finger and thumb and said he was not dead but half choked; so they wrapped him in cotton wool and warmed him, and he opened his eyes and sneezed.

"Now," said the big man (he was an Englishman who had just moved into the bungalow), "don't frighten him, and we'll see what he'll do."

It is the hardest thing in the world to frighten a mongoose, because he is eaten up from nose to tail with curiosity. The motto of all the mongoose family is "Run and find out"; and Rikki-tikki was a true mongoose. He looked at the cotton wool, decided that it was not good to eat, ran all round the table, sat up and put his fur in order, scratched himself,

---

1. *Segowlee* (see GOW lee) *cantonment* was a large British military camp in Segowlee, India.
2. *Chuchundra* (choo CHUN druh)

and jumped on the small boy's shoulder.

"Don't be frightened, Teddy," said his father. "That's his way of making friends."

"Ouch! He's tickling under my chin," said Teddy.

Rikki-tikki looked down between the boy's collar and neck, snuffed at his ear, and climbed down to the floor, where he sat rubbing his nose.

"Good gracious," said Teddy's mother, "and that's a wild creature! I suppose he's so tame because we've been kind to him."

"All mongooses are like that," said her husband. "If Teddy doesn't pick him up by the tail, or try to put him in a cage, he'll run in and out of the house all day long. Let's give him something to eat."

They gave him a little piece of raw meat. Rikki-tikki liked it immensely, and when it was finished he went out into the veranda and sat in the sunshine and fluffed up his fur to make it dry to the roots. Then he felt better.

"There are more things to find out about in this house," he said to himself, "than all my family could find out in all their lives. I shall certainly stay and find out."

He spent all that day roaming over the house. He nearly drowned himself in the bathtubs, put his nose into the ink on a writing table, and burned it on the end of the big man's cigar, for he climbed up in the big man's lap to see how writing was done. At nightfall he ran into Teddy's nursery to watch how kerosene lamps were lighted, and when Teddy went to bed Rikki-tikki climbed up too; but he was a restless companion, because he had to get up and attend to every noise all through the night and find out what made it. Teddy's mother and father came in, the last thing, to look at their boy, and Rikki-tikki was awake on the pillow. "I don't like that," said Teddy's mother; "he may bite the child."

"He'll do no such thing," said the father. "Teddy's safer with that little beast than if he had a bloodhound to watch him. If a snake came into the nursery now—"

But Teddy's mother wouldn't think of anything so awful.

Early in the morning Rikki-tikki came to early breakfast in the veranda, riding on Teddy's shoulder, and they gave him banana and some boiled egg; and he sat on all their laps one after the other, because every well-brought-up mongoose always hopes to be a house mongoose someday and have rooms to run about in, and Rikki-tikki's mother (she used to live in the general's house at Segowlee) had carefully told Rikki what to do if ever he came across Englishmen.

Then Rikki-tikki went out into the garden to see what was to be seen. It was a large garden, only half cultivated, with bushes as big as summer houses of roses, lime and orange trees, clumps of bamboos, and thickets of high grass. Rikki-tikki licked his lips. "This is a splendid hunting ground," he said, and his tail grew bottle-brushy at the thought of it, and he scuttled up and down the garden, snuffling here and there till he heard very sorrowful voices in a thornbush.

It was Darzee, the tailorbird, and his wife. They had made a beautiful nest by pulling two big leaves together and stitching them up the edges with fibers, and had filled the hollow with cotton and downy fluff. The nest swayed to and fro, as they sat on the brim and cried.

"What is the matter?" asked Rikki-tikki.

"We are very miserable," said Darzee. "One of our babies fell out of the nest yesterday, and Nag ate him."

"H'm!" said Rikki-tikki; "that is very sad—but I am a stranger here. Who is Nag?"

Darzee and his wife only cowered down in the nest without answering, for from the thick grass at the foot of the bush came a low hiss—a horrid cold sound that made Rikki-tikki jump back two clear feet. Then inch by inch out of the grass rose up the head and spread hood of Nag, the big black cobra, and he was five feet long from tongue to tail. When he had lifted one third of himself clear of the ground, he stayed balancing to and fro exactly as a dandelion tuft balances in the wind, and he looked at Rikki-tikki with the wicked snake's eyes that never change their expression, whatever the snake may be thinking of.

"Who is Nag?" he said. "*I* am Nag. Look, and be afraid!"

He spread out his hood more than ever, and Rikki-tikki saw the spectacle mark on the back of it that looks exactly like the eye part of a hook-and-eye fastening. He was afraid for the minute; but it is impossible for a mongoose to stay frightened for any length of time, and though Rikki-tikki had never met a live cobra before, his mother had fed him on dead ones, and he knew that all a grown mongoose's business in life was to fight and eat snakes. Nag knew that too, and at the bottom of his cold heart he was afraid.

"Well," said Rikki-tikki, and his tail began to fluff up again, "marks or no marks, do you think it is right for you to eat fledglings out of a nest?"

Nag was thinking to himself, and watching the least little movement in the grass behind Rikki-tikki. He knew that mongooses in the garden meant death sooner or later for him and his

family, but he wanted to get Rikki-tikki off his guard. So he dropped his head a little and put it on one side.

"Let us talk," he said. "You eat eggs. Why should not I eat birds?"

"Behind you! Look behind you!" sang Darzee.

Rikki-tikki knew better than to waste time in staring. He jumped up in the air as high as he could go, and just under him whizzed by the head of Nagaina,[3] Nag's wicked wife. She had crept up behind him as he was talking, to make an end of him; and he heard her savage hiss as the stroke missed. He came down almost across her back, and if he had been an old mongoose, he would have known that then was the time to break her back with one bite; but he was afraid of the terrible lashing return stroke of the cobra. He bit, indeed, but did not bite long enough, and he jumped clear of the whisking tail, leaving Nagaina torn and angry.

"Wicked, wicked Darzee!" said Nag, lashing up as high as he could reach toward the nest in the thornbush; but Darzee had built it out of the reach of snakes, and it only swayed to and fro.

Rikki-tikki felt his eyes growing red and hot (when a mongoose's eyes grow red, he is angry), and he sat back on his tail and hind legs like a little kangaroo, and looked all around him, and chattered with rage. But Nag and Nagaina had disappeared into the grass. When a snake misses its stroke, it never says anything or gives any sign of what it means to do next. Rikki-tikki did not care to follow them, for he did not feel sure that he could manage two snakes at once. So he trotted off to the gravel path near the house, and sat down to think. It was a serious matter for him.

If you read the old books of natural history, you will find they say that when the mongoose fights the snake and happens to get bitten, he runs off and eats some herb that cures him. That is not true. The victory is only a matter of quickness of eye and quickness of foot—snake's blow against mongoose's jump—and as no eye can follow the motion of a snake's head when it strikes, that makes things much more wonderful than any magic herb. Rikki-tikki knew he was a young mongoose, and it made him all the more pleased to think that he had managed to escape a blow from behind. It gave him confidence in himself, and when Teddy came running down the path, Rikki-tikki was ready to be petted.

But just as Teddy was stooping, something flinched a little in the dust, and a tiny voice said: "Be careful. I am death!" It was Karait, the dusty brown snakeling that lies for choice on the dusty earth; and his bite is as dangerous as the cobra's. But he is so small that nobody thinks of him, and so he does the more harm to people.

Rikki-tikki's eyes grew red again, and he danced up to Karait with the peculiar rocking, swaying motion that he had inherited from his family. It looks very funny, but it is so perfectly balanced a gait that you can fly off from it at any angle you please; and in dealing with snakes this is an advantage. If Rikki-tikki had only known, he was doing a much more dangerous thing than fighting Nag, for Karait is so small, and can turn so quickly, that unless Rikki bit him close to the back of the head, he would get the return stroke in his eye or lip. But Rikki did not know: his eyes were all red, and he rocked back and forth, looking for a good place to hold. Karait struck out.

---

3. *Nagaina* (nih GY nuh)

Word Bank	**flinched** (FLINCHT) *v.*: drew back or away, as if from something dangerous; winced
	gait (GAIT) *n.*: a manner of walking, stepping, or running

Rikki jumped sideways and tried to run in, but the wicked little dusty gray head lashed within a fraction of his shoulder, and he had to jump over the body, and the head followed his heels close.

Teddy shouted to the house: "Oh, look here! Our mongoose is killing a snake"; and Rikki-tikki heard a scream from Teddy's mother. His father ran out with a stick, but by the time he came up, Karait had lunged out once too far, and Rikki-tikki had sprung, jumped on the snake's back, dropped his head far between his forelegs, bitten as high up the back as he could get hold, and rolled away. That bite paralyzed Karait, and Rikki-tikki was just going to eat him up from the tail, after the custom of his family at dinner, when he remembered that a full meal makes a slow mongoose, and if he wanted all his strength and quickness ready, he must keep himself thin.

He went away for a dust bath under the castor-oil bushes, while Teddy's father beat the dead Karait. "What is the use of that?" thought Rikki-tikki. "I have settled it all"; and then Teddy's mother picked him up from the dust and hugged him, crying that he had saved Teddy from death, and Teddy's father said that he was a providence, and Teddy looked on with big scared eyes. Rikki-tikki was rather amused at all the fuss, which, of course, he did not understand. Teddy's mother might just as well have petted Teddy for playing in the dust. Rikki was thoroughly enjoying himself.

That night, at dinner, walking to and fro among the wineglasses on the table, he could have stuffed himself three times over with nice things; but he remembered Nag and Nagaina, and though it was very pleasant to be patted and petted by Teddy's mother, and to sit on Teddy's shoulder, his eyes would get red from time to time, and he would go off into his long war cry of "*Rikk-tikk-*

tikki-tikki-tchk!"

Teddy carried him off to bed and insisted on Rikki-tikki sleeping under his chin. Rikki-tikki was too well bred to bite or scratch, but as soon as Teddy was asleep he went off for his nightly walk round the house, and in the dark he ran up against Chuchundra, the muskrat, creeping round by the wall. Chuchundra is a brokenhearted little beast. He whimpers and cheeps all the night, trying to make up his mind to run into the middle of the room, but he never gets there.

"Don't kill me," said Chuchundra, almost weeping. "Rikki-tikki, don't kill me."

"Do you think a snake-killer kills muskrats?" said Rikki-tikki scornfully.

"Those who kill snakes get killed by snakes," said Chuchundra, more sorrowfully than ever. "And how am I to be sure that Nag won't mistake me for you some dark night?"

"There's not the least danger," said Rikki-tikki; "but Nag is in the garden, and I know you don't go there."

"My cousin Chua, the rat, told me —" said Chuchundra, and then he stopped.

"Told you what?"

"H'sh! Nag is everywhere, Rikki-tikki. You should have talked to Chua in the garden."

"I didn't—so you must tell me. Quick, Chuchundra, or I'll bite you!"

Chuchundra sat down and cried till the tears rolled off his whiskers. "I am a very poor man," he sobbed. "I never had spirit enough to run out into the middle of the room. H'sh! I mustn't tell you anything. Can't you *hear*, Rikki-tikki?"

Rikki-tikki listened. The house was as still as still, but he thought he could just catch the faintest *scratch-scratch* in the world—a noise as faint as that of a wasp walking on a windowpane—the dry scratch of a snake's scales on brickwork.

"That's Nag or Nagaina," he said to

himself; "and he is crawling into the bathroom sluice.[4] You're right, Chuchundra; I should have talked to Chua."

He stole off to Teddy's bathroom, but there was nothing there, and then to Teddy's mother's bathroom. At the bottom of the smooth plaster wall there was a brick pulled out to make a sluice for the bath water, and as Rikki-tikki stole in by the masonry curb where the bath is put, he heard Nag and Nagaina whispering together outside in the moonlight.

"When the house is emptied of people," said Nagaina to her husband, "*he* will have to go away, and then the garden will be our own again. Go in quietly, and remember that the big man who killed Karait is the first one to bite. Then come out and tell me, and we will hunt for Rikki-tikki together."

"But are you sure that there is anything to be gained by killing the people?" said Nag.

"Everything. When there were no people in the bungalow, did we have any mongoose in the garden? So long as the bungalow is empty, we are king and queen of the garden; and remember that as soon as our eggs in the melon bed hatch (as they may tomorrow), our children will need room and quiet."

"I had not thought of that," said Nag. "I will go, but there is no need that we should hunt for Rikki-tikki afterward. I will kill the big man and his wife, and the child if I can, and come away quietly. Then the bungalow will be empty, and Rikki-tikki will go."

Rikki-tikki tingled all over with rage and hatred at this, and then Nag's head came through the sluice, and his five feet of cold body followed it. Angry as he was, Rikki-tikki was very frightened as he saw the size of the big cobra. Nag coiled himself up, raised his head, and looked into the bathroom in the dark, and Rikki could see his eyes glitter.

"Now, if I kill him there, Nagaina will know; and if I fight him on the open floor, the odds are in his favor. What am I to do?" said Rikki-tikki-tavi.

Nag waved to and fro, and then Rikki-tikki heard him drinking from the biggest water jar that was used to fill the bath. "That is good," said the snake. "Now, when Karait was killed, the big man had a stick. He may have that stick still, but when he comes in to bathe in the morning he will not have a stick. I shall wait here till he comes. Nagaina—do you hear me? I shall wait here in the cool till daytime."

There was no answer from outside, so Rikki-tikki knew Nagaina had gone away. Nag coiled himself down, coil by coil, round the bulge at the bottom of the water jar, and Rikki-tikki stayed still as death. After an hour he began to move, muscle by muscle, toward the jar. Nag was asleep, and Rikki-tikki looked at his big back, wondering which would be the best place for a good hold. "If I don't break his back at the first jump," said Rikki, "he can still fight; and if he fights—O Rikki!" He looked at the thickness of the neck below the hood, but that was too much for him; and a bite near the tail would only make Nag savage.

"It must be the head," he said at last; "the head above the hood; and when I am once there, I must not let go."

Then he jumped. The head was lying

---

4. A *sluice* (SLOOS) is a channel for draining water.

a little clear of the water jar, under the curve of it; and, as his teeth met, Rikki braced his back against the bulge of the red earthenware to hold down the head. This gave him just one second's purchase,[5] and he made the most of it. Then he was battered to and fro as a rat is shaken by a dog—to and fro on the floor, up and down, and round in great circles; but his eyes were red, and he held on as the body cartwhipped over the floor, upsetting the tin dipper and the soap dish and the fleshbrush, and banged against the tin side of the bath. As he held, he closed his jaws tighter and tighter, for he made sure[6] he would be banged to death, and, for the honor of his family, he preferred to be found with his teeth locked. He was dizzy, aching, and felt shaken to pieces when something went off like a thunderclap just behind him; a hot wind knocked him senseless, and red fire singed his fur. The big man had been wakened by the noise, and had fired both barrels of a shotgun into Nag just behind the hood.

Rikki-tikki held on with his eyes shut, for now he was quite sure he was dead; but the head did not move, and the big man picked him up and said: "It's the mongoose again, Alice; the little chap has saved *our* lives now." Then Teddy's mother came in with a very white face, and saw what was left of Nag, and Rikki-tikki dragged himself to Teddy's bedroom and spent half the rest of the night shaking himself tenderly to find out whether he really was broken into forty pieces, as he fancied.

When morning came he was very stiff, but well pleased with his doings. "Now I have Nagaina to settle with, and she will be worse than five Nags, and there's no knowing when the eggs she spoke of will hatch. Goodness! I must go and see Darzee," he said.

Without waiting for breakfast, Rikki-tikki ran to the thornbush where Darzee was singing a song of triumph at the top

of his voice. The news of Nag's death was all over the garden, for the sweeper had thrown the body on the rubbish heap.

"Oh, you stupid tuft of feathers!" said Rikki-tikki angrily. "Is this the time to sing?"

"Nag is dead—is dead—is dead!" sang Darzee. "The valiant Rikki-tikki caught him by the head and held fast. The big man brought the bang-stick, and Nag fell in two pieces! He will never eat my babies again."

"All that's true enough; but where's Nagaina?" said Rikki-tikki, looking carefully round him.

"Nagaina came to the bathroom sluice and called for Nag," Darzee went on; "and Nag came out on the end of a stick—the sweeper picked him up on the end of a stick and threw him upon the rubbish heap. Let us sing about the great, the red-eyed Rikki-tikki!" And Darzee filled his throat and sang.

"If I could get up to your nest, I'd roll all your babies out!" said Rikki-tikki. "You don't know when to do the right thing at the right time. You're safe enough in your nest there, but it's war

5. Here, *purchase* means advantage.
6. Here, *made sure* means he felt sure.

Word Bank	**valiant** (VAL yint) *adj.*: brave

for me down here. Stop singing a minute, Darzee."

"For the great, the beautiful Rikki-tikki's sake I will stop," said Darzee. "What is it, O Killer of the terrible Nag?"

"Where is Nagaina, for the third time?"

"On the rubbish heap by the stables, mourning for Nag. Great is Rikki-tikki with the white teeth."

"Bother[7] my white teeth! Have you ever heard where she keeps her eggs?"

"In the melon bed, on the end nearest the wall, where the sun strikes nearly all day. She hid them there weeks ago."

"And you never thought it worthwhile to tell me? The end nearest the wall, you said?"

"Rikki-tikki, you are not going to eat her eggs?"

"Not eat exactly; no. Darzee, if you have a grain of sense you will fly off to the stables and pretend that your wing is broken, and let Nagaina chase you away to this bush! I must get to the melon bed, and if I went there now she'd see me."

Darzee was a featherbrained little fellow who could never hold more than one idea at a time in his head; and just because he knew that Nagaina's children were born in eggs like his own, he didn't think at first that it was fair to kill them. But his wife was a sensible bird, and she knew that cobras' eggs meant young cobras later on; so she flew off from the nest, and left Darzee to keep the babies warm, and continue his song about the death of Nag. Darzee was very like a man in some ways.

She fluttered in front of Nagaina by the rubbish heap and cried out, "Oh, my wing is broken! The boy in the house threw a stone at me and broke it." Then she fluttered more desperately than ever.

Nagaina lifted up her head and hissed, "You warned Rikki-tikki when I would have killed him. Indeed and truly, you've chosen a bad place to be lame in." And she moved toward Darzee's wife, slipping along over the dust.

"The boy broke it with a stone!" shrieked Darzee's wife.

"Well! It may be some consolation to you when you're dead to know that I shall settle accounts with the boy. My husband lies on the rubbish heap this morning, but before night the boy in the house will lie very still. What is the use of running away? I am sure to catch you. Little fool, look at me!"

Darzee's wife knew better than to do *that*, for a bird who looks at a snake's eyes gets so frightened that she cannot move. Darzee's wife fluttered on, piping sorrowfully, and never leaving the ground, and Nagaina quickened her pace.

Rikki-tikki heard them going up the path from the stables, and he raced for the end of the melon patch near the wall. There, in the warm litter about the melons, very cunningly hidden, he found twenty-five eggs, about the size of a bantam's eggs,[8] but with whitish skin instead of shell.

"I was not a day too soon," he said; for he could see the baby cobras curled up inside the skin, and he knew that the minute they were hatched they could each kill a man or a mongoose. He bit off the tops of the eggs as fast as he could, taking care to crush the young cobras, and turned over the litter from time to time to see whether he had missed any. At last there were only three eggs left, and Rikki-tikki began to chuckle to himself, when he heard Darzee's wife screaming:

---

7. *Bother*, here, means never mind.
8. *Bantam's eggs* are tiny eggs of a small chicken.

Word Bank	cunningly (KUN ing lee) *adv.*: cleverly or craftily
	mourning (MORN ing) *n.*: the state of grieving over a death

"Rikki-tikki, I led Nagaina toward the house, and she has gone into the veranda, and—oh, come quickly—she means killing!"

Rikki-tikki smashed two eggs, and tumbled backward down the melon bed with the third egg in his mouth, and scuttled to the veranda as hard as he could put foot to the ground. Teddy and his mother and father were there at early breakfast; but Rikki-tikki saw that they were not eating anything. They sat stone-still, and their faces were white. Nagaina was coiled up on the matting by Teddy's chair, within easy striking distance of Teddy's bare leg, and she was swaying to and fro singing a song of triumph.

"Son of the big man that killed Nag," she hissed, "stay still. I am not ready yet. Wait a little. Keep very still, all you three. If you move I strike, and if you do not move I strike. Oh, foolish people, who killed my Nag!"

Teddy's eyes were fixed on his father, and all his father could do was to whisper, "Sit still, Teddy. You mustn't move. Teddy, keep still."

Then Rikki-tikki came up and cried: "Turn round, Nagaina; turn and fight!"

"All in good time," said she, without moving her eyes. "I will settle my account with *you* presently. Look at your friends, Rikki-tikki. They are still and white; they are afraid. They dare not move, and if you come a step nearer

I strike."

"Look at your eggs," said Rikki-tikki, "in the melon bed near the wall. Go and look, Nagaina."

The big snake turned half round and saw the egg on the veranda. "Ah-h! Give it to me," she said.

Rikki-tikki put his paws one on each side of the egg, and his eyes were blood-red. "What price for a snake's egg? For a young cobra? For a young king cobra? For the last—the very last of the brood? The ants are eating all the others down by the melon bed."

Nagaina spun clear round, forgetting everything for the sake of the one egg; and Rikki-tikki saw Teddy's father shoot out a big hand, catch Teddy by the shoulder, and drag him across the little table with the teacups, safe and out of reach of Nagaina.

"Tricked! Tricked! Tricked! *Rikk-tck-tck*!" chuckled Rikki-tikki. "The boy is safe, and it was I—I—I that caught Nag by the hood last night in the bathroom." Then he began to jump up and down, all four feet together, his head close to the floor. "He threw me to and fro, but he could not shake me off. He was dead before the big man blew him in two. I did it. *Rikki-tikki-tck-tck*! Come then, Nagaina. Come and fight with me. You shall not be a widow long."

Nagaina saw that she had lost her chance of killing Teddy, and the egg lay between Rikki-tikki's paws. "Give me the egg, Rikki-tikki. Give me the last of my eggs, and I will go away and never come back," she said, lowering her hood.

"Yes, you will go away, and you will never come back; for you will go to the rubbish heap with Nag. Fight, widow! The big man has gone for his gun! Fight!"

Rikki-tikki was bounding all round Nagaina, keeping just out of reach of her stroke, his little eyes like hot coals. Nagaina gathered herself together and

flung out at him. Rikki-tikki jumped up and backward. Again and again and again she struck, and each time her head came with a whack on the matting of the veranda, and she gathered herself together like a watchspring. Then Rikki-tikki danced in a circle to get behind her, and Nagaina spun round to keep her head to his head, so that the rustle of her tail on the matting sounded like dry leaves blown along by the wind.

He had forgotten the egg. It still lay on the veranda, and Nagaina came nearer and nearer to it, till at last, while Rikki-tikki was drawing breath, she caught it in her mouth, turned to the veranda steps, and flew like an arrow down the path, with Rikki-tikki behind her. When the cobra runs for her life, she goes like a whiplash flicked across a horse's neck.

Rikki-tikki knew that he must catch her, or all the trouble would begin again. She headed straight for the long grass by the thornbush, and as he was running Rikki-tikki heard Darzee singing his foolish little song of triumph. But Darzee's wife was wiser. She flew off her nest as Nagaina came along, and flapped her wings about Nagaina's head. If Darzee had helped they might have turned her; but Nagaina only lowered her hood and went on. Still, the instant's delay brought Rikki-tikki up to her, and as she plunged into the rathole where she and Nag used to live, his little white teeth were clenched on her tail, and he went down with her—and very few mongooses, however wise and old they may be, care to follow a cobra into its hole. It was dark in the hole; and Rikki-tikki never knew when it might open out and give Nagaina room to turn and strike at him. He held on savagely and struck out his feet to act as brakes on the dark slope of the hot, moist earth.

Then the grass by the mouth of the hole stopped waving, and Darzee said:

"It is all over with Rikki-tikki! We must sing his death song. Valiant Rikki-tikki is dead. For Nagaina will surely kill him underground."

So he sang a very mournful song that he made up all on the spur of the minute, and just as he got to the most touching part the grass quivered again, and Rikki-tikki, covered with dirt, dragged himself out of the hole leg by leg, licking his whiskers. Darzee stopped with a little shout. Rikki-tikki shook some of the dust out of his fur and sneezed. "It is all over," he said. "The widow will never come out again." And the red ants that live between the grass stems heard him, and began to troop down one after another to see if he had spoken the truth.

Rikki-tikki curled himself up in the grass and slept where he was—slept and slept till it was late in the afternoon, for he had done a hard day's work.

"Now," he said, when he awoke, "I will go back to the house. Tell the coppersmith, Darzee, and he will tell the garden that Nagaina is dead."

The coppersmith is a bird who makes a noise exactly like the beating of a little hammer on a copper pot; and the reason he is always making it is because he is the town crier to every Indian garden, and tells all the news to everybody who cares to listen. As Rikki-tikki went up the path, he heard his "attention" notes like a tiny dinner gong; and then the steady "*Ding-dong-tock*! Nag is dead—*dong*! Nagaina is dead! *Ding-dong-tock*!" That set all the birds in the garden singing, and the frogs croaking, for Nag and Nagaina used to eat frogs as well as little birds.

When Rikki got to the house, Teddy and Teddy's mother (she still looked very white, for she had been fainting) and Teddy's father came out and almost cried over him; and that night he ate all that was given him till he could eat no more, and went to bed on Teddy's shoulder, where Teddy's mother saw him when she came to look late at night.

"He saved our lives and Teddy's life," she said to her husband. "Just think, he saved all our lives!"

Rikki-tikki woke up with a jump, for all mongooses are light sleepers.

"Oh, it's you," said he. "What are you bothering for? All the cobras are dead; and if they weren't, I'm here."

Rikki-tikki had a right to be proud of himself; but he did not grow too proud, and he kept that garden as a mongoose should keep it, with tooth and jump and spring and bite, till never a cobra dared show its head inside the walls.

Recalling

1. What circumstances brought Rikki-tikki to the bungalow? Who lives there?

2. Why did Nag and Nagaina want to kill Teddy's family?

3. How does Rikki-tikki protect the family?

4. What was the ultimate fate of the cobras?

Interpreting

5. What are some of the characteristics of a mongoose? Give examples of these traits, based on evidence from the story.

6. Explain how Kipling arouses sympathy for Nagaina.

7. Describe the other animals' reactions to Rikki-tikki's victory.

Concluding

8. Give specific examples of animals in the story that have humanlike personalities.

9. The theme of good versus evil is represented in the story. Explain how.

Examining Fiction

A **conflict** is a struggle between two opposing forces. An **external conflict** is a struggle with a force outside oneself. Examples of external conflicts are a person's disagreement with another person, a conflict with nature, or a clash with society. The story, *Rikki-Tikki-Tavi*, is a good example of a story with an external conflict.

1. Suppose the characters in *Rikki-Tikki-Tavi* were human. Which type of external conflict would be portrayed: man versus man, man versus society, or man versus nature?

2. At what point does this conflict reach its climax?

3. How is the conflict resolved?

Thinking About Fiction

In literature, many events are written in **chronological order**. This means that the events are described in the order in which they occur, going forward from the beginning of the story, to the middle of the story, and then to the end. Suppose the story had been written as a flashback. Would that have affected the suspense as the plot developed?

Creating and Writing

Visualize the cobra kingdom's reaction upon receiving word of Rikki-tikki's victory over Nag and Nagaina. Describe a meeting of the cobras. Imagine that they have assembled to discuss the consequences of Nag and Nagaina's defeat. How do you think the cobras reached their decision that "...never a cobra dared show its head inside the walls"? Try to write a dialogue among the cobras, in which they discuss this decision in detail. Proofread your dialogue for accuracy in spelling, punctuation, and grammar.

Into • *A Day's Wait*

Young. Inexperienced. Sick. Afraid. This is a mixture that is ready to explode into shaking sobs and uncontrollable tears. Or it can be contained, feeling like a lead weight until it almost sinks the patient. The narrator is diagnosed with the flu, but he is young, and he doesn't know...

Focus

A Day's Wait is about a boy experiencing an **internal conflict**. In an internal conflict, there is a war going on inside a person, and the person is in emotional pain. The narrator of *A Day's Wait* is being pulled in two directions, and his fear and illness leave him with little energy to resolve the conflict. The story is told from the father's point of view. The father is not aware of the battle raging inside the boy until near the end of the story. He—and we—see only some outer signs of a conflict. Can you spot those signs as you read the story? Perhaps you will be able to guess what is worrying the narrator. When you discover the boy's secret, ask yourself: could that have happened to me? In contrast to the internal conflict of the boy, the relationship between father and son is one of love and kindness; between the two of them, there is no conflict at all.

About the Author

American author **ERNEST HEMINGWAY** was born in 1899 in Oak Park, Illinois. Hemingway participated in both World Wars. He began his writing career after World War I, when he took a position with the *Toronto Star*. He went on to become one of America's most famous authors. He was awarded the Nobel Prize both for his novels and his short stories. Hemingway died in 1961. Two themes that run through his works are adventure and courage. Courage is exhibited by the main character in *A Day's Wait*.

A DAY'S WAIT

ERNEST HEMINGWAY

He came into the room to shut the windows while we were still in bed and I saw he looked ill. He was shivering, his face was white, and he walked slowly as though it ached to move.

"What's the matter, Schatz?"[1]

"I've got a headache."

"You better go back to bed."

"No. I'm all right."

"You go to bed. I'll see you when I'm dressed."

But when I came downstairs he was dressed, sitting by the fire, looking a very sick and miserable boy of nine years. When I put my hand on his forehead I knew he had a fever.

"You go up to bed," I said, "you're sick."

"I'm all right," he said.

When the doctor came he took the boy's temperature.

"What is it?" I asked him.

"One hundred and two."

Downstairs, the doctor left three different medicines in different colored capsules with instructions for giving them. One was to bring down the fever, another a purgative, the third to over-

come an acid condition. The germs of influenza can only exist in an acid condition, he explained. He seemed to know all about influenza and said there was nothing to worry about if the fever did not go above one hundred and four degrees. This was a light epidemic of flu and there was no danger if you avoided pneumonia.

Back in the room I wrote the boy's temperature down and made a note of the time to give the various capsules.

"Do you want me to read to you?"

"All right. If you want to," said the boy. His face was very white and there were dark areas under his eyes. He lay still in the bed and seemed very detached from what was going on.

I read aloud from Howard Pyle's *Book of Pirates*; but I could see he was not following what I was reading.

"How do you feel, Schatz?" I asked him.

"Just the same, so far," he said.

I sat at the foot of the bed and read

---

1. *Schatz* (SHOTS) is a German nickname of affection.

to myself while I waited for it to be time to give another capsule. It would have been natural for him to go to sleep, but when I looked up he was looking at the foot of the bed, looking very strangely.

"Why don't you try to go to sleep? I'll wake you up for the medicine."

"I'd rather stay awake."

After a while he said to me, "You don't have to stay in here with me, Papa, if it bothers you."

"It doesn't bother me."

"No, I mean you don't have to stay if it's going to bother you."

I thought perhaps he was a little light-headed and after giving him the prescribed capsules at eleven o'clock I went out for a while. It was a bright, cold day, the ground covered with a sleet that had frozen so that it seemed as if all the bare trees, the bushes, the cut brush and all the grass and the bare ground had been varnished with ice. I took the young Irish setter for a little walk up the road and along a frozen creek, but it was difficult to stand or walk on the glassy surface and the red dog slipped and slithered and I fell twice, hard, once dropping my gun and having it slide away over the ice.

We flushed a covey of quail under a high clay bank with overhanging brush and I killed two as they went out of sight over the top of the bank. Some of the covey lit in trees but most of them scattered into brush piles and it was necessary to jump on the ice-coated mounds of brush several times before they would flush. Coming out while you were poised unsteadily on the icy, springy brush they made difficult shooting, and I killed two, missed five, and started back pleased to have found a covey close to the house and happy there were so many left to find on another day.

At the house they said the boy had refused to let anyone come into the room.

"You can't come in," he said. "You mustn't get what I have."

I went up to him and found him in exactly the position I had left him, white-faced, but with the tops of his cheeks flushed by the fever, staring still, as he had stared at the foot of the bed.

Word Bank

varnished (VAR nisht) *v.*: coated with varnish; gave a glossy appearance to

slithered (SLITH erd) *v.*: moved or walked with a sliding motion, as a snake; slid unsteadily down a surface, from side to side

flushed (FLUSHT) *v.*: drove out of hiding

covey (CUV ee) *n.*: a small group of game birds, especially partridges or quail

poised (POYZD) *v.*: balanced

I took his temperature.

"What is it?"

"Something like a hundred," I said. It was one hundred and two and four tenths.

"It was a hundred and two," he said.

"Who said so?"

"The doctor."

"Your temperature is all right," I said. "It's nothing to worry about."

"I don't worry," he said, "but I can't keep from thinking."

"Don't think," I said. "Just take it easy."

"I'm taking it easy," he said and looked straight ahead. He was evidently holding tight on to himself about something.

"Take this with water."

"Do you think it will do any good?"

"Of course it will."

I sat down and opened the *Pirate* book and commenced to read, but I could see he was not following, so I stopped.

"About what time do you think I'm going to die?" he asked.

"What?"

"About how long will it be before I die?"

"You aren't going to die. What's the matter with you?"

"Oh, yes, I am. I heard him say a hundred and two."

"People don't die with a fever of one hundred and two. That's a silly way to talk."

"I know they do. At school in France the boys told me you can't live with forty-four degrees. I've got a hundred and two."

He had been waiting to die all day, ever since nine o'clock in the morning.

"You poor Schatz," I said. "Poor old Schatz. It's like miles and kilometers. You aren't going to die. That's a different thermometer. On that thermometer thirty-seven is normal. On this kind it's ninety-eight."

"Are you sure?"

"Absolutely," I said. "It's like miles and kilometers. You know, like how many kilometers we make when we do seventy miles in the car?"

"Oh," he said.

But his gaze at the foot of the bed relaxed slowly. The hold over himself relaxed too, finally, and the next day it was very slack and he cried very easily at little things that were of no importance.

Word Bank	**commenced** (cum MENST) *v.*: began

Recalling

1. What is the doctor's diagnosis of the boy's ailment?

2. What is the boy's reaction to his illness? What is his mistake?

3. Why doesn't the father reassure him immediately by telling him that everything is fine?

4. Why does the father stop reading aloud? What does the father tell the boy that puts the boy at ease?

Interpreting

5. Why is the title of the story so appropriate?

6. How does the boy show courage in facing his internal conflict? How does he show concern for his father?

7. How does the boy behave the next day? Why do you think he behaves this way?

Concluding

8. Imagine yourself in the boy's place. What would you have felt inside? How would you have behaved in this situation?

Examining Fiction

Unlike an external conflict, which is a struggle between two characters, an **internal conflict** is a struggle within one character. The character may be facing an important decision or struggling with a confusing, frightening idea. In *A Day's Wait*, the boy experiences such a struggle.

1. What fear is the boy struggling to master?

2. When does the struggle begin?

Thinking About Fiction

The conflict in *A Day's Wait* is not stated directly, because it takes place within the boy's mind. As you read the story, you can make inferences about what is going on inside the boy's mind, based on what he says and does. When you realize that certain actions and statements seem out of character, you begin to understand what the boy is afraid of. One indication of the boy's internal conflict is his reluctance to go to sleep.

1. Many of the boy's actions reveal his internal conflict. Find two such actions (besides his difficulty going to sleep) and describe them in your own words.

2. The boy also makes statements that seem unusual. Reread the story and find two statements that point to an internal conflict.

Creating and Writing

Did you ever say or do anything that led to a misunderstanding? Describe your recollection of the incident, using vivid details and conversation. Include information about the setting and the characters involved.

Into • *Kid at the Stick*

Match men against gravity, and you have flight. Match men against gravity, throw in some danger, and you have suspense. In *Kid at the Stick*, a new pilot is doing just fine until he falls ill. When he loses consciousness, his eleven-year-old son desperately contacts the control tower for help. Could an eleven-year-old land a plane? Herb Stillman, in the control tower, thinks he can help the boy. Swanson, Herb's boss, is sure he cannot, and taunts him about something in Herb's past. As turmoil rages within Herb, time begins to run out for the kid at the stick.

Focus

In *Rikki-Tikki-Tavi*, we learned about external conflict. We identified internal conflict in *A Day's Wait*. In *Kid at the Stick*, external and internal conflicts shape the plot, each influencing the other. How do the events of the story (external conflict) shape Herb's thoughts? How do Herb's thoughts (internal conflict) shape his actions in the story? Notice that the external conflict in the story intensifies and builds to a climax, while the internal conflict starts out with great intensity, but lessens as the story progresses.

In addition to conflict, the story has **suspense**. When a story is written skillfully, the reader feels an intense need to "find out what happens in the end." How does an author create this feeling in the reader? Part of the answer lies in the way the story unfolds. A suspense story is often constructed in the following way. A problem arises, causing anxiety in the reader. Just as the problem seems to overwhelm the hero, it is solved. The reader breathes a sigh of relief but, almost immediately, a new, bigger problem arises. When that one, too, is solved, and the sigh of relief over, yet another, even bigger problem arises, and so on until the story's climax. By that time, a great amount of suspense has built up in the reader's mind and, when the problem is finally solved completely, the reader feels tremendously relieved and satisfied to have "survived" so much!

About the Author

MIKE MILLER is an American author who wrote articles for popular magazines in the 1950s. The story you have just read was first published in 1957, at a time when aviation was beginning to transform aspects of American culture. By 1963 there were more than 100,000 registered aircraft in the United States. *Kid at the Stick*, with both the elements of suspense and adventure, makes for enjoyable and intriguing reading.

KID AT THE STICK

Mike Miller

The yellow Cub, so tiny against its Rocky Mountain background, banked into a slow rolling turn as it entered the flight pattern. Beneath it and to its left, fifteen-foot letters spelled out "Mt. View Airpark—Tredway, Colo.," across two hangar tops.

Flying the pattern at 800 feet above the airport, the plane continued downward for a minute or two, seeming to float in the sea of cloudless blue sky. Then it started another lazy bank to the left. Now on his base leg the pilot watched for a signal light from the tower. The signal came immediately—green, all-clear-to-land. Another turn left, this one steep. Its engine throttled back, the Cub glided to the runway.

Inside the tower a tall blond youth turned to his companion, "Cub's down, Herb. Hear any more from that Mayday?"

Herb Stillman at the control board shook his earphoned head. It had been several minutes now since he'd heard the weak, indistinct "Mayday" signal which meant a plane in distress. It had been all but drowned out by the loudspeaker's static.

Herb adjusted the receiver band. Then the volume control. The earphones produced less static, but no more of a signal than the loudspeaker had. Another tender turn of the band. Still nothing.

It was slow, tedious work, but the kind Herb Stillman was made for. The kind the boys at the airport liked to tease him about. They said worrying over details would make an old man out of him. Well, maybe so. Quite a few gray hairs peppered his black crewcut. Too many for thirty-five years. But he continued to work the controls, his eyes glued to the knobs and dials which were his element.

| Word Bank | **bank** (BAYNK) *n.*: a controlled tilt made by a turning plane |
| | **Mayday** (MAY DAY) *n.*: an international radiotelephone distress signal used by ships and aircraft |

Suddenly, clearly, it came again: "Mayday! Help me. Please help me!"

It was a kid's voice! Every terror a child's mind can hold registered in his crying, panicked voice. Terror of height, of being alone, of facing the unknown. Those terrors and a dozen more.

"Dad's sick. Please...I don't know how to fly this airplane!"

For a brief second Herb sat paralyzed. He'd handled Maydays before, plenty of them. But a kid...Was a kid trying to fly his dad's airplane?

Herb shook himself slightly, clearing the daze from his mind. "Get Swanson," he said to Don Pierson. "Then call CAA."[1]

The younger man scrambled from his desk, then turned back when he reached the door. "You sure you want Swanson? He'll hit the panic button for sure when he hears this."

"I don't want him, no," said Herb. "But he's the acting manager."

The frantic voice continued over the phones and speaker, sobbing, crying, then shrieking. "Mayday! Please help me. Somebody help me!"

Herb had the microphone in his hand. "Aircraft in distress. This is Mountain View radio at Tredway. This is Mountain View radio at Tredway. We read you. We read you."

There was no acknowledgment from the plane. The same voice was calling more hysterically than ever when Herb switched his set back from "Send" to "Receive." Then there was nothing but sobs.

Herb didn't try to transmit another call. It was no use trying. As long as he could hear the kid's voice he knew the plane's radio was set on "Send." It could receive nothing until the boy let go of the mike switch.

The door burst open behind Herb, and heavy thumping followed as a big man crossed the floor to his desk. It would be Swanson. Swanson, majority stockholder in the airport corporation, and therefore acting manager while the boss was away. Swanson, who didn't know anything about planes except that gassing and hangaring[2] them was good business.

He looked more blubbery, sweatier, more scared even than usual. "What's this about a kid in an airplane? You can't bring a kid to this airport! He'll crash, you fool—"

At that instant the loudspeaker went silent. Herb ignored Swanson and grabbed for the mike. "Aircraft in distress. This is Tredway. Can you hear me? Can you hear me?"

From the phones and the speaker came the tiny voice again, still scared, but a shade less hysterical. "I can hear you...Can you help me?"

"Hello. Hello. This is Tredway again. Listen, I can't talk to you when you push the button on your mike. You've got to release it when you're not talking. Otherwise you won't be able to hear me. Do you understand that?"

"Yes. That's what Dad told me, before he...before he passed out. I just remembered."

"Who are you? Do you know where you are?"

"I don't know where I am. I'm lost."

Swanson grabbed Herb's shoulder. "Don't bring him here. We don't want kids cracking up on this field. Do you hear me, Stillman? Don't *bring* him here!"

Herb felt his stomach tighten with

---

1. The *CAA*, the Civil Aeronautics Administration (now the Federal Aviation Agency) regulates the flow of traffic in the air and is responsible for the safety of planes in flight.
2. *Hangaring* (HANG ur ing) is providing shelter for airplanes.

fear. Not with a fear like Swanson's, or even like the boy's. Theirs was a fear of the unknown. Herb's was the fear of an airman who knew and respected the element of the pilot. He reached for a cigarette, broke it in his hand.

"I…I don't suppose there's anyone in the plane with you besides your dad, is there?"

"No," said the boy. Seconds of silence followed. "Dad was flying and then he said he was going to be sick. So he set the plane to fly itself. And he showed me how to run the radio."

Herb looked at the two other men in the tower. Swanson appeared ready to pass out. Pierson's face reflected his disbelief. *They're scared*, he thought. *They're scared and they've never even been through this before. What if they were like me? I brought my best friend in for a crack-up. I couldn't even bring Heggen down. And he was a pilot.*

"Can you help us, Mister?" asked the voice from the plane.

"Sure we can, son," said Herb. He forced calm reassurance through his dry throat. "My name is Herb. What's yours? And where were you headed?"

The boy's name was Frankie Morgan. He and his dad had left Stafford, Kansas, that morning about seven. About twenty minutes ago his father had complained of sudden and terrible pains. The men in the tower knew the rest.

"Where were you headed, Frankie?" asked Herb.

"Tredway," said the sobbing boy. "In Colorado."

At the mention of Tredway, Swanson came instantly to his feet. Before he could speak, Herb turned to him.

"Get on the phone downstairs, Swanson, and call the Air Force. See if they have any planes flying in this area. We've got to locate that boy."

"The Air Force! Of course!" Swanson cried. "I'll call them now.

They can handle this. They're used to these things."

"Nobody's used to these things," said Herb. "But get on the phone. And, Don, you get on your mike. Use every frequency you've got but this one. Clear all air traffic in the area. No unauthorized planes to fly within seventy-five miles of Tredway from zero to ninety degrees."

He heard Pierson's voice drone out its emergency message. In spite of himself he asked, why try? A man who knows nothing about flying cannot fly an airplane. Make it a kid who knows nothing, and…

But, maybe, just maybe, the kid does know a bit about flying. He picked up his mike. "Frankie, you're still with me, aren't you?"

"I hear you, Mr. Herb." The voice wasn't steady, not by a long shot. But it was a good deal steadier than it had been. *The kid's got some guts about him*, thought Herb. "How old are you, Frankie?"

"Eleven."

Herb stared at the mike in his hand. Eleven. Just eleven. He'd figured, or at least hoped, the kid might be fourteen or fifteen. But eleven…

"Frankie, have you flown much with your dad?"

"No. Dad hasn't had the plane long. He just got his license last week. This is my second ride in it."

Herb started to speak, hesitated, then went ahead. The kid had to learn the score sooner or later.

"Frankie, I'm going to level with you. You and your dad are in a tight spot. I can't fly your airplane from here. You're the only person that can fly it. So you're going to have to learn how, Frankie, and it's not going to be easy. But you can do it, Frankie. It won't be easy—but I can tell you how."

The response came fast. Every time the kid spoke, he seemed just a little more confident, a little more capable. "I think I can do it, Mr. Herb. You tell me how, and I think I can fly this airplane."

No one but a kid would have looked at it that way—an eleven-year-old kid at that. Any younger and the boy would have been simply too young to learn. Much older, and he'd have realized what he was up against. Maybe eleven wasn't the wrong age after all. Maybe eleven was just right.

Swanson burst back into the tower, almost giggling with his news. "Air Force has three planes, jets, in the area. They're fanning out from here toward Stafford. Also sending a helicopter in case the kid goes down. Those boys can take care of the situation now. Uh, Stillman, you just sign off. Tell the kid to switch to Air Force frequency."

Herb looked blankly at Swanson. He couldn't believe that such a man existed. Just then Pierson's voice broke in. "I've got the first jet on my set now. He's spotted an airplane headed for Tredway. An Ercoupe. Ask the boy if that's him."

"Frankie, this is Herb again. Do you know what kind of plane you're flying? Is it an Ercoupe?"

"It sure is, Mr. Herb."

"Roger!" yelled Pierson. "Number two jet's flying just over his nose at twelve o'clock."

"Is an airplane flying straight towards you, Frankie?"

"Yes, I see a plane coming. Now it's turning."

"That's him all right!" said Pierson. "Jet pilot says the Ercoupe's headed dead on Tredway. Fifty miles out. We'll get him here yet, Herb."

"What good'll that do?" asked Swanson, his eyes glazing again with fear. "He'll crash, and unless we turn this over to the military, they'll blame us. Tell the Air Force to figure something out. They've got to take over."

Herb started to curse, the veins in his neck and hands pulsating with his desire to blast the man. Then he turned again to the mike.

"Good news, Frankie. You're headed straight for Tredway. All you've got to do is keep coming the way you're headed."

"But what if the plane starts to turn? How will I know how to turn it back?"

"I'll tell you about all that pretty soon, Frankie. Just hold on."

He turned to Swanson. "Okay,

Swanson. We know when he left Stafford —roughly two and a half hours ago— and we know where he's headed. Right here at Tredway. If he's fifty miles out, that leaves him about thirty minutes of flying time before arrival.

"Most Ercoupes carry about six hours' fuel in their tanks, but we'll want to make sure. And we'll want to make sure he was full up on gas when he left Stafford. Why don't you get back on the phone and call Stafford field? If you can verify these two facts, we'll know the plane has fuel for three hours of flying time left when it gets here."

"I don't like this, Stillman. I'll check, but I am turning this matter over to the Air Force as soon as I get the information." As Swanson barged through the door, he spoke again. "And what if he does have three hours when he gets here? Is that any better than three minutes?"

Herb closed his eyes, then opened them again, very slowly. "I wish I knew, Swanson. I really wish I knew."

Picking up the mike again, he spoke to the boy. "We're almost ready for a flying lesson, Frankie. Still think you can do it?"

"I...I'll sure try, Mr. Herb."

"Good boy, Frankie. Now, first, do you know if your airplane has what they call an automatic pilot? You said that before your dad passed out, he set the plane to flying itself?"

"I don't know, Mr. Herb. Dad just kept adjusting a little knob."

"Look at the knob, Frankie. Tell me if it has any writing on it."

"It's got stuff on it, Mr. Herb. It has an arrow and the words 'Nose up' and another arrow and the words 'Nose down.' "

"Trim tab," said Pierson. "I didn't think that plane would have auto pilot. It's just trimmed out."

"That's what I was afraid of," said Herb. "Tell those jets to advise us the second that kid goes off straight and level. And Don, better call the hospital, too. We'll need doctors and an ambulance for the father...if they get here."

Herb waited a few seconds before picking up the mike again. Now it would begin—talking the kid in and down. He shuddered as he remembered one other time he'd had to do it. Heggen's plane. And he remembered Heggen's body, twisted and broken, blown thirty feet from the wreckage. He closed his eyes. "Okay, Frankie, here we go on lesson one. Do you know what your control wheel is? Maybe your dad calls it a stick."

"Sure," said the boy. "He always calls it the stick."

"Well, Frankie. First off, we're going to use your stick to turn with..."

And so started the toughest teaching job in Herb Stillman's career.

And so started, too, the race— against time, against distance, against fear.

"Now listen to this, Frankie. Let's play like we want to turn right. All you've got to do is turn the wheel a lit- tle bit to the right. Then your plane will bank in that direction. Got that?"

"Sure."

"Okay, but to stop the plane from turning you've got to do more than turn the wheel back to where it was. You not only bring it back to where it was but you turn it to the left a bit, too. Then you bring it back to where it was again."

Even to Herb, as he listened to his own voice, it sounded difficult. It sounded confusing. But turns and banks were the easiest to learn.

Should he teach the kid compass or navigation? No, because the jets were with him. Rudder control? No need— Ercoupe rudders synchronize with ailerons. Throttle? He'd have to know that. Oil gauge? Carburetor heat con- trol? No. RPM's?[3] No, too confusing for an eleven-year-old mind. Air-speed indi- cator?[4] Yes.

The minutes passed swiftly, too swiftly, while the instruction went so slowly. If Herb could only have *shown* the kid, not just talked to him. And the talk had to sound so casual, so under- standing when the kid didn't get a point. Otherwise he'd panic again.

The panic came anyway, just after the boy had seemed to catch on so well.

---

3. *RPM's* are engine revolutions per minute.
4. The *air-speed indicator* (in dih KAY tor) is a control that indicates air speed.

Banking had been easy, almost too easy. Use of the throttle didn't seem too hard for the boy. And climbs and glides had been satisfactory.

But when Herb attempted to combine the operations, the boy lost his nerve. "I'll crash...I'll crash; I can't do it. I can't turn the wheel and push the throttle too. *Help* me, Mr. Herb..."

Pierson's face went white. "Golly, Herb, you can't blame him. He's only eleven."

Herb didn't blame him. But he didn't have time to sympathize with him either, not with the Rocky Mountain range a few short miles ahead.

"Listen to me, Frankie, and get this straight! Quit bawling! Your dad's in there, too. Are you going to keep crying and crash, or are you going to be a man and bring your dad to the hospital?" He uttered a silent prayer.

"Okay, Mr. Herb," a voice answered meekly. "I'll try again."

Suddenly Swanson was in the room, more nervous than Herb had ever seen him. "He's out of gas," he bellowed. "He's out of gas."

"What?" said Herb. "Who's out of gas? What are you talking about?"

"He didn't have your six hours' to start with—not from Stafford anyway. He had six hours' fuel when he left Kansas City this morning, at four o'clock. The kid started out from Stafford all right. But his father just picked him up there. He'd been visiting his grandparents."

It wasn't possible. It wasn't reasonable. Herb picked up the mike.

"Frankie, I've got a question for you. Did you and your dad stop anywhere for gas after he left Stafford?"

"No, sir. We didn't land at all."

"Do you remember if your dad said anything about landing between Kansas City and Stafford?"

"Sure, I remember. Grandpa asked him if he flew straight down from home without stopping and Dad said 'yes.'"

"Okay, Frankie. That's all I wanted to know." He put down the mike and turned to Swanson. "I don't understand why they didn't gas up at Stafford."

"Because the pumps weren't open then." Swanson paced the room. "They didn't open until nine o'clock." The man started bawling. "It's all over...all over."

"Swanson," said Herb, "get out of here!"

Pierson spoke. "The kid's coming in pretty close, Herb. About a mile out. You going to bring him straight in for a landing?"

Herb stared at the widening speck in the sky. "He'd crash for sure," he said. "He's still so clumsy with the controls. I've got to let him circle the field once. That'll give him practice at four more turns. Maybe that'll be enough..."

You're teaching a man how to fly and he's sharp, but not sharp enough. So you give him a dozen, or four dozen, turns under supervision before you teach him to land. So now you're teaching this kid. So you give him four practice turns before his first solo landing.

"Frankie, we're ready now for you to circle the field. Remember, every time you turn you've got to add power. Otherwise you'll stall out."

"I...I'll remember, Mr. Herb."

"And remember this, too. You're a long way from the field, so we can make the turns gentle. This first one won't even be a complete ninety-degree turn. Just half a turn, so you'll be parallel to the runway. Now, give your plane extra power and bank a little bit to the

---

Word Bank   **bellowed** (BELL ode) *v.*: roared like a bull; cried out in a deep, blaring voice

right."

He watched as the boy followed his directions, turned a halting forty-five degrees, then leveled off and flew straight again. The plane, which had come in from the northeast, now flew into the south.

"Next time add just a little more power, Frankie. Now here's the deal. You're flying south now. We'll make four more turns and you'll be heading south again. Then you'll land. But I want to warn you about something. If you have any engine trouble, or run out of gas, don't worry. You don't have to land on a runway, and I'll tell you how to get down safely."

"Do you think I'll run out of gas, Mr. Herb?"

"Of course not, but I don't want you to be scared in case you do run into any trouble."

Herb smiled as the boy made his second turn. It was up to acceptable stan-

dards in any student's log book.

The tower door opened and Swanson came in again.

Swanson, veins showing through the puffy skin of his neck, screamed at Herb. "Stillman, you're fired! You killed one man on one of these landings. Now you're going to crash that boy! At my airport! Get out of this tower…"

He didn't finish. He saw Herb lay down the mike, he saw Herb's face, and something told Swanson he had best get out of there fast.

Herb picked up his mike. "Ready for another turn, young fellow?"

The bank wasn't as good as the oth-

ers had been. He lost altitude. If the boy had been too near the ground… Herb thought about that other time, about Heggen.

Almost imploringly, he looked at Don Pierson. "Am I doing the right thing, Don? Do you think I'm doing what's best?"

Pierson avoided Herb's eyes. "I…I don't know. I only know that, since I've worked with you, you've never done the wrong thing."

I did the wrong thing once, Herb thought. *At least most people think I did.*

Heggen in the snow-blinded plane—flying with windows frosted and ice on the wings. Herb talking him in by radio. Heggen should never have been flying that day—but he was. And he trusted his friend and instructor to bring him in safely.

Herb felt the explosion again. Sleeping and waking he'd felt it for seven years now.

Did I say something that made him think he was on the ground? L-rd help me, I'm sure he said he could see after I got him to twenty feet, that he didn't need more help!

Herb gulped a deep breath, and now the hand that held the mike was shaking as he watched the Ercoupe finish the downwind, and fastest, leg of its pattern. "Another one to your left, Frankie. This is your next to last turn."

Again a flawless bank—no. He hadn't added enough power. The plane lost altitude.

"Lower your nose! Add power!" A split second later the turn was complete. Herb breathed heavily.

He walked to the window and stared for the first time at the crowds below—pilots, passengers, reporters, and photographers. He knew what he could expect from them if the boy should crash. Could he stand it if a second crash were added to his record and his mind?

"Mr. Herb," said a trusting voice

from the plane. "Isn't it about time for me to turn?"

I don't care about the record! I don't care what the crowds might think!

Herb took a last glance at the plane and walked to the public-address broadcaster. Then he spoke—his voice sounding deep and strong as it broke the news to the field.

"Attention! Attention! This is an emergency. Repeat. Emergency. Prepare crash trucks and ambulances. Clear all runways and taxi strips. All noncrash personnel stand clear of the ramp and flightline.

"An eleven-year-old boy is at the controls of the Ercoupe to the north. *We are going to bring him in.*"

Below, the airport became a madhouse. Plane owners ran to their aircraft on the flightline. Four or five were already taxiing back to their hangars. Mechanics ran to board crash trucks. Two ambulances were poised at the ramp already, waiting....

Herb was back at the mike. "This is your last turn, Frankie. Then you're going to land. Make this turn the best of the day."

It was, by far, the best of the day.

Everything was perfect. Like so many kids, this one was a natural flyer. If only he'd had even an hour or two more of flying time.

The plane, about three quarters of a mile out, was headed straight down the runway.

"Okay, Frankie, we're going down. We'll do it by losing altitude just a little at a time. Cut back on the throttle and pull back your stick just a little, until the indicator says ninety."

A few seconds passed. "It does, Mr. Herb. It says ninety."

"Now lower your nose. Until it says a hundred."

"Okay. It does."

Herb studied the angle of descent. Not steep enough. The plane, which he'd kept high for turning practice, was too high for a normal glide path. It might overshoot the runway.

"Pull back on the throttle some more, Frankie. All the way back if you have to. Until the indicator says eighty-five. And remember to hold back your stick."

The glide looked better now, with the engine throttled clear back. But eighty-five was a shade too slow. About ninety was right for an Ercoupe. He'd hold the angle for a few more minutes, then have Frankie lower his nose:

"It's hard to hold the wheel back, Mr. Herb. It pulls forward."

"Hold it back anyway, Frankie. You're doing fine."

Herb remembered his own first landings. With the throttle back and the nose trying to drop, the stick *had* been hard to hold. It had seemed drawn to the firewall[5] by a powerful magnet.

More seconds passed. Now the plane was at four hundred and an eighth of a mile from the landing strip. "What's your speed, Frankie?"

"It's eighty."

"Okay, hold it there."

It wasn't hard to imagine what the boy was going through. Up high, at three thousand, maneuvers had probably seemed slow. Moves are leisurely, easy. At four hundred the ground would be blurred. Houses, streets, poles would be whizzing past.

"Don't look straight down, Frankie. Look out from your plane, a little to one side.

"Lower your nose, Frankie. Until the indicator says ninety."

Lower and lower the plane came. It looked smooth. It looked professional. It looked like any routine landing at any airport. But Herb Stillman knew differently. He knew the pilot was only eleven. And scared.

Three hundred feet, then two hun-

---

5. The *firewall* is the separation between the engine and the pilot.

dred. Past the boundary markers.

Herb's throat was dry. "Looks good, Frankie…good…that's it…hold her at ninety…good boy…"

One hundred feet. He could hear the engine now. Even throttled back the prop gave the plane a small share of lift—and insurance.

Then he heard and saw it at the same instant. The cough, the sputter, the propeller dwindling from a blur to a windmilling visibility. Out of gas!

"Mr. Herb! Mr. Herb! It stopped! Help me!"

"Hold on, Frankie!" Herb yelled.

The boy held on. He cried, he screamed, but he held on.

Seventy-five feet. Fifty. "You're doing wonderful, Frankie. Don't talk. Just keep it up."

Then thirty feet. Twenty. Now was the time, the moment that makes all the difference. Now was the time an approach becomes a landing—a dead-stick landing.

"Pull back on your stick a little more, Frankie…now a little more… more yet."

Fifteen feet, then lower.

"Keep pulling back, Frankie. A little more all the time. Now more. More."

The plane's nose had lifted, gliding the plane parallel to the ground, yet descending to it. The plane was in a perfect altitude.

"Now! All the way back, Frankie! Pull the stick back as far as it will go!"

Five feet. Three. He was almost there. Another second…

"He's down!" screamed Pierson. "He made it! He made it!"

"Let go of the stick, Frankie! Let go of it completely. The plane will take care of itself now."

It did just that. Headed down the runway, still at forty or forty-five miles an hour, it lost speed in a hurry.

Then it stopped completely. And before the small person inside it had time to open the cabin cover, an ambulance, two crash trucks, and a carload of photographers arrived.

Swanson was there, too—posing alternately with the boy, then beside the ambulance, where the boy's father had just been placed.

Herb had never left the tower. Seeing the Ercoupe, abandoned on the runway, he called maintenance to dispatch a tractor to tow it in. No one answered.

"I'm going to get a tractor," he told Pierson. "Hold down the fort for a few minutes."

Downstairs, in the waiting room, more than a hundred persons milled around. Herb heard someone say, "The guy's going to be all right. It was an appendix, but the doc says they got him in time."

Suddenly someone shouted, "There he is!" and all eyes turned to Herb. The room was silent for a moment; then a cheer went up, almost deafening in its volume.

And, just as suddenly, the shouting died away as a red-haired crash-truck driver forced his way through the crowd. He was leading a boy, blond and wide-eyed. The driver whispered something to him. The boy looked up at Herb, still fifteen feet away. "Mr. …Mr. Herb?" he asked.

Herb felt mist in his eyes. He could only nod and smile.

Then the boy came running to him and was hugging him and crying. Neither of them said anything; there was no need.

Recalling

1. What was Herb's reaction upon hearing the word "Mayday" spoken by a child?

2. What did Frankie do that made it impossible for Herb to communicate with him? How did Herb solve this problem later?

3. Did Frankie have enough gasoline? How did Herb figure that out?

4. What situation from the past haunted Herb as he helped Frankie land?

Interpreting

5. How did Mr. Swanson's attitude change from the beginning of the story to its end?

6. Explain why Herb felt that "...maybe eleven wasn't the wrong age after all. Maybe eleven was just right."

7. Describe the scene at the airfield after Frankie landed.

Concluding

8. Give an example of how Mr. Swanson undermined Herb's confidence in himself.

9. Imagine you are Frankie. Could you have followed Herb's directions? What did you learn about flying a plane from this story?

Examining Fiction

A **conflict** is a struggle between two forces. In some short stories, there is both an external and internal conflict. In *Kid at the Stick*, an external conflict occurs when an eleven-year-old boy, Frankie, is forced to fly and land a plane. An internal conflict arises in Herb, the person in the control tower, because he is haunted by an earlier, similar experience.

1. Identify some of the conflicts in the story. Tell whether each conflict is internal or external, and explain why you think so.

2. Are the resolutions to these conflicts realistic? Why or why not?

3. Describe the different emotions Herb experiences throughout the incident.

Thinking About Fiction

Suspense is a tool that writers use to sustain the reader's interest. An important part of suspense is uncertainty. What keeps the reader interested is the intense desire to find out what happens in the end. One of the components of suspense is danger. In *Kid at the Stick*, the suspense is heightened by a life and death situation.

1. What details does the author use to increase the suspense?

2. Suppose Mr. Swanson's attitude had been different. Would that have changed the degree of suspense in the story?

Creating and Writing

Have you ever been in a situation that was dangerous? How did you feel? What did you do to get out of the situation? How did you feel after it was over?

Write a journal entry in which you answer all of the above questions in complete sentences. Write in detail about the dangerous situation, explain how you got into it, and tell how you got out of it.

Into • *Look Back at the Sea*

Look Back at the Sea starts out calmly. The story is told in a matter-of-fact voice that describes a girl floating on a raft in the ocean. The author adds a few details recalling a relaxing day at the beach to add mood, and the picture is complete. Suddenly, a conflict arises, danger is presented, and the reader settles in for the telling of a suspenseful story. What are the features of a well-written short story? A story needs a plot, interesting characters, and a clearly described setting. What makes a short story suspenseful is often an added dash of danger. Try to identify the conflict in this story—is it internal, external, or both? Can you find the turning point as the suspense increases? Why is it that the idea of being unaware of a danger about to be faced works so well in short fiction?

Focus

Remember that suspense equals conflict plus danger. Remember, also, that a suspense story almost always builds suspense one level at a time; things go from bad to worse as the story progresses. Think about the way most suspense stories begin. *Kid at the Stick* and *Look Back at the Sea* are good examples. How does beginning the story in this way increase the suspense in the story?

About the Author

BETSY BYARS has been called "one of the best writers for children in the world." Born in North Carolina in 1928, Byars had no early aspirations to become an author. She began writing in 1950 and sold her first article to the *Saturday Evening Post*. She has been granted countless awards and honors for her work, including the 1970 Newbery Award. Her stories are filled with adventure and humor, and she is well known for her realistic portrayal of children as they grow and change.

Look Back at the Sea

Betsy Byars

Clara lay on the float with her head resting on her arms. Her eyes were closed. The smooth, rhythmic rise and fall of the waves soothed her.

She was glad she had found the float that morning in the hall closet, all bunched up in a plastic ball; glad she had spent the morning straightening it out, blowing it up.

The sun was warm on her back. The water that lapped over the sides of the float was cool on her stomach. She dipped her hands into the water and made a few strokes to keep the float from drifting back into the breakers. Then she folded her arms back under her cheek.

Overhead the gulls were crying. The sound seemed soothing. She was sleepy, relaxed.

She lifted her head. The float was in the same spot, had not drifted either way. She dipped her arms into the water, paddling slowly, idly. She watched the shore, the long white curving beach, the dunes blown up from the beach into a double line. The dunes had overtaken the trees in some places, and the twisted trunks stuck up in the sand.

Clara closed her eyes. I think I'll just stay out here until it's time to go home, she thought.

Clara blinked her eyes against the glare. The salt spray had dried on her arms, giving a frosted look to her skin. She touched her arm with her tongue, tasted salt. She closed her eyes.

Word Bank	**dunes** (DOONZ) *n.*: a sand hill or sand ridge formed by the wind, usually in desert regions or near the ocean

She lay without moving, her hands trailing in the water. She could hear the waves breaking on the shore, but it was like the distant boom of thunder. Her breathing grew regular. She drifted toward sleep. "Mnnn," she sighed.

Clara awoke with a start as a spray of cold water slapped across her back. She lifted her head and looked around in irritation.

She saw the swell of a wave rising behind her, the white crest of foam. For a moment Clara thought she had drifted into the breakers and was about to be washed up onto the beach. She looked ahead to see how close the beach was. She saw another wave.

A cold fear gripped her. These were not the long gentle waves of the shore, but the dark choppy waters of the sea. Her shoulders tightened. She gasped air into her lungs. Slowly, holding on to the float with tight cold hands, she lifted her head.

There were only waves, rising then falling to reveal more waves. She turned and glanced over her shoulder. A wave broke over her legs and sent cold spray across her back again. She ducked her head. She waited tensely, afraid to move.

As the float rose on the crest of the next wave, she lifted her head and saw the faint gray line of the shore on the horizon. The solid hump of the hotels, stores, and houses at the end of the island told her how far away she had drifted.

Word Bank	**swell** (SWELL) *n.*: a long, often huge wave or waves coming one after the other
	horizon (hor I zun) *n.*: a line or circle that forms the apparent boundary between earth and sky

She began to paddle. Her arms dipped into the sea again and again, her cupped hands pulling through the cold water. She did not look up, just kept drawing her arms mechanically through the sea like a swimmer. Spray slapped across her face, but she did not stop to wipe it away. When she paused, finally, to rest her trembling arms, she looked up and saw the shore was no nearer.

She put her head down. She lay with her eyes closed, blocking the sea, the waves, the distant island, from her mind.

Suddenly the sun went behind a cloud, and Clara felt the chill of the wind. Her teeth began to chatter, her legs to shake. The float wiggled unsteadily, too, and Clara clutched the sides. She tried to breathe deeply, regularly. Stay calm, she told herself. A spray of water hit her face, and she spit out salt water. Stay calm, she repeated.

There was nothing gentle or comforting about the sea now. This was a mean hang-on-if-you-can kind of motion.

Suddenly Clara heard the sound of an engine. Her spirits surged. Her head snapped up. A boat was on the horizon.

"Over here!" she screamed, waving her arm. "Help me. I'm over here!"

It was a cabin cruiser, moving steadily toward the island, rolling slightly with the motion of the waves. Clara could see a man on deck, facing away from her, into the wind.

"Help! I'm over here! *Help*!"

How could he not hear her? Clara struggled to sit up on the float. "I'm over here. I'm—" Suddenly the float flexed over a wave and bucked like a horse. Clara yelped, flopped down, and clutched the plastic. When the motion of the float was steady again, she raised her head.

"I'm over here!"

The boat had already moved past her. She could smell the fumes from the exhaust. The sound of the engine was growing fainter. The man on deck had gone into the cabin.

"Come back!" she yelled louder. "Help me! Come back!"

The boat grew smaller, the sound fainter, and Clara's shoulders sagged. Her nose began to run.

Then she lowered her head and started crying, making no effort to wipe her wet face. "Why didn't he see me?" she moaned.

Suddenly a wave hit the float broadside. The float rose, dipped with a sickening lunge, and rose again. Clara felt her stomach twist with nausea. She tightened her hold. As the float rose again, she closed her eyes and waited for the sickness to pass.

A second wave broke over the side of the float, and water filled her nostrils. She choked and gagged, and as she threw back her head for air, she saw there was nothing in sight now but the sea. She was overcome with a kind of loneliness she had only read about.

She twisted in a desperate move, churning the water with her hands, turning the float around. There was the island. The lighthouse. She felt a moment of relief.

She thought she heard another boat. She raised her head. There had to be boats! There were hundreds in the marina. She

waited, but the only sound she heard now was the waves.

There was an unreal feeling to it all, she thought, as she searched the horizon for boats. Her eyes stung with salt and tears. It was as if she had gone to sleep in one ocean and awakened in another.

She began to paddle again, moving her arms through the cold water. This made her feel better, more in control. She kept her head down so she could not see that she was not getting closer to the island. Indeed, the island seemed to be drifting farther away.

Clara had been clinging to the float for two hours. She no longer yelled or cried or paddled toward the retreating island. She lay with her eyes squeezed shut, her body as stiff and unmoving as one of those bodies uncovered in

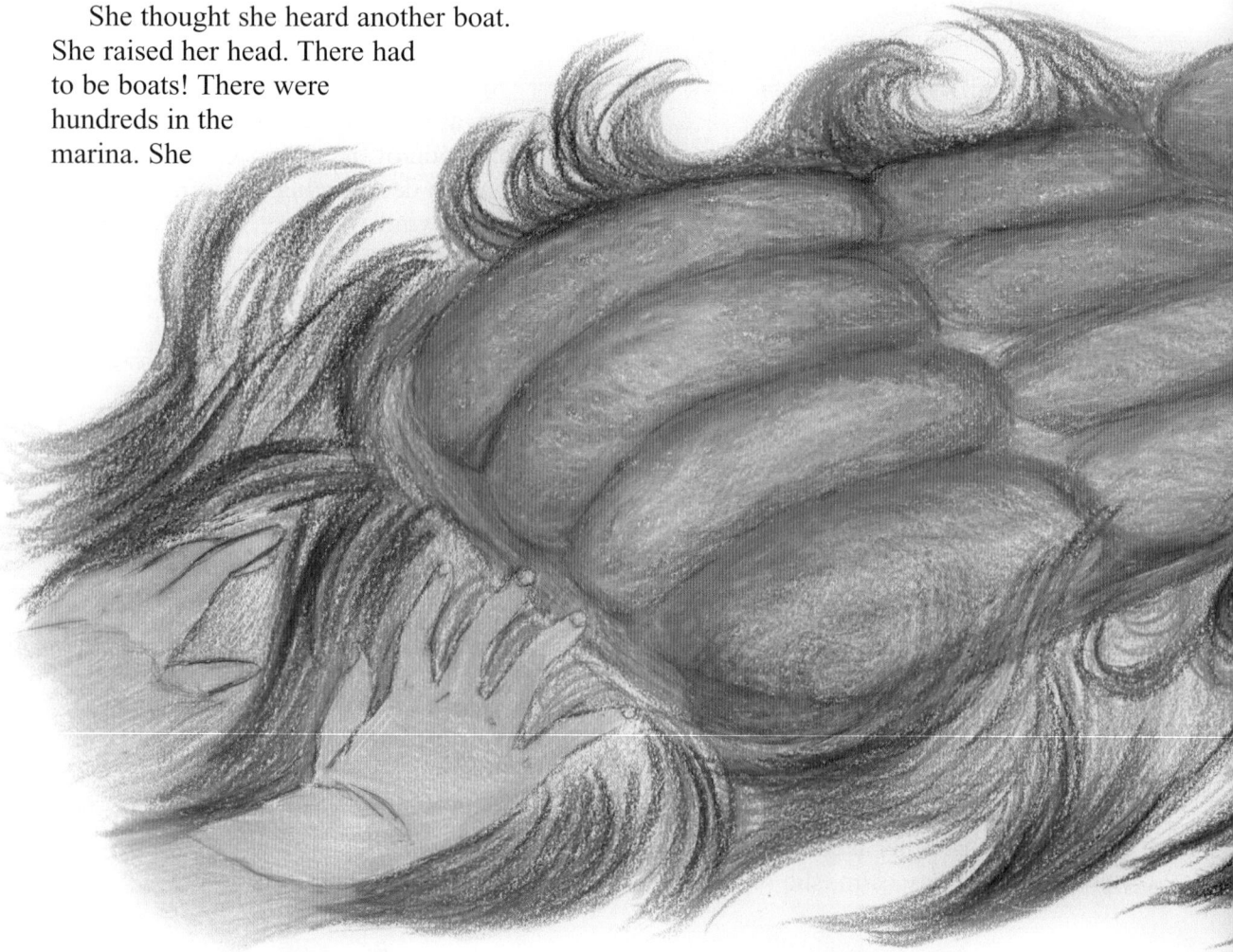

Pompeii,[1] petrified[2] in a moment of fear.

The waves were high and choppy now, and there was no rhythm to the movements of the float. It was like an amusement park ride designed to keep people off balance. The float went up, turned sideways, tipped, was hit broadside by waves, slid between waves—up, down, sideways.

Occasionally when the float made a particularly wrenching move, Clara would moan, but it was the sound of someone beyond hope. She had long since given up any thought of rescue. She felt as if she had been drawn far away from the normal world, into one of those spots that sailors fear, where the sea ignores the laws of nature and goes wild, a spot marked on old maps by drawings of dragons and reptiles.

Clara had no idea how long she had been on the raft—all her life, it seemed. The part of her life spent on dry land—walking, sleeping, eating, doing normal things—seemed like a brief, vague dream. This was hard cold reality.

A wave slapped against the float, and Clara suddenly felt it tipping over. She screamed and clutched the raft tighter, but her scream was cut short. The raft flipped over and Clara was thrown into the sea. Her head went under water, and she came up choking. She slung her wet hair from her face and looked around. The float was drifting away.

Clara swam after it. She reached out. The current pulled the float just beyond her grasp. She struggled through the waves, her eyes on the float, gasping for breath, swallowing salt water.

Her fingers touched the corner of the float and she fumbled to hold it. The float slipped away on the crest of a wave. She touched it again. It was gone. It was as if a playful hand were jerking the float out of her reach.

Clara began to swim. Another wave rose and she sank into the trough between waves. The float was out of sight. Clara was gripped with a terrible fear.

She waited, treading water anxiously, her eyes on the rolling waves. She caught sight of the float then, on the crest of a wave, and she struck out. Her arms and legs moved with a strength she had not known she had. Her teeth were clenched, her mouth clamped shut. A wave hit her face, and she plunged through it. She was gaining.

She swam again, lifting her head. The float was within reach. She scissored her legs in one last spurt and felt her fingers close on the thin plastic. Tears ran down her cheeks as she pulled herself up.

She lay across the float for a moment, her legs trailing in the choppy water. She coughed. She was exhausted. Her strength had gone as quickly as it had come. She could not lift her legs onto the float.

As she lay there, arms and legs trembling with fatigue and cold, she noticed something printed on the float. She blinked her eyes to clear them. NOT TO BE USED AS A LIFE PRESERVER, she read. She rested her face against the letters. Now they tell me. She closed her stinging eyes.

---

1. *Pompeii* (POM pay) was an ancient city of Rome buried by volcanic ash.
2. *Petrified* (PEH trih FYD) means paralyzed or rigid.

Word Bank	**marina** (ma REEN uh) *n.*: landing pier for docking small boats

Then slowly, gasping with the effort, she threw one leg over the float. She rested. She pulled the other leg up and stretched out as gingerly as an old dog. She closed her eyes. Her heart was pounding in her ears.

She lay there, clutching the sides of the float with both hands, legs shaking, knees knocking, waiting tensely for the next wave that could throw her again into the sea.

This time, she said through her clenched teeth, this time I won't let go.

She glanced over her shoulder. The waves were tinted red by the sinking sun. She glanced skyward. The clouds were moving in, gray and foreboding. A lone gull, white as snow, dipped in the darkening sky.

I will not let go, she said again.
I will not let go...I will not let go...
Clara was so intent on staying on the raft that she had not heard the sound of the approaching boat. She had not heard the men's voices.

"Hey, girl, are you all right?"

"She's not moving."

"She's got to be alive. Look how tightly she's holding on."

I will not let go...

Clara had not seen the boat pull up behind her, did not feel the raft bump against the boat. And when human hands grabbed her stiff arm, she screamed like a wild person. "Nooooo!" She flung her head back, still screaming, and was lifted out of the water like something baited and caught from the sea.

She was clutching the float so tightly that it came out of the water with her. When the men lifted her over the side, it flopped back into the water and bobbed away on the choppy sea.

Clara grabbed at the air, but the man said, "You don't need that anymore. You're all right. You're with us."

She was on her knees, staring around, blank-eyed.

"You're all right," he said in a softer voice. "Get a blanket," he told someone.

Clara began to shiver. Her teeth clattered. She wrapped her arms around herself.

"Here, here."

Still on her knees, still shaking violently, Clara was wrapped in a blanket and helped to her feet. When her trembling legs would not support her, she was lifted and carried below and put on a bunk.

There she realized for the first time that she had been saved. She began to cry, sobbing into the blanket, shivering harder than ever.

"It's all right," the man said. He was rubbing her arms now, trying to get some heat into her body. "You're on our boat. We're taking you to the island."

He spoke in the soothing tone people use to calm frightened animals. "We aren't a half-hour from the bay. You'll be home soon."

Clara nodded, then lifted her head. "Thank you," she said through her salt-parched lips.

"I bet your parents are worried sick. We'd call ahead, but our radio's out."

"It's just my father and sister."

"Well, I know they're worried sick. How did it happen?"

"I don't know. One minute I was floating by the beach and I closed my eyes and when I woke up—well, I was out where you found me."

Suddenly Clara sat up. "I want to go up on deck," she said.

"Well, now, I don't know whether you ought to be doing that or not," the man said. "You just—"

"I want to see the ocean. I have to."

"Well, wrap up." The man tightened the blanket around her, threw a towel over her head, and helped her up the narrow steps.

As they came onto the deck, the man said, "There's a helicopter. It was probably searching for you."

"If they know I'm gone."

"They know."

Clara sat in one of the chairs and pulled her legs up under the blanket. There was the island—the lighthouse, the long curving shore. Then she let her eyes look back at the sea.

"Sea's getting higher," the man said.

Clara nodded, her eyes on the waves.

From the boat the waves looked high and rolling, with an occasional crest of foam, but not a dangerous sea. Then the boat dipped between waves, wavered, and Clara clutched the arms of her chair. As the boat lunged forward, she shuddered.

"Cold?"

"No." She licked her upper lip and tasted salt. She looked at the man. "I'm just—" She paused to find the right word, realized there wasn't one, and substituted "glad." She smiled.

"This has been quite a day for us, young lady. I was thinking, before we spotted you, that I had something to brag about—we caught more than a hundred blues today. Now I really got something to brag about. It's been quite a day."

"For me too," Clara said.

The boat moved over the waves, and Clara leaned forward in her seat. She watched the water with a new kind of intensity. They rounded the end of the island, and Clara rose from her seat as they came into the bay.

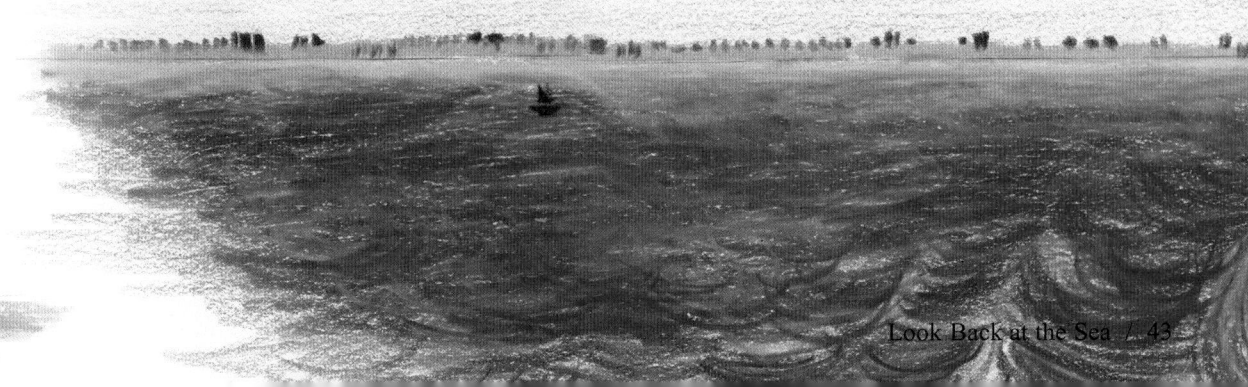

Recalling

1. What happens to Clara as she falls asleep on the raft?

2. How does Clara react when she realizes that she is lost at sea?

3. What does Clara do to save herself from drowning?

4. When Clara is finally saved and brought onto the boat, where does she want to go?

Interpreting

5. At the opening of the story, what is the setting in which Clara finds herself? What effect did the setting have on her?

6. Why do you think Clara's reaction to being rescued was screaming, "Noooo"?

7. Look back at the answer to question number 4. Why do you think Clara wanted to go there?

Concluding

8. Imagine yourself in Clara's position. How would you have kept yourself calm?

Examining Fiction

Writers create suspense by describing situations that are both uncertain and perilous. The danger in these situations can be physical or emotional, or both. Many readers enjoy suspenseful stories because they look forward to finding out how the story ends.

1. When does the reader first realize that Clara is in danger?

2. How do Clara's repeated attempts to keep afloat and to be rescued increase the suspense?

Thinking About Fiction

Suspense is created through details that intensify the crisis in the situation. Take note of details in the following description of Clara's attempt to stay afloat: "A wave slapped against the float, and Clara suddenly felt it tipping over. She screamed and clutched the raft tighter, but her scream was cut short."

1. Now, find the paragraph that begins, "As she lay there…" (page 41). List the details, in this and the next few paragraphs, that help create suspense.

2. Are there specific words and phrases that make you feel this suspense? Which ones? Write them down.

Creating and Writing

Imagine that you have been asked to write a review of several suspenseful stories. Think of some stories that you have read that would keep readers on the edge of their seats. Choose the one you like most and write a review of the story. You can use *Look Back at the Sea* if you cannot think of another. Make sure you explain how the story contains the key ingredients of suspense: uncertainty and danger. Proofread your review for accuracy in spelling, punctuation, grammar, and sentence structure.

Into • *Stolen Day*

Where does the inner world leave off and the outer world begin? If someone tells you that the food you just ate is spoiled, does your stomach start to hurt? If you hear that the air pollution level is high, do you suddenly have the urge to cough? Imaginative people are often more suggestible (easily influenced by suggestion) than are practical, down-to-earth individuals, and imaginative children are even more unclear about what is real and what is imagined. In *Stolen Day*, a young boy sees a friend who has a serious illness. The boy begins to feel sick, too—or does he? As you read the story, do not be too quick to answer that question, or to judge the narrator. If you think back, you may remember having an experience very much like his. Perhaps, now, you can look back at your younger self with an understanding that you lacked at the time.

Focus

Stolen Day is a story built around **character**. What is of interest to the reader is not an exciting sequence of events, but the portrayal of a young boy's personality. The narrator possesses certain human weaknesses familiar to us all. The author reveals these shortcomings slowly as the story unfolds. Do you think this boy will grow up to be honest? Can you analyze his character? How might he put some of his talent to good use as an adult? If you were his parent, which part of his nature would you reinforce, and which part would you try to improve?

About the Author

SHERWOOD ANDERSON was born in 1876 in a small town in Ohio. As a young man, he ran a very successful paint business, while privately working on his writing. According to the legend, one day in 1912, he just walked out of his business and never returned. From that time on, he devoted himself to writing. Many of Anderson's stories deal with growing up and are based on his childhood memories. Sherwood Anderson died in 1941. He is especially remembered for his short stories, such as *Stolen Day*.

It must be that all children are actors. The whole thing started with a boy on our street named Walter, who had inflammatory rheumatism. That's what they called it. He didn't have to go to school.

Still, he could walk about. He could go fishing in the creek or the waterworks pond. There was a place up at the pond where in the spring the water came tumbling over the dam and formed a deep pool. It was a good place. Sometimes you could get some big ones there.

I went down that way on my way to school one spring morning. It was out of my way but I wanted to see if Walter was there.

He was, inflammatory rheumatism and all. There he was, sitting with a fish pole in his hand. He had been able to walk down there all right.

It was then that my own legs began to hurt. My back too. I went on to school but, at the recess time, I began to cry. I did it when the teacher, Sarah Sugget, had come out into the schoolhouse yard.

She came right over to me.

"I ache all over," I said. I did, too.

I kept on crying and it worked all right.

"You'd better go on home," she said.

So I went. I limped painfully away. I kept on limping until I got out of the schoolhouse street.

Then I felt better. I still had inflammatory rheumatism pretty bad but I could get along better.

I must have done some thinking on the way home.

"I'd better not say I have inflammatory rheumatism," I decided. "Maybe if you've got that, you swell up."

I thought I'd better go around to where Walter was and ask him about that, so I did—but he wasn't there.

"They must not be biting today," I thought.

I had a feeling that, if I said I had inflammatory rheumatism, Mother or my brothers and my sister Stella might laugh. They did laugh at me pretty often, and I didn't like it at all.

"Just the same," I said to myself, "I have got it." I began to hurt and ache again.

Stolen Day

by Sherwood Anderson

I went home and sat on the front
steps of our house. I sat there a long
time. There wasn't anyone at home
but Mother and the two little ones.
Ray would have been four or five
then and Earl might have been three.

It was Earl who saw me there. I
had got tired of sitting and was lying
on the porch. Earl was always a
quiet, solemn little fellow.

He must have said something to
Mother, for presently she came.

"What's the matter with you?
Why aren't you in school?" she
asked.

I came pretty near telling her
right out that I had inflammatory
rheumatism. But I thought I'd better
not. Mother and Father had been

Word
Bank

solemn (SAHL UM) *adj.*:
serious; grave

speaking of Walter's case at the table just the day before. "It affects the heart," Father had said. That frightened me when I thought of it. "I might die," I thought. "I might just suddenly die right here; my heart might stop beating."

On the day before, I had been running a race with my brother Irve. We were up at the fairgrounds after school, and there was a half-mile track.

"I'll bet you can't run a half mile," he said. "I bet you I could beat you running clear around the track."

And so we did it and I beat him, but afterward my heart did seem to beat pretty hard. I remembered that, lying there on the porch. "It's a wonder, with my inflammatory rheumatism and all, I didn't just drop down dead," I thought. The thought frightened me a lot. I ached worse than ever.

"I ache, Ma," I said. "I just ache."

She made me go in the house and upstairs and get into bed.

It wasn't so good. It was spring. I was up there for perhaps an hour, maybe two, and then I felt better.

I got up and went downstairs. "I feel better, Ma," I said.

Mother said she was glad. She was pretty busy that day and hadn't paid much attention to me. She had made me get into bed upstairs and then hadn't even come up to see how I was.

I didn't think much of that when I was up there; but when I got downstairs where she was, and when, after I had said I felt better and she only said she was glad and went right on with her work, I began to ache again.

I thought, "I'll bet I die of it. I bet I do."

I went out to the front porch and sat down. I was pretty sore at Mother.

"If she really knew the truth, that I have inflammatory rheumatism and I may just drop down dead any time, I'll bet she wouldn't care about that either," I thought.

I was getting more and more angry the more thinking I did.

"I know what I'm going to do," I thought; "I'm going to go fishing."

I thought that, feeling the way I did, I might be sitting on the high bank just above the deep pool where the water went over the dam, and suddenly my heart would stop beating.

And then, of course, I'd pitch forward, over the bank into the pool; and, if I wasn't dead when I hit the water, I'd drown sure.

They would all come home to supper and they'd miss me.

"But where is he?"

Then Mother would remember that I'd come home from school aching.

She'd go upstairs, and I wouldn't be there. One day during the year before, there was a child got drowned in a spring. It was one of the Wyatt children.

Right down at the end of the street there was a spring under a birch tree and there had been a barrel sunk in the ground.

Everyone had always been saying the spring ought to be kept covered, but it wasn't.

So the Wyatt child went down there, played around alone, and fell in and got drowned.

Mother was the one who had found the drowned child. She had gone to get a pail of water, and there the child was, drowned and dead.

This had been in the evening when we were all at home, and Mother had come running up the street with the dead, dripping child in her arms. She was making for the Wyatt house as hard as she could run, and she was pale.

She had a terrible look on her face. I remembered then.

"So," I thought, "they'll miss me, and there'll be a search made. Very likely there'll be someone who has seen me sitting by the pond fishing, and there'll be a big alarm and all the town will turn out and they'll drag the pond."

I was having a grand time, having died. Maybe, after they found me and had got me out of the deep pool, Mother would grab me up in her arms and run home with me as she had run with the Wyatt child.

I got up from the porch and went around the house. I got my fishing pole and lit out for the pool below the dam. Mother was busy—she always was—and didn't see me go. When I got there, I thought I'd better not sit too near the edge of the high bank.

By this time I didn't ache hardly at all, but I thought.

"With inflammatory rheumatism you can't tell," I thought.

"It probably comes and goes," I thought.

"Walter has it and he goes fishing," I thought.

I had got my line into the pool and suddenly I got a bite. It was a regular whopper; I knew that. I'd never had a bite like that.

I knew what it was. It was one of Mr. Fenn's big carp.

Mr. Fenn was a man who had a big pond of his own. He sold ice in the summer, and the pond was to make the ice. He had bought some big carp and put them into his pond; and then, earlier in the spring when there was a freshet, his dam had gone out.

So the carp had got into our creek, and one or two big ones had been caught—but none of them by a boy like me.

The carp was pulling and I was pulling and I was afraid he'd break my line, so I just tumbled down the high

| Word Bank | **carp** (KARP) *n.*: large freshwater fish |
| | **freshet** (FRESH it) *n.*: a sudden rise in the level of a stream; flooding caused by heavy rain or rapidly melting snow or ice |

bank, holding onto the line and got right into the pool. We had it out, there in the pool. We struggled. We wrestled. Then I got a hand under his gills and got him out.

He was a big one all right. He was nearly half as big as I was myself. I had him on the bank and I kept one hand under his gills and I ran.

I never ran so hard in my life. He was slippery, and now and then he wriggled out of my arms; once I stumbled and fell on him, but I got him home.

So there it was. I was a big hero that day. Mother got a washtub and filled it with water. She put the fish in it, and the neighbors came to look. I got into dry clothes and went down to supper—and then I made a break that spoiled my day.

There we were, all of us, at the table, and suddenly Father asked what had been the matter with me at school. He had met the teacher, Sarah Suggett, on the street, and she told him how I had become ill.

"What was the matter with you?" Father asked; and before I thought what I was saying, I let it out.

"I had the inflammatory rheumatism," I said—and a shout went up. It made me sick to hear them, the way they all laughed.

It brought back all the aching again, and like a fool I began to cry.

"Well, I have got it—I have," I cried, and I got up from the table and ran upstairs.

I stayed there until Mother came up. I knew it would be a long time before I heard the last of the inflammatory rheumatism. I was sick all night, but the aching I now had wasn't in my legs or in my back.

Studying THE SELECTION

Recalling

1. Why didn't Walter have to go to school? Despite this, what was he still able to do?

2. Which illness did the narrator of the story believe he had?

3. At first, why didn't the narrator tell his mother about his "illness"?

4. What did the narrator do later on, after he got almost no attention from his mother?

5. How did the father find out that his son was "sick"?

6. How did the members of his family respond when Walter told them what was wrong?

Interpreting

7. Why did the boy begin to cry only after the teacher came into the school yard?

8. After his mother's response, that she was glad he was feeling better, the boy began to ache all over again. Why did he react that way?

9. Look back to question number 6, and remember the response of his family, when the narrator told them about his "illness." What does the family's reaction to the narrator tell the reader about the narrator's character traits? What else might the narrator have done in the past? What kind of person do you think he was?

10. At the conclusion of the story, the boy says, "I was sick all night, but the aching I now had wasn't in my legs or in my back." What do you think the boy has learned from his experiences that day?

Concluding

11. If you were the boy in the story, would you have told your family what was "wrong" with you? Why or why not?

Examining Fiction

As the story unfolds, the boy's character traits are revealed through his words, thoughts, and actions, and from the way other characters react to him.

1. What causes the boy to convince himself that he has inflammatory rheumatism?

2. What deeply felt emotion causes the boy to exclaim "I had the inflammatory rheumatism"?

Thinking About Fiction

By comparing and contrasting characters, you can come to a better understanding of them. When **comparing** characters, you look at ways in which they are alike. When **contrasting** them, you look for ways that they are different.

1. Think back to the story *A Day's Wait*. Identify a character trait that the main character shares with the boy in *Stolen Day*.

2. How do the boys in *A Day's Wait* and *Stolen Day* react to their fears? Are their reactions similar, or do they differ? What do their reactions show about them? How do their families react to them? What does this show about the nature of these families? Answer each of these questions.

Creating and Writing

Think of a person you know well. Write a detailed character sketch of this person. Assume your reader knows nothing about the person.

- First, list all of the traits that make this person unique.

- Then, write a first draft, making sure that you have included enough detail to make this person come alive.

- Revise your paper, correcting any spelling or punctuation errors, and then write your final draft. You also may want to include some anecdotes (brief stories) that illustrate this person's character, with specific details about his or her interactions with others.

Blueprint FOR READING

Into • *The Strangers That Came to Town*

Have you ever been "the new kid on the block"? Did you ever go to a summer camp where everyone knew everyone else—except for you? Have you ever joined a class that had been together for years? How were you treated? How did you feel? How long did it take until you felt as though you were part of the group? Now, let's take a look at how you, the newcomer, behaved to everyone else. Were you friendly, or were you very shy? Did you greet people first, or did you wait to be greeted? Did you volunteer to help others or did you worry only about yourself? What about when you were part of an old group and somebody else was new? Were you friendly to newcomers, or did you ignore them? Were you the first to welcome someone, or were you afraid your friends would laugh at you if you did? *The Strangers That Came to Town* is about the changes that take place when some new people come to an old town.

Focus

Why do people behave the way they do? Sometimes they are imitating others; sometimes they are doing what they are told to do; sometimes they have certain principles by which they live. In *The Strangers That Came to Town*, you will read about many types of behavior, some of it admirable, some of it, not. What makes each character behave a certain way? Another way of asking this question is, what motivates each character? People may be motivated by feelings like idealism, greed, fear, or love. As you read the selection, ask yourself what is motivating the behavior of each character. The author wants you to ask this question, because the message of the story can be found in its answer.

About the Author

American author **AMBROSE FLACK** was born in 1902, and grew up in Syracuse, New York. His family members were great admirers of the twenty-sixth president of the United States, Theodore Roosevelt. He describes his meeting with the President in a well-known story, *Theodore Roosevelt and My Gold Fountain Pen*. Ambrose Flack wrote many stories with children as the central characters. *The Strangers That Came to Town* is such a story. Many of his writings were published in popular magazines.

Ambrose Flack

The Strangers That Came to Town

The first of April came dark and stormy, with silver whips of lightning cracking open the lowering clouds that seemed to skim the treetops. My brother Tom and I, recovering from chest colds, tired of reading and listening to the radio, turned to the big living-room window of our house on Syringa Street.

"Here they come, Mother," cried Tom when a big truck drove up in the teeming rain and stopped in front of the empty cottage across the street.

Mother hurried in from the kitchen and we three looked out. That truck, we knew, contained the Duvitch family and all their earthly possessions.

Mr. Duvitch and the biggest boy carefully helped Mrs. Duvitch from the seat and walked her into the house, supporting her all the way. Another big boy, carrying a well-bundled baby, followed. A stream of young Duvitches, accompanied by a big brown houndlike dog, poured out of the back of the truck and stood in a huddle in the rain.

The barnyard sounds we heard escaped from two crates of hens the Duvitches had fetched along and from a burlap bag in which a small flock of ducks had been stowed. While the livestock made noises according to its kind, the Duvitches were quiet—almost solemn. They showed no elation at finding themselves in a new neighborhood and a very pretty neighborhood at that.

All afternoon Mother, Tom and myself had been watching out for them, with rather mixed emotions. For the Duvitches were immigrants and the first of their nationality to settle in our small smug town. Coming to our obscure part of the state a year before, they had moved into a rotting old farmhouse two miles north of town, long abandoned. After the slashing hurricane of mid-March, the moss-rotten dwelling looked like the house in the fairy tale that remained standing only because it did not know which way to fall and the Duvitches were forced to give it up.

"I wonder if Mrs. Duvitch is ill," murmured Mother, looking through the rain at the dreary street scene.

"She must be," said Tom. "I wonder if it'll be all right for Andy and me to help 'em move in their stuff."

This request, as Mother well knew, was not inspired by genuine feeling for the Duvitches but by curiosity and she shook her head. It was a strict family rule that any illness which kept us out of school would automatically keep us indoors.

But the Duvitches got along very well without help from us. As it turned out, they were old hands at moving. For years before coming to America they had been on the move, to escape starvation, separation, possible assassination. Every child capable of two-legged locomotion pitched in and helped carry the things from the truck. In no time at all, it seemed, the truck was empty and the Duvitches were shut up tight in their new home.

That was the signal for Mother to step into the kitchen. She returned swathed in her hooded raincoat, carrying a basket containing a vacuum jug of chicken soup, a baked tuna-fish dish, steaming hot; a loaf of fresh bread and a chocolate cake. These she took to the house across the street and gave basket and all to the boy who answered her knock. It wasn't her plan to stop for a visit that day but to wait a week or so and call when the Duvitches were all settled.

The next day when the three of us—Mother, Tom and myself—were having lunch, we heard a faint tap at the back door. I answered it and there stood a pale dark-eyed boy, looking very solemn, holding our basket. It contained the empty vacuum jug, casserole dish and cake plate, all of which shone, and a tiny very shapely potted rose tree, an exquisite pink-tipped bud, the handsomest plant—and the only plant of its kind—ever seen in that neighborhood.

"I send them a few scraps of food," murmured Mother, a few seconds later, deeply touched, "and get this queenly gift!"

That was our last traffic with the Duvitch family for over two years. When Mother stopped to visit them a week after their coming, the little girl who opened the door a few inches said, "Mamma sick; she stay in bed today." Mrs. Duvitch never crossed the street to our house and Mother, a rather formal woman, made no further attempts to see the family. But Father disagreed when she remarked that she thought the Duvitches probably wished to be left alone.

Syringa Street seemed to be a friendly street. It was a crooked maple-shady country lane that wound through the town without losing its charm. The sidewalk here and there was almost lost in weeds and the ditches, in places, were brightened by clumps of orange day lilies. Widely spaced cottages, some of them smothered in vines, only seemed to make the neighborhood more rural. There were brilliant flower gardens, vegetable plots, fruit trees—and a few henhouses. The children, who enjoyed all the benefits of country life while actually living in town, were quite numerous. Behind the facades of the street's dwellings there was probably no more greed, envy, superstition or intolerance than lurked behind the doors of any average dwelling in any average American town. The cardinal[1] virtues, no doubt, were all represented. Yes, Syringa Street seemed to be a friendly street.

But the Duvitches were marked people. They were the one struggling family in a prosperous community—and poverty, amid prosperity, is often embarrassing and irritating to the prosperous. They were considered unattractive physically. They were so meek! The Duvitches never fought back.

The women started in on Mrs. Duvitch because she "never showed her face." It is true, she was rarely if ever seen in the daytime, emerging from her dwelling only after dark in warm weather, to sit on the veranda, where she found privacy behind the ragged trumpet creeper. But this gave rise to the rumor that she was the victim of an obscure skin disease and that every morning she shook scales out of the bed sheet. (When my father heard that one, he went out to the pantry and mixed himself a tall drink.)

---

1. *Cardinal* (KAR din al) means most important.

Mr. Duvitch, too, was classified as an untouchable. His job, a rather malodorous[2] one, was with the local rendering plant as a laborer. It followed that the Syringa Street young, meeting him on the street, sometimes stopped their noses as they passed him by—a form of torment all the more acute when Mr. Duvitch had to share it with the children that happencd to be with him.

Black hard luck seemed to be their lot.

A few weeks after they moved to Syringa Street they suffered a tragedy they were all summer in recovering from—Mr. Duvitch lost two weeks' pay while gathering mushrooms in Tamarack Swamp. Inside of a year and a half, three Duvitch boys had lost, among them, by various mishaps, two fingers, one eye and an ear lobe. They were forever being cut up, bruised, mutilated by things falling, breaking, cracking and exploding.

A mild case of typhoid, mass cases of whooping cough and measles—all plagued the family within a year of their arrival. Their only bright spot here was Dr. Switzer, one of the town's kindliest souls. He declined to accept fees, but was several times seen leaving the Duvitch cottage, carrying off a handsome house plant and looking very pleased. The Duvitches' dog, Kasimar, acted just like the family to which he belonged—like one of the world's poorest canine relations. He seemed to be afraid of his own shadow and no one had ever heard him bark or growl.

Because they cast their eyes on the sidewalk as one passed them by and spoke only when spoken to, the young Duvitches, like their parents, were considered antisocial. They were regarded as born scavengers too, for they spent hours foraging[3] in the town dump, where they often picked up their footgear, some of their pants and shirts and furnishings for the house as well. They went on country excursions to gather watercress, dandelion greens, mushrooms and wild berries; and the few apples and tomatoes they occasionally concealed under their blouses didn't make the farmers on whom they poached much poorer. Tom and I raided tomato patches and robbed apple trees just for the fun of it.

That first September four Duvitches—Irving, Benny, Abe and Esther—registered at the local grammar school. Mrs. Lovejoy, the principal, said they were bright, conscientious, pathetically eager but almost pathologically[4] shy. Before she could put a stop to it, some of their classmates scoffed at the leaf-lard-and-black-bread sandwiches they ate for lunch, huddled in one corner of the recreation room, dressed in their boiled-out ragpickers' clothes. After school they headed straight for home, never lingering on the playground.

Even the tradesmen to whom the Duvitches gave good money were either curt with them or downright rude. Mrs. Frithjof Kinsella, the proprietor of the general store and a big jolly Viking who could be heard two blocks away, extended credit to almost everybody in town and had a way of insulting her customers so heartily that they all loved her for it. The Duvitches, however, Mrs. Kinsella very carefully did not insult (a form of insult in itself) and neither did she extend them credit.

But Mother, remembering the potted rose tree, always had a friendly word and a smile for the young Duvitches

Word Bank	canine (KAY nyn) *n.*: dog

2. *Malodorous* (mal OWE dur ess) means strong or bad-smelling.
3. *Foraging* (FOR uh jing) means searching about.
4. *Pathologically* (PATH uh LAHJ ik lee) means abnormally.

when she saw them and a bone for Kasimar when he found courage to venture across the road. Father was the only man on Syringa Street who tipped his hat to sixteen-year-old Maria Duvitch, when he met her coming home from her piece-work job in Miller's Box Factory. It may have been that their European travail[5] made it easy for them to endure such a trifle as humiliation in America.

"I think," said Father one fine Saturday morning in July two years after the Duvitches had come to Syringa Street, "that it would be very pleasant for Andy, Tom and myself to pitch our tent out at Durston's Pond and spend the night. We could fish and swim. That is," he added, "if Mother can spare us."

"I can spare you very well," Mother said cheerfully.

She had a notion it did menfolk good to get away occasionally and in this instance the sacrifice came easily, because camp life was little to her liking. She packed a hamper of food, Tom and I fetched a tent from the attic and Father looked over his fishing tackle. An hour after lunch we were driving through rolling farm country out to Durston's Pond, four miles north of town.

We often had the serene little lake all to ourselves but on our arrival that afternoon we found half a dozen male Duvitches in possession. They had been fishing for several hours, casting from the shore, dropping their lines over the wooden bridge that spanned Cat Creek where it flowed into the pond and trolling for bass from a flat-bottomed rowboat.

Tom and I, Philistines[6] like our friends, ignored the Duvitch boys but Father went up to Mr. Duvitch, who was fishing from the shore, and put out his hand.

"Good afternoon, Mr. Duvitch! It's nice to see you and the boys here. What a beautiful day! Are Mrs. Duvitch and the girls all well?"

Mr. Duvitch was a little fellow, a lean starveling of a man with watery blue eyes and a kicked-about look. Gratitude for being agreeably noticed showed in his mosquito-bitten face as he took Father's hand and his tremulous smile showed broken teeth.

"I know the mosquitoes are biting," Father went on pleasantly, "but are the fish?"

Proudly, oh, so proudly, Mr. Duvitch exhibited the catch that would probably feed his family for the better part of a week: a fine mess of bass, perch and sunfish, all of them alive, as far as I could see, and swimming around in the oaken washtub in which they had been dropped. Father gave Mr. Duvitch hearty congratulations and said we couldn't hope to do as well but that we'd try.

We three pitched the tent on a little knoll over the pond, and then Father, with a happy sigh, lay down on the blanket for a nap in the sun. Tom and I played a game of chew-the-peg on the grassy bank above the water and, later on, made several trips to the tent, for the camera, the field glasses, the sun lotion. On a trip for a cold drink from the vacuum jug and to fetch towels and soap, we stopped to look again at the Duvitches' catch of fish.

Mr. Duvitch and the boys had moved away and were fishing in a small arm of the pond below us. None of them seemed visible. Tom and I, our glances meeting over the big cake of soap in my hand, were similarly and wickedly inspired—the thing was irresistible. We held a brief whispering conversation; and then, egged on by him and quite willing on my own, I played a shameful

---

5. Their *travail* (truh VAYL) means their agony and intense pain.
6. Here, *Philistines* (FILL ih STEENZ) refers to people with little to no sensitivity.

trick on the Duvitches, the memory of which will come back to the end of my days to plague me. Without considering further, I dropped the cake of soap into the tub of fish.

"Let's go," whispered Tom after we had watched the soap sink to the bottom.

We swam out to the raft, diving and frolicking in the deep water. After a while the Duvitches, calling it a day, assembled at a spot on the shore below our tent, happy in the knowledge of a good catch to take home.

In a little while Tom and I could hear their muffled exclamations of disbelief and dismay. Father woke up and joined our neighbors in a conclave,[7] looking down at the tub of fish near his feet. After a few moments he produced the whistle he carried on all our country excursions and blew it piercingly three times, the proclamation of emergency. This meant that Tom and I must come at once.

Looking as guilty as we felt, we swam in and joined the group gathering around the tub. In the midst of our stricken neighbors stood Father, holding the half-melted cake of soap in his palm silently but accusingly, for the fish had perished miserably in the soapy water and were unfit to eat. Not only had Tom and I snatched precious food from their mouths but we had brazenly[8] advertised the contempt in which we held them.

Father's eyes were narrow slits of

7. A *conclave* (KAHN klayv) is a private gathering.
8. *Brazenly* (BRAY zin lee) means boldly and shamelessly.

blue fire in his white face. I had never seen him so angry. One look at Tom and me told him everything. Words would have been superfluous and my brother and I bowed our heads in acknowledgment of our guilt.

"You will begin," Father said in a voice I didn't recognize, "by saying you're sorry."

Our stunned neighbor wiped his blinking eyes as he listened to our mumbled words, which Father made us repeat when they were inaudible. But there was no hostility, no animosity toward us in the man and it was obvious also that he considered himself too humble to receive an apology, finding it, like most of life's troubles, a mockery to be endured without protest. His sons showed no resentment, either, only a kind of resignation in their minds, which carried almost atavistic memories[9] of century-old oppression by country barons and landed gentry.

One-eyed Manny Duvitch, as it turned out, had told Father he had seen me drop something in the tub of fish (before he learned that it had been a cake of soap). Now he looked guiltier than Tom and I. Because he had been the witness and accuser, it was as if he considered himself to be the troublemaker, deserving the punishment. The two real culprits were the young lords of the ruling manor, with unlimited license, exempt from chastisement.[10] To Manny, the fortunate, the well-to-do, were also the privileged.

"Do you realize," said Father coldly, looking from Tom to me, "that in certain primitive communities the sort of stunt you've pulled would be punishable by death?"

Tom and I did not reply.

"Turn over the tub," said Father abruptly, addressing us as if we were strangers.

We turned it over. The gray soapy water ran away in bubbly rivulets, disappearing in the coarse mat of turf, and the poisoned fish lay exposed on the grass—quiet, strangled, open-mouthed—and somehow looking as if they were mutely protesting their horrid unnatural fate.

"Count the fish," Father ordered us, his voice like steel.

Tom and I got down on our knees.

"How many are there?" demanded Father.

"Sixty-one," I said.

"How many bass?"

"Twelve."

Father handed Mr. Duvitch two dollars, the price of a day's rental of the rowboat. Then, looking both the avenging angel and executioner, he ordered Tom and me, with our tackle and bait, off the land we had disgraced—into exile, out on Durston's Pond.

"And you are not to come back," he gave out in the same steely tones, "until you've caught sixty-one fish to repay Mr. Duvitch. See to it that among them you bring in at least a dozen bass."

Father stepped up to the tent on the knoll to fetch our shirts and dungarees. These he rolled into a tight ball and shot like a bolt into the rowboat. He then turned his back to us and, thus disowned, Tom and I lost no time in rowing out on the pond. Father's decisions, even with Mother present, were never reversed and swift execution, from which there was no appeal, followed his sentences.

Word Bank

contempt (kun TEMPT) *n.*: scorn

superfluous (suh PER floo uss) *adj.*: being more than is sufficient; unnecessary; needless

animosity (AN ih MAHS ih tee) *n.*: ill-will; dislike

mutely (MYOOT lee) *adv.*: silently

---

9. *Atavistic* (AT uh VISS tik) *memories* are memories inherited from prior generations.
10. *Exempt from chastisement* (CHASS tyz mint) means not subject to punishment.

Out in the middle of the big pond we dropped anchor, threaded our steel rods and, baiting our hooks, began to fish. I knew that if it took us all summer to catch them, we dared not set foot ashore without sixty-one fish. Almost at once Tom pulled in a good-sized bass and ten minutes later two yellow perch were added to our string. The crestfallen Duvitches went home. Father threw himself on the blanket, furiously smoking a cigar. That was about four in the afternoon.

Oh, the mosquitoes! They were bad enough at the time, and while the light held, but after we had been fishing for three hours and had caught eight fish, they swarmed out of the swampland surrounding the pond in legions.

After an hour of it we wanted to leap overboard. They got in our ears, our noses, our eyes, even in our mouths, and nestling in our hair, they bit through to our scalps. I remembered tales of Indian prisoners in Alaska, turned loose on the tundra[11] by their captors, where they died of the mosquitoes in two hours. Several times we slipped over the side of the boat, immersing ourselves in the water to escape the bloodthirsty clouds. The night dragged on while the whining swarms grew thicker.

"Andy, what time is it?"

"Ten o'clock, Tom."

"Is that all?" Tom groaned and pulled in another bass and killed six or eight mosquitoes in one slap. Two hours passed and midnight was ghostly on Durston's Pond.

The moon, bright as day, sailed high in the purple sky, dimming the starfire, casting a great white shaft of quivering radiance on the water, but it was all hideous. The big yellow disk sank in a gauzy cloud bank, then disappeared for good and the stars shone out with renewed splendor.

"Andy, what time is it?"

"Two o'clock, Tom."

---

11. *Tundra* (TUN druh) is any of the vast, nearly treeless plains of the world's arctic regions.

The treetops whispered as if in conspiracy against us. Owls hooted—mockingly we thought—and bats circled over our heads, making us feel thoroughly alone. Our only solace was the campfire Father kept burning near the tent, which flared like a beacon of light in the dark. We went on fishing as our tormentors bit and sang. Each hour was an eternity of frenzy and I fairly panted for the light of dawn to come, but even now I cannot decide which was worse, that night with the mosquitoes on Durston's Pond or the following day in the blistering heat.

"Andy—"

"It's four o'clock, Tom, and we've got sixteen fish."

Dawn came but even I, a highly impressionable youngster of seventeen, did not enjoy that calm effulgent[12] majesty of daybreak. A long stretch on Durston's Pond, under the July sun, still faced us.

The rising sun was red, casting glimmering circles of rose-colored light on the windless surface of the pond. The mosquitoes thinned, the fish continued to bite. But as we fished the sun mounted steadily and by eleven it had fulfilled its awful prophecy and became a ball of fire in the cloudless skies. Tom and I began to bake in the heat waves that shimmered over the pond and we were steamed in the scalding vapory mist.

"I wish it was night again, Andy," groaned Tom after sweating out two hours of it. "This is worse than the mosquitoes."

"At least we won't get any infections from our bites, Tom," I said feebly.

"The sun's cauterizing them."

"We might get sunstrokes, though. We're liable to, without our hats. But I don't care if I do. I'd rather be unconscious."

Tom was only fifteen and I think he hated me that day. I, the older, should have been his protector against participation in crime, not his accomplice. I wanted to row him in, then come back to finish the business alone, but there on the green Eden-like shore stood Father, stationed there barring the way.

Tom and I weighed our hooks down to the deep cold water. We caught two more bass and half a dozen sunfish.

By one o'clock groups of people gathered on the shore, for word of the drama that was being enacted on Durston's Pond had spread through the town. Some of the visitors praised Father for his stern discipline; others berated him. He went right on reading his magazine and smoking his cigar, as indifferent to their praise as he was to their criticism.

Local fishermen who knew the lake and something about the angling ability of the average youngster made gloomy estimates as to the possible length of our exile on the water. A few had us fishing until the snow flew. They made bets too. Would Tom and I have the guts to stick it out? Most of the bets were against us.

But we sat there in the rowboat, without food, through the hottest day of the summer.

No breeze stirred. No cloud obscured the sun. Even the bird life of the swamp, usually a medley of song, was silent and dead. Tom was drooping visibly in the glare and I tried hard not to look at his scorched face.

Between three and four we dropped lines in a school of yellow perch and pulled up no less than twenty. The bass

---

Word Bank

solace (SAHL uss) *n.*: comfort

cauterizing (KAUT er IZE ing) *v.*: burning, with a hot iron

berated (bee RAYT id) *v.*: scolded; expressed sharp, stern disapproval of

---

12. *Effulgent* (ih FUL jint) is a brilliant radiance.

continued to bite in the deep black holes off the swamp, which bristled with tree trunks. Benumbed, half-blinded, moving like automatons,[13] Tom and I geared ourselves for the home stretch.

When the sun, dropping low, had lost its fury and the hard blue enamel of the sky began to pale, I pulled up the thirteenth bass, which was our sixty-first fish.

Turned lobster-red, fairly devoured, famished and drooping from lack of sleep, we put together our rods and with our remaining strength rowed to where Father was waiting.

He received us coolly, making no comment on our condition. At once he asked to see the fish and we held them up by the strings.

"Count them," he said.

Obviously we would receive permission to land only when we had produced the required number, which was the price of our freedom.

"Sixty-one," said Tom.

"Including thirteen bass," I added.

"Very good," said Father in businesslike tones. "We will now restore to Mr. Duvitch his rightful property."

Tom and I took care not to play the part of triumphant heroes, even of redeemed sinners—that would not have suited our parent. Certainly, in

_____

13. *Automatons* (aw TOM uh tahnz) are machine-like robots.

appearance, we were more condemned than redeemed. But when we tottered out of the rowboat something in me was quietly rejoicing. I guessed that Father was secretly proud of our fortitude and I realized, too, that all through the night he had suffered with us.

We walked through the crowd of visitors on the lake shore, climbed into the car and silently drove to the Duvitch cottage. Mrs. Duvitch and the children were not visible but we found Mr. Duvitch sitting on the porch.

When he saw Tom and me and we silently handed him the strings of fish, he gulped and swallowed hard. For a moment he could not speak. Then, in a voice that was raw with emotion, he protested that he had not wished us to suffer so. Suppose we had fallen overboard in the dark?

"Will you shake hands with the boys?" asked Father.

Instead, Mr. Duvitch broke down. My brother and I did not know where to look and during those moments we suffered more acutely than we had suffered in the clouds of mosquitoes and under the broiling sun. After our neighbor had composed himself, he seized our hands and bowed his head over them. There was something Biblical in the man's gesture. Anyway, it was my greatest lesson in humility.

When Mother, who had heard about our exile on the pond from a neighbor, saw us she burst into tears. She tried to embrace us but we drew back painfully. While she was rubbing salves and ointments on our seared backs and necks, somebody knocked at the kitchen door and Father opened it to find Mrs. Duvitch standing there—the first time she had crossed the street to our house.

In her pale swaying hand Mrs. Duvitch held a porcelain teacup, ornamented with pink rosebuds and golden leaves—a relic from the old country and, as it turned out, her most cherished possession.

Her voice, thin and wispy from fright and shock, was difficult to follow. But we gathered that she had brought the teacup over as a peace offering and as a plea for our forgiveness to her family for the living purgatory,[14] no matter whose fault, through which my brother and I had passed. When Mother declined the teacup and assured Mrs. Duvitch that she would not have it otherwise with Tom and me, our neighbor, unable to find her tongue, made a little eloquent sign with her hands that was for thanks and that looked like a silent blessing. She quietly turned and went away; and again I felt that I had witnessed a profound moment.

Mother continued her ministrations[15] to Tom and me and put us to bed. Despite our skin, which stuck to sheet and pillowcase, we slept like creatures drugged.

"It is high time," Tom and I heard Father say calmly, sanely, to Mother around noon the next day when we woke up, "for this senseless feeling against the Duvitches to stop and I'm willing to do still more to stop it. Tonight we are having supper with them. I've just seen Mr. Duvitch and he remarked that since Andy and Tom caught the fish, he'd feel better if we all shared in them. I suggested a fish-fry picnic supper and with a few hints from me, and some encouragement, he invited us over. It may be an ordeal but we ought to be able to bear it."

We walked across the street at six o'clock, not knowing what to expect.

---

14. Here, *purgatory* (PURG uh TOR ee) means drawn-out punishment.
15. *Ministrations* (MIN ih STRAY shunz) are acts of aid and relief.

All the Duvitches, dressed in their Sunday best, bright and flushed and shining as we had never seen them, received us at the door as if we had been royalty. They looked at Tom and me and delicately looked away—I shuddered when I thought of what my brother and I would have had to endure had this been any other family.

Instead of a wretched abode we found a scantily furnished home that shone with cleanliness and smelled of spicy garden pinks. In its almost barren simplicity there was something comely.[16] A few of the stands, chairs and tables had the intimate quality of what is fashioned by the human hand. These, together with odds and ends the family had brought from the old country and others resurrected from the town dump and mended, painted, waxed and polished, made for a kind of native household harmony. The house plants (no window was without several) delighted Mother. Mrs. Duvitch was raising little orange and lemon trees from seed and experimenting with a pineapple plant growing in a butter tub.

At once we were conscious of a remarkable difference in the demeanor of the family. The children, thrilled by their first party, by the family's first recognition in this country, kept showing their pleasure in wide delighted smiles. I couldn't believe they were the same timid downcast youngsters one met on the street and saw in school; they seemed to have been touched by a wand. The Duvitches' home was their castle: sustained and animated[17] by the security of its four walls, shut away from a world of contempt and hostility, they were complete human beings. In their own house their true personalities emerged.

As the host Mr. Duvitch was a man we were seeing for the first time.

Overjoyed to have neighbors in his house, he was so full of himself that I was conscious of an invisible stature in him which made him seem quite as tall as Father. He beamed and feasted his eyes on us. Saying very little, he managed to make us feel a great deal and he constantly sought his wife's eyes with glances of delight over the wonder of what was happening.

David, the oldest boy, helped his father serve a bottle of homemade blackberry wine.

We ate fried fish and good food of the American picnic variety at a long plank table set out in the back yard under an apple tree. The young Duvitches passed things politely, never helping themselves first, and their thanks upon receiving a dish were almost ceremonial. They waited patiently for their plates and ate every scrap of food.

Father kept the conversation going. His every word was listened to, every childish eye riveted on him while he spoke.

Tom and I, fascinated by the family's metamorphosis, almost forgot about our blisters and our stings. As father told stories and jokes, we discovered that the Duvitches had a gift for gaiety, for laughter, all but extinguished but still capable of resurrection. They were merry people who had suffered too much. How strange to see the boys and

---

16. *Comely* (KUM lee) means pleasing and attractive.
17. *Sustained and animated* means supported and given life.

| **Word Bank** | **demeanor** (dih MEEN ur) *n.*: conduct, behavior; facial appearance |
| | **metamorphosis** (MET uh mor FO siss) *n.*: a profound change |

girls throw back their heads and laugh when Father said something that was funny, but not terribly funny.

After supper we were ushered to the open summer kitchen, the coolest room in the house, for entertainment.

David played folk songs on his accordion. Mr. Duvitch turned out to be an amateur ventriloquist; he made the dog Kasimar talk Polish, the cat Jan talk Russian and a doll named Sophia, talk English. Mrs. Duvitch read aloud to us, translating as she went along, a letter her mother had received from the great actress Modjeska, whom her family had known long ago.

I could tell that the Duvitches were a great revelation to Father and that he had enjoyed the evening tremendously.

"To think," he murmured as if talking to himself, while we were crossing the street, "that they should turn out to be gentle people of cultivation and accomplishment. Looked down on and ignored by their inferiors!"

I like to believe that the oil paintings of George Washington, Abraham Lincoln and Thomas Jefferson, which hung in our living room, helped to establish the Duvitches in our community. Even the fountain tinkling in the lily pool in our garden might have helped. In that town, oil paintings and flowing fountains were the symbols of wealth and aristocracy. Only a few mansions on Sycamore Hill were adorned with such.

Because our home was graced with these symbols, we had always been classified with the town's great, which gave us such prestige in the neighborhood that people often followed our lead. Obviously the Duvitches were important in Father's eyes, shown by the rigorous sentence he had imposed on Tom and me for our misuse of them. Added to that, we had recognized the family by taking a meal with them in their own house. People, often persuaded to accept what we accepted, to believe what we believed, began to think the Duvitches must really count, after all. Most of our neighbors decided that if they were good enough for a highly educated man like Father (the only college graduate on Syringa Street), they were good enough for them. The galvanized community began to look upon things in a different light and it soon became the fashion to give the Duvitches the favorable nod.

Mother invited Mrs. Duvitch to a tea party, where her delicate manners, and the fine needlework which engaged her, won the approval of the local housewives who were present. On hot days our neighbor asked one of her big boys to carry the pineapple plant (which Mother had advertised well) into the back yard; and since botanical rarities were irresistible in that town of gardens, people were soon stopping by the fence for a look at the tropical specimen. After a while Mrs. Duvitch found courage to ask these people into her house and, if Mr. Duvitch was at home, he told the visitors stories about life in the old country. It was then that the neighborhood learned about the family's European past.

The children ceased stopping their noses when Mr. Duvitch passed them by and it wasn't long before the young Duvitches were able to enjoy outside companionship when they found time to play. They blossomed out in school and they were soon shining in school plays and festivals. Even Kasimar began to

| **Word Bank** | galvanized (GAL vuh nyzd) *v.*: motivated |

take on the ways of an American dog, daring to bark and growl on occasion.

Nathan Duvitch, who was seventeen, could throw and hit a baseball as far as anybody his age in town. When I learned this, and let it be known, he was asked to join one of the local ball clubs. David, invited to play his accordion at a country dance, turned out to be a magician with the instrument and ended up being one of the community's most popular players. Mrs. Frithjof Kinsella gave One-eyed Manny an after-school job in her store and later on told Mother he was worth three boys put together.

The community presently had reason to be grateful for Mrs. Duvitch's presence. It turned out that she had a great gift for nursing, and no fear of death, no fear of disease, contagious or otherwise. In times of severe illness Dr. Switzer often suggested that she be sent for—her own girls could take over at home. There were almost no nurses in town and the nearest hospital was over a hundred miles away. When Mrs. Duvitch quietly slipped into a sickroom, she never failed to bring along a sedative influence, a kind of sanity. After an hour or two of her serene presence, the patient was calmed and comforted and the family reassured.

People began to turn to the Duvitches in all kinds of trouble. A boy who got in a bad scrape, a bitter family quarrel, a baby who had come into the world deformed—the elder Duvitches, with their old-world wisdom and gift for accepting the inevitable, could sit by the hour and argue gently and convincingly against disgrace, false pride, grief, fear.

Most surprising of all, Mr. Duvitch, in one respect, turned out to be characteristically American. One Saturday afternoon when my ball team was playing Nathan's, Father met him in the local ball park.

"Chust like de American boy," Mr. Duvitch exploded when Nathan made a timely hit that drove in two runs. Our neighbor choked with pride and went on: "Nathan's battering averich three hunnert tventy-sevened!"

On a cold snowy afternoon in winter Mr. Duvitch stopped at our house and presented Father (who had enormous hands, much bigger than any of the Duvitches') with a handsome pair of leather mittens, lined with fur, which had a slightly acrid ashy odor.

"No doubt one of the boys resurrected them from a heap of ashes in the dump," remarked Father, drawing on the mittens, which fitted perfectly. "Why should I value them any the less? *Who* would have dreamed that the Duvitches would have so much more to offer us than we have to offer them?"

Word Bank	sedative (SED uh TIV) *adj.*: tending to calm or soothe acrid (AK rid) *adj.*: bitter

Recalling

1. What brought the Duvitches to the neighborhood?

2. Why didn't the Duvitch family have any friends?

3. What sort of prank did Tom and Andy play on the Duvitches?

4. How did Tom and Andy's father react to their prank? How did Mr. Duvitch react?

5. What was Tom and Andy's punishment?

6. What caused the neighborhood to finally accept the Duvitches?

Interpreting

7. Why do you think Father disagreed with Mother "when she remarked that she thought the Duvitches probably wished to be left alone"?

8. What does the narrator mean when he states, "their European travail made it easy for them to endure such a trifle as humiliation in America"?

9. After Tom and Andy came back to dry land after bringing in all the fish, "something in [Andy] was quietly rejoicing." What was Andy rejoicing about?

10. How did the Duvitches act within the confines of their own home? Describe the interior of the Duvitch home. Were their manners and their home what you would have expected?

11. Father remarks at the end of the story, "Who would have dreamed that the Duvitches would have so much more to offer us than we have to offer them?" In what ways did the Duvitches enrich their community?

Concluding

12. To "justify" means: to "provide good grounds or reasons for something." Why do people try to justify their behavior, even when they know that what they have done is wrong?

Examining Fiction

Understanding a character's motives gives you deeper understanding of a story. Think about the main characters in *The Strangers That Came to Town*.

1. What caused the boys to pull the prank on the Duvitches? Do you think it was out of malicious intent, or out of mischief?

2. What motivated Father to punish Tom and Andy the way he did? Do you think the punishment was too severe, or do you think the punishment was appropriate?

Thinking About Fiction

What motivates an individual? If you know that about a person, you must understand that person well. Usually, we look at a person's actions and come to certain conclusions about what motivated those actions. Writers of fiction often show us a character's actions and leave it to us to determine what the character's motivation is. It sometimes requires a lot of observing and thinking to figure out just what motivated a person to take certain action. Often, two observers will come to different conclusions about what someone's motives were in a certain situation.

1. What motivated the children of the town to ridicule the Duvitches?

2. What motivated Father to invite the Duvitches to dinner?

3. What motivated the community to finally accept the Duvitches? Frequently, people have mixed motives, some good, some selfish. Do any of the characters in the story have fixed motives?

Creating and Writing

Imagine that you are one of the Duvitches. Write a diary entry about what life was like for you, when you first moved to town. Describe how you felt starting in a new school and being treated in a demeaning way. Then write a second diary entry, describing life after having supper with your neighbors. Include details about how life began to change for the better.

Blueprint FOR READING

Into • *Barnum's First Circus*

Have you ever seen a drawing or heard some music and asked yourself, "How did the artist think of that?" We can imagine that Laura Benét—the author of *Barnum's First Circus*—must have gone to a circus and thought, "how did someone think of doing this?" She invented a story about young Phineas Barnum, the creator of America's first and most famous circus. She imagined the type of personality that would combine the desire to entertain others with a fascination for the strange and different. In addition, this person would be organized and energetic. The young Phineas Barnum portrayed in the story has all these qualities. Although the story itself may not have actually happened, given what we know about the accomplishments of Phineas Barnum, it certainly could have!

Focus

An author uses a variety of techniques to bring a character to life. They may use **direct characterization**, in which they tell the reader what the character looks like, how the character behaves, or even what the character is thinking. Another technique is **indirect characterization**. This requires the reader to judge the character from the character's own dialogue or actions. Most authors will use a combination of both types of characterization in order to keep the story interesting and varied. Which type of characterization do you think is more difficult to write?

About the Author

LAURA BENÉT was born in 1884 in Brooklyn, New York. Originally a social worker, she had no intention of becoming a writer. Both of her brothers, Stephen Vincent and William Rose, were writers. When William Rose started to work at the *Literary Review*, she began occasionally sending her work to them. Later she started to write children's stories. Laura Benét also wrote numerous biographies that were well-received. She went on to publish five books of poetry. Laura Benét considered *Barnum's First Circus*—a collection of her short stories—her best work for children. She died in 1979 in New York.

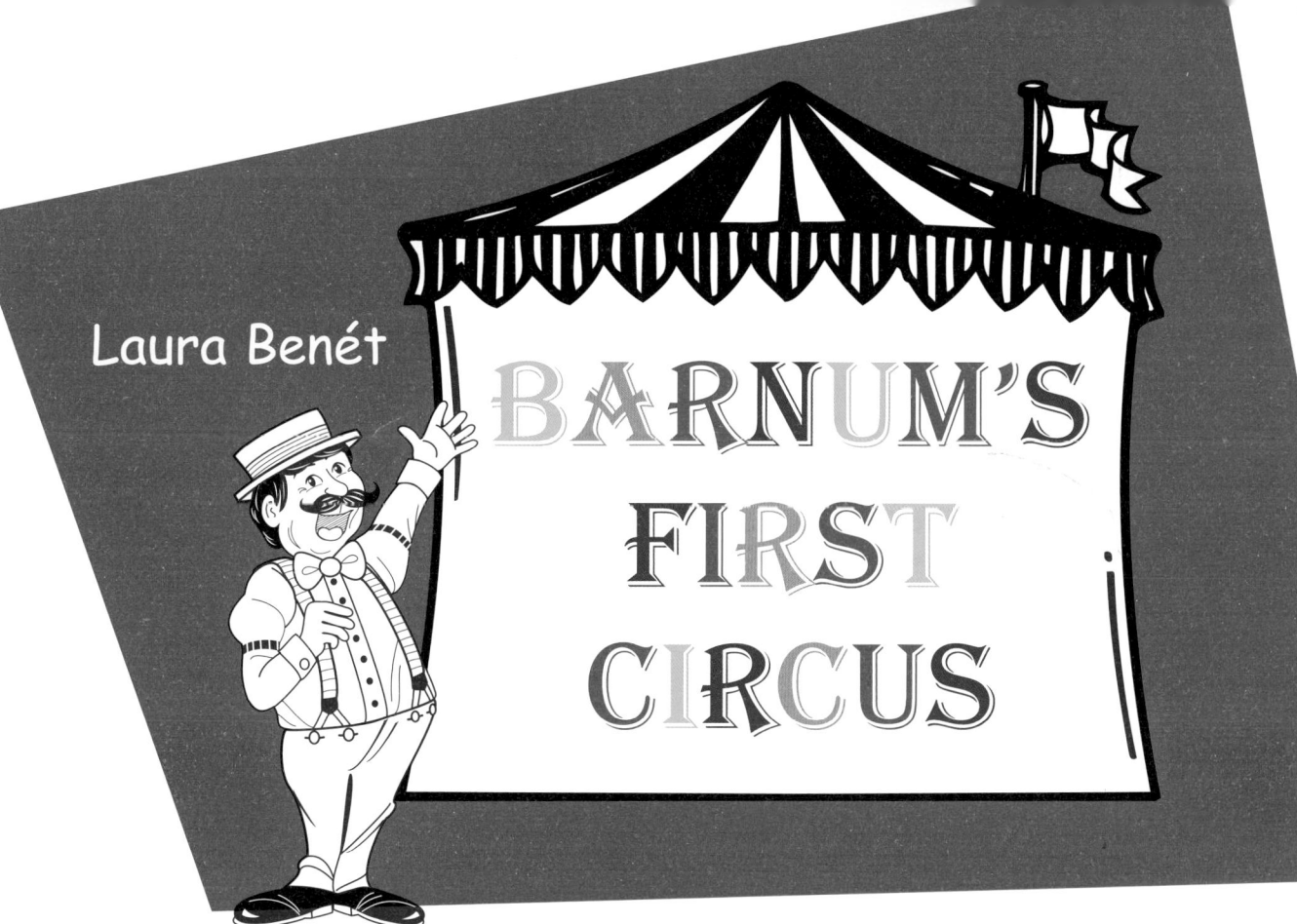

Laura Benét

BARNUM'S FIRST CIRCUS

"Phineas," remarked his father, pushing back his coffee cup and carefully wiping the ends of his walrus mustache, "you can tend store for me mebbe two or three days. The mare's going to take your mother and me to the county seat." He looked across the table at his thirteen-year-old son.

Phineas Taylor Barnum, a stocky, broad-shouldered lad bursting with vitality, stopped munching a doughnut, and his eyes danced. This piece of news was too good to be true. He had often helped his father in the store, but to have it in charge…that would be wonderful!

"Yes, sir," he answered respectfully.

His father went briskly on with the tale of his instructions. "If Noah Totten's drinking, don't give him credit.

And don't give the Widow Sweeney any, neither. Cash in hand is the rule, unless circumstances is a mite unusual. Seeing apples are good this year, you can take two or three barrels in exchange for groceries. But remember, business is likely to be brisk, and you're to tend to your job and not talk your head off. You've got a good head on your shoulders when you choose to use it. That's all. And don't make me use that strap hanging up in the barn when I come back Saturday." His keen eyes twinkled slightly.

Barnum Senior, citizen of the town of Bethel, Connecticut went to "hitch up." Barnum Junior, rejoicing in his unexpected freedom from school, put on his hat and took his way to his father's small corner store.

The day being October and a chill wind blowing, he began his business day by doing what his father would have said was needless extravagance. He started a fire in the rusty iron stove in the center of the store. The fire, made out of shavings, old boxes, and good hard cordwood, had not been going fifteen minutes before Phineas' first customer arrived.

It *was* the Widow Sweeney, shawled and bonneted, peering out of near-sighted, pinkish-rimmed eyes that were much like a rabbit's. She slammed the store door behind her so that everything on the shelves rattled, and delighted by the good fire, crept near it, untying her bonnet strings.

"Well, if it ain't Barnum's boy!" she said in a pleased tone. The son should be much easier to deal with than the father.

"Now, I want you," she continued, consulting a list, "to tie up a pound of white sugar and a passel of apples and raisins and two pounds of coffee and a pound of rice and a pint of sorghum molasses."

Young Barnum went to the shelves and began weighing out the various articles, to which the Widow Sweeney kept adding other items. At last everything was ready. In his pleasantest tone, he stated: "One dollar, if you please, Missus Sweeney."

The Widow started back. "No sass from you, Phineas Barnum. This is on credit today. I'm a poor woman and I pay up my bills all at once, twice a year."

"Pa said 'no credit'—that I was to take cash only," answered Pa's representative. "I'm sorry, but you've got a long credit column already, Missus Sweeney."

Finding her first method of bluster did not work, the Widow began to wheedle. "Now, you're a good boy and not raised for impudence. Haven't I got the nicest little calf only two weeks old that I was calculating on giving your Pa in payment, if he'd continue my credit awhile?"

"Is it an all right calf?" asked the youthful storekeeper bluntly.

> **Word Bank**
>
> **sorghum molasses** (SORE gum muh LASS iss) *n.*: sweet syrup made from the juicy stalks of a cereal grass
>
> **impudence** (IMP yoo duntz) *n.*: bold and shameless rudeness

"Of course, it's all right. It's as pretty as can be. But it's got a curious failing—an extra eye."

"Oh!" Joy gleamed in Phineas' own eyes. If he could only get hold of that calf for purposes of his own! "Pa's been wanting a calf," he answered. "Is it a bull?"

"No, a heifer."

"Well, marm—" He hesitated, the thought of the ready strap at the back of his mind, but decided he'd have to take a chance. "If you'll let me stop around tonight and see it when I close up store, I can let you have these things now."

The delighted Widow assented, warmed herself thoroughly at the stove, and then went on her way. Meanwhile, Phineas Barnum resolved to show off that three-eyed calf behind the barn at a penny a peep—or maybe he'd make it two cents for a look. What a find for the show he was planning!

His next customer was a red-headed boy, younger than himself, who painfully lugged in two pecks of apples to be exchanged for potatoes. As he set the half-bushel basket down with a thump, a snake glided across the uneven, splintered floor toward the heat.

"Hi, help me get him, Phin! He musta got out of my pocket!" screeched Hiram Fletcher. Young Barnum recaptured the snake in a wink, stowing him in a small and dark box.

"Can you do tricks with him?" he inquired interestedly.

"Only caught him yesterday, so how'm I to know?" said Hiram, surprised by the idea.

"Bring him around to my house Saturday afternoon. Meet me behind the barn. We'll have a circus," said Phineas in an excited whisper. He saw three farmers entering. "There's lots of things I can tell you but I've got to tend store now."

Hiram chuckled. "I'll see you later, and I'll get Rafe and George and Buckle Ewing, too."

Farmers were apt to stay indefinitely on such a raw day. Phineas prepared for them by fetching out a couple of rickety wooden stools (the third could perch on the molasses barrel) and mending the fire.

"Hey, Phineas," said the first farmer, Ezra Dean, a hard-bitten Yankee with rugged features and a long jaw. "Give me a plug of chewing tobacco."

The busy storekeeper cut it and was paid. "One nickel more," he requested briskly.

Ezra dumped his weather-beaten purse out on the counter for inspection. Not a cent was in it.

"I'll give you a hopping bean instead, boy!" he offered. "I know you like tricks."

"But does it really hop? Lemme see for sure."

Ezra winked at the other men and produced a small brown object from his pocket. Placing it on the bottom of a broken cracker box, he carried it to the stove. Yes, the heat caused it to skip about here and there on the piece of board. The dance was uncanny. The farmers stood and watched interestedly.

Word Bank	**assented** (uh SENT id) *v.*: agreed
	indefinitely (in DEF in it lee) *adv.*: having no fixed or specific limit
	uncanny (un CAN ee) *adj.*: mysterious; weird

"Ain't seen a contraption like that in a month of Sundays," remarked the oldest of the three, Mose Painter. Phineas put it carefully into his pocket.

As he waited on children, giggling schoolgirls, New England housewives (for the store had filled up), Phineas caught snatches of conversation from the group of farmers.

"Just try walking easy by that mill, come twilight, and you'll hear a voice, a high, queer voice, like a spirit's," was one statement.

"I didn't know that the old mill was haunted."

"Well, 'tis, and Steve Carter's lost his watch chain and swears he had it when he was going by there, week or so ago."

"Time someone got to the bottom of this," said Mose Painter.

The very same evening, Phineas, who had been to see Widow Sweeney's three-eyed calf, took a walk past the old Franklin mill on the village outskirts. He didn't believe what the men at the store had said, and anyway, he was more curious than afraid. In the moonlight the stone mill looked as peaceful as the stream that flowed beside it. Suddenly, from an upper window of the mill came easy, conversational tones.

"Good boy," uttered a clipped mocking voice, and then a dark shadow flew past him. Something with straw clinging to it jingled at his feet. Squatting on a stone, Phineas drew from his pocket a bit of bread and a cheese rind he kept

for just such emergencies. The shadow drew nearer and perched on his finger. It was a raven!

"Good night," it said, "good night, good night. Have no fear, no fear."

Adroitly, Phineas caught it, slipped it into a bag he had brought, and picked up the object on the ground. It was nothing less then Steve Carter's gold watch chain! What a surprise Steve would have on Saturday!

The raven would be a great addition to the side show. He could teach it to talk in no time. It must have flown over from some other township, where someone else had begun its education. He might rent a skull for it to perch on, if there was anyone about who had one handy. There was never going to be another exhibition like this one he planned. No, sir!

Next morning Phineas had Hiram, with George, his brother and side-partner, take a brisk turn about Bethel. One went east, one west, until they covered the whole town. In their hands they carried a pile of hand-printed advertisements that were stuck under front doors or pushed at anyone the boys happened to meet.

After three long days of storekeeping, Phineas had collected a goodly sum in his father's till as well as half-a-dozen barrels of fall pippins. Now it was Saturday noon. His father was still away, but he'd done his level best, and at three o'clock he planned to close up the store until evening.

"Barnum's Saturday Show" was opening at four o'clock for a nickel admission and a penny apiece extra for special side shows. Of course it couldn't begin until Phineas appeared.

The crowd that gathered at the back of the Barnums' barn at four o'clock that day was enormous. At a rude turnstile made of two crossed laths stood

SOLD HERE

See the Three-Eyed Calf

Meet Jupiter, the Domestic Snake!

Barnum's boy himself, hair tousled, face red with excitement.

"This way, ladies and gentlemen," he shouted, "to see the Three-Eyed Calf, the only specimen of its kind in captivity. Meet Jupiter, the Domestic Snake that snuggles up to you like an infant! See the Magic Bean worked by Unseen Force, and Lupo, the Raven that talks and brings forth gold. Last chance, cash and tickets!"

"That boy of Barnum's has a gift of gab," said the tired mother of two fretting children. "First-rate showman! He'll make money or I miss my guess."

Farmers, curious to see, were driving up in carts and buggies, with children between their knees. Big boys were stamping in, leading younger brothers and sisters by the hand.

"This way, this way, to the Calf. Put your money on the Three-Eyed Calf," called one of Barnum's assistants.

He was instantly corrected by his chief. "Say a lot more, Hi, about its unusual points—like this: 'The One and Only Calf in Captivity That Has an Extra Eye,'" shouted Phineas.

Meantime, a fearless brother, younger than Phineas, was riding Zeke, the Runaway Colt, around a chalked ring, sticking on its back despite frantic kickings and plungings. This feature, the only ten-cent one, was marvelously popular. When Bethel's crop of dimes

"Sor-ry," croaked the raven, and Steve Carter, eyes popping, was beckoned forward to receive his missing watch chain.

"I *declare*," was all he could say.

As a final feature, the hopping bean began gamboling briskly on a table. Young Phineas had learned exactly how much heat to give it from his warm, perspiring palm.

SOR-RY

had been taken in, the raven was produced.

"Step up here," announced the showman to late comers. "Plenty of room to stand. Step up!" Then, "What do you like best, Lupo?" he asked the raven.

"Gold," said Lupo in a hoarse and impressive tone.

"What next to that?"

"Chain," croaked the raven.

"And then?"

"Gold chain."

"Now tell the gentleman whose watch chain you took that you're sorry."

Word Bank	**gamboling** (GAM buh ling) *v.*: skipping; dancing; frolicking

Homemade doughnuts and cider were being circulated to the still admiring crowd when hoofs were heard approaching briskly, and a tired man came into view on the far side of the barn. In the buggy were visible the wide shoulders of Pa Barnum, his wife by his side.

Barnum Senior's astonishment when he saw the gathering on the lot back of his barn was followed by a grim expression about the jaw. That fool boy of his, who was so keen on freaks and shows, had gone and closed up the store (yes, it was shut and silent when he passed it) and lost the late Saturday afternoon trade. He'd show him! He could not help being perked up over his son's talents, but he'd have to teach him a lesson for all that.

"Phineas," he called in tones to wake the dead, "you come here and stop this fooling."

Some little distance away, he seemed to see a familiar form, to hear a familiar voice. "Calf," it was saying.

Calf! Was it possible there was a new heifer? Excitedly, Barnum stopped the buggy, threw the reins to his wife, got out, and stamped over to the circus enclosure.

"Nickel, please, Mister Barnum," requested the gatekeeper. Inwardly raging, Barnum paid it and continued his search.

"Excuse me, folks," he kept saying until suddenly, in a pen near him, he saw one of the finest little heifer calves. It was sound in wind and limb, the only defect being a curious third eye immediately

over the regular one on the left side.

"Where on earth did Phineas…?"

Then father and son met face to face. Young Barnum's countenance was as bland as cream. "Hey, Pa," he said. "See the calf you got from the Widow Sweeney."

"How much did you have to give for it?" roared his father.

"Not a penny. It was a present in payment."

"Well—and what do you have to say about closing the store and losing my Saturday-afternoon trade?"

"I was going to reopen this evening," stated Phineas confidently, "and what I've taken in on entrances will make up for any loss. I've got a good sight of money in here, Pa, and it's all yours!" He gleefully rattled the contents of a tin can.

Parent looked at son with sudden added respect.

"You've not cheated anyone to get hold of these critters?" Barnum Senior indicated in one sweeping gesture the calf, the raven, the snake, and the colt. "I nearly stepped on that blamed snake," he exploded as it wiggled near his boots.

"No, Pa, I didn't cheat. When folks come in to celebrate, I like to show them a thing or two," Phineas said.

His father scratched his head. "I always took it you had smartness in you," was his comment.

Young Barnum looked triumphantly around. The crowd was scattering. His father had made up with him and gone peering into this box and that pen to see what else he could see.

But, somehow, the barn lot wasn't quite large enough. Some day there must be a big white tent pegged down at the corners, or—maybe—a hall. In his imagination such a hall swelled and grew bigger until he had it peopled with weird shapes. He'd like a family of dwarfs—a mummy—a giant—and a voice that would fill space with its ringing music and make echoes come out of the air. Some day he'd have that, too!

Word Bank	bland (BLAND) *adj.*: mild; expressionless

Recalling

1. Why is Phineas placed in charge of his father's store?

2. What rules does Mr. Barnum make in regard to managing the store?

3. How does Widow Sweeney convince Phineas to allow her to take her items on credit, even though it is against the rules?

4. What sort of wonders did Phineas gather for his show? How did he obtain each one?

5. Was his show a success?

Interpreting

6. Do you think it was right for Phineas to accept the calf from Widow Sweeney in place of payment? Keep in mind how his father had cautioned him before leaving.

7. One mother, who brought her two children to the show, said, "First-rate show-man! He'll make money or I miss my guess." Do you agree with her? Why or why not?

8. When Mr. Barnum came home and saw what his son had done, he was proud. If you were Phineas' father, would you have reacted in the same manner? Why or why not?

Concluding

9. *Barnum's First Circus* is a fictional story based on facts. Which parts of the story do you think are fact, and which parts do you think are fiction?

Examining Fiction

The author of *Barnum's First Circus* uses both **direct** and **indirect characterization**. Sometimes, she directly describes a character. At other times she reveals personality and traits through the character's speech and action, as well as through the other characters' reactions. Read the following passages from the story. Is the author using direct or indirect characterization?

1. "Phineas Taylor Barnum, a stocky, broad-shouldered lad bursting with vitality, stopped munching a doughnut, and his eyes danced."

2. " 'I was going to reopen this evening,' stated Phineas confidently."

3. "His father scratched his head. 'I always took it you had smartness in you,' was his comment."

Thinking About Fiction

A reasonable conclusion drawn from given information is an **inference**. When an author uses indirect characterization, the reader is forced to make inferences, based on the character's words and actions. After reading the story, you may have inferred that Phineas had several obvious character traits.

1. At what point in the story did you make the inference that at only age thirteen, Phineas was a good businessman?

2. Present evidence from the story that Phineas had a great imagination and could see value in things that other people considered profitless.

3. Where in the story do you see Phineas' ability to get people to willingly do what he asks them to do?

Creating and Writing

Phineas Barnum went on to become the founder of "The Greatest Show on Earth." He was a brilliant and creative promoter. Now it's your turn to plan a show! Design an advertising poster and a brochure for your show. Think about the "acts" you will feature and how you can present your advertising in the most intriguing way.

Into • *A Secret for Two*

Deep feelings can be expressed in many different ways. Sometimes, words of love are spoken. Sometimes, gifts are exchanged. Sometimes, time, loyalty, and devotion create such a strong bond that neither words nor gifts are needed. A bond such as this can exist between two people. It can also—and it often does—exist between a person and an animal. In *A Secret for Two*, Pierre, a man, and Joseph, a horse, share a love for one another that runs so deep that one cannot live without the other.

Focus

Most short stories have one **major character** and several **minor characters**. Generally the story is built around the major character. The author uses the minor characters to develop the plot or the characterization of the major character. The reader is usually given a detailed description of the major character, while the minor characters are described briefly. *A Secret for Two* is different because a minor character, Joseph, plays a very important role in the story. Perhaps this is because the focus of the story is not really Pierre, the main character, or even Joseph, the minor one. The focus is the bond that exists between the two of them.

About the Author

QUENTIN REYNOLDS was born in 1902 in Brooklyn, New York. Even though he received a law degree, Reynolds eventually became a journalist. During World War II Reynolds served as an international war correspondent in Moscow, North Africa, Sicily, Tehran, and Palestine. Much of his writing reflects his wartime experiences. Winston Churchill, the Prime Minister of England at that time, highly praised Reynolds' works. Reynolds was also a sportswriter and a writer of short stories. He died in 1965. He is remembered fondly for one of his most beloved stories, *A Secret for Two*.

A Secret for Two

Quentin Reynolds

Montreal[1] is a very large city, but, like all large cities, it has some very small streets. Streets, for instance, like Prince Edward Street, which is only four blocks long, ending in a cul-de-sac. No one knew Prince Edward Street as well as did Pierre Dupin,[2] for Pierre had delivered milk to the families on the street for thirty years now.

During the past fifteen years the horse which drew the milk wagon used by Pierre was a large white horse named Joseph. In Montreal, especially in that part of Montreal which is very French, the animals, like children, are often given names. When the big white horse first came to the Provincale[3] Milk Company, he didn't have a name. They told Pierre that he could use the white horse henceforth. Pierre stroked the softness of the horse's neck; he stroked the sheen of its splendid belly, and he looked into the eyes of the horse.

"That is a kind horse, a gentle and faithful horse," Pierre said, "and I can see a beautiful spirit shining out of the eyes of the horse. I will name him after Joseph, a kind and gentle and faithful and a beautiful name."

Within a year Joseph knew the milk route as well as Pierre. Pierre used to boast that he didn't need reins—he never touched them. Each morning

---

1. *Montreal* (MAHN tree all) is a large city in Quebec where French and English are both official languages.
2. *Pierre Dupin* (pea ERR due PAAN)
3. *Provincale* (pro vaan SAHL)

Word Bank	**cul-de-sac** (KUL DUH SAK) *n.*: a passage or street that is closed at one end
	sheen (SHEEN) *n.*: luster; glimmer

Pierre arrived at the stables of the Provincale Milk Company at five o'clock. The wagon would be loaded and Joseph hitched to it. Pierre would call *"Bon jour, vieille, ami,"*[4] as he climbed into his seat and Joseph would turn his head and the other drivers would smile and say that the horse would smile at Pierre. Then Jacques,[5] the foreman, would say, "All right, Pierre, go on," and Pierre would call softly to Joseph, *"Avance, mon ami,"*[6] and this splendid combination would stalk proudly down the street.

The wagon, without any direction from Pierre, would roll three blocks down St. Catherine Street, then turn right two blocks along Roslyn Avenue; then left, for that was Prince Edward Street. The horse would stop at the first house, allow Pierre perhaps thirty seconds to get down from his seat and put a bottle of milk at the front door and would then go on, skipping two houses and stopping at the third. So down the length of the street. Then Joseph, still without any direction from Pierre, would turn around and come back along the other side. Yes, Joseph was a smart horse.

Pierre would boast at the stable of Joseph's skill. "I never touch the reins. He knows just where to stop. Why, a blind man could handle my route with Joseph pulling the wagon."

So it went on for years—always the same. Pierre and Joseph both grew old together, but gradually, not suddenly. Pierre's huge walrus mustache was pure white now and Joseph didn't lift his knees so high or raise his head quite as much. Jacques, the foreman of the stables, never noticed that they were both getting old until Pierre appeared one day carrying a heavy walking stick.

"Hey, Pierre," Jacques laughed. "Maybe you got the gout,[7] hey?"

"Mais oui,[8] Jacques," Pierre said uncertainly. "One grows old. One's legs get tired."

"You should teach the horse to carry the milk to the front door for you," Jacques told him. "He does everything else."

He knew every one of the forty families he served on Prince Edward Street. The cooks knew that Pierre could neither read nor write, so instead of following the usual custom of leaving a note in an empty bottle if an additional quart of milk was needed they would sing out when they heard the rumble of his wagon wheels over the cobbled street, "Bring an extra quart this morning, Pierre."

Pierre had a remarkable memory. When he arrived at the stable he'd always remember to tell Jacques, "The Paquins[9] took an extra quart this morning; the Lemoines[10] bought a pint of cream."

Jacques would note these things in a little book he always carried. Most of the drivers had to make out the weekly bills and collect the money, but Jacques, liking Pierre, had always excused him from his task. All Pierre had to do was to arrive at five in the morning, walk to his wagon, which was always in the same spot at the curb, and deliver his

---

4. *Bon jour, vieille ami* (BAHN ZHOOR, vee AY ah MEE) is French for "hello, old friend."
5. *Jacques* (ZHAHK)
6. *Avance, mon ami* (ah VAHNCE, MONE ah MEE) is French for "forward, my friend."
7. *Gout* (GOWT) is a disease common in the elderly causing swelling of the joints.
8. *Mais oui* (MAY WEE) is French for "but yes."
9. *Paquins* (pah KAHNZ)
10. *Lemoines* (luh MWAHNZ)

milk. He returned some two hours later, got stiffly from his seat, called a cheery "*Au 'voir*"[11] to Jacques and then limped slowly down the street.

One morning the president of the Provincale Milk Company came to inspect the early morning deliveries. Jacques pointed Pierre out to him and said, "Watch how he talks to that horse. See how the horse listens and how he turns his head toward Pierre? See the look in that horse's eyes? You know, I think those two share a secret. I have often noticed it. It is as though they both sometimes chuckle at us as they go off on their route. Pierre is a good man, Monsieur[12] President, but he gets old. Would it be too bold for me to suggest that he be retired and be given perhaps a small pension?" he added anxiously.

"But of course," the president laughed. "I know his record. He has been on this route now for thirty years and never once has there been a complaint. Tell him it is time he rested. His salary will go on just the same."

But Pierre refused to retire. He was panic-stricken at the thought of not driving Joseph every day. "We are two old men," he said to Jacques. "Let us wear out together. When Joseph is ready to retire—then I, too, will quit."

Jacques, who was a kind man, understood. There was something about Pierre and Joseph which made a man smile tenderly. It was as though each drew some hidden strength from the other. When Pierre was sitting in his seat, and when Joseph was hitched to the wagon, neither seemed old. But when they finished their work, then Pierre would limp down the street slowly, seeming very old indeed, and the horse's head would drop and he would walk very wearily to his stall.

Then one morning Jacques had dreadful news for Pierre when he arrived. It was a cold morning and still pitch-dark. The air was like iced wine that morning and the snow which had fallen during the night glistened like a million diamonds piled together.

Jacques said, "Pierre, your horse, Joseph, did not wake this morning. He was very old, Pierre, he was twenty-five, and that is like seventy-five for a man."

"Yes," Pierre said, slowly. "Yes, I am seventy-five. And I cannot see Joseph again."

"Of course you can," Jacques soothed. "He is over in his stall, looking very peaceful. Go over and see him."

Pierre took one step forward then turned. "No…no…you don't understand, Jacques."

Jacques clapped him on the shoulder. "We'll find another horse just as good as Joseph. Why, in a month you'll teach him to know your route as well as Joseph did. We'll…"

The look in Pierre's eyes stopped him. For years Pierre had worn a heavy cap, the peak of which came low over his eyes, keeping the bitter morning wind out of them. Now Jacques looked into Pierre's eyes and he saw something which startled him. He saw a dead, lifeless look in them. The eyes were mirroring the grief that was in Pierre's heart and his soul. It was as though his heart and soul had died.

"Take today off, Pierre," Jacques said, but already Pierre was hobbling off down the street, and had one been

---

11. *Au 'voir* (ah VWAHR), short for au revoir, is French for "good-bye."
12. *Monsieur* (mih SYUH) is French for "mister."

Word Bank	pension (PEN shun) *n.*: a payment received periodically by a retired person

near one would have seen tears streaming down his cheeks and have heard half-smothered sobs. Pierre walked to the corner and stepped into the street. There was a warning yell from the driver of a huge truck that was coming fast and there was a scream of brakes, but Pierre apparently heard neither.

Five minutes later an ambulance driver said, "He's dead. Was killed instantly."

Jacques and several of the milk-wagon drivers had arrived and they looked down at the still figure.

"I couldn't help it," the driver of the truck protested, "He walked right into my truck. He never saw it, I guess. Why, he walked into it as though he was blind."

The ambulance doctor bent down. "Blind? Of course the man was blind. See those cataracts? This man has been blind for five years." He turned to Jacques. "You say he worked for you? Didn't you know he was blind?"

"No…no…" Jacques said, softly. "None of us knew. Only one knew—a friend of his named Joseph…It was a secret, I think, just between those two."

Word Bank	**cataract** (KAT UH RAKT) *n.*: a condition of the eye in which the lens becomes cloudy and vision is impaired

Recalling

1. Where does Pierre live? What does he do for a living? Who is Joseph, and how does he help Pierre on the job?

2. What allowances do Pierre's customers make for him, because he doesn't know how to read or write?

3. What happens to Joseph one morning? How does Pierre react?

4. How do we discover that Pierre is blind?

Interpreting

5. Explain how Jacques helps Pierre run his route.

6. Describe Pierre's reaction, when asked to retire. Why do you think he reacts this way?

7. How is it possible that no one ever knew that Pierre was blind?

8. Why is the story titled *A Secret for Two*? Is this an appropriate name for this story? Can you suggest a better name? If so, what would it be?

Concluding

9. Give reasons as to why the tie between Pierre and Joseph was so strong.

10. Explain how the friendship between Pierre and Joseph is similar to a relationship between two human beings.

Examining Fiction

The **major character** in a story is given many different character traits. A **minor character** plays a small role in the story and therefore is not a major focus of the author. Many times a story explores the relationship between two or more characters.

1. Identify the major character in *A Secret for Two*. Who are the minor characters?

2. What are the differences between the role Jacques plays in the story and the role Joseph plays?

3. Examine the relationship between Pierre and Joseph. How does it help move the story along?

Thinking About Fiction

Sometimes a character in a story may have a problem that is not obvious to the reader until the end of the story. In *A Secret for Two*, we do not discover that Pierre is blind until the conclusion.

1. Suppose the author had revealed to us earlier that Pierre was blind. How would that have changed the effect of the story?

2. Pretend you are Jacques, and you realize that Pierre is blind. What would you say, to try to convince him that all was not lost, when Joseph died?

3. Is there anybody or anything in the story that makes life difficult for Pierre? If so, what or who is it?

Creating and Writing

Many times people have special relationships with animals or pets. Write a story in which the major character has a special bond with a pet. Perhaps the main character is lonely and cannot form a friendship with another person; perhaps the animal fulfills a special need for the person. Make your characters unique and believable.

Into • "My Journey Is Still Long"

As the story opens, a young boy, Kofi Akakpo, is walking through an African village of mud huts, the aroma of fried fish and plantain heavy in the air. By the story's end, he is standing outside a modern apartment building, the sounds of cars coming and going, humming in his ears. At the age of twelve, Kofi decided he would escape the poverty and ignorance of his birthplace and make a better life for himself. The key to this, he knew, was education. But how could he get an education? Kofi answered this question in the only way he knew. He would walk across the desert to Algiers, from there to Morocco, on to Spain, to France, to Germany, Austria, Yugoslavia, Bulgaria, and finally, to Turkey, where he would meet an American airman who had promised to help him. How did he survive the heat, snakes, hunger, thirst, wild animals, border guards and, above all, loneliness? *"My Journey Is Still Long"* is based on a true story. After reading it one can only conclude that, of the wonders of the world, the human spirit is the greatest of them all.

Focus

The structure of *"My Journey Is Still Long"* is an interesting mix of narrative and journal entries. The narrative is written in the third person, and the journal entries are written in the first person. The two voices are so skillfully blended that the reader is hardly conscious of the shift from one voice to the other. What does each format add to the story? Do you think the story would have been better had it been told entirely in one or the other format? Both the narrative and the journal entries draw a picture of Kofi, the main character. Which of Kofi's qualities comes through from the narrative and which from the journal entries? Keep in mind that when narrators speak, we receive only whatever information they give us, but when characters speak, we learn about the speakers themselves.

About the Author

The American author, **CHARLES L. SANDERS**, was born in 1932. A successful reporter, author, columnist, and editor, Sanders became the managing editor of *Ebony Magazine* in 1968. He was responsible for opening the first overseas office of *Ebony*, in Paris. During his time in Paris, he wrote a weekly column for *Jet Magazine*. In addition to his literary accomplishments, Sanders was deeply involved in the NAACP. Charles Sanders died in Chicago in 1990. *"My Journey Is Still Long"* describes the adventures of a teenager, Kofi Akakpo, whose search began in 1962.

"My Journey Is Still Long"

Charles L. Sanders

One walks through the villages of mud-and-wattle huts that ring Accra, Ghana, and sees women frying great baskets of fish and plantain which they spoon over *kenkey* and sell to anyone who will buy. They cook the seafood, fruit, and millet goo right on the street and keep the pots warm by banking their fires with dry leaves and wads of newspapers and magazines.

An old copy of a magazine was about to be tossed into such a fire one day in 1962 when 12-year-old Kofi Akakpo, a Hausa tribesman in the village of Nima, pulled it from a pile of waste paper, sat under a jacaranda tree, and became fascinated by the pictures of the people who looked like Hausas but had fine houses and clothes and cars and lived across the sea in the U.S.A.

Kofi kept the magazine for weeks, showed it to everyone in his village, and searched each page for the name of someone who might become his "pen pal" and tell him all about America and its people who looked like him. In the "Letters to the Editor," he saw a name he liked: Charles W. Simmons, Capt., U.S. Air Force. There was an APO number, and Kofi began writing down all the things he wanted to say. He wrote that he was a poor boy who had learned to read and write at a school where he worked as a clean-up boy. He said he swept the classrooms before dawn and then stood outside a window or door each day to listen to others recite their lessons. He studied the blackboards, he said, and rewrote everything on them before washing them for the next day's classes. In case Capt. Simmons would not believe his story, he gave as a reference the name of the man who ran the school.

The boy wrote that he wanted an education in America so that he could return to Africa and become a leader of his people. If Capt. Simmons helped him, he would "be your slave for a period of ten years." Then Kofi Akakpo signed the letter with a new name: Charles W. Wayo. The "Charles W." was, of course, the first name and initial of Capt. Simmons. The "Wayo" was Hausa for "man with smart brain." Then the boy walked to the post office in Accra and sent the letter on its way.

Capt. Simmons was impressed. He began writing to the boy, and he and friends sent him money, books, and clothes, and paid for a year of school. Charles (everyone was calling him that by now) won highest honors in his class and soon became First Boy in the entire school.

But Charles still dreamed of an education in American schools. By late 1963, when he was 14, he had decided what he would do. "I am leaving Ghana," he wrote to Capt. Simmons. "I am coming to you so that I will have a chance to complete my studies and then come back home to be the kind of leader that Africa needs."

Recalls Capt. Simmons, who was stationed in Ankara, Turkey, at the time: "I wrote back and praised his ambition, but I didn't think much more about his coming to me. After all, he was just a little kid, he was an entire continent away from me, and I wasn't able to send for him."

But Charles had made up his mind. He had saved 24 Ghanaian *cedis* (about $25) from the money that Capt. Simmons had sent him. He had gone to the U.S. Information Service Library in Accra and checked a map of the world. On the map, Turkey was, after all, only a few inches from Accra.

Getting up very early one morning, he put on a shirt and his khaki shorts. He took another shirt and made a bundle containing a towel, a pencil, and a writing pad. He told his mother that he was going into the bush to trap birds. His mother, who, he says, smiles all the time and is called Dede Aku, told him to come to her and hold her hand. "I think she knew I was planning something big because she looked real scared," Charles says. But, speaking Hausa, she told him to "come back home before the sun goes to bed."

Charles went into the bush, sat under a tree, said his prayers, cried a little, then began talking to G-d as if he were speaking to someone he knew real well: "This is going to be a real dangerous trip, and I have nobody to go with me but You. It's up to You to protect me, because I'm going to find Captain Simmons. Good-bye."

He walked into Accra, stopped at a gas station, and bought a small calendar and map. Then he went to a market and bought two or three loaves of bread and a pound of onions. He put everything into his bundle and headed in a direction he thought was north. He thinks he walked about 45 miles the first day. That night he sat under a tree and ate a little of the bread and an onion. Then he opened his blue writing pad and wrote the first of the entries that would become a remarkable diary of his long journey, his fears and loneliness, his struggle to survive the bush and the desert, and his frequent talks to G-d who he believed would protect him from everything:

I think I walked about 45 miles the first day

1st Jan. 1964

This night I am going to sleep in the bush here. I have left home all alone without the knowledge of my parents to go to look for my friend Capt. Charles Wesley Simmons of the US Air Force. I am about 45 miles from home (I mean Nima). My friend, the above, lives in Turkey. I am going to walk until I get to him. I must have to go to school. I am poor, I have no money, I can't get any-where but walk. Legs were made before engines. Anyway, I am scared a little bit. G-d help me. Good night. Till tomorrow.

2nd Jan. 1964

Tonight, the sky is bright. I can see clearly. I have walked a lot and my legs are angry. I don't want to quarrel with them. So both of us must rest. I am about 100 miles from home now. I am almost beginning to know what lies ahead. I have bread and fried fish in my bundle. The fish is smelling, so I will eat all quick. The day's walk has been interesting. I saw many creatures. Never have I seen such beautiful animals play-ing all over in their kingdom. They did not bother me, except one antelope which kept running in the direction I am heading. I wondered why. Well, I am sleepy, so I will climb up an orange tree and pass the night peacefully. Good night.

3rd Jan. 1964

Today I passed many villages and picked some food on the village mar-kets. Nobody bothered me. The night is cold. Oh, I remember home. I am very homesick. Tonight, I can imagine my parents sitting by the warm coal pot fire, while I am very cold here. Anyway who asked me to leave the house? Nobody. I must bear the cold as a man.

I have only khaki shorts on and my jumper. The mosquitoes are having a great feast on my legs. May G-d help me from fever. I am tired, so good night.

4th Jan. 1964

I was nearly killed yesterday. This is how: I was asleep for about two hours when I felt something heavy on my stomach. Opened my eyes. A big black snake crawling over me, heading oppo-site direction. Nearly screamed. Somebody held my throat and pressed my body very strong and still till my would-be assailant towed itself away. I regained consciousness. I don't think I can sleep tonight, just sit here and continue tomorrow. I don't think I am far away from Togo now. Good night.

Month after month Charles followed the north-south route from Agadés into Algeria, past the old French Foreign Legion outpost of Tamanrasset (former-ly Ft. Laperrine), across the Tropic of Cancer, into the desert way-stations of In Salah, El Goléa, Ghardaia—the 1,000-mile route which leads straight up to Algiers on the Mediterranean. He spent long periods pacing himself, mov-ing when he could from outpost to out-post, walking most of the way, but accepting rides on camels and on the one or two trucks that passed. It took him weeks to cross, for example, the Ahaggar—the moun-tain range which is one of the most cruel of all Sahara areas. It is here that the sun is so intense that the normally gray-brown rock has turned black, and hard-blown sand has pol-ished the sides of mountains until

Camel ride!

they appear as huge mirrors that reflect the sun into one's eyes with an unbearable glare. At first, Charles tried covering his eyes with his hands and looking out through the spaces between his fingers, while using his shirt to cover his head. But the rocks cut his feet and the sand was too hot to bear. He tore the shirt into shreds, wrapped his feet, and told himself, he says, that "G-d will not let my brains boil." He began walking at night, hiding from the sun during the day in the shade of rocks and dunes. Somewhere between Agadés and In Salah, Charles made these entries in his diary:

Ahaggar

5th July 1965

I am losing my strength very fast, so I must write something about myself before I die, so that you will know who I was. My name is Charles Wayo. My mother is called Dede Aku, my father is of the poorest family of Kwashie. They live in house No. E6/12 in the village of Nima, near Accra, Ghana. I left my home to find my friend, Capt. Charles W. Simmons, US Air Force, TUSLOG DOT30 APO254, New York. I had no money to take a plane, so I walked. Bury me where you find me and no ceremonies. Don't let my parents see my body for they will die. They love me and I love them, too. Tell them I am sorry that I have not lived to my word. But I have no power over death. Tell my brother that I loved him and still love him. Tell him to clothe himself with manhood and get some education and one day he will be great. I am growing weaker now. Bye. There comes something now I cannot see well.

12th July 1965

This story is too miraculous to tell you here. But I will say it in short. Some French army men riding on the Sahara picked me up while dying. So, after all, G-d has taken mercy on my youth and granted me another pardon. Now the Frenchmen have left me with two month's supply of food after treating me for three days. They can't keep anyone longer than that. They brought me somewhere and said I should sit here and a truck will come soon and pick me up. I have sardines, some strange long bread which could be used to spank someone. I have a water can, etc. May the L-rd guard, guide, and protect those men. And I was picked up again by some Arabs yesterday, and I am riding on top of a truck now. It is about 24 feet long and well packed with goods. I am enjoying it. The two men are sitting in front and I am right at the back. I am moving much faster now…

Within two months, Charles had made his way to El Goléa in north-central Algeria. Then, riding on a cart with an old Arab, he reached Ghardaia by October. From there he walked on to the villages of Laghouat and Djelfa. In each place he made friends with Arabs, and they gave him water and such food as they had. At Djelfa, the Sahara had ended and Charles began seeing signs pointing to Algiers and the sea. He reached Algiers at the end of October. In his diary he wrote:

1st Nov. 1965

I am well glad to see such a fantastic city as Algiers. It is beautiful, and being here means that Wayo has conquered the Sahara. I am now halfway to Turkey, and only G-d knows that this is really me. I will not write anymore in my diary, for I am cold and still have a long way to go. Maybe I will write again when I reach my goal. Now I am going to Morocco, for someone has told me it is better to get to Turkey from there. Good-bye.

The road to Algiers

Following railroad tracks, Charles slipped across the border into Morocco and made his way to Fez and Meknes, then to Rabat, and finally to Tangier. He went to the Tangier docks, slipped aboard a ferry, and hid among barrels. Hours later he found himself across the Strait of Gibraltar at the port of Algeciras, Spain. He had reached Europe at last, but the route he had taken had landed him thousands of miles west of the Turkish city where Capt. Simmons lived.

In Spain, Charles underwent a remarkable change. This was the first "white" country he had ever seen, and, as he walked through Algeciras, he saw poor white people for the first time. No white man he had seen in Africa had been poor. But on the streets of Algeciras he saw white beggars—white people who were hungry, whose clothes were as ragged as his. As he left the city, following the signs that pointed toward Madrid, he saw white peasants along the road. In Cadiz, a beggar woman reached out and pleaded with him for a coin.

"I hated that woman," Charles recalls. "All of a sudden, and for the very first time in my life, I hated some-body, really hated somebody. I hated that woman and all the white people I was seeing in their own country for the first time. These are the people, I thought to myself, who made me believe all my life that they were superior to me, an African. These are the people whose books made me think that their cities were so rich that even the streets shone like mirrors and nobody was ever hungry and nobody ever wanted a place to sleep. I looked at those people who had not only conquered Africa, but had set themselves up as masters of the whole world, and I hated them for making me and my brother and my parents and so many other people of Africa believe that we would never have what white men had, and that we weren't supposed to ever hope for the same things. Just look there, I thought, one of them is begging me, and I'm one of those Africans that they've always said are useless, without brains, fit only to be slaves."

In Seville, Charles passed a cathedral and felt only contempt for those who he knew must be inside saying their prayers. He despised even those Spaniards who waved to him and called him "Amigo," and he pushed away the hands that tried to brush dirt from his hair. In Madrid, he stole fruit from the markets not only because he was hungry, but because, he says, he wanted to see how it felt to take something from white people for the first time.

The hate was with him, he says, until he made his way across the border at Hendaye and began walking through southern France. "I walked into the first little French village knowing that I looked real bad," he remembers. "I had on an old overcoat that a man had given me in Morocco when winter began setting in, and that old coat was filthy and smelling, and my hair must have been about four inches long. People stared at me and spoke in French, which I couldn't understand. But when I pointed to my stomach, they understood that I was hungry and gave me food. When I got into a village and cupped my hands to my mouth, the French knew that I was thirsty and gave me water. In one village I just said the word 'Paris' and some people took me by the hands, led me to a road, gave me food, and smiled as I waved goodbye. I walked all the way to Paris and none of the people in the villages treated me bad. They treated me just like the African village people had done, and I knew for the first time that white people and black people could be just the same. I knew they could be poor, and get sick and everything, one just like the other. I stopped hating white people, and, if anything, I became more determined than ever to reach my goal and show them that Africans can build trains and buildings and big ships, too, and even be superior to them in some ways."

In Paris, Charles met an American couple who listened to his story, then helped him telephone Capt. Simmons to say that he was safe and on his way. Capt. Simmons sent him $50, but Charles lost the money before he could get to a train. "I felt so stupid about losing it," he says, "that I didn't want to phone him a second time. I just started walking all over again."

Charles was an old hand at slipping across borders ("Sometimes the border guards

outdoor market in Paris

would ask for a passport, but I'd shake my head, then they'd look me up and down, shake their heads, and wave me on through"), so he had no trouble getting into Germany. He stayed in Aachen for a while, then went on to Cologne. It was here that he learned to hitchhike. "I met some boys on the road," he says, "and they showed me how to put my finger up in the air and make cars stop." He hitchhiked to Bonn, then walked to Wiesbaden, then followed the *autobahn* to Mannheim, Frankfurt, and Munich. Then he walked over the Austrian border which, he says, "was the easiest of all to cross." He thumbed his way across Austria, crossed into Yugoslavia, and began walking toward Belgrade. At Zagreb, he met an old couple who gave him food. "They watched me eat," he recalls, "and put their hands to their hearts to tell me they were my friends. Then I pointed toward the sky and spread my hands over them, which meant 'G-d bless you.' They understood and both of them cried."

Cologne neighborhood

A Swiss tourist gave Charles a ride into Belgrade, then he walked on to Dimitrovgrad. To get across the Bulgarian border he used sign language to make some farmers understand. They hid him under hay in their cart, crossed a border checkpoint, and kept him out of sight until they reached Sofia. Charles was very near to Ankara now. Only the Turkish border

Rooftops of Zagreb

remained. "When I got there," he says, "I started figuring out how I'd slip past this last gate between me and Capt. Simmons. Then I saw an old man with a very long beard. I think he was Greek, but he could speak a little English and understand what I wanted to do. He thought for a while, then told me to grab his hand and talk real fast when we came close to the crossing point. I did just like he said and we walked right past the guards. I spent two days with that old man because he told me he had some friends who would be coming along to take a truckload of dates to Istanbul. Sure enough, they came and I rode all the way to Istanbul."

In Istanbul, Charles met four white American sailors from the *S.S. Saratoga*. He told them his story. Though one sailor asked him, "If you're a real African, where's the elephant bone you're supposed to wear in your nose?" he took him to the train station, bought a ticket to Ankara, and sent him on his way.

Charles thinks about the trip now and says, "When that train got to Ankara, I just didn't believe I was really me. I thought about the bush and the Sahara and all the things I had been through on that long journey, and then there I was in the very city where Capt. Simmons lived. I prayed to G-d and thanked Him for guarding and guiding me, then I started trying to find my friend.

"The first thing I did was ask somebody where the American Embassy was located. Then I went there to see if they had Capt. Simmons's address. They said no, but there was a Marine guard there and he showed me where the Air Force officers lived."

It was the end of May, 1966—nearly 2 years since the day that Charles had left his village home, and his heart was pounding, he says, as he stopped airman after airman and asked, "Do you know Capt. Charles W. Simmons? Do you know where he lives?" Finally someone showed Charles the Simmons apartment, and he says his hands were trembling with excitement as he walked upstairs and knocked on the door. He knocked twice, three times, again and again. But nobody was at home. "I sat right down on the steps and cried," he says, "but then a Negro airman came into the building and saw me there. I told him what had happened, and he said, 'Aw, fellow, come on in my house and relax. Simmons and his family will be back later on.'"

Hours later a car drove into the parking lot and a man, a woman, and some children got out and went into the apartment that had the Simmons name on the door. Charles went there and knocked again. When the door opened, he was so scared that he couldn't say a word. But then a very kind-faced man shouted, "You're Charles Wayo, aren't you?" Charles managed to say "Yes, sir, it's me." The man grabbed him and said "Well, I'll just be…" Charles's friend had been found.

Captain Simmons's apartment

Recalling

1. Where did Kofi Akakpo find Captain Charles Simmons's name? Why did Kofi choose Simmons as a pen pal?

2. Why did Kofi choose "Charles W." as his own first name and middle initial? Why did Kofi choose "Wayo" as his last name?

3. What was Charles Wayo's dream? What did he decide he had to do in order to make his dream come true?

4. What did Charles see for the first time, when he traveled to Spain?

Interpreting

5. Why do you think the story is titled *"My Journey is Still Long"*? Is this a good name for the story? Why or why not?

6. When Charles arrived in Spain, he was suddenly filled with hatred for the people and the country. Why?

7. Charles had to journey from country to country, until he finally reached his destination. What do you think motivated him to make such a long, difficult, and dangerous journey?

Concluding

8. If you were Charles, would you have kept going, even after encountering the snake, and then having to cross the Ahaggar, the cruel mountain range?

Examining Fiction

In *"My Journey Is Still Long,"* the major character is Charles Wayo. He is the central figure, and the person about whom we learn the most.

1. Can you name three personal qualities of Charles Wayo that particularly interested you?

2. Where in the story did you find evidence of these characteristics?

Thinking About Fiction

You have learned that a conclusion made by a reader, based on the information given, is an inference. Remember, the author does not always tell the reader everything about the character.

1. What inferences can you make about Charles based on the following facts?
    a. He studied the blackboard and wrote down everything he saw on it, before washing it off.
    b. He persevered under dangerous circumstances, and traveled through many countries, to find Captain Simmons.

2. Find two details in the story that support the inference that Charles is a determined and dedicated individual.

Creating and Writing

Nowadays, traveling is convenient and pleasurable most of the time. Describe a trip you took to visit someone who is important to you. Include one or two sentences that show a contrast between the ease of your travel and the difficulty of Charles's journey.

Into • *The Dinner Party*

The country is India. The time is early 20th century, when Great Britain ruled much of the world. The topic is one that has been argued about for centuries: who has more inner strength—a man or a woman? The guests at the dinner party have their opinions, the colonel has his opinion, and the American has his opinion. But the deciding vote goes to...the cobra!

Focus

The Dinner Party is written in a style called **realism**. This means that the characters, dialogue, and setting are very true to life and that the story could have happened. Notice how simple the dialogue and description are. Just enough details are provided to introduce the characters and create an atmosphere. Those details that are included, however, are so clear and real, that the reader does not even notice how little background is given.

Setting is very important to this story. In a few, well-chosen words, the author transports the reader to colonial India. One can almost feel the warm, fragrant night air and hear the delicate clink of crystal and china above the hum of mosquitoes and the dinner-table conversation. The setting of the story has to be in India, as the story's "punch line" depends upon the presence of a cobra. The theme of the story is discipline and self-control. This theme was a common one in British literature at the turn of the century. Setting, characterization, and theme all work together to form this beautifully crafted story.

About the Author

MONA GARDNER was born in 1900 in Seattle, Washington, but lived in Hong Kong, South Africa, and California. She traveled extensively through many exotic countries during her lifetime. Many of her works of fiction take place in Asia. *The Dinner Party* is one of Gardner's best-known works. Notice how Gardner used her travels to create a successful context for this popular story.

Word Bank

attaché (At uh SHAY) *n.*: a person who is on the staff of an ambassador or diplomat

naturalist (NAT chur uh list) *n.*: one who studies natural science

rafters (RAFT erz) *n.*: beams of a ceiling

rupees (ROO peez) *n.*: Indian currency; at the time of the story, one rupee was worth about ten cents

veranda (ver AND uh) *n.*: an open porch, extending along one or more sides of a building, at the ground level

The Dinner Party
Mona Gardner

The country is India. A colonial official and his wife are giving a large dinner party. They are seated with their guests—army officers and government attachés and their wives, and a visiting American naturalist—in their spacious dining room, which has a bare marble floor, open rafters, and wide glass doors opening onto a veranda.

A spirited discussion springs up between a young girl who insists that women have outgrown the jumping-on-a-chair-at-the-sight-of-a-mouse era and a colonel who says that they haven't.

"A woman's unfailing reaction in any crisis," the colonel says, "is to scream. And while a man may feel like it, he has that ounce more of nerve control than a woman has. And that last ounce is what counts."

The American does not join in the argument but watches the other guests. As he looks, he sees a strange expression come over the face of the hostess. She is staring straight ahead, her muscles contracting slightly. With a slight gesture she summons the servant standing behind her chair and whispers to him. The servant's eyes widen, and he quickly leaves the room.

Of the guests, none except the American notices this or sees the servant place a bowl of milk on the veranda just outside the open doors.

The American comes to with a start. In India, milk in a bowl means only one thing—bait for a snake. He realizes there must be a cobra in the room. He looks up at the rafters—the likeliest place—but they are bare. Three corners of the room are empty, and in the fourth the servants are waiting to serve the next course. There is only one place left—under the table.

His first impulse is to jump back and warn the others, but he knows the commotion would frighten the cobra into striking. He speaks quickly, the tone of his voice so arresting that it sobers everyone.

"I want to know just what control everyone at this table has. I will count to three hundred—that's five minutes—and not one of you is to move a muscle. Those who move will forfeit fifty rupees. Ready!"

The twenty people sit like stone images while he counts. He is saying "…two hundred and eighty…" when, out of the corner of his eye, he sees the cobra emerge and make for the bowl of milk. Screams ring out as he jumps to slam the veranda doors safely shut.

"You were right, Colonel!" the host exclaims. "A man has just shown us an example of perfect control."

"Just a minute," the American says, turning to his hostess. "Mrs. Wynnes, how did you know that cobra was in the room?"

A faint smile lights up the woman's face as she replies: "Because it was crawling across my foot."

Recalling

1. What does the colonel say is "...a woman's unfailing reaction in any crisis"?

2. What does the servant place on the veranda? What does this signify?

3. How does the American prevent everyone from moving?

4. How did the hostess know there was a cobra in the room?

Interpreting

5. At the dinner party, the colonel and the young girl have an argument. What does it concern?

6. Describe how the American realizes that the snake is under the table.

7. How are the personalities of the American and the hostess similar?

Concluding

8. Give an example of a demonstration of self-control from the story.

9. What is the narrator's opinion regarding the nature of women?

Examining Fiction

The Dinner Party takes place in a foreign country. The **setting**—or the time and place where the action occurs—influences the tone of the story, and makes the plot realistic and believable.

1. Which details inform you that the story takes place when India was under British rule?

2. Examine the effect of the setting on the story. If the story were to take place in another location or in a different era, would the atmosphere and tone be the same?

Thinking About Fiction

Minor characters play an important role in *The Dinner Party.* Identify two minor characters and explain how these characters advance the plot and provide support for the theme.

Creating and Writing

In your opinion, which character in the story exhibited the greatest courage and self-discipline: the American or the hostess? Choose one of these two characters, and compose a letter in which he or she writes to a friend or relative about the dinner party. Write from the point of view of this character, and express the feelings and emotions he or she had, as the episode unfolded. Include details of setting, and make the letter sound dramatic and convincing.

Blueprint FOR READING

Into • *The Third Level*

Train stations are a world unto themselves. People rushing here and there, announcements of arrivals and departures echoing in the vast rooms, and always, the sense of adventure that fills the air, as trains depart to places all over the map. Most imaginative people like to think about what it would be like to travel to new and unfamiliar places. But there are always the few who want to travel not to another place, but to another time. Some wish they could leap ahead to a world of space travel and robot workers. Others yearn to live in the past, when the living was simple and the townspeople knew one another. Charley was just such a person. He loved the 1890s—and he almost found a way to get there.

Focus

Setting plays a very important role in *The Third Level*. The story is set in Grand Central Station, one of the largest train terminals in the world. The hustle and rush of the station mirror the hurried complicated lives of the story's characters. The time of the story is the second half of the 20th century, a period of growing anxiety, in which life has become more hurried and stressful than it was in the 19th century. The theme of the story is modern man's longing to escape this stress and return to a time of greater peacefulness. The 1890s represent this peaceful time. The author sets part of the story in the Grand Central Station of 1894, and part of it in a small American town in the same year. In this story, setting and theme are so tightly interwoven that it is difficult to separate the two.

About the Author

JACK FINNEY was born in 1911 in Wisconsin. He is famous for suspense and science fiction novels. Finney began his writing career in the mid-1940s, and is the author of many diverse works. A common theme in his writing is the desire to escape from the unpleasant present to a more tranquil past. One of his early works was a series of short stories called *The Third Level*. These stories revolve around time travel. The story you are about to read is from that collection. He died in 1995 in California.

THE
THIRD LEVEL

Jack Finney

Courtesy: The Library of Congress

The presidents of the New York Central and the New York, New Haven and Hartford railroads will swear on a stack of timetables that there are only two. But I say there are three, because I've been on the third level at Grand Central Station.[1] Yes, I've taken the obvious step: I talked to a psychiatrist friend of mine, among others. I told him about the third level at Grand Central Station, and he said it was a waking-dream wish fulfillment.[2] He said I was unhappy. That made my wife kind of mad, but he explained that he meant the modern world is full of insecurity, fear, war, worry and all the rest of it, and that I just want to escape. Well, who doesn't? Everybody I know wants to escape, but they don't wander down into any third level at Grand Central Station.

But that's the reason, he said, and my friends all agreed. Everything points to it, they claimed. My stamp collecting,

---

1. *Grand Central Station* is a busy, large New York City train station.
2. *Waking-dream wish fulfillment* means a daydream in which an unconscious wish seems as if it came true.

for example; that's a "temporary refuge from reality." Well, maybe, but my grandfather didn't need any refuge from reality; things were pretty nice and peaceful in his day, from all I hear, and he started my collection. It's a nice collection, too, blocks of four of practically every U.S. issue, first-day covers, and so on. President Roosevelt[3] collected stamps, too, you know.

Anyway, here's what happened at Grand Central. One night last summer I worked late at the office. I was in a hurry to get uptown to my apartment so I decided to take the subway from Grand Central because it's faster than the bus.

Now, I don't know why this should have happened to me. I'm just an ordi-nary guy named Charley, thirty-one years old, and I was wearing a tan gabardine suit and a straw hat with a fancy band; I passed a dozen men who looked just like me. And I wasn't trying to escape from anything; I just wanted to get home to Louisa, my wife.

I turned into Grand Central from Vanderbilt Avenue, and went down the steps to the first level, where you take trains like the Twentieth Century.[4] Then I walked down another flight to the second level, where the suburban trains leave from, ducked into an arched door-

---

3. *President Roosevelt* (ROZE uh VELT) refers to Frankin D. Roosevelt (1882-1945), a U.S. president from 1933-1945.
4. *The Twentieth Century* refers to a train that ran between New York City and Chicago.

Word Bank

refuge (REF yooj) *n.*: a safe haven or sanctuary; a place of shelter

gabardine (GAB er DEEN) *n.*: a durable fabric used in making suits and dresses

way heading for the subway—and got lost. That's easy to do. I've been in and out of Grand Central hundreds of times, but I'm always bumping into new doorways and stairs and corridors. Once I got into a tunnel about a mile long and came out in the lobby of the Roosevelt Hotel. Another time I came up in an office building on Forty-sixth Street, three blocks away.

Sometimes I think Grand Central is growing like a tree, pushing out new corridors and staircases like roots. There's probably a long tunnel that nobody knows about feeling its way under the city right now, on its way to Times Square, and maybe another to Central Park. And maybe—because for so many people through the years Grand Central has been an exit, a way of escape—maybe that's how the tunnel I got into…But I never told my psychiatrist friend about that idea.

The corridor I was in began angling left and slanting downward and I thought that was wrong, but I kept on walking. All I could hear was the empty sound of my own footsteps and I didn't pass a soul. Then I heard that sort of hollow roar ahead that means open space and people talking. The tunnel turned sharp left; I went down a short flight of stairs and came out on the third level at Grand Central Station. For just a moment I thought I was back on the second level, but I saw the room was smaller, there were fewer ticket windows and train gates, and the information booth in the center was wood and old-looking. And the man in the booth wore a green eyeshade and long black sleeve protectors. The lights were dim and sort of flickering. Then I saw why; they were open-flame gaslights.

There were brass spittoons on the floor. And across the station a glint of light caught my eye; a man was pulling a gold watch from his vest pocket. He snapped open the cover, glanced at his watch, and frowned. He wore a derby hat, a black four-button suit with tiny lapels, and he had a big, black, handlebar mustache. Then I looked around and saw that everyone in the station was dressed like eighteen-ninety-something; I never saw so many beards, sideburns and fancy mustaches in my life. A woman walked in through the train gate; she wore a dress with leg-of-mutton sleeves and skirts to the top of her high-buttoned shoes. Back of her, out on the tracks, I caught a glimpse of a locomotive, a very small Currier & Ives[5] locomotive with a funnel-shaped stack. And then I knew.

---

5. *Currier & Ives* was a printing company in the 1800s that published pictures of American life and nature scenes.

Courtesy: The Library of Congress

Word Bank	**corridor** (KOR ih DOOR) *n.*: a long passageway or hallway in a building, often with doors opening to rooms off of it

To make sure, I walked over to a newsboy and glanced at the stack of papers at his feet. It was *The World*; and *The World* hasn't been published for years. The lead story said something about President Cleveland.[6] I've found that front page since, in the Public Library files, and it was printed June 11, 1894.

I turned toward the ticket windows knowing that here—on the third level at Grand Central—I could buy tickets that would take Louisa and me anywhere in the United States we wanted to go. In the year 1894. And I wanted two tickets to Galesburg,[7] Illinois.

Have you ever been there? It's a wonderful town still, with big old frame houses, huge lawns, and tremendous trees whose branches meet overhead and roof the streets. And in 1894, summer evenings were twice as long, and people sat out on their lawns, the men smoking cigars and talking quietly, the women waving palm-leaf fans, with the fireflies all around, in a peaceful world. To be back there with the First World War still twenty years off, and World War II over forty years in the future… I wanted two tickets for that.

The clerk figured the fare—he glanced at my fancy hatband, but he figured the fare—and I had enough for two coach tickets, one way. But when I counted out the money and looked up, the clerk was staring at me. He nodded at the bills. "That ain't money, mister," he said, "and if you're trying to skin[8] me you won't get very far," and he glanced at the cash drawer beside him. Of course the money in his drawer was old-style

6. *President Cleveland* refers to Grover Cleveland (1837-1908), the twenty-second (1885-1889) and twenty-fourth (1893-1897) president of the United States.
7. *Galesburg* is a small city in the western part of Illinois.
8. *To skin* is an old-fashioned way of saying "to cheat."

bills, half again as big as the money we use nowadays, and different-looking. I turned away and got out fast. There's nothing nice about jail, even in 1894.

And that was that. I left the same way I came, I suppose. Next day, during lunch hour, I drew three hundred dollars out of the bank, nearly all we had, and bought old-style currency (that really worried my psychiatrist friend). You can buy old money at almost any coin dealer's, but you have to pay a premium. My three hundred dollars bought less than two hundred in old-style bills, but I didn't care; eggs were thirteen cents a dozen in 1894.

But I've never again found the corridor that leads to the third level at Grand Central Station, although I've tried often enough.

Louisa was pretty worried when I told her all this, and didn't want me to look for the third level any more, and after a while I stopped; I went back to my stamps. But now we're both looking, every weekend, because now we have proof that the third level is still there. My friend Sam Weiner disappeared! Nobody knew where, but I sort of suspected because Sam's a city boy, and I used to tell him about Galesburg— I went to school there—and he always said he liked the sound of the place. And that's where he is, all right. In 1894.

Because one night, fussing with my stamp collection, I found—Well, do you know what a first-day cover is? When a new stamp is issued, stamp collectors buy some and use them to mail envelopes to themselves on the very first day of sale; and the postmark proves the date. The envelope is called a first-day cover. They're never opened: you just put blank paper in the envelope.

That night, among my oldest first-day covers, I found one that shouldn't have been there. But there it was. It was there because someone had mailed it to

Word Bank

currency (KUHR uhn see) *n.*: money
premium (PREE mee um) *n.*: an extra amount charged in addition to the usual price

my grandfather at his home in Galesburg; that's what the address on the envelope said. And it had been there since July 18, 1894—the postmark showed that—yet I didn't remember it at all. The stamp was a six-cent, dull brown, with a picture of President Garfield.[9] Naturally, when the envelope came to Granddad in the mail, it went right into his collection and stayed there—till I took it out and opened it.

The paper inside wasn't blank. It read:

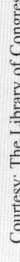

941 Willard Street
Galesburg, Illinois
July 18, 1894

Charley:

I got to wishing that you were right. Then I got to believing you were right. And, Charley, it's true; I found the third level! I've been here two weeks, and right now, down the street at the Daly's, someone is playing a piano, and they're all out on the front porch singing "Seeing Nelly Home." And I'm invited over for lemonade. Come on back, Charley and Louisa. Keep looking till you find the third level! It's worth it, believe me!

Sam

The note was signed Sam.

At the stamp and coin store I go to, I found out that Sam bought eight hundred dollars' worth of old-style currency. That ought to set him up in a nice little hay, feed and grain business; he always said that's what he really wished he could do, and he certainly can't go back to his old business. Not in Galesburg, Illinois, in 1894. His old business? Why, Sam was my psychiatrist.

---

9. *President Garfield* refers to James A. Garfield (1831-1881), who was the twentieth president of the United States in 1881.

Recalling

1. How does Charley find the "third level" of Grand Central Station?

2. Why can't Charley purchase the tickets to Galesburg?

3. What prevents him from traveling to Galesburg, after he has the correct currency?

4. How does Charley discover that the "third level" really exists?

Interpreting

5. Explain why Charley thinks that Grand Central Station is "growing like a tree."

6. Describe Galesburg, Illinois in 1894. Why does it appeal to Charley?

7. What was Louisa's reaction, when Charley told her about his experience on the "third level"?

8. Why is it that Sam cannot practice his profession in Galesburg, Illinois, in 1894?

Concluding

9. Give examples of Charley's desire to escape from the modern world.

10. Explain Charley's preference for the past over the present.

11. What can be concluded from the effect that Sam's letter has on Charley?

Examining Fiction

The time and location in which a story takes place is the **setting**. In some stories, the element of time is essential to its theme or meaning. In *The Third Level*, time shifts from the present to the past. The author uses this to contrast modern culture with an earlier period.

1. Contrast the atmosphere of Grand Central Station in the present with the Grand Central Station of the past.

2. Explain why it is that the shift in time plays such an important role in illustrating the problems of today's society.

Thinking About Fiction

Often, the setting of a story is only implied by the author. Look back at the story to do the following exercises.

1. List the details that suggest that the "third level" exists in the past.

2. From these details, can you predict what life would be like for Charley, if he could return to the past?

Creating and Writing

Was life years back more tranquil and pleasant than it is in the present? Write a story in which you return to the past. Which era would you choose? How would you get there? How would you get back? Include details that clearly show that you are in the past. Use changes in setting to contrast the quality of life in an earlier time to life in modern times.

Into • *Rip Van Winkle*

How does the world change in twenty years? It depends upon which twenty years we are speaking of. If a war takes place during the twenty-year span, major changes can occur. Freedom can be won or lost; wealth can appear instantly or disappear suddenly; laws can be changed for better or for worse; and, tragically, people can be robbed of friends and family. People who live through a war experience the changes gradually and grow accustomed to them. But what if a person slept through a war, only to wake up shortly after it was over? What would he think of the world he woke up to? What would the world think of him? Rip Van Winkle fell asleep when King George ruled the American colonies. He woke up when George Washington was the President of the United States. Being Rip Van Winkle, he was puzzled, but not too shaken. Like the true American that he was, he adapted to the change and never looked back.

Focus

The setting of *Rip Van Winkle* is the beautiful Hudson River Valley. Much of the story is devoted to describing the mountains, the river, the valley, and the sky above them. The setting is timeless; it never changes. However, the people who live along the Hudson River *do* change. They grow up, go to war, and establish a new government. Washington Irving contrasts the parts of life that are changeless, or permanent, with the parts of life that are changing, or temporary. Where does Rip Van Winkle fit in? On the one hand, his twenty years' slumber causes physical changes in him. He wakes up stiff, bearded, and gray-haired. On the other hand, his real "self" is as unchanging as the mountains. Neither his wife's scolding, nor his own poverty, nor even a fantastic meeting with strange, little men on the mountain changes him. The lazy, friendly, helpful, incompetent, stubborn, maddening, sweet-natured Rip is like a rock. He doesn't change in the story, and he hasn't changed in the two hundred or so years since he was "born." *Rip Van Winkle* is an American treasure!

About the Author

WASHINGTON IRVING was born in 1783 in New York. He was one of the first American fiction writers to receive international acclaim. While abroad, Irving published a series of short stories containing some of his most beloved works— *The Legend of Sleepy Hollow* and *Rip Van Winkle* are among them. Irving returned to the United States, to spend the last years of his life in his home along the Hudson River. He died in 1859 in New York.

Rip Van Winkle
Washington Irving

Whoever has made a voyage up the Hudson[1] must remember the Catskill Mountains.[2] They are a branch of the great Appalachian[3] family, and are seen away to the west of the river, swelling up to a noble height, and lording it over the surrounding country. Every change of season, every change of weather, indeed, every hour of the day, produces some change in the magical hues and shapes of these mountains, and they are regarded by all the good wives, far and near, as perfect barometers. When the weather is fair and settled, they are clothed in blue and purple, and print their bold outlines on the clear evening sky; but, sometimes, when the rest of the landscape is cloudless, they will gather a hood of gray vapors about their summits, which, in the last rays of the setting sun, will glow and light up like a crown of glory.

At the foot of these fairy mountains, the voyager may have seen the light smoke curling up from a village, whose shingle roofs gleam among the trees, just where the blue tints of the upland melt away into the fresh green of the nearer landscape. It is a little village, of great antiquity, having been founded by some of the Dutch colonists, in the early times of the province. There were some of the houses of the original settlers standing within a few years,[4] built of small yellow bricks brought from

1. The *Hudson* refers to the Hudson River in the eastern part of New York State.
2. The *Catskill Mountains* are in the southeastern part of New York State.
3. The *Appalachians* (AP uh LAY shunz) are a group of mountains extending from the southeastern part of Canada to northern Alabama.
4. *Within a few years* means until recently. This story was written in the early 19th century.

Holland, having latticed windows and gable fronts, surmounted with weathercocks.

In that same village, and in one of these very houses, which was sadly timeworn and weather-beaten, there lived many years since, while the country was yet a province of Great Britain, a simple, good-natured fellow, of the name of Rip Van Winkle. He was a descendant of the Van Winkles who figured so gallantly in the chivalrous days of Peter Stuyvesant.[5] He inherited, however, but little of the martial character of his ancestors. I have observed that he was a simple, good-natured man; he was, moreover, a kind neighbor, and an obedient, henpecked husband. Indeed, to the latter circumstance might be owing that meekness of spirit which gained him such universal popularity; for those men are most apt to be conciliating[6] abroad who are under the discipline of shrews at home. Their tempers, doubtless, are rendered pliant in the fiery furnace of domestic trouble, which is worth all the sermons in the world for teaching the virtues of patience and long-suffering. A quarrelsome wife may, therefore, in some respects, be

considered a tolerable blessing; and if so, Rip Van Winkle was thrice blessed.

Certain it is, that he was a great favorite among all the good wives of the village, who took his part in all family squabbles, and never failed, whenever they talked those matters over in their evening gossipings, to lay all the blame on Dame Van Winkle. The children of the village, too, would shout with joy whenever he approached. He assisted at their sports, made their playthings, taught them to fly kites and shoot marbles, and told them long stories of ghosts, witches, and Indians. Whenever he went dodging about the village, he was surrounded by a troop of them, hanging on his coat skirts, clambering on his back, and playing a thousand tricks on him with impunity;[7] and not a dog would bark at him throughout the neighborhood.

The great error in Rip's character was an insuperable dislike of all kinds of profitable labor. It could not be from the want of perseverance; for he would sit on a wet rock, with a rod as long and heavy as a Tartar's lance,[8] and fish all day without a murmur, even though he should not be encouraged by a single nibble. He would carry a fowling piece[9] on his shoulder for hours together, trudging through woods and swamps, and up hill and down dale, to shoot a few squirrels or wild pigeons. He would never refuse to assist a neighbor even in the roughest toil, and was a foremost man at all country frolics for husking Indian corn, or building stone fences. The women of the village, too, used to employ him to run their errands, and to do such little odd jobs as their less obliging husbands would not do for them. In a word, Rip was ready to attend to anybody's business but his own; but as to doing family duty, and keeping his farm in order, he found it impossible.

In fact, he declared it was of no use to work on his farm; it was the most pestilent[10] little piece of ground in the whole country; everything about it went wrong, and would go wrong, in spite of him. His fences were continually falling to pieces; his cow would either go astray or get among the cabbages; weeds were sure to grow quicker in his fields than anywhere else; the rain always made a point of setting in just as he had some outdoor work to do; so that his estate had dwindled away under his management, acre by acre, until there was little more left than a mere patch of Indian corn and potatoes, and was the worst-conditioned farm in the neighborhood.

His children, too, were as ragged and wild as if they belonged to nobody. His son Rip promised to inherit the habits, with the old clothes, of his father. He was generally seen trooping like a colt at his mother's heels, equipped in a pair of his father's castoff galligaskins,[11] which he had to hold up with one hand, as a fine lady does her train in bad weather.

Rip Van Winkle, however, was one of those happy mortals, of foolish, well-oiled dispositions, who take the

---

5. *Peter Stuyvesant* (STY vih sint) (1592-1672) was the last governor of the Dutch colony of New Netherland. It was taken over in 1664 by the British and renamed New York.
6. *Conciliating* (kun CILL ee AYT ing) means friendly.
7. *With impunity* (im PYOON ih tee) means without fearing punishment.
8. A *Tartar's* (TAR terz) *lance* was a long spear used by a Mongolian tribesman.
9. A *fowling piece* was a lightweight gun used for shooting wild birds.
10. Here, *pestilent* (PESS tih lint) means bothersome.
11. *Galligaskins* (GAL ih GASS kinz) were loose knee-length trousers.

Word Bank

chivalrous (SHIV ihl rihs) *adj.*: gallant; courteous

martial (MAR shuhl) *adj.*: warlike; military

pliant (PLY uhnt) *adj.*: easily bent; flexible

obliging (uh BLY jing) *adj.*: ready to do favors

world easy, eat white bread or brown, whichever can be got with least thought or trouble, and would rather starve on a penny than work for a pound.[12] If left to himself, he would have whistled life away in perfect contentment, but his wife kept continually dinning in his ears about his idleness, his carelessness, and the ruin he was bringing on his family. Morning, noon, and night, her tongue was incessantly going, and everything he said or did was sure to produce a torrent of household eloquence. Rip had but one way of replying to all lectures of the kind, and that, by frequent use, had grown into a habit. He shrugged his shoulders, shook his head, cast up his eyes, but said nothing. This, however, always provoked a fresh volley from his wife; so that he would take to the outside of the house—the only side which, in truth, belongs to a henpecked husband.

Rip's sole domestic adherent[13] was his dog Wolf, who was as much henpecked as his master; for Dame Van Winkle regarded them as companions

in idleness, and even looked upon Wolf with an evil eye, as the cause of his master's going so often astray. True it is, in all points of spirit befitting an honorable dog, he was as courageous an animal as ever scoured the woods—but what courage can withstand the terrors of a woman's tongue? The moment Wolf entered the house his crest fell, his tail drooped to the ground, or curled between his legs, he sneaked about with a gallows air, casting many a sidelong glance at Dame Van Winkle, and at the least flourish of a broomstick or ladle, he would fly to the door, yelping.

Times grew worse and worse with Rip Van Winkle as years of matrimony rolled on; a tart temper never mellows with age, and a sharp tongue is the only edged tool that grows keener with constant use. For a long while he used to console himself, when driven from home, by frequenting a kind of perpetual club of the sages, philosophers, and other idle personages of the village, which held its sessions on a bench before a small inn, designated by a portrait of His Majesty George the Third.[14] Here they used to sit in the shade through a long, lazy summer's day, talking listlessly over village gossip, or telling endless sleepy stories about nothing. But it would have been worth any statesman's money to have heard the profound discussions that sometimes took place, when by chance an old newspaper fell into their hands from some passing traveler. How solemnly they would listen to the contents, as drawled out by Derrick Van Bummel, the schoolmaster, a dapper, learned little man, who was not to be daunted by the most gigantic word in the dictionary; and how sagely they would deliberate upon public events some months after they had taken place.

The opinions of this club were completely controlled by Nicholas Vedder, a patriarch[15] of the village, and landlord of the inn, at the door of which he took his seat from morning till night, just moving sufficiently to avoid the sun and keep in the shade of a large tree; so that the neighbors could tell the hour by his movements as accurately as by a sundial. It is true he was rarely heard to speak, but smoked his pipe incessantly. His adherents, however, perfectly understood him, and knew how to gather his opinions. When anything that was read or related displeased him, he was observed to smoke his pipe vehemently, and to send forth short, frequent, and angry puffs; but when pleased, he would inhale the smoke slowly and tranquilly, and emit it in light and placid clouds; and sometimes, taking the pipe from his mouth, and letting the fragrant vapor curl about his nose, would gravely nod his head in token of perfect approbation.

From even this stronghold the unlucky Rip was at length routed by his wife, who would suddenly break in upon the tranquillity of the assemblage and call the members all to naught; nor was that august[16] personage, Nicholas Vedder himself, sacred from the daring tongue of this terrible shrew, who charged him outright with encouraging her husband in habits of idleness.

---

12. The *pound* is the basic unit of British currency, and was used in the Colonies.
13. An *adherent* (ad HEER int) is a supporter.
14. *His Majesty George the Third* (1738-1820) was the king of England who ruled the American Colonies until the American Revolution in 1776.
15. A *patriarch* (PAY tree ark) is a respected and honored old man.
16. *August* (aw GUST) means well-respected and dignified.

Word Bank	keener (KEEN er) *adj.*: quicker; sharper

Poor Rip was at last reduced almost to despair; and his only alternative, to escape from the labor of the farm and clamor of his wife, was to take gun in hand and stroll away into the woods. Here he would sometimes seat himself at the foot of a tree, and share the contents of his wallet[17] with Wolf, with whom he sympathized as a fellow sufferer in persecution. "Poor Wolf," he would say, "thy mistress leads thee a dog's life of it; but never mind, my lad, whilst I live thou shalt never want a friend to stand by thee!" Wolf would wag his tail, look wistfully in his master's face, and if dogs can feel pity, I believe he returned the sentiment with all his heart.

In a long ramble of the kind on a fine autumnal day, Rip had unconsciously scrambled to one of the highest parts of the Catskill Mountains. He was after his favorite sport of squirrel shooting, and the still solitudes[18] had echoed and reechoed with the reports of his gun. Panting and fatigued, he threw himself, late in the afternoon, on a green knoll, covered with mountain herbage, that crowned the brow of a precipice. From an opening between the

trees he could overlook all the lower country for many a mile of rich woodland. He saw at a distance the lordly Hudson, far, far below him, moving on its silent but majestic course, with the reflection of a purple cloud, or the sail of a lagging bark,[19] here and there sleeping on its glassy bosom, and at last losing itself in the blue highlands.

On the other side he looked down into a deep mountain glen, wild, lonely, and shagged, the bottom filled with fragments from the overhanging cliffs, and scarcely lighted by the reflected rays of the setting sun. For some time Rip lay musing on this scene. Evening was gradually advancing. The mountains began to throw their long blue shadows over the valleys. He saw that it would be dark before he could reach the village, and he heaved a heavy sigh when he thought of encountering the terrors of Dame Van Winkle.

As he was about to descend, he heard a voice from the distance, hallooing, "Rip Van Winkle! Rip Van Winkle!" He looked round, but could see nothing but a crow winging its solitary flight across the mountain. He thought his fancy[20] must have deceived him, and turned again to descend, when he heard the same cry ring through the still evening air: "Rip Van Winkle! Rip Van Winkle!" At the same time Wolf bristled up his back, and giving a low growl, skulked to his master's side, looking fearfully down into the glen. Rip now felt a vague apprehension stealing over him; he looked anxiously in the same direction, and perceived a strange figure slowly toiling up the rocks, and bending under the weight of something he carried on his back. He was surprised to see any human being in this lonely and unfrequented place, but supposing it to be someone of the neighborhood in need of his assistance, he hastened down to yield it.

On nearer approach he was still more surprised at the singularity of the stranger's appearance. He was a short, square-built old fellow, with thick, bushy hair and a grizzled beard. His dress was of the antique Dutch fashion—a cloth jerkin[21] strapped round the waist—several pairs of breeches, the outer one of ample volume, decorated with rows of buttons down the sides, and bunches at the knees. He bore on his shoulder a stout keg that seemed full of liquor, and made signs for Rip to approach and assist him with the load. Though rather shy and distrustful of this new acquaintance, Rip complied with his usual readiness; and mutually relieving one another, they clambered up a narrow gully, apparently the dry bed of a mountain torrent. As they ascended, Rip every now and then heard long rolling peals, like distant thunder, that seemed to issue out of a deep ravine, or rather cleft, between lofty rocks, toward which their rugged path conducted. He paused for an instant, but supposing it to be the muttering of one of those transient thundershowers which often take place in mountain heights, he proceeded. Passing through the ravine, they came to a hollow, like a small amphitheater,[22] surrounded by perpendicular precipices, over the brinks of which trees shot their branches, so that

---

17. Here, *wallet* is a bag for carrying supplies.
18. *Still solitudes* (SAHL ih toodz) are lonely, quiet places.
19. A *bark* is a small boat.
20. His *fancy* is his imagination.
21. A *jerkin* is a fitted, short jacket frequently made of leather.
22. An *amphitheater* (AM fih THEE ih ter) is an open rounded stadium with tiers of seats surrounding it.

| **Word Bank** | **majestic** (muh JES tuk) *adj.*: regal; grand |
| | **wistfully** (WHIST fuh lee) *adv.*: showing longings; wishfully |

you only caught glimpses of the azure sky and the bright evening cloud. During the whole time Rip and his companion had labored on in silence; for though Rip marveled greatly what could be the object of carrying a keg of liquor up this wild mountain, yet there was something strange and incomprehensible about the unknown, that inspired awe and checked familiarity.

On entering the amphitheater, new objects of wonder presented themselves. On a level spot in the center was a company of odd-looking personages playing at ninepins. They were dressed in a quaint, outlandish fashion; some wore short doublets,[23] others jerkins, with long knives in their belts, and most of them had enormous breeches, of style similar to that of the guide's. Their visages,[24] too, were peculiar. One had a large beard, broad face, and small piggish eyes. The face of another seemed to consist entirely of nose, and was sur-mounted by a white sugar-loaf hat,[25] set off with a little red cock's tail. They all had beards, of various shapes and colors. There was one who seemed to be the commander. He was a stout old gentleman, with a weather-beaten countenance; he wore a laced doublet, broad belt and hanger,[26] high-crowned hat and feather, red stockings, and high-heeled shoes, with roses in them. The whole group reminded Rip of the figures in an old Flemish[27] painting, in the parlor of the village parson, which had been brought over from Holland at the time of the settlement.

What seemed particularly odd to Rip was that, though these folks were evidently amusing themselves, yet they maintained the gravest faces, the most mysterious silence, and were the most melancholy party of pleasure he had ever witnessed. Nothing interrupted the stillness of the scene but the noise of the balls, which, whenever they were

rolled, echoed along the mountains like rumbling peals of thunder.

As Rip and his companion approached them, they suddenly stopped their play, and stared at him with such fixed, statue-like gaze, and such strange, lackluster countenances, that his heart turned within him, and his knees smote together. His companion now emptied the contents of the keg into large flagons,[28] and made signs to him to wait upon the company. He obeyed with fear and trembling; they quaffed[29] the liquor in profound silence, and then returned to their game.

By degrees Rip's awe and apprehension subsided. He even ventured, when no eye was fixed upon him, to taste the beverage, which he found had much of the flavor of excellent Holland gin. He was naturally a thirsty soul, and was soon tempted to repeat the draft.[30]

One taste provoked another; and he repeated his visits to the flagon so often that at length his senses were overpowered, his eyes swam in his head, his head gradually declined, and he fell into a deep sleep.

On waking, he found himself on the green knoll whence he had first seen the old man of the glen. He rubbed his eyes—it was a bright sunny morning. The birds were hopping and twittering among the bushes, and the eagle was wheeling aloft, and breasting the pure mountain breeze. "Surely," thought Rip, "I have not slept here all night." He recalled the occurrences before he fell asleep. The strange man with a keg of liquor—the mountain ravine—the wild retreat among the rocks—the woebegone party at ninepins—the flagon—"Oh! that flagon! that wicked flagon!" thought Rip—"what excuse shall I make to Dame Van Winkle?"

He looked round for his gun, but in place of the clean, well-oiled fowling piece, he found an old firelock lying by him, the barrel incrusted with rust, the lock falling off, and the stock worm-

eaten. He now suspected that the grave roisters[31] of the mountain had put a trick upon him, and, having dosed him with liquor, had robbed him of his gun. Wolf, too, had disappeared, but he might have strayed away after a squirrel or partridge. He whistled after him and shouted his name, but all in vain;

23. *Doublets* (DUB lits) are tight waist-length jackets.
24. *Visages* (VIZ ij ez) are faces.
25. A *sugar-loaf hat* is a cone-shaped tall hat.
26. A *hanger* is a short sword.
27. *Flemish* refers to an area in western Europe now part of Belgium, France, and the Netherlands.
28. *Flagons* (FLAG inz) are large containers with handles and spouts that hold liquid.
29. *Quaffed* (KWAHFD) means drank.
30. Here, *draft* means drink.
31. *Roisters* (ROY sterz) are noisy merrymakers.

| **Word Bank** | **incomprehensible** (IN com pree HEN sih bul) *adj.*: not possible to understand |
| | **melancholy** (MEL in KAHL ee) *n.*: a feeling of sadness |

the echoes repeated his whistle and shout, but no dog was to be seen.

He determined to revisit the scene of the last evening's gambol,[32] and if he met with any of the party, to demand his dog and gun. As he rose to walk, he found himself stiff in the joints. "These mountain beds do not agree with me," thought Rip, "and if this frolic should lay me up with a fit of the rheumatism, I shall have a blessed time with Dame Van Winkle." With some difficulty he got down into the glen. He found the gully up which he and his companion had ascended the preceding evening; but to his astonishment a mountain stream was now foaming down it, leaping from rock to rock, and filling the glen with babbling murmurs. He, however, made shift to scramble up its sides, working his toilsome way through thickets of birch, sassafras, and witch hazel, and sometimes tripped up or entangled by the wild grapevines that twisted their coils or tendrils from tree to tree, and spread a kind of network in his path.

At length he reached to where the ravine had opened through the cliffs to the amphitheater; but no traces of such opening remained. The rocks presented a high wall over which the torrents came tumbling in a sheet of feathery foam, and fell into a broad, deep basin, black from the shadows of the surrounding forest. Here, then, poor Rip was brought to a stand. He again called and whistled after his dog; he was only answered by the cawing of a flock of idle crows, who seemed to look down and scoff at the poor man's perplexities.[33] What was to be done? The morning was passing away, and Rip felt famished for want of his breakfast. He grieved to give up his dog and gun; he dreaded to meet his wife; but it would not do to starve among the mountains. He shook his head, shouldered the rusty firelock, and, with a heart full of trouble and anxiety, turned his steps homeward.

As he approached the village, he met a number of people, but none whom he knew, which somewhat surprised him, for he had thought himself acquainted with everyone in the country round. Their dress too, was of a different fashion from that to which he was accustomed. They all stared at him with equal marks of surprise, and whenever they

cast their eyes upon him, invariably stroked their chins. The recurrence of this gesture induced Rip to do the same, when, to his astonishment, he found his beard had grown a foot long!

He had now entered the outskirts of the village. A troop of strange children ran at his heels, hooting after him, and pointing at his gray beard. The dogs, too, not one of which he recognized for an old acquaintance, barked at him as he passed. The very village was altered; it was larger and more populous. There were rows of houses which he had never seen before, and those which had been his familiar haunts had disappeared. Strange names were over the doors—strange faces at the windows—everything was strange. His mind now misgave him; he began to doubt whether both he and the world around him were not bewitched. Surely this was his native village, which he had left but the day before. There stood the Catskill Mountains—there ran the silver Hudson at a distance—there was every hill and dale precisely as it had always been—Rip was sorely perplexed. "That flagon last night," thought he, "has addled[34] my poor head sadly."

It was with some difficulty that he found the way to his own house, which he approached with silent awe, expecting every moment to hear the shrill voice of Dame Van Winkle. He found the house gone to decay—the roof fallen in, the windows shattered, and the doors off the hinges. A half-starved dog that looked like Wolf was skulking about it. Rip called him by name, but the cur snarled, showed his teeth, and passed on. This was an unkind cut indeed. "My very dog," sighed poor Rip, "has forgotten me!"

He entered the house, which, to tell the truth, Dame Van Winkle had always

32. *Gambol* is playing.
33. *Perplexities* (per PLEX ih teez) are confusions.
34. *Addled* (AD dild) is confused.

kept in neat order. It was empty, forlorn, and apparently abandoned. This desolateness overcame all his fears— he called loudly for his wife and children—the lonely chambers rang for a moment with his voice, and then all again was silence.

He now hurried forth, and hastened to his old resort, the village inn—but it too was gone. A large, rickety wooden building stood in its place, with great gaping windows, some of them broken and mended with old hats and petticoats, and over the door was painted, "The Union Hotel, by Jonathan Doolittle." Instead of the great tree that used to shelter the quiet little Dutch inn of yore, there now was reared a tall naked pole, with something on the top that looked like a red nightcap,[35] and from it was fluttering a flag, on which was a singular assemblage of stars and stripes—all this was strange and incomprehensible. He recognized on the sign, however, the ruby face of King George, under which he had smoked so many a peaceful pipe; but even this was singularly changed. The red coat was changed

for one of blue and buff, a sword was held in the hand instead of a scepter, the head was decorated with a cocked hat,[36] and underneath was painted in large characters, GENERAL WASHINGTON.

There was, as usual, a crowd of folk about the door, but none that Rip recollected. The very character of the people seemed changed. There was a busy, bustling tone about it, instead of the accustomed tranquillity. He looked in vain for the sage Nicholas Vedder, with his broad face, double chin, and fair long pipe, uttering clouds of tobacco smoke instead of idle speeches; or Van Bummel, the schoolmaster, doling forth the contents of an ancient newspaper. In place of these, a lean, bilious-looking[37] fellow, with his pockets full of handbills, was talking vehemently about rights of citizens—elections—members of Congress—liberty—Bunker's hill—heroes of seventy-six—and other words, which were a perfect Babylonish jargon[38] to the bewildered Van Winkle.

The appearance of Rip, with his long, grizzled beard, his rusty fowling piece, his uncouth dress, and an army of women and children at his heels, soon attracted the attention of the tavern politicians. They crowded round him, eyeing him from head to foot with great curiosity. The orator bustled up to him, and drawing him partly aside, inquired "on which side he voted?" Rip stared in vacant stupidity. Another short but busy little fellow pulled him by the arm, and, rising on tiptoe, inquired in his ear, "whether he was Federal or Democrat?"[39] Rip was equally at a loss to comprehend the question, when a knowing, self-important old gentleman, in a sharp cocked hat, made his way through the crowd, putting them to the right and left with his elbows as he passed, and planting himself before Van Winkle, with one arm akimbo,[40] the other resting on his cane, his keen eyes

and sharp hat penetrating, as it were, into his very soul, demanded in an austere tone, "what brought him to the election with a gun on his shoulder, and a mob at his heels; and whether he meant to breed a riot in the village?"

"Alas! gentlemen," cried Rip, somewhat dismayed, "I am a poor quiet man, a native of the place, and a loyal subject of the King, G-d bless him!"

Here a general shout burst from the bystanders—"A Tory![41] a Tory! a spy! a refugee! hustle him! away with him!" It was with great difficulty that the self-important man in the cocked hat restored order; and demanded again of the unknown culprit, what he came there for, and whom he was seeking. The poor man humbly assured him that he meant no harm, but merely came there in search of some of his neighbors, who used to keep about the tavern.

"Well—who are they?—name them."

Rip bethought himself a moment, and inquired, "Where's Nicholas Vedder?"

There was a silence for a little while, when an old man replied, in a thin, piping voice, "Nicholas Vedder! Why, he is dead and gone these eighteen years! There was a wooden tombstone in the graveyard that used to tell all about him, but that's rotten and gone too."

"Where's Brom Dutcher?"

"Oh, he went off to the army in the

---

35. *Red nightcap* refers to a red cloth liberty cap that was a symbol of freedom.
36. A *cocked hat* is a three-cornered hat.
37. *Bilious-looking* (BILL yiss LOOK ing) is appearing ill-tempered.
38. *Babylonish jargon* (BAB ih LONE ish JAR gun), here, means language that cannot be understood.
39. *Federal or Democrat* refers to member of the Federalist Party or the Democrat-Republican Party. In the early years of the United States these were the two political parties.
40. *Akimbo* (uh KIM boe) is having the hand on the hip and the elbow held out.
41. During the American Revolution, an American who sided with the British was called a *Tory.*

beginning of the war; some say he was killed at the storming of Stony Point[42]—others say he was drowned in a squall at the foot of Anthony's Nose.[43] I don't know—he never came back again."

"Where's Van Bummel, the school-master?"

"He went off to the wars too, was a great militia general, and is now in Congress."

Rip's heart died away at hearing of these sad changes in his home and friends, and finding himself thus alone in the world. Every answer puzzled him, too, by treating of such enormous lapses of time, and of matters which he could not understand: war—Congress—Stony Point; he had no courage to ask after any more friends, but cried out in despair. "Does nobody here know Rip Van Winkle?"

"Oh, Rip Van Winkle!" exclaimed two or three; "oh, to be sure! that's Rip Van Winkle yonder, leaning against the tree."

Rip looked, and beheld a precise copy of himself, as he went up the

mountain; apparently as lazy and certainly as ragged. The poor fellow was now completely bewildered. He doubted his own identity, and whether he was himself or another man. In the midst of his bewilderment, the man in the cocked hat demanded who he was, and what was his name.

"G-d knows," exclaimed he, at his wit's end; "I'm not myself—I'm somebody else—that's me yonder—no—that's somebody else got into my shoes—I was myself last night, but I fell asleep on the mountain, and they've changed my gun, and everything's changed, and I'm changed, and I can't tell what's my name, or who I am!"

The bystanders began now to look at each other, nod, wink significantly, and tap their fingers against their foreheads. There was a whisper, also, about securing the gun, and keeping the old fellow from doing mischief, at the very suggestion of which the self-important man in the cocked hat retired quickly. At this critical moment a woman pressed through the throng to get a peep at the gray-bearded man. She had a chubby child in her arms, which, frightened at his looks, began to cry. "Hush, Rip," cried she, "hush, you little fool; the old man won't hurt you." The name of the child, the air of the mother, the tone of her voice, all awakened a train of recollections in his mind. "What is your name, my good woman?" asked he.

"Judith Gardenier."

"And your father's name?"

"Ah, poor man, Rip Van Winkle was his name, but it's twenty years since he went away from home with his gun, and never has been heard of since—his dog came home without him; but whether he shot himself, or was carried away by the Indians, nobody can tell. I was then but a little girl."

Rip had but one question more to ask; but he put it with a faltering voice:

"Where's your mother?"

"Oh, she too had died but a short time since; she broke a blood vessel in a fit of anger at a New England peddler."

There was a drop of comfort, at least, in this intelligence.[44] The honest man could contain himself no longer. He caught his daughter and her child in his arms. "I am your father!" cried he—"Young Rip Van Winkle once—old Rip Van Winkle now!—Does nobody know poor Rip Van Winkle?"

All stood amazed, until an old woman, tottering out from among the crowd, put her hand to her brow, and peering under it in his face for a moment, exclaimed, "Sure enough! it is Rip Van Winkle—it is himself! Welcome home again, old neighbor. Why, where have you been these twenty long years?"

Rip's story was soon told, for the whole twenty years had been to him as but one night. The neighbors stared when they heard it; some were seen to wink at each other, and put their tongues in their cheeks; and the self-important man in the cocked hat, who, when the alarm was over, had returned to the field, screwed down the corners of his

---

42. *Stony Point* is a village on the Hudson River.
43. *Anthony's Nose* is a mountain on the Hudson River.
44. Here, *intelligence* means news.

mouth, and shook his head—upon which there was a general shaking of the head throughout the assemblage.

It was determined, however, to take the opinion of old Peter Vanderdonk, who was seen slowly advancing up the road. He was a descendant of the historian of that name, who wrote one of the earliest accounts of the province. Peter was the most ancient inhabitant of the village, and well versed in all the wonderful events and traditions of the neighborhood. He recollected Rip at once, and corrobated his story in the most satisfactory manner. He assured the company that it was a fact, handed down from his ancestor the historian, that the Catskill Mountains had always been haunted by strange beings. That it was affirmed that the great Henry Hudson, the first discoverer of the river and country, kept a kind of vigil there every twenty years, with his crew of the *Half-Moon*; being permitted in this way to revisit the scenes of his enterprise and keep a guardian eye upon the river and the great city called by his name. That his father had once seen them in

their old Dutch dresses playing at ninepins in a hollow of the mountain; and that he himself had heard, one summer afternoon, the sound of their balls, like distant peals of thunder.

To make a long story short, the company broke up, and returned to the more important concerns of the election. Rip's daughter took him home to live with her; she had a snug, well-furnished house, and a stout, cheery farmer for a husband, whom Rip recollected for one of the urchins that used to climb upon his back. As to Rip's son and heir, who was the ditto of himself, seen leaning against the tree, he was employed to work on the farm; but showed an hereditary disposition to attend to anything else but his business.

Rip now resumed his old walks and habits; he soon found many of his former cronies, though all rather the worse for the wear and tear of time; and preferred making friends among the rising generation, with whom he soon grew into great favor.

Having nothing to do at home, and being arrived at that happy age when a

man can be idle with impunity, he took his place once more on the bench at the inn door, and was reverenced as one of the patriarchs of the village, and a chronicle of the old times "before the war." It was some time before he could get into the regular track of gossip, or could be made to comprehend the strange events that had taken place during his sleep. How that there had been a Revolutionary War—that the country had thrown off the yoke of old England—and that, instead of being a subject of His Majesty George the Third, he was now a free citizen of the United States. Rip, in fact, was no politician; the changes of states and empires made but little impression on him; but there was one species of despotism under which he had long groaned, and that was—petticoat government. Happily that was at an end; he had got his neck out of the yoke of matrimony, and could go in and out whenever he pleased, without dreading the tyranny of Dame Van Winkle. Whenever her name was mentioned, however, he shook his head, shrugged his shoulders, and cast up his eyes; which might pass either for an expression of resignation to his fate, or joy at his deliverance.

He used to tell his story to every stranger that arrived at Mr. Doolittle's hotel. He was observed, at first, to vary on some points every time he told it, which was, doubtless, owing to his having so recently awaked. It at last settled down precisely to the tale I have related, and not a man, woman, or child in the neighborhood but knew it by heart. Some always pretended to doubt the reality of it and insisted that Rip had been out of his head, and that this was one point on which he always remained flighty. The old Dutch inhabitants, however, almost universally gave it full credit. Even to this day they never hear a thunderstorm of a summer afternoon about the Catskills but they say Henry Hudson and his crew are at their game of ninepins; and it is a common wish of all henpecked husbands in the neighborhood, when life hangs heavy on their hands, that they might have a quieting draft out of Rip Van Winkle's flagon.

Recalling

1. In order to give the reader a clearer sense of atmosphere, or "feel," of the village, the author uses descriptive images. Write about the tranquil village in which Rip lived. Use descriptions from the story.

2. What is the "great error" in Rip Van Winkle's character?

3. Where does Rip go to escape? Whom does he meet, and where is he led?

4. Identify three changes that Rip notices, as he enters the village after his long slumber.

5. Who reassures the townspeople that Rip was asleep for twenty years? What does this person tell them about the people on the mountain?

Interpreting

6. Describe Rip's character at the beginning of the story. What do you like or dislike about him?

7. Rip's best friend was his dog, Wolf. Why do you think the dog was such an ally for Rip in his situation?

8. Do you think Rip's life was better before or after his sleep? Why?

Concluding

9. Given the choice, would you drink from Rip Van Winkle's flagon? Describe what life would be like for you, if you fell asleep for twenty years and then woke up.

Examining Fiction

Signs of the passage of time may be changes in the character's appearance and in features of the setting. After Rip awakened from his deep sleep, changes in his environment and in people's appearance made him realize that something strange had occurred.

1. When Rip enters the village, what changes in history and in politics does he discover?

2. Why is Rip's situation at home so much better after he has awakened from his deep sleep, than it was before he fell asleep?

Thinking About Fiction

Washington Irving uses a technique of comparing and contrasting setting and changing events. *Rip Van Winkle* is a good example of how a writer advances the plot of a story by comparing what stays the same and contrasting it with what is changeable.

1. When Rip entered the village after he awoke from his deep slumber, he expected the villagers to approach him in their usual friendly manner. Compare and contrast the villagers' reactions to him before he drank the wine, to their reactions after he awoke from his twenty-year sleep.

2. What differences did Rip notice in the appearance of the mountains, after he awoke from his long "nap"?

Creating and Writing

Make up an incident in your life that causes you to fall asleep for twenty years. Describe the setting before you fell asleep and after you woke up. Include many details about setting, as well as a description of your reaction when you awaken. Proofread your writing for accuracy in spelling, punctuation, and grammar.

Into • *A Boy and a Man*

On an icy mountain, a man falls twenty feet into a crack in the ground and he can't climb out. Then he hears a voice. "Hello!" Rudi calls. But Rudi has no rope and he is only a boy. If he goes for help, the man will freeze to death before he returns. This is how this suspense story begins. When we think of suspense stories, we assume that it is the plot that is creating the suspense. Actually, it is often the atmosphere combined with the plot that creates it. As you read the story, see if you can find words or phrases that create the atmosphere and increase the suspense.

Focus

A story consists of narrative and dialogue. The **narrative** is written in the author's voice, and gives the reader information about setting, plot, and characterization. The **dialogue** is written in a character's voice, and also gives us information about setting, plot, and characterization, but in a more indirect way. Both the narrative and dialogue create the story's atmosphere. In *A Boy and a Man*, the narrative tells us that the setting is a mountain.

The crevasse was about six feet wide at the top and narrowed gradually as it went down.

We know from the dialogue that someone has fallen into the crevasse. The narrative and dialogue add to our sense of anxiety.

"Hello!" Rudi called.
"Hello—" a voice answered from the depths.
"How long have you been there?"
"About three hours"…
"Do you have a rope?" asked the voice.
"No."
"How many of you are there?"
"Only me."

With each piece of information, the suspense grows. What will happen to this man? Night is falling. The air is freezing. The boy is alone. The reader can almost feel the cold and isolation of the mountainside. An atmosphere has been created.

About the Author

JAMES RAMSEY ULLMAN was born in 1907 in New York City. He was a newspaper writer, playwright, and theatrical producer. He had a love of adventure and traveled extensively. These passions, as well as his love of mountain climbing, are expressed in his many writings. In 1963, Ullman accompanied the first American expedition to Mount Everest, in spite of his being too ill to actually climb the mountain. He died in 1971 in Massachusetts.

A Boy and a Man

James Ramsey Ullman

The crevasse was about six feet wide at the top and narrowed gradually as it went down. But how deep it was Rudi could not tell. After a few feet the blue walls of ice curved away at a sharp slant, and what was below the curve was hidden from sight.

"Hello!" Rudi called.

"Hello—" A voice answered from the depths.

"How far down are you?"

"I'm not sure. About twenty feet, I'd guess."

"On the bottom?"

"No. I can't even see the bottom. I was lucky and hit a ledge."

The voice spoke in German, but with a strange accent. Whoever was down there, Rudi knew, it was not one of the men of the valley.

"Are you hurt?" he called.

"Nothing broken—no," said the voice. "Just shaken up some. And cold."

"How long have you been there?"

"About three hours."

Word Bank	**crevasse** (kruh VASS) *n.*: a very deep and wide break or opening
	gradually (GRAJ oo lee) *adv.*: slowly

Rudi looked up and down the crevasse. He was thinking desperately of what he could do.

"Do you have a rope?" asked the voice.

"No."

"How many of you are there?"

"Only me."

There was a silence. When the voice spoke again, it was still quiet and under strict control. "Then you'll have to get help," it said.

Rudi didn't answer. To get down to Kurtal would take at least two hours, and for a party to climb back up would take three. By that time it would be night, and the man would have been in the crevasse for eight hours. He would be frozen to death.

"No," said Rudi, "it would take too long."

"What else is there to do?"

Rudi's eyes moved over the ice-walls: almost vertical, smooth as glass. "Have you an ax?" he asked.

"No. I lost it when I fell. It dropped to the bottom."

"Have you tried to climb?"

"Yes. But I can't get a hold."

There was another silence. Rudi's lips tightened, and when he spoke again his voice was strained. "I'll think of something," he cried. "I'll think of *something*!"

"Don't lose your head," the voice said. "The only way is to go down for help."

"But you'll—"

"Maybe. And maybe not. That's a chance we'll have to take."

The voice was as quiet as ever. And, hearing it, Rudi was suddenly ashamed. Here was he, safe on the glacier's surface, showing fear and despair, while the one below, facing almost certain death, remained calm and controlled. Whoever it was down there, it was a real man. A brave man.

Rudi drew in a long, slow breath.

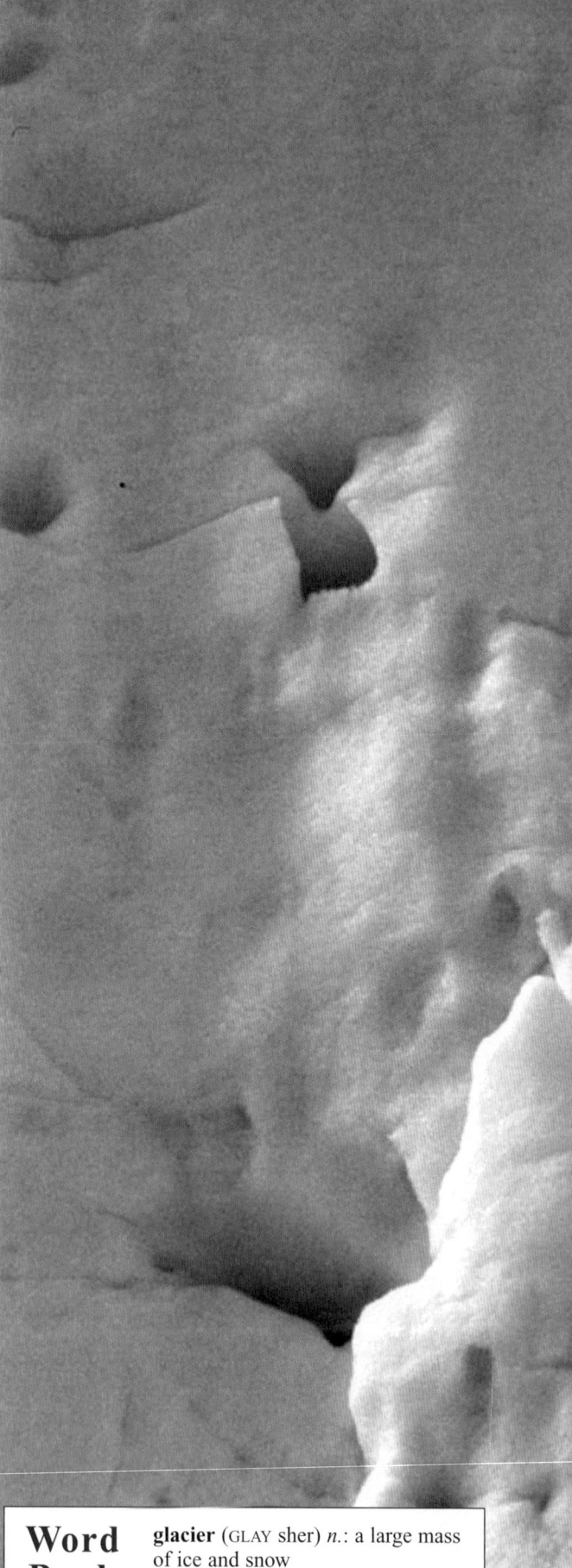

glacier (GLAY sher) *n.*: a large mass of ice and snow

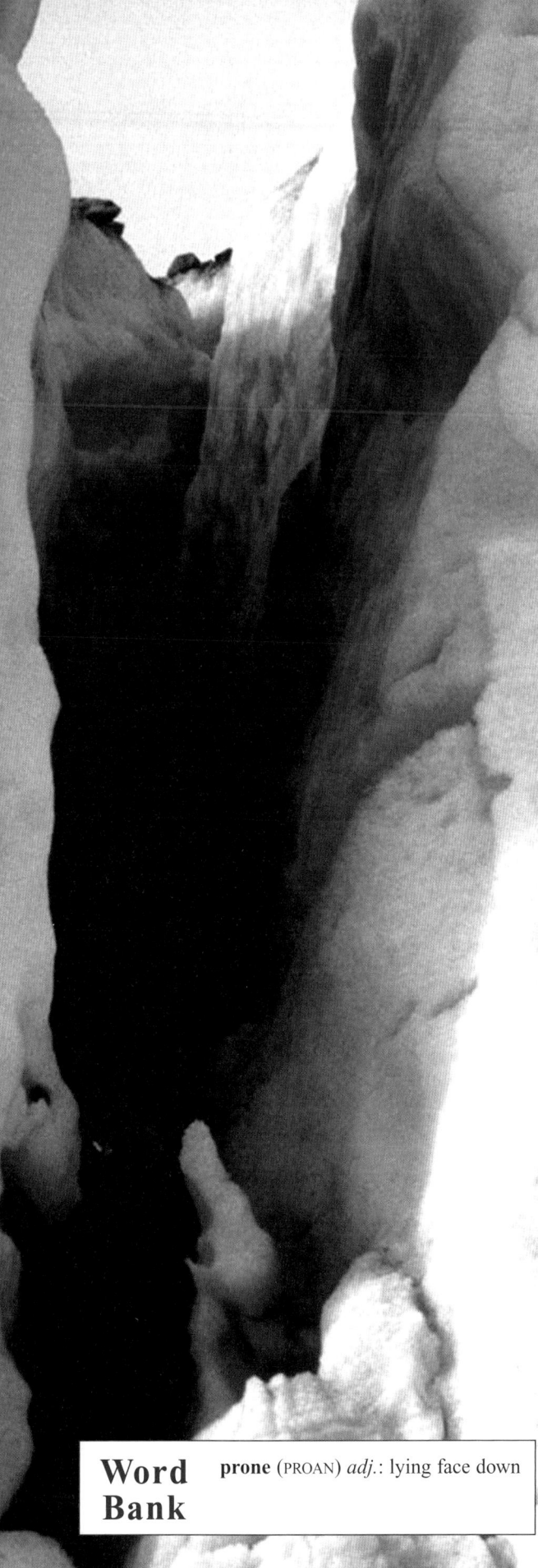

With his climbing-staff he felt down along the smooth surface of the ice walls.

"Are you still there?" said the voice.

"Yes," he said.

"You had better go."

"Wait—"

Lying flat on the glacier, he leaned over the rim of the crevasse and lowered the staff as far as it would go. Its end came almost to the curve in the walls.

"Can you see it?" he asked.

"See what?" said the man.

Obviously he couldn't. Standing up, Rudi removed his jacket and tied it by one sleeve to the curved end of the staff. Then, holding the other end, he again lay prone and lowered his staff and jacket.

"Can you see it now?" he asked.

"Yes," said the man.

"How far above you is it?"

"About ten feet."

Again the staff came up. Rudi took off his shirt and tied one of its sleeves to the dangling sleeve of the jacket. This time, as he lay down, the ice bit, cold and rough, into his bare chest; but he scarcely noticed it. With his arms extended, all the shirt and half the jacket were out of sight beneath the curve in the crevasse.

"How near are you now?" he called.

"Not far," said the voice.

"Can you reach it?"

"I'm trying."

There was the sound of scraping bootnails; of labored breathing. But no pull on the shirtsleeve down below.

"I can't make it," said the voice. It was fainter than before.

"Wait," said Rudi.

For the third time he raised the staff. He took off his trousers. He tied a trouser-leg to the loose sleeve of the shirt. Then he pulled, one by one, at all the knots he had made: between staff and jacket, jacket and shirt, shirt and trousers. He pulled until the blood

hear a scraping sound below, and he knew that the man was clawing his boots against the ice-wall, trying both to lever himself up and to take as much weight as possible off the improvised lifeline. But the wall obviously offered little help. Almost all his weight was on the lifeline. Suddenly there was a jerk, as one of the knots in the clothing slipped, and the staff was almost wrenched from Rudi's hands. But the knot held. And his hands held. He tried to call down, "All right?" but he had no breath for words. From below, the only sound was the scraping of boots on ice.

How long it went on Rudi could never have said. Perhaps only for a minute or so. But it seemed like hours. And then at last—at last—it happened. A hand came into view around the curve of the crevasse wall: a hand grip-

pounded in his head and the knots were as tight as his strength could make them. This done, he stepped back from the crevasse to the point where his toes had rested when he lay flat. With feet and hands he kicked and scraped the ice until he had made two holes. Then, lying down as before, he dug his toes deep into them. Without trousers and shirt the cold rose from the ice into his blood and bones. He lowered the staff and knotted clothes like a sort of crazy fishing line.

The trousers, the shirt and half of the jacket passed out of sight. He was leaning over as far as he could.

"Can you reach it now?" he called.

"Yes," the voice answered.

"All right. Come on."

"You won't be able to hold me. I'll pull you in."

"No you won't."

He braced himself. The pull came. His toes went taut in their ice-holds and his hands tightened on the staff until the knuckles showed white. Again he could

Word Bank   taut (TAWT) *adj.*: tense; tightly stretched

But heavy. Indescribably heavy. Rudi's hands ached and burned, as if it were a rod of hot lead that they clung to. It was not a mere man he was holding, but a giant, or a block of granite. The pull was unendurable. The pain was unendurable. He could hold on no longer. His hands were opening. It was all over.

And then it *was* over. The weight was gone. There was a scraping sound close beneath him; a hand on the rim of ice; a figure pulling itself up onto the lip of the crevasse. The man was beside Rudi, turning to him, staring at him.

"Why—you're just a boy!" he said in astonishment.

Rudi was too numb to move or speak. Taking the staff from him, the man pulled up the line of clothes, untied the knots and shook them out.

ping the twisted fabric of his jacket, and then a second hand rising slowly above it. A head appeared. A pair of shoulders. A face was raised for an instant and then lowered. Again one hand moved slowly up past the other.

But Rudi no longer saw it, for now his eyes were shut tight with the strain. His teeth were clamped, the cords of his neck bulged, the muscles of his arm felt as if he were being drawn one by one from the bones that held them. He began to lose his toe-holds. He was being dragged forward. Desperately, frantically, he dug in with his feet, pressed his whole body down, as if he could make it part of the glacier. Though freezing cold, he was pouring with sweat. Somehow he stopped the slipping. Somehow he held on. But now suddenly the strain was even worse, for the man had reached the lower end of the staff. The slight "give" of the stretched clothing was gone, and in its place, was rigid deadweight on a length of wood. The climber was close now.

Word Bank

bulged (BUHLJD) *v.*: swelled outward

"Come on now. Quickly!" he said.

Pulling the boy to his feet, he helped him dress. Then he rubbed and pummeled him until at last Rudi felt the warmth of returning circulation. "Better?" the man asked, smiling.

Rudi nodded. And finally he was able to speak again. "And you, sir," he said, "you are all right?"

The man nodded. He was warming himself now: flapping his arms and kicking his feet together. "A few minutes of sun and I'll be as good as new."

Nearby, a black boulder lay embedded in the glacial ice, and, going over to it, they sat down. The sunlight poured over them like a warm bath. Rudi slowly flexed his aching fingers and saw that the man was doing the same. And then the man had raised his eyes and was looking at him.

"It's a miracle how you did it," he said. "A boy of your size. All alone."

"It was nothing," Rudi murmured.

"Nothing?"

"I—I only—"

"Only saved my life," said the man.

For the first time, now, Rudi was really seeing him. He was a man of perhaps thirty, very tall and thin, and his face, too, was thin, with a big hawklike nose and a strong jutting chin. His weather-browned cheeks were clean-shaven, his hair black, his eyes deep-set and gray. And when he spoke, his voice was still almost as quiet as when it had been muffled by the ice-walls of the crevasse. He is—what?—Rudi thought. Not Swiss, he knew. Not French or German. English, perhaps? Yes, English…And then suddenly a deep excitement filled him, for he knew who the man was.

"You are Captain Winter?" he murmured.

"That's right."

"And I—I have saved—I mean—"

Rudi stopped in confusion, and the Englishman grinned. "You've saved," he said, smiling, "one of the worst imbeciles that ever walked on a glacier. An imbecile who was so busy looking up at a mountain that he couldn't even see what was at his feet."

Rudi was wordless—almost stunned. He looked at the man, and then away in embarrassment, and he could scarcely believe what had happened. The name of Captain John Winter was known through the length and breadth of the Alps. He was the foremost mountaineer of his day, and during the past ten years had made more first ascents of great peaks than any other man alive. Rudi had heard that he had come to Kurtal a few days before. He had hoped that at least he would see him in the hotel or walking by in the street. But actually to meet him—and in this way! To pull him

Word Bank	**pummeled** (PUM meld) *v.*: thump and pound; to strike repeatedly
	jutting (JUT ting) *v.*: projecting outward
	imbecile (IM buh sil) *n.*: a simple-minded person

from a crevasse—save him…It was incredible!

Captain Winter was watching him. "And you, son," he asked. "What is your name?"

Somehow the boy got his voice back. "Rudi," he said. "Rudi Matt."

"Matt?" Now it was the man's turn to be impressed. "Not of the family of the great Josef Matt?"

"He was my father," Rudi said.

Captain Winter studied him with his gray eyes. Then he smiled again. "I should have known," he said. "A boy who could do what you've done—"

"Did you know my father, sir?"

"No, unfortunately I didn't. He was before my day. But ever since I was a boy I have heard of him. In twenty years no one has come to the Alps and not heard of the great guide, Josef Matt."

Rudi's heart swelled. He looked away. His eyes fixed on the vast mountain that rose before them, and then he saw that Captain Winter was watching it too.

Unconsciously the Englishman spoke his thoughts. "Your father was—" He caught himself and stopped.

"Yes," said Rudi softly, "he was killed on the Citadel."

There was a silence. Captain Winter reached into a pocket and brought out an unbroken bar of chocolate. "Lucky I fell on the other side," he grinned.

He broke the bar in two and handed half to Rudi.

"Oh, no, sir, thank you. I couldn't."

"When I meet a boy your age who can't eat chocolate," said Winter, "I'll be glad to stay in a crevasse for good."

Rudi took it, and they sat munching. The sun was warm on their thawing bodies. Far above, it struck the cliffs and snowfields of the Citadel, so brightly that they had to squint against the glare.

Then there was Winter's quiet voice again. "What do you think, Rudi?"

"Think, sir?"

"Can it be climbed?"

"Climbed? The Citadel?"

"Your father thought so. Alone among all the guides of Switzerland, he thought so." There was another pause. "And I think so too," said Captain Winter.

The boy was peering again at the shining heights. And suddenly his heart was pounding so hard that he was sure the Englishman must be able to hear it. "Is—is that why you have come here, sir?" he asked. "To try to climb the Citadel?"

"Well, now—" Winter smiled. "It's not so simple, you know. For one thing, there's not a guide in the valley who would go with me."

"I have an uncle, sir. He is—"

"Yes, I know your uncle. Franz Lerner. He is the best in Kurtal, and I've spoken to him. But he would not go. Anything but that, he said. Any other peak, any route, any venture. But not *that*, he said. Not the Citadel."

"He remembers my father—"

"Yes, he remembers your father. They all remember him. And while they love and respect his memory, they all think he was crazy." Winter chuckled softly. "Now they think *I'm* crazy," he added. "And maybe they're right too," he said.

"What will you do, sir?" asked Rudi. "Not try it alone?"

"No, that crazy I'm not." Winter slowly stroked his long jaw. "I'm not certain what I'll do," he went on. "Perhaps I'll go over to the next valley. To Broli. I've been told there is a guide there—a man called Saxo. Do you know him?"

"Yes—Emil Saxo. I have never met him, but I have heard of him. They say he is a very great guide."

"Well, I thought perhaps I'd go and talk with him. After a while. But first I must reconnoiter some more. Make my plans. Pick the route. If there *is* a route."

"Yes, there is! Of course there is!"

Rudi had not thought the words. They simply burst out from him. And now again he was embarrassed as the man looked at him curiously.

"So?" said Captain Winter. "That is interesting, Rudi. Tell me why you think so."

"I have studied the Citadel many times, sir."

"Why?"

"Because—because—" He stopped. He couldn't say it.

"Because you want to climb it yourself?"

"I am not yet a grown man, sir. I know I cannot expect—"

"I wasn't a grown man either," said the Captain, "when I first saw the Citadel. I was younger than you—only twelve—and my parents had brought me here for a summer holiday. But I can still remember how I felt when I looked up at it, and the promise I made myself that some day I was going to climb it." He paused. His eyes moved slowly upward. "Youth is the time for dreams, boy," he murmured. "The trick is, when you get older, not to forget them."

Rudi listened, spellbound. He had never heard anyone speak like that. He had not known a grown man could think and feel like that.

Then Winter asked:

"This east face, Rudi—what do you think of it?"

"Think of it, sir?"

"Could it be climbed?"

Rudi shook his head. "No, it is no good. The long chimney[1] there—you see. It looks all right; it could be done. And to the left, the ledges"—he pointed—"they could be done too. But higher up, no. They stop. The chimney stops, and there is only smooth rock."

"What about the northeast ridge?"

"That is not good either."

"It's not so steep."

"No, it is not so steep," said Rudi. "But the rocks are bad. They slope out, with few places for holds."

"And the north face?"

Rudi talked on. About the north face, the west ridge, the southwest ridge. He talked quietly and thoughtfully, but with deep inner excitement, for this was the first time in his life that he had been able to speak to anyone of these things which he had thought and studied for so long…And then suddenly he stopped, for he realized what he was doing. He, Rudi Matt, a boy of sixteen who worked in the kitchen of the Beau Site Hotel, was presuming to give his opinions to one of the greatest climbers in the world.

But Captain Winter had been listening intently. Sometimes he nodded. "Go on," he said now, as Rudi paused.

Word Bank	reconnoiter (REE cun oy ter) *v.*: to make an exploratory or preliminary survey, inspection, or examination

---

1. *Chimney* (CHIM nee) is a word specific to mountain climbing, which means a narrow, deep crack in a cliff face.

"But I am only—"

"Go on."

And Rudi went on…

"That doesn't leave much," said the captain a little later.

"No, sir," said the boy.

"Only the southeast ridge."

"Yes, sir."

"That was the way your father tried, wasn't it?"

"Yes, sir."

"And you believe it's the *only* way?"

"Yes, sir."

Captain Winter rubbed his jaw for a moment before speaking again. Then— "That also is very interesting to me, Rudi," he said quietly, "because it is what I believe too."

Later, they threaded their way down the Blue Glacier. For a while they moved in silence. Then Captain Winter asked:

"What do you do, Rudi?"

"Do, sir?"

"Are you an apprentice guide? A porter?"

Rudi swallowed. "No, sir."

"What then?"

He could hardly say it. "A—dishwasher."

"A dishwasher?"

"In the Beau Site Hotel. It is my mother, sir. Since my father died, you see, she is afraid—she does not want—"

Rudi swallowed again. "I am to go into the hotel business," he murmured.

"Oh."

Again they moved on without speaking. It was now late afternoon, and behind them the stillness was broken by a great roaring, as sun-loosened rock and ice broke off from the heights of the Citadel.

When they reached the path Rudi spoke again, hesitantly. "Will you please do me a favor, sir," he asked.

"Of course," said Winter.

"Before we come to the town we will separate. And you will please not tell anyone that I have been up here today?"

The Englishman looked at him in astonishment. "Not tell anyone? You save my life, boy, and you want me to keep it a secret?"

"It was nothing, sir. Truly. And if you say that I have been in the mountains, my mother and uncle will hear, and I will be in trouble." Rudi's voice took on a note of urgency. "You will not do it, sir? You will promise—please?"

Winter put a hand on his shoulder. "Don't worry," he said. "I won't get you in trouble." Then he smiled and added: "Master Rudi Matt—dishwasher."

They walked down the path. The sun sank. Behind them, the mountain roared.

Recalling

1. What discovery does Rudi make at the beginning of the story?

2. Why does Rudi decide to save the man by himself and not go for help?

3. How does Rudi go about saving the man? What "equipment" does he use in his rescue?

4. Whom does Rudi save? What is this man's occupation and reputation?

5. Who was Rudi's father, and how did he die?

Interpreting

6. Rudi is told that "youth is the time for dreams..." What was Rudi's dream?

7. Which obstacles have kept Rudi from realizing his dream?

8. What do you think is the significance of the title, *A Boy and a Man*? Do you think it is an appropriate title for this story? Why or why not?

Concluding

9. Keeping dreams a secret is important for some people. Why do you think this is so?

Examining Fiction

Atmosphere may be thought of as the personality of a place. This is what makes the crevasse more than just a crack in the ice.

1. Reread the first page of the story. Write a paragraph describing how the crevasse looks, feels, and sounds.

2. Choose one of the following adjectives, and explain how it describes the atmosphere of the story: suspenseful, tragic, calm, exciting, scary, joyful, tense, sad, or peaceful.

Thinking About Fiction

The author creates a great deal of suspense in this story. Quote two passages from the story that add to the suspense.

Creating and Writing

Imagine that Captain Winter and Rudi have decided to climb the Citadel together. Write a short piece in which you convey the atmosphere, as they climb up the mountain. Include details that create suspense, and vivid description, so that a reader may actually "see" and "feel" the mountain and the characters, as they attempt their treacherous climb.

Blueprint FOR READING

Into • *The Hummingbird That Lived Through Winter*

What makes an artist special? It is not only that the artist can draw. An artist notices details that the average person overlooks. A good writer has the same ability. An event that you might report in three sentences becomes, in the hands of a writer, an entire short story. The writer describes a setting, creates a mood, adds dialogue, and inserts touches here and there that make the story come alive. The plot of *The Hummingbird That Lived Through Winter* is not very complicated or suspenseful. Rather, the story is like a beautiful miniature painting with wonderful details. When you have read the story, you will see that you have a picture in your mind—a mental image—of Dikran's house and garden. Most of us have read some stories in which the setting was described so skillfully that we have it tucked away in our memories as though it were real. Perhaps Dikran's little kitchen will become part of your "memory bank," too.

Focus

How does an author create a mental image? You might guess, at first, that the more description the author provides, the stronger the image will be. This is not necessarily so. What is more important than the number of details provided, is how clear those images are. As we all know, too many details are boring. A few strong images stay in the readers' minds and encourage the readers to use their imaginations to complete the picture. As you read the story, notice the adjectives used by the author. He chooses simple, clear adjectives and trusts the reader to imagine the rest. Almost without our noticing, we imagine how things look, feel, and even smell in Dikran's kitchen. The story's "life" is dependent on the author's writing and the reader's imagination.

About the Author

WILLIAM SAROYAN was born in 1908 in Fresno, California and died there in 1981. Born to an Armenian-American family, Saroyan's heritage is expressed in many of his works. Saroyan's work was first published when he was still a teenager. A prolific writer, Saroyan was awarded many literary prizes during his lifetime. In 1940, he received the Pulitzer Prize for Literature which he turned down, because he objected to wealthy persons patronizing the arts. Saroyan's Armenian background is expressed in *The Hummingbird That Lived Through Winter*.

The Hummingbird That Lived Through Winter

William Saroyan

*There was a hummingbird once which in the wintertime
did not leave our neighborhood in Fresno, California.
I'll tell you about it.*

Across the street lived old Dikran, who was almost blind. He was past eighty and his wife was only a few years younger. They had a little house that was as neat inside as it was ordinary outside—except for old Dikran's garden, which was the best thing of its kind in the world. Plants, bushes, trees—all strong, in sweet black moist earth whose guardian was old Dikran. All things from the sky loved this spot in our poor neighborhood, and old Dikran loved *them*.

One freezing Sunday in the dead of winter, as I came home from Sunday School I saw old Dikran standing in the middle of the street trying to distinguish what was in his hand. Instead of going into our house to the fire, as I had wanted to do, I stood on the steps of the front porch and watched the old man.

He would turn around and look upward at his trees and then back to the palm of his hand. He stood in the street at least two minutes and then at last he came to me. He held his hand out, and in Armenian he said, "What is this in my hand?"

I looked.

"It is a hummingbird," I said half in English and half in Armenian. Hummingbird I said in English because I didn't know its name in Armenian.

"What is that?" old Dikran asked.

"The little bird," I said. "You know. The one that comes in the summer and stands in the air and then shoots away.

Word Bank	**distinguish** (diss TIN gwish) *v.*: to see as being separate or different; to recognize a difference in

The one with the wings that beat so fast you can't see them. It's in your hand. It's dying."

"Come with me," the old man said. "I can't see, and the wife's not home. I can feel its heart beating. Is it in a bad way? Look again, once."

I looked again. It was a sad thing to behold, this wonderful little creature of summertime in the big rough hand of the old peasant. Here it was in the cold of winter, absolutely helpless and pathetic, not suspended in a shaft of summer light, not the most alive thing in the world, but the most helpless and heartbreaking.

"It's dying," I said.

The old man lifted his hand to his mouth and blew warm breath on the little thing in his hand which he could not even see. "Stay now," he said in Armenian. "It is not long till summer. Stay, swift and lovely."

We went into the kitchen of his little house, and while he blew warm breath on the bird he told me what to do.

"Put a tablespoon of honey over the gas fire and pour it into my hand, but be sure it is not too hot."

This was done.

After a moment the hummingbird began to show signs of fresh life. The warmth of the room, the vapor of the warm honey—and, well, the will and love of the old man. Soon the old man could feel the change in his hand, and after a moment or two the hummingbird began to take little dabs of the honey.

"It will live," the old man announced. "Stay and watch."

The transformation was incredible. The old man kept his hand generously open, and I expected the helpless bird to shoot upward out of his hand, suspend itself in space, and scare the life out of me—which is exactly what happened.

The new life of the little bird was magnificent. It spun about in the little kitchen, going to the window, coming back to the heat, suspending, circling as if it were summertime and it had never felt better in its whole life.

The old man sat on the plain chair, blind but attentive. He listened carefully and tried to see, but of course he couldn't. He kept asking about the bird, how it seemed to be, whether it showed signs of weakening again, what its spirit was, and whether or not it appeared to be restless; and I kept describing the bird to him.

When the bird was restless and wanted to go, the old man said, "Open the window and let it go."

"Will it live?" I asked.

"It is alive now and wants to go," he said. "Open the window."

I opened the window, the hummingbird stirred about here and there, feeling the cold from the outside, suspending itself in the area of the open window, stirring this way and that, and then it was gone.

"Close the window," the old man said.

We talked a minute or two and then I went home.

The old man claimed the hummingbird lived through that winter, but I never knew for sure. I saw hummingbirds again when summer came, but I couldn't tell one from the other.

One day in the summer I asked the old man.

<table>
<tr><td>**Word Bank**</td><td>**pathetic** (puh THET ik) *adj.*: extremely pitiful; bringing to mind pity, sympathy, or sorrow
shaft (SHAFT) *n.*: beam or beacon of light</td></tr>
</table>

suspending (sus SPEN ding) *v.*: hanging from above

"Did it live?"

"The little bird?" he said.

"Yes", I said. "That we gave the honey to. You remember. The little bird that was dying in the winter. Did it live?"

"Look about you", the old man said. "Do you see the bird?"

"I see hummingbirds", I said.

"Each of them is our bird", the old man said. "Each of them, each of them", he said swiftly and gently.

Recalling

1. What is Dikran holding in his hand? Why can't he identify it himself?

2. At what time of year does the story begin? How does this affect the health of the bird?

3. How does Dikran save the bird's life?

Interpreting

4. Describe Dikran's garden.

5. Explain why Dikran lets the bird go free.

6. Explain Dikran's message when he says, "Each of them is our bird."

Concluding

7. Give examples of the way Dikran shows his compassion for all living creatures.

Examining Fiction

The setting is a significant element in a short story. However, sometimes an author provides only a few specifics, leaving it to the reader to create a detailed mental image of the setting.

Think about the setting of the story and what it conveys about Dikran. What do Dikran's home and garden tell us about his character?

Thinking About Fiction

Point of view is the perspective from which an author tells a story. *The Hummingbird That Lived Through Winter* is written from the narrator's perspective.

1. Suppose the hummingbird could speak in English. Write several sentences from the point of view of the hummingbird about the way Dikran cared for him.

2. Describe an unusual way that the hummingbird could repay Dikran's kindness.

Creating and Writing

In *The Hummingbird That Lived Through Winter*, a man's love for the beauty of nature is obvious. The deep appreciation that Dikran has for the bird and its beauty has a profound effect on the reader. Write a short story that shows an appreciation of nature. Perhaps your major character will have character traits that are as simple and touching as Dikran's. Try to create a setting with vivid, clear images.

Into • *The Sparrow*

The Sparrow is not really a story; it is closer to what is called a **vignette**: a short, touching scene. It is easy to identify its theme, which is clearly stated in the last paragraph. It is also easy to see how every part of the vignette—the setting, the characters, and the narrative—all help convey the theme.

How can you, as a reader, get the most out of this little story? You must use your "mind's eye" and picture the scene in your imagination. If you do, you will probably feel the same way that the author did when he saw how much the mother bird loved her baby. This is the author's goal: to share with you, the reader, a beautiful experience and a deeper understanding of the world.

Focus

The **theme** of a story is the main idea conveyed by the story. Sometimes, the theme is obvious; the title or a line in the story may state it clearly. At other times, the reader must think about the story and analyze the plot, characters, and dialogue and see if a single, important idea runs through them. The next step, of course, is to ask yourself whether the theme's "truth" is, indeed, true!

About the Author

IVAN TURGENEV was born in 1818 in Russia. He was a master writer, among the first Russian authors to receive international acclaim. In spite of wealthy parents and upbringing, Turgenev was devoted to helping the poor. He traveled widely, and spent much time outside of Russia. He died in 1883 in France. The day of his funeral was a day of national mourning; the funeral was attended by representatives of 180 different organizations, who all came together to pay tribute to a master of Russian literature.

IVAN TURGENEV   # THE SPARROW

I was returning from a day's hunting and was walking toward the house along an alley in my garden. My dog was running ahead of me.

Suddenly she slowed her pace and began to advance stealthily, as though she had caught scent of game.

I looked down the path and saw a young sparrow with a streak of yellow near its beak and a bit of puff on its head. It had fallen out of the nest. (A strong wind was swaying the birch trees.) The tiny bird sat there trying helplessly to use its barely grown wings.

My dog was stealing up to the infant sparrow when, abruptly, an old black-chested bird fell like a stone right in front of the dog's face, and with all its feathers standing on end, misshapen, uttering a desperate and pitiful chirp, it hopped once and then again in the direction of the dog's open jaw.

The bird had thrown itself in front of the dog to shield its young one, but its own small body was trembling with terror, its little voice was frenzied and hoarse, and it was numb with fright—it was sacrificing itself!

What a huge monster the dog must have seemed to the mother sparrow! Nevertheless, it could not bear to stay on its high, safe perch in the tree. A force stronger than its will to remain alive made it hurl itself to the rescue.

My Treasure, the dog, stopped still and then backed up. Evidently she, too, recognized that force…

I hastened to call off the puzzled dog and went on my way, awed.

Yes, do not laugh. I was awed by that small, heroic bird—by its impulse of love.

Love, I felt more than ever, is stronger than death and the fear of death. Only through love is life sustained[1] and nourished.

---

1. *Sustained* (suh STAYND) means supported.

| **Word Bank** | **alley** (AL lee) *n.*: a path in a park or garden |
| | **awe** (AW) *n.*: overwhelming feeling of admiration, fear, or wonder |

frenzied (FRENZ eed) *adj.*: desperately agitated

pace (PAYS) *n.*: the rate of movement in stepping and walking

stealthily (STEHL thil ee) *adv.*: proceeding in a secret fashion

Recalling

1. Who was returning from a day's hunt?

2. Why did the dog slow its pace?

3. Who came to the defense of the baby bird?

4. What was the dog's reaction?

5. Which emotion is "...stronger than death and the fear of death," according to the narrator?

Interpreting

6. Name the emotions that the mother bird was feeling as she faced the dog.

7. Describe what interaction the narrator saw between the dog and the birds.

8. Explain how the mother bird defended her baby.

Concluding

9. Explain the statement, "Only through love is life sustained and nourished."

Examining Fiction

In a short story, the theme is the underlying idea and is revealed as the plot develops. In a story with a stated theme, the theme is established directly. In *The Sparrow* the theme is made clear by the author at the end of the story. The details and events of the story support the theme.

1. What is the theme of *The Sparrow*?

2. Restate the events and details that support the theme.

3. Compare the feelings and reactions of the mother bird to those of a human mother. Do you think that these emotions are common to all living creatures?

Thinking About Fiction

To **paraphrase** means to rewrite text in your own words. When we paraphrase a stated theme, it helps us better understand the theme. Paraphrase the stated theme of *The Sparrow*.

Creating and Writing

A mother's love for her children is an enduring theme in literature. Write a fictitious paragraph that supports this theme. The story may be about people or animals. Be sure that the details and events of your story fit the theme. Proofread for accuracy in spelling, punctuation, and grammar.

Into • *Zoo*

Zoo is a short, humorous work of science fiction. As in *The Sparrow*, the author makes the theme very clear to the reader in the last few lines of the story. In *The Sparrow*, however, the author states the theme openly, whereas in *Zoo*, the last bit of dialogue only hints at or implies the theme. When you have read the story, see if you can clearly express the story's theme in one or two sentences. Then, ask yourself whether you agree or disagree with the author.

Focus

The settings and, to some extent, characterizations, in science fiction make it different from all other types of literature. Outer space, undiscovered planets, weird creatures, and unimagined scientific advances are what make science fiction unique. But the themes of sci-fi stories are similar to those of all other forms of literature. Issues of life, war, conflict, suffering, and other universal topics are as popular in science fiction as they are in any other form of literature. Perhaps we like science fiction because we can discuss very important topics from a distance. It may be easier to discuss good or evil behavior when it is taking place light years away!

About the Author

American author **EDWARD D. HOCH** was born in 1930. He is well known for his mysteries and works of science fiction. A graduate of the University of Rochester, Hoch first began working as a researcher for the Rochester Public Library, and a copywriter for an advertising agency. Hoch's sense of humor and imaginative style have contributed greatly to his success as an author. He was the winner of the 1967 award from the Mystery Writers of America. His work, *Zoo*, is an example of his creative and amusing style.

Edward D. Hoch
Zoo

The children were always good during the month of August, especially when it began to get near the twenty-third. It was on this day that the great silver spaceship carrying Professor Hugo's Interplanetary Zoo settled down for its annual six-hour visit to the Chicago area.

Before daybreak the crowds would form, long lines of children and adults both, each one clutching his or her dollar, and waiting with wonderment to see what race of strange creatures the Professor had brought this year.

In the past they had sometimes been treated to three-legged creatures from Venus, or tall, thin men from Mars, or even snakelike horrors from somewhere more distant. This year, as the great

Word Bank

interplanetary (IN ter PLAN uh tehr ee) *adj.*: occurring between planets or between planets and the sun

clutching (KLUCH ing) *v.*: holding tightly with the hands

wonderment (WUN der mint) *n.*: amazement

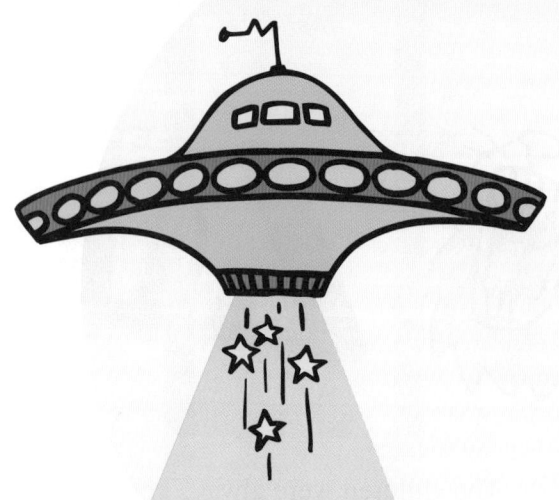

round ship
settled slowly to
earth in the huge
tri-city parking area
just outside of Chicago,
they watched with awe as
the sides slowly slid up to
reveal the familiar barred
cages. In them were some wild
breed of nightmare—small, horse-
like animals that moved with quick,
jerking motions and constantly chattered
in a high-pitched tongue. The citizens of
Earth clustered around as Professor Hugo's
crew quickly collected the waiting dollars,
and soon the good professor himself made an
appearance, wearing his many-colored rainbow
cape and top hat. "Peoples of Earth," he called into
his microphone.

The crowd's noise died down and he continued.

"Peoples of Earth, this year you see a real treat for your single dollar—the little-known horse-spider people of
Kaan—brought to you across a million miles of space at great
expense. Gather around, see them, study them, listen to them, tell
your friends about them. But hurry! My ship can remain here only
six hours!"

And the crowds slowly filed by, at once horrified
and fascinated by these strange creatures that looked
like horses but ran up the walls of their cages like spiders.
"This is certainly worth a dollar," one man remarked, hurrying away. "I'm going home to get the wife."

Word Bank	**breed** (BREED) *n.*: lineage; stock; strain; sort; kind; group
	clustered (KLUS terd) *v.*: gathered into a group or bunch
	filed (FY uhld) *v.*: marched in a line, one after the other

All day long it went like that, until ten thousand people had filed by the barred cages set into the side of the spaceship. Then, as the six-hour limit ran out, Professor Hugo once more took the microphone in hand. "We must go now, but we will return next year on this date. And if you enjoyed our zoo this year, telephone your friends in other cities about it. We will land in New York tomorrow, and next week on to London, Paris, Rome, Hong Kong, and Tokyo. Then on to other worlds!"

He waved farewell to them, and as the ship rose from the ground, the earth peoples agreed that this had been the very best Zoo yet…

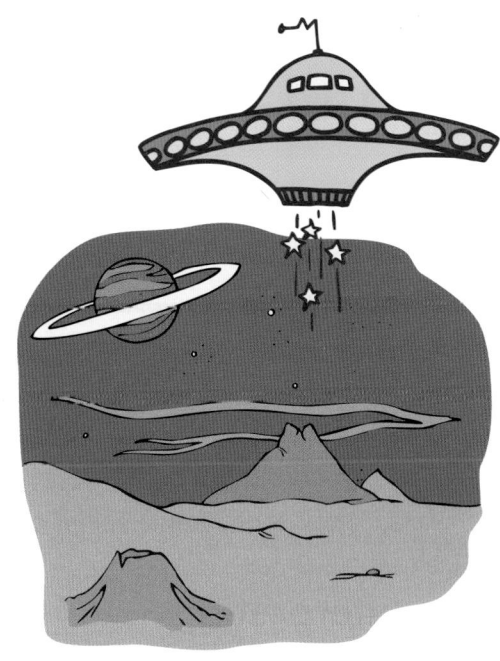

Some two months and three planets later, the silver ship of Professor Hugo settled at last onto the familiar jagged rocks of Kaan, and the odd horse-spider creatures filed quickly out of their cages. Professor Hugo was there to say a few parting words, and they scurried away in a hundred different directions, seeking their homes among the rocks.

In one house, the she-creature was happy to see the return of her mate and offspring. She babbled a greeting in the strange tongue and hurried to embrace them. "It was a long time you were gone. Was it good?"

And the he-creature nodded. "The little one enjoyed it especially. We visited eight worlds and saw many things."

The little one ran up the wall of the cave. "On the place called Earth it was the best. The creatures there wear garments over their skins, and they walk on two legs."

"But isn't it dangerous?" asked the she-creature.

"No," her mate answered. "There are bars to protect us from them. We remain right in the ship. Next time you must come with us. It is well worth the nineteen commocs it costs."

And the little one nodded. "It was the very best Zoo ever…"

Word Bank | **jagged** (JAG id) *adj.*: raggedly notched; sharply irregular on the surface or borders

Recalling

1. What causes the great excitement in Chicago?

2. What did Professor Hugo bring for the exhibition? What is the reaction of the People of Earth?

3. How do the horse-spider people of Kaan react to the People of Earth?

Interpreting

4. Did the People of Earth view the horse-spider people of Kaan differently than the creatures of Kaan viewed the People of Earth? Explain.

5. Professor Hugo ignored the appearance of the creatures from Kaan, and referred to them as people. What can you infer from this about their sensitivities and capabilities?

Concluding

6. What is the advantage of viewing a situation from more than one point of view?

Examining Fiction

The message of a story is its theme. In *Zoo*, the theme is revealed through the reactions of both the People of Earth and the horse-spider people of Kaan. The unique elements of the plot, the creatures of Kaan, and the setting are the elements that combine to create the theme.

1. Compare and contrast the ways in which the People of Earth and the People of Kaan view each other.

2. What does the story suggest about the way we view people or things that we consider abnormal?

3. What do you think is the theme of *Zoo*?

Thinking About Fiction

In the science fiction tale, *Zoo*, the ironic twist at the conclusion gives the reader information needed to make inferences regarding the theme of the story.

1. What was the surprise at the end of the story?

2. What did you learn when you read this conclusion?

3. Why does the irony of the ending make the story more effective and enjoyable?

Creating and Writing

Imagine that you have been chosen by Professor Hugo to seek out new and exciting creatures to bring to Earth. He has told you to send him a preliminary report. Record your initial reaction to these creatures. Include any change in your feelings that occurred once you began to communicate with the creatures. Include details about the appearance of the creatures and their home worlds. Your report should consist of at least one or two well-developed paragraphs. Make sure your spelling, punctuation, and grammar are correct.

Blueprint FOR READING

Into • *The Clearing*

Farming is hard work. Clearing the land of trees, digging up roots, plowing the soil, planting, watering, harvesting—what could be harder? Sometimes, just getting along with the neighbors is the more challenging job! As the story opens, the narrator and his brother are working at clearing some farmland. The Hinton boys, who live on the farm over the hill, begin to throw rocks at them for no apparent reason. Mr. Hinton, their father, is angry and unfriendly. Why? What does the future hold for these neighbors who get off to such a "rocky" start? Is there anything the narrator and his family can do to improve the situation—or would it be best for them to just avoid these bitter people?

Focus

The theme of *The Clearing* is developed through the interaction of the characters. The Hintons start out as hostile neighbors who pelt the narrator and his brother with stones. The boys' father, Pa, predicts that the families will never get along. Mom predicts that they will, once they get to know each other. As the two families are brought together by circumstance, they begin to appreciate one another's good points. What quality in each character allows this to happen? What different character trait might have kept the ill feeling between the two families alive? What is the author's message about conflict and its resolution? As you read the story, see if you can identify the character who best expresses the story's theme.

About the Author

American author **JESSE STUART** was born in 1907 in a log cabin in Kentucky. He is considered the genuine voice of Appalachian America. In addition to teaching much of his life, he was also a prolific writer. His first work, published in 1934, established his reputation as a "mountain bard," a title that remained with him throughout his career. Stuart died in 1984. His works of fiction are remembered and valued by the American public, for their humor, insight, and creative use of Appalachian dialect.

THE CLEARING

Jesse Stuart

Finn and I were pruning the plum trees around our garden when a rock came cracking among the branches of the tree I was pruning.

"Where did that come from?" I asked Finn, who was on the ground below piling the branches.

"I don't know," he said.

Then we heard the Hinton boys laughing on the other side of the valley. I went back to pruning. In less than a minute, a rock hit the limb above my head, and another rock hit at Finn's feet. Then I came down from the tree. Finn and I started throwing rocks. In a few minutes, rocks were falling like hailstones around them and around us. The land was rocky on both sides of the valley, and there were plenty of rocks to throw.

One of their rocks hit Finn on the foot, and one of our rocks hit the largest Hinton boy's head.

"Think of it," Finn said. "We fight before we know each other's names! What will it be as time goes on?"

We fought all afternoon with rocks. At sunset the Hinton boys took off up the path and over the hill. We went home. When Pa asked why we hadn't finished pruning the trees, we told him.

"I told you," he said to Mom. "You'll see whether we can live apart!"

"Wait until we get to know each other," Mom said.

"But how are we ever going to know people like them?" Pa asked.

"Oh, something will happen," she replied calmly. "You'll see."

The next day, Mort Hinton was with his boys. They climbed higher on the hill, cutting the briers and brush and tree branches and stacking them neatly into piles. Finn and I pruned our trees.

"I'll say one thing for the Hintons," Mom said. "They're good workers."

"When they don't throw rocks," Finn said.

On the fourth day, my guinea hens[1] flew across the valley where the Hintons were clearing land.

"Get these hens back on your side of the valley," Mort Hinton yelled. "Get 'em back where they belong."

---

1. *Guinea hens* (GINN ee HENZ) are fowl with round bodies and speckled feathers. Their heads have no feathers.

| Word Bank | **pruning** (PROON ing) *v.:* trimming; cutting back |
| | **briers** (BRY ers) *n.:* thorns; thistles |

I didn't want to put my hens in the hen house. But I had to. I knew Mort Hinton would kill them. I wanted to tell him that they would help his land. They'd get rid of insects that might destroy his crop. But I was afraid to tell him anything.

A week had passed before my guinea hens got out and flew across the valley.

"If you don't keep your hens on your side of the valley," Mort Hinton hollered to me, "I'll wring their necks."

That night I put my guinea hens in again. I fixed the hen house so they couldn't get out and roam the hills as they had always done. While Finn, Pa, and I cleared land on one side of the valley, the Hintons cleared on the other side.

When April came and the Hintons had finished clearing the hill and had burned the brush, Mort Hinton brought a skinny mule hitched to a plow and started plowing the new ground. He plowed slowly the first day. The second day my hens got out again and flew across the valley to the plowed ground. Mort Hinton caught two of them. The others flew back home when he tried to catch them. Then he yelled across to where we were plowing our new ground and told us what he had done.

"Your hens were on his land," Mom said. "He told you to keep them off his land."

Mort Hinton plowed his new ground by working from daylight until dusk, while the boys carried armloads of roots

THAT HILL OVER THERE IS NOT A

Though we'd never been close enough to the Hintons to talk with them, and we didn't want to get that close, we found ourselves trying to do more work than the four of them. Each day that early March, rain or sunshine, four Hintons worked on their side of the valley, and Pa, Finn, and I worked on our side. One day a Hinton boy hollered at us, "You can't clear as much land as we can."

"Don't answer him," Pa said.

from the field and stacked them in great heaps. By the first of May, they had made this ground soil like a garden. Then came a rainy season in early May, and they carried baskets of tobacco plants and set them in the newly plowed rows.

"They're workers, all right," Pa said.

On a dark night about a week later, I watched a moving light from my upstairs window. It came from the direction of the Hintons, over the hill and down into

Word Bank	**hitch** (HICH) *v.*: tie; to fasten
	heaps (HEEPS) *n.*: piles

the valley below our house. In a few minutes, I heard footsteps on the porch. Then there was a loud knock on our door. I heard Pa get out of bed and open the door.

"I'm Mort Hinton," a voice said. "My wife sent for your wife."

I heard Mom getting out of bed.

"I'll be ready in a minute," she called out.

Neither Pa nor Mort said another word.

baby," were Mom's first words as she sat down for a cup of coffee.

"What did they name the baby?" Glenna asked.

"They've not named her yet," Mom said. "I think they plan to call her Ethel. They're tickled to death. Three boys and now a girl!"

"What kind of people are they, anyway?" Pa asked.

"Like other people," Mom said. "They don't have much furniture in

"I'll be back when everything is all right," Mom said as she hurried off.

I watched the lantern fade from sight as Mort Hinton and Mom went down the path into the deep valley below the house. In two minutes or more, it flashed into sight again when they reached Hinton's tobacco field. The light moved swiftly up and over the hill.

The next morning, Pa cooked breakfast for us. He muttered about the Hintons as he stood near the hot stove frying eggs.

"They are friendly enough when they need something over there," Pa said.

We were ready to sit down to breakfast when Mom came home.

"Dollie Hinton's got a healthy girl

their house. They're working hard to pay for their farm."

"Will they be any better neighbors?" Pa asked.

"I think so," Mom said. "That hill over there is not a fence between us any longer."

"There's more than a hill between us," I said. "What about my hens Mort Hinton caught? Did he say anything about 'em last night?"

"And what about the Hinton boy that hit me on the foot with a rock?" Finn said. "I'd like to meet up with him sometime."

By the time we had finished our breakfast, Mort Hinton was plowing the young tobacco. His three sons were hoeing the tender plants with long-handled hoes.

"You'd think Mr. Hinton would be sleepy," Mom said. "He didn't go to bed last night. And the boys slept on the hay in the barn loft."

Pa, Finn, and I didn't have too much sympathy for the Hintons. Through the dining-room window, we could look across the valley and watch Mort keep the plow moving steadily. We watched his boys dig with their hoes, never looking up from the ground.

"This will be a dry, sunny day," Pa said. "We'll burn the brush piles on the rest of our clearing."

We gathered our pitchforks, hoes, and rakes and went to the hill where we had cleared ground all spring. There were hundreds of brush piles on our twenty acres of cleared ground. The wind was still. The sun had dried the dew from the leaves that carpeted the ground between the brush piles.

"It's the right time to burn," Pa said. "I can't feel any wind. The brush has aged in these piles until it is as dry as powder."

Pa struck a match to the brush pile at the bottom of the clearing. The fire started with little leaps over the leaf-carpeted ground. Finn, Pa, and I set fire to the bottom of the clearing until we had a continuous line of fire going up the slope. Then a wind sprang up from nowhere. And when flames leaped from brush pile to brush pile, Pa looked at me.

"This is out of control," Pa said. "Grab a hoe and start raking a ring."

"I'm afraid we can't stop it," Finn said. "We'll have to work fast

FINN & I TALKED WITH

to save the orchards."

"Run to the house and get Sal and Glenna," Pa yelled.

"Look, Pa," Finn said, pointing down the hill.

Mort Hinton was in front. He was running up the hill. His three sons were running behind him, each with a hoe across his shoulder.

"It's out of control," Pa shouted to Mort before he reached us.

ABOUT FISHING

"We've come to help," Mort said.

"Can we keep it from the orchards?" Pa asked.

"Let's run to the top of the hill and fire against it," Mort said. "I've burnt hundreds of acres of clearings on hillsides, and I always fire the top first and let it burn down! I fire the bottom last. Maybe we'll not be too late to save the orchards!"

Mort ran up the hill and we followed. Finn and I didn't speak to his boys, and they didn't speak to us. But when we started raking a ring side by side, we started talking to the Hintons. We forgot about the rock fight. Now wasn't the time to remember it, when flames down under the hill were shooting twenty to thirty feet high. In no time, we raked the ring across the top of the clearing. And the fire Mort Hinton set

control, we raked a ring down the west side near the peach orchard. Mort set a line of fire along this ring and let it burn toward the middle of the clearing. Then we raked a ring on the east side and fired against the fire that was approaching our plum trees and our house. Soon the leaping flames met in the clearing. We had the fire under control. Our clearing was burned clean as a whistle.

"How much do I owe you?" Pa asked Mort Hinton.

"You don't owe me anything," Mort said. "We're just paying you back for the help your wife gave us."

"Then let's go to the house for dinner," Pa said.

"Some other time," Mort said. "We must go home and see about Dollie and the baby."

As we went down the hill, Finn and I

THE HINTON BOYS . . .

along the ring burned fiercely down the hill and made the ring wider and wider. Only once did fire blow across the ring, and Pa stopped it then.

As soon as we had this spot under

talked with the Hinton boys about fishing and wildbee trees, while Pa and Mort laughed and talked about weather and crops.

& WILDBEE TREES

Recalling

1. Describe the first encounter between Finn, the narrator, and the Hintons.

2. Mom says, "Oh, something will happen. You'll see," in reference to the Hintons. What did happen, later on in the story, that proved Mom right?

3. Why do Finn, his brother, and his father move so quickly as they work next to the Hintons?

4. What do the Hintons need from Mom? Further along in the story, what does the narrator's family need from the Hintons?

5. As the story comes to its conclusion, what changes of attitude take place?

Interpreting

6. What is the narrator implying when he says, "There's more than a hill between us"?

7. How do the two families view each other and treat each other by the time the story has ended?

8. What do the boys discuss at the end of the story? What do they think of each other now?

Concluding

9. Often, first impressions of others are inaccurate. Describe a situation in which your feelings about a person changed dramatically.

Examining Fiction

Noticing how characters develop in a story will help you understand theme. In *The Clearing*, the narrator's family learns how to put personal feelings aside in a time of need.

1. Cite examples from the story that show how the family learns to do this.

2. What is the theme of the story?

Thinking About Fiction

Often, the title of a short story refers to its main character or event. However, sometimes an author chooses a title that emphasizes an important element of the theme.

1. Why did the author call this story, *The Clearing*?

2. How does the title refer to its theme?

3. If you had written this story, what would you have used for a title?

Creating and Writing

Imagine that a family has moved in next door to you. Your brother has begun having fights with them. How would you convince him that it is important to be on good terms with neighbors, and that he should stop behaving so badly? Write a short monologue in which you try to persuade your brother to be more friendly with your new neighbors.

Blueprint FOR READING

Into • *Home on the Range*

Have you ever had a day when everything went wrong? How did you react? Did you throw up your hands in despair and say, "I give up!"? Or did you laugh at each misadventure and try again? Whether we face our trials and problems with tears or with laughter, most of us can't help chuckling at somebody else's "bad day" (assuming it isn't really bad). A lot of comedy—especially slapstick comedy—is about likeable people who slip on the ice, miss trains, or fall into potholes! What we usually love about these comic heroes is their good-natured acceptance of all these difficulties. Underneath our laughter, is a fondness for the characters and a respect for their optimism. They, like the boys in this story, always come out on top!

Focus

This story has two themes—family loyalty and the benefit of a positive attitude. The story opens with the first theme. The boys, motivated by their love and appreciation of their mother, offer to help her out. Shortly afterwards, they find they must help out their father as well. The affection the brothers have for their father is so obvious that even a stranger can see it. We observe the way their father treats them, and we see why they love him so much. Another father might have scolded his sons for the mess that he found and blamed them for ruining his chance for advancement. This father does neither. He immediately sizes up the situation, realizes that his sons have been trying their hardest to help him, and expresses his appreciation to them. It is clear that the father considers his family the most important part of his life.

The second theme, the power of a positive attitude, is what creates the humor in the story. *Home on the Range* is humorous because the boys are so upbeat about each "disaster." As things get worse and worse for the boys, they get funnier and funnier for the reader! Everyone wins in the end in this delightful story, and the reader walks away chuckling.

About the Author

BEATRICE JOY CHUTE was born in 1913 in Minnesota, one of three sisters who all became authors. A resident of New York, Chute found writing "a difficult, demanding, and very interesting profession." According to Chute, the key to success for a writer is the willingness to constantly rewrite. The short story, *Home on the Range*, is one of Chute's earlier works, and is a good example of her charming and creative style. She died in 1987 in New York.

Home on the Range

B. J. Chute

Jeff Abbott parked the lawn mower against a tree and spoke to the hammock. "Get up, useless. It's your turn."

The hammock stirred and said, "Go away."

Jeff sighed, took hold of the ropes, and tipped it neatly upside down. His brother Tommy popped forth and landed sprawling on the grass.

"Ups-a-daisy," said Jeff brightly and settled down in a patch of shade.

Tommy said, "I hope you're sitting on a wasp." He hauled the lawn mower into position and leaned dreamily on the handle.

"Quit stalling," said Jeff.

"I'm not stalling. Jeff, won't it be wonderful if Dad gets that job?"

"You'll still have to mow the lawn," Jeff pointed out realistically. "And anyway it's no good worrying about it until Dad gets back home tomorrow night."

"*With* Mr. Wilson," Tommy reminded him. "If I was Mr. Wilson, I'd make Dad manager of the Wilson and Arnold branch store here without even thinking about it."

"Well, Mother's planning a slap-bang dinner, and there's nothing like a good dinner to make a man feel mellow, especially Mother's fried chicken. One taste of that, Mr. Wilson'll make Dad vice-president."

"I'll settle for manager."

"I'll settle for you mowing the lawn. It's rising around your ankles."

Word Bank	**mellow** (MEL oh) *adj.*: made gentle by age or experience; pleasant; agreeable; laid-back

Tommy sighed and was about to start work when the front door opened and their mother came out, wearing a blue housedress and an anxious expression. Tommy waved to her companionably.

"Have a hammock," he invited.

She declined with thanks, but crossed the lawn to join them.

"Your Aunt Dorothy just phoned. Uncle Jim fell down the basement stairs and sprained his ankle."

"Gee, that's tough! Anything we can do to help?"

"That's just it. Dorothy has a bad cold and the twins are behaving like wild Indians. She wanted to know if I could drive out and spend the night with her, and I said I'd call back."

Jeff got to his feet. "Of course you'll go. She can't possibly be expected to manage alone."

"You're sure you don't mind? You'll have to make supper out of scraps, I'm afraid—I'll shop for Mr. Wilson's dinner tomorrow morning."

"Don't give us a second thought," Jeff said airily. "I'll keep an eye on the house and little Thomas will mow the lawn."

Little Thomas permitted himself a low passionate growl. Mrs. Abbott said, "The laundryman will be coming. Oh, and Jeff, they've promised to send a man to look at the stove. The back burners don't light right."

"Back burners," Jeff repeated. "Okay. Now you go and call Aunt Dorothy and tell her the Marines are coming."

By the time they had seen their mother off in the family car, Tommy and Jeff were feeling highly competent and domestic. Tommy shot through the lawn mowing and, when the doorbell rang, Jeff welcomed the laundryman hospitably and retired upstairs to sort sheets and towels.

The doorbell rang again.

Jeff shouted down, "Tommy, if that's the man to fix the stove, tell him it's the back burners." Silence answered him. "Tommy?" More silence. "Hey, Tommy! Who is it?"

A hollow voice rose from the front hall. "Telegram," said Tommy. "From Dad."

Waving two bath towels, Jeff hurtled down the stairs and met Tommy coming up. Wordlessly, Tommy put the yellow envelope into his brother's hands, put his head into his own hands, and sat down on the bottom step. Jeff opened the telegram:

PLANS CHANGED. FLYING DOWN. WILL ARRIVE TONIGHT WITH WILSON. EXPECT US DINNER ABOUT SIX O'CLOCK. LOVE.

"Tonight!" There was a flopping sound as Jeff landed beside Tommy. "Good grief! What do we do now?"

"Phone Mother and tell her to come home."

"Thomas! We can't. Nowhere to catch her. And she couldn't get back in time if we did."

Tommy thought a moment, then nodded gloomy agreement. "Well, how about wiring Dad and telling him to change his plans?"

"They'd have left by now." Jeff clutched his hair. "This is awful. Mother had everything planned to give Mr. Wilson a superdeluxe dinner, and now…Tommy! I've got the solution. *We'll get the dinner.*"

"You're mad," said Tommy.

Jeff consulted his watch and ignored his brother. "It's not four-thirty yet, and they won't be here until six. By that time, we'll have a delicious dinner all ready to welcome Mr. Wilson."

"Mother said there was only scraps for our dinner. You can't feed Mr. Wilson on scraps."

"Listen, chum, if Mother was home

she'd cook up something, wouldn't she? She's always making something out of nothing. Well, we can do the same. You want Mr. Wilson to be happy, don't you?"

"For Pete's sake! Of course I do."

"Very well, then." Jeff seized his brother and pushed him kitchenward. "The first thing we do is plan a menu, starting of course with soup." He found a cookbook and dived into "Soups." "Four pounds chicken—one cup chopped clams. The things people think of! Tommy, look in the cupboard and see what kind of canned soups we've got."

"How about cream of mushroom?"

"Fine. We just heat that. Now, for the main course—beef roulade, veal short-cake, roast chicken. H'mm." He changed his tactics. "Tell you what, we'll pick our vegetables first. What have we got?"

"Bag of peas. Six potatoes. We could have baked potatoes."

Jeff, who had been voyaging danger-ously among the meats again, shook his head. "We shall want the oven."

"We shall?"

Jeff nodded solemnly. "I've decided on corned-beef-and-rice casserole, if we have any corned beef. Take a look, will you, Thomas my boy?"

"I suppose," said Thomas my boy between his teeth, "that you're being executive. Oh, well." He investigated the cupboard again and came out wav-ing the corned beef.

"Now, find an onion and some toma-toes. The casserole takes thirty minutes, so it should go in the oven about five-thirty." He licked his pencil and made a note. "This is going to be easy. Soup, casserole, peas, potatoes—I think mashed would be nice. Let's see, pota-toes on at five-twenty, peas at five-forty, set table at five-forty-five—"

"Trains stop only on signal," said Tommy. "Passengers with baby ele-phants must leave their trunks in the baggage car."

"Hush," said Jeff. "Now, for dessert, we want something fancy. I think cake would be nice."

"I thought you were in the oven."

"That comes later. The cake will be out by the time the casserole goes in, which is why I have the timetable you were so rude about. Don't apologize."

"Who's apologizing?"

Jeff listened. No one was. He returned to his menu. "There's a recipe here for chocolate roll that sounds deli-cious. It's like a jelly roll, only it has whipped cream inside." He spread the cookbook out on the table. "I'll start that, and you do the casserole. First, you fix the rice and tomatoes."

"How much rice?" said Tommy resignedly.

Jeff referred to his cookbook again. "Four cups cooked rice. That would mean four cups uncooked rice, I should think. You just put it in water and boil it." He got down on his knees and start-ed prowling around the saucepan cup-board. "Do you think Mother has a jelly-roll pan?" he inquired from its depths, added something about darkest Africa, and then gave a happy yelp. "Ah, got it!" There was a tremen-dous crash, rather like two armadillos locked in mortal com-bat, and Jeff came out hastily backward with two muffin pans and a

Word Bank	**armadillo** (ARM uh DILL oh) *n.*: a small insect-eating mammal with an armor-like shell

whole troop of small custard-cups pursuing him hotly. He had, however, the jelly-roll pan in one hand and the casserole in the other, so there was triumph on his brow as well as a sieve.

Tommy said, "The rice is on. Do I skin the tomatoes?"

"I suppose. Let's see, six tablespoons of cake flour. Tommy, what's cake flour?"

"Flour you use in cakes, I should think."

"Brilliant deduction," said Jeff ungratefully. "Flour's flour," he decided, measured six tablespoons, added cocoa, salt, and baking powder, and then discovered he was supposed to sift the mixture three times. This seemed pointless and enraged him, and by the time he was through the third sifting the air was cloudy with flour dust. It cheered him enormously, on emerging, to discover that his brother was knee-deep in tomato skins. "There must be a better way to do that, Tommy. You're not getting anywhere."

Tommy, who knew a better way, offered Jeff the knife. Jeff backed off and made noises appropriate to a man who is very busy with a chocolate roll.

"Three-quarters cup sugar," said Jeff, measuring like mad. "You know, Tommy, this is all quite simple. I hope Mr. Wilson appreciates home cooking."

Tommy was trying to arrange a separation between his nose and a large piece of tomato skin, and his reply was slightly blurred, as if with anguish.

"Four eggs," said Jeff cheerfully. "Beat egg whites stiff but not dry. H'mm, that's odd. You beat the yolks separately. Tommy, if you were an egg—"

Tommy put down his knife in exasperation. "I've got enough tomato skin on me to be a tomato," he said crossly. "Look, Jeff, can't I just cut 'em up and dump 'em into the saucepan?"

"Dump away," said Jeff. "I need you." He was holding an egg in each hand and staring at them. As Tommy came over, he outlined the problem in simple terms. "The recipe says to separate the yolks and whites. I'm in a very receptive mood if you have any suggestions."

"Sure," said Tommy with frightening clearheadedness. "I've watched Mother do it a hundred times. You simply take an egg, like this, and tap it against the side of the bowl—OOPS!"

"Have another egg," said Jeff hospitably, and added with admiration, "Who would ever have believed that a little egg with no feet could run up a person's sleeve so fast? Can I help you, pal—a vacuum cleaner or a bathtub or something?"

Tommy, between clenched teeth, declined aid and mopped himself up austerely with a dish towel, then held out a stern hand for another egg. "I merely hit it a little too hard," he said, cracked this one more skeptically and let the white trickle out slowly. "There. Now, grab the yolk before it slides."

Jeff automatically reached out his hand, palm up. Tommy dropped the yolk into it.

This time it was Jeff who did his speaking between clenched teeth, and by the time Tommy

found a bowl for the yolks he was in a clearly fragile mood. Tommy tried another egg, and its yolk crept in with the white. In the next few minutes, they learned an astonishing amount about adhesion. When at last four yolks and four whites had gone their separate ways, they were both exhausted and Tommy staggered back thankfully to his rice which was beginning to bubble.

Jeff began to beat the egg white to the tune of "Danny Boy." "Lookit the purty white mountain peaks it makes," he invited, admiring his handiwork. "Tommy, it says here to fold in the sugar. How do you fold in sugar?"

"I'm busy," said Tommy, who didn't know.

"I guess it just means stir." Jeff dumped in the sugar, stirred briskly, and took a taste. "Umm, delicious. How are your tomatoes doing?"

Tommy poked one with a fork. "I think they're holding their own." He leaped as the doorbell rang. "Maybe that's another telegram, saying they're not coming."

"It's probably the man about the stove." He watched Tommy go, returned to his egg whites, then broke off as the phone rang. "Too many bells in this house," he said grumpily and went to answer it.

The phone call was from a neighbor. The doorbell had been pushed by a vacuum-cleaner salesman. When the cooks returned to the kitchen, they were greeted by a strange rich scent.

"My tomatoes!" Tommy shrieked and grabbed the saucepan. The bottom layer had turned a melancholy black and was clinging sulkily to the pan; the top layer was in its original state.

"Put 'em in another saucepan and start over again," Jeff advised, glanced at the clock, and added, "Jeepers, we've got to hurry." He combined his eggs, added vanilla, and dumped in the flour mixture all in one dump. This turned

out to be a grievous error. The flour took a cordial dislike to the eggs and humped itself up in a series of hillocks. Jeff, wielding a spoon, would whack one hillock into place, only to see another rise behind it, and when, inspired, he tried to correct the situation with the egg beater, the egg beater bogged down in the batter. With the aid of two spoons, a knife, and his fingers, Jeff finally got the batter loose and decided that the lumps would bake themselves out in the oven.

He began to issue instructions like an overwrought general. "Tommy, line the jelly-roll pan with waxed paper and grease the paper. You'd better hurry," he added. "I think the lumps are gaining on me." He hit them fiercely on their heads with his spoon, then glanced over his shoulder to see how Tommy was getting along, caught sight of the stove, and gave a horrified howl.

"Tommy—LOOK!"

Tommy looked. The rice was boiling over.

Sequestered—there in the saucepan of water, each separate little grain had been hard at work, swelling triumphant-

Word Bank	cordial (KOR jil) *adj.*: friendly and warm
	hillocks (HILL ahks) *n.*: small hills
sequestered (sih KWES terd) *v.*: secluded; set off; set apart	

ly. Now the time had come when the overcrowding became acute, and rice poured out over the sides of the pan in a tremendous white waterfall, inundating the stove, sweeping heedlessly over the burners, and cascading to the floor.

It was a stupendous and stirring spectacle. People travel thousands of miles to see Niagara Falls; great natural events like the San Francisco earthquake become historic. Here, in the Abbott kitchen, the whole world was ricebound, and the majestic beauty of the show should have held Jeff and Tommy in hushed appreciation.

It didn't.

Jeff shouted, "Get a bucket!"

Tommy yelled for the fire department.

Jeff howled, "Do something!" and Tommy howled right back "What?" which was a good question.

It was Jeff who finally thought of turning out the fire. The flood began slowly to subside, leaving rice fields and swamps.

Jeff paddled back to his brother and eyed him severely. "What did you measure that stuff with? A bushel basket?"

"It's four cupfuls, like you said," Tommy defended himself. "It's not my fault if only four cupfuls makes a full-scale blizzard."

"Well, clean it up," said Jeff morosely, then looked at the clock. "No, don't. I need you. Is the waxed paper greased? Where's my spoon? Where's—?"

"Stop roaring," said Tommy soothingly. He shoved the pan under his brother's nose, and Jeff poured in the batter, arranging the lumps as neatly as possible. Together, they put the finished product reverently into the oven, trying to avoid trampling on rice.

"Bakes twelve minutes," said Jeff. "Don't let me forget it. Now, where are we with the corned-beef casserole?"

"Well," said Tommy, in a masterpiece of understatement, "we have the rice."

Jeff, who was standing on one foot, scraping the rice off his shoe, conceded the truth of this statement. He drew a deep breath.

"From here on, everything's much simpler. You put the corned beef and rice into the casserole, make a sauce with the tomatoes and some onion…"

"What tomatoes?"

"They're not well?" said Jeff anxiously.

"Some are burned and some are raw. We cater to all tastes."

"Well, put the raw ones on the bottom and arrange the burned ones where they won't show." He seized the casserole and began alternating corned beef and rice in a cheflike frenzy. Tommy peered into the cookbook to see what came next and suddenly announced, "You should have greased the casserole first."

Jeff gave the cry of a wounded hippopotamus. "Now he tells me! Well, it's too late. Here, you take your tomatoes now, Tommy, add salt, pepper, Worcestershire sauce, and onion. Go find an onion and chop it."

"*You* chop it," Tommy suggested winningly.

"No, you. I'm busy." Jeff pointed

indignantly at the clock. "Now I've forgotten what time the chocolate roll went in." He opened the oven, gazed inside, and gave one of those wounded howls which were becoming a trademark with him. "It hasn't even begun to—Oh."

"Difficulty?"

"We forgot to light the oven."

"Then I suppose," said Tommy profoundly, "that it didn't bake."

"My boy, you're an absolute genius." Jeff lit the oven in some bitterness of spirit, suddenly remembered the potato problem, and dived for the cookbook again. "Peel and boil for twenty to thirty minutes," he read. "Tommy, you peel things so nicely…"

"No." Tommy, who was sobbing quietly over his onion, was in no mood for more responsibilities.

Jeff retired into the potatoes, and almost at once he began to understand what his brother had been through with the tomatoes. The devotion of a potato to its peel is a very touching thing, and after about ten minutes of the most earnest endeavor it began to seem to Jeff that it was cruel to separate them. He gave up trying to peel thin and started peeling thick. This resulted in a splendid pile of potato peels and six miniature white marbles. He impaled one of these on the point of his knife and turned it around, examining it intently from all sides. "Look, Tommy, isn't nature amazing?"

Tommy looked up with wet eyes and blinked. "What's *that* thing?"

"That," said Jeff informatively, "is a potato. I have six of the dear little, wee little things." He sighed deeply. "Tommy, do you think we need potatoes with all that rice?"

"Potatoes," said Tommy, who was a good brother, "are very fattening—onion's chopped, Jeff. What do I do with it now?"

"Mix it with the rest of the stuff and pour it over the corned beef and rice."

"I hope Mr. Wilson likes rice," said Tommy, mixing his sauce artistically. "A man who doesn't like rice is going to feel awfully out of things in this house. There—now what?"

"Now, it goes into the oven. Great leaping lemondrops, the chocolate roll!" Jeff leaped for the stove. "It's been in there at least ten minutes too long."

"How does it look?" said Tommy.

"Well…it has a lot of strange little bubbles on top, and in the middle it seems sort of depressed. Do you think it's done?"

Tommy joined him and peered. "Reminds me of that rubber mat on the porch."

"Are you insinuating[1]…?"

"No, no, of course not. Just a sudden mood of reminiscence." Tommy scowled at the chocolate roll. "You know, Jeff, I think you'd better take it out. It's five-thirty already, and the casserole has to go in. And, anyway, if that roll gets any browner it will be black."

"You put things so nicely." Jeff took the pan out of the oven and made another grab for the cookbook. "F' Pete's sake!"

"Now what?" Tommy shoved in the casserole, closed the door, and turned alertly to his brother's aid in what

---

1. *Insinuating* (in SIN you AYT ing) means hinting.

appeared to be yet another crisis.

"The roll's supposed to be turned out onto a towel dusted with confectioner's sugar. I call that very eccentric.[2] Get me a towel and some sugar, quick."

Tommy obeyed. Jeff sprinkled the towel with sugar and then turned his cake out onto it. "Now," he said, "we roll it up and wrap it in the towel, working rapidly." He worked rapidly, producing a neat, professional-looking roll.

"Jeff," said Tommy quietly.

"Looks nice, doesn't it?"

"It looks very nice," said Tommy, "but I think you've made two slight errors. In the first place, you didn't take the waxed paper off…"

"Oh," said Jeff, rather blankly.

"And, in the second place," said Tommy, "when it says roll up and wrap in towel, I think it means that you roll it up first and *then* wrap it in the towel. The way things are now, you've got the waxed paper and the towel where the whipped cream goes."

"So I have," said Jeff. A respectful sort of pall[3] settled on the scene, but then the natural optimism of the Abbotts reasserted itself. "Well, look at it this way. It has to be unrolled when it's cool enough to put the cream in, and at that time we merely zip off the towel and the paper in one brisk motion."

"I hope you're right."

"Of course I'm right. Now what have we got left to do?"

"Shell peas, whip cream, set table, and…"

The back doorbell rang suddenly.

Jeff and Tommy leaped in duet. "If that's the man about the stove at a time like this," said Jeff, "I shall boil him in a saucepan and wrap him up in the chocolate roll." He strode to the door and flung it open dramatically.

A small man with a black bag clutched in one hand looked at him meekly and said, "Is this the Abbott house?"

"We expected you hours ago," Jeff said fretfully as he held the door open and followed him into the kitchen. "It's the back burners, but I guess you'll have to wait a few minutes before you fix them, on account of the stove's sort of busy."

The little man looked doubtful. "But I…"

"We won't keep you waiting long," Jeff assured. "You just sit down in this chair."

"Jeff," said Tommy in a hoarse stage whisper, "the peas aren't shelled yet. If we don't get them on pretty soon, we'll have to eat them for dessert."

Jeff clutched his brow and turned despairingly to the stove-man. "Look, can you shell peas?"

"Peas?"

"It's very simple," said Jeff apologetically, "and you'd be doing us a big favor." He put a bowl and the bag of peas onto the little man's lap and gazed at him trustingly. "I have to whip the cream and Tommy has to set the table, and if we don't get the peas on we'll really be in the soup."

"Soup!" Tommy yelled, catching the key word.

"Oh, murder! Get a can opener and another saucepan." Jeff rushed around like a neurotic[4] beetle, explaining as he rushed. "You see, the trouble is that my father's bringing a man home to dinner, and my mother's gone to visit my aunt who has twins and a husband with a sprained ankle and a cold. Well, *she* has the cold and her husband has the ankle." He paused to make sure this was all quite clear. The little man nodded dazedly, and Jeff went on. "So, this man that my father's bringing home is the

---

2. *Eccentric* (ek SEN trik) means odd.
3. Here, *pall* (PAHL) means an effect of gloom.
4. *Neurotic* (nuh ROT ik) means nervous.

president of the Wilson and Arnold stores—Tommy, where's that saucepan?"

"In your hand."

"Oh. Well, Mr. Wilson is thinking of making my father manager of the branch store here, so we're trying to get a nice dinner that will impress him. There's nothing like a good dinner to make a man feel mellow, and our aim in life is mellowing Mr. Wilson. He's probably a crab by nature," Jeff finished cheerfully. "I'd better whip the cream."

Tommy, table-setting, came out of the dining room. "What china shall we use, and where's the salt-and-pepper shakers?"

"Use the best, we want to be impressive. I don't know where the shakers are." Jeff whirred his egg beater like a helicopter. "Put some water on to boil for the peas, will you, Tommy? And while you're there, take a look at the casserole."

Tommy filled a saucepan, put it on the stove, and then opened the oven door. He gasped, "Wow, that's hot," and backed off, looking pensive. Then he poked it cautiously with a spoon. "Jeff, you remember what the cookbook said about greasing the casserole? Well, the book was right."

"It stuck?"

"The rice," said Tommy precisely, "appears to have formed a thin coat of cement across the bottom. It would make a marvelous tennis court."

Jeff pondered this melancholy news bulletin. "We'll serve it from the top," he decided resourcefully. "Tommy, this cream won't whip."

"Are you sure?"

"Positively. I'm beginning to have a vague feeling that Mother orders special cream for whipping." He gave the egg beater a disgusted shake and splashed cream on the floor. "How can we have a chocolate-cream roll without cream?"

"How about spreading jelly on it instead? After all, it's second cousin to a jelly roll."

"I never spread jelly on a second cousin," said Jeff, "but we can try."

He undid the towel around the cake and proceeded to unwrap. To say that cake, towel, and waxed paper had become devoted to each other would be to understate the case. The paper clung to the bottom of the roll, and the towel clung to its interior. The cake itself, discouraged by the way things were going, peeled off in chunks.

Tommy tried hard to think of something reassuring to say, but there was a quality about the cake that defied comfort. "We could spread the towel with

jelly," he offered. "Some towels have a very delicate flavor."

Jeff glared at the object he had produced. It was a sort of a chocolate towel, richly frosted with waxed paper. For anyone with a taste for towels and paper, it would make a most delectable and unusual dessert.

"Tommy," said Jeff.

"Yes, old man?" said Tommy in a hushed, respectful voice.

"What would you say to burying this quietly in the garbage can?"

"It would be kinder," said Tommy.

"That's what I thought." Jeff lifted the ruins solemnly and started toward the garbage can, then put his foot squarely into the cream he had splashed on the floor. There was one moment when it looked as though Jeff would successfully defy the laws of gravity. In that moment, he grabbed for support at the stove-man's knee.

The stove-man's knee had a bowlful of shelled peas sitting on it. There was, therefore, a double crash—Jeff falling (with cake) and bowl falling (with peas). The peas, gladsomely released, scooted all over the kitchen floor. The cake only got as far as Jeff's lap.

He sat there on the floor, thinking long hard thoughts.

Tommy started to his rescue and then stopped, sniffing. From the oven a thin spiral of smoke wound its way out into the room.

The afternoon had trained Tommy to think fast in an emergency. He seized a potholder in one hand, turned off the oven with the other, drew the casserole out and eyed it somberly.

Jeff looked up from the cake in his lap. "There goes your tennis court, Tommy," said Jeff.

"There goes our dinner," said Tommy.

They looked around the room. They had mushroom soup and, if Tommy could find the salt-and-pepper shakers, they would have salt and pepper. Otherwise, their dinner now consisted of a well-burned casserole with a paved floor, a bowlful of shelled peas racing from door to window, and a chocolate roll which Jeff was still sitting under.

The stove-man got down on his knees and began silently to follow the peas around the floor. After a moment, Tommy joined in.

Jeff rose and began scraping his trousers.

The swinging door from the dining room opened suddenly. Jeff stared for a moment, then shouted "Dad!" Tommy, who had been trying to coax a pea out from under the refrigerator, looked up and echoed the shout.

Mr. Abbott got as far as "Hello, kids" and then saw the kitchen.

Called Jeff, "Where's Mr. Wilson?"

"Isn't he coming, I hope?" said Tommy, seeing a ray of light.

"Mr. Wilson?" Their father stopped staring at the kitchen and stared at his sons. "Didn't he...?"

At that moment, the stove-man crawled out from under the table, clutching a handful of migratory peas.

Mr. Abbott gave him one unbelieving look. "MR. WILSON!"

Jeff said "Oh, no" in a soft, stricken whisper.

"Good evening, Mr. Abbott," said the pea fancier, getting to his feet.

Tommy, two jumps behind on the plot, said alertly. "This isn't Mr. Wilson, Dad. This is the man to fix the stove." It then dawned on him that

his father was in a better position to recognize Mr. Wilson than he was, and a quiver went over him like a ship meeting up with an iceberg.

Mr. Abbott gulped. "I had to stop off at the office, and I told Mr. Wilson to come on ahead and—What happened? Where's your mother?"

Tommy in a small voice explained about Aunt Dorothy. "So Mother went there," he finished, "and Jeff and I made the—the dinner, and when the stove-man came we asked him to shell peas because we were so short on time…"

"You asked Mr. Wilson to shell the peas?"

"We didn't know he was Mr. Wilson; we thought he was the stove-man."

Jeff said unhappily, "Gee, Dad, we're awfully sorry. We were just trying to make things nice."

Mr. Abbott put his arms over his sons' shoulders. "It's all right," he said. "We'll clean up this mess and go to a restaurant." He turned to Mr. Wilson. "I've got those reports you asked to see, sir. If you want to…"

Mr. Wilson shook his head. "It won't be necessary," he said crisply. "There's a plane back in about an hour. I'm taking that."

Mr. Abbott pulled his sons a little closer to him reassuringly. "I'm sorry you feel that way, sir," he said.

"Nothing to be sorry about," said Mr. Wilson. "I'm a man of quick decisions, that's all, and there's no sense hanging around once I've made up my mind. I'm too busy." He leaned over to scrape a smashed pea off his shoe and added, "I'll send you the contract to sign first thing in the morning."

"The—contract?"

"As manager." Mr. Wilson nodded.

"Just what I want. Man with the kind of kids who'll put in a whole afternoon's hard work trying to fix things up nice for their father's guest. I knew you were a good businessman, Mr. Abbott, but I take an interest in my managers' homes, too. It makes a difference to me what their sons think of them."

"We—" said Jeff and Tommy.

"—and what they think of their sons," said Mr. Wilson.

"I—" said Mr. Abbott.

"Exactly," said Mr. Wilson. "And now, if I might just have a cup of coffee before I go…"

Jeff and Tommy looked at each other. "I'll boil the water," said Jeff.

"I'll measure out the instant coffee," said Tommy. "Very carefully, watching the teaspoon for any false moves. Cooking is *so* simple."

Jeff nodded solemnly. "Given plenty of time, a lot of space, and absolute quiet, Mr. Wilson, I think we should be able to produce one cup of coffee."

"Two," said Mr. Wilson. "One for me, and one for my new manager."

Jeff gave him an appreciative look. "I'd like to know who said too many cooks spoil the boss," said Jeff. "He sure was wrong."

Recalling

1. Who was coming to the Abbotts' house for dinner? Why?

2. What was Mrs. Abbott planning to do?

3. Why do the boys decide to cook dinner? List the items on the menu.

4. State the reason Mr. Wilson arrives before Mr. Abbott.

Interpreting

5. Why did the mother have to leave the house?

6. Describe the results of the boys' cooking.

7. Retell, in your own words, why Mr. Wilson wanted Mr. Abbott as his manager.

Concluding

8. Give an example of the loyalty and devotion that the boys show their father.

9. What is the universal theme of this story?

Examining Fiction

Home on the Range was first published as contemporary fiction in a magazine. Even though the story takes place many years ago, its theme, or general message, is timeless and universal. This universal theme has value and meaning for people all over the world.

1. Identify the details that point to the universal theme of the story.

2. Explain why the theme is as relevant today, as it was when the story was first written.

Thinking About Fiction

Many times it is helpful to summarize the events of a story, in order to remember it more easily. A summary consists of the most important incidents. These steps will be helpful in writing a summary:

a. Read the story.

b. Select the most important incidents in the story.

c. Put them in chronological order (the order in which they occurred), and write about them.

d. Briefly restate the most relevant facts of the story.

Write a brief summary of *Home on the Range*. Make sure to include the most important events and to keep them in sequential order.

Creating and Writing

Life has changed a great deal since the writing of *Home on the Range*. Our world is filled with the products of modern technology: microwaves, fax machines, cellular phones, and computers are all part of our daily lives. Even the foods on the boys' menu might be different today, given how health-conscious we have become. Perhaps Mrs. Abbott would have a career outside the home, as is currently the case for so many women in the United States.

If the Abbotts lived today, their lifestyle would be significantly altered by the influence of technology. Although this would affect elements of the plot and the setting, the universal theme would remain the same. Think about the ways the products of modern technology would alter the plot and the setting. Recreate the story, as it would occur in the present day. Incorporate technological advances and current attitudes. Remember to remain true to the universal theme—the value of family devotion—as expressed in the original story.

Into • *The Sound of Summer Running*

The Sound of Summer Running is about the power of language—and the powerlessness of language. As we read the beautiful phrases Douglas, the hero, uses to describe the way a new pair of sneakers feels to a teenager, we marvel that words can capture so much feeling. But, deep inside, we know that there is one part of that feeling that can never be put on paper. The words can only serve as arrows that point to feelings. They say: "There are some deep feelings I have, don't you have them, too?" And, if we do, we nod our heads and say, "Yes! I know just what you mean. But my feelings just can't be completely expressed in words."

So, when we say this story is about the power of language, we mean that it uses language to remind us of feelings that we once had, or to alert us to feelings that we have now. When we say the story is about the powerlessness of language, we mean that once we have been made aware of those feelings, we recognize that no words can fully express what we feel.

Focus

What is the theme of *The Sound of Summer Running*? That is not an easy question to answer. Is the theme summertime? Is it youth? Is it dreams? Surely it cannot be sneakers! Perhaps the theme is energy—that magical burst of feeling we have at certain moments in our lives. Have you ever walked outside in the early morning of a crisp autumn day and felt you could "conquer the world"? Have you ever breathed the sweet, mild air of a spring night and been suddenly filled with hopes and dreams? Douglas is a boy full of energy and ideas. The sneakers that he yearns for are the magic key that unlocks all that energy and sends his spirit soaring.

About the Author

American author **RAY BRADBURY** was born in 1920 in Waukegan, Illinois. Well known for his science fiction, Bradbury has been writing since 1942. In 1947, he received the O. Henry Award for Short Stories. One of his works was selected for the Science Fiction Hall of Fame. *The Sound of Summer Running* is not a work of science fiction, but Bradbury's fanciful style is evident in the story.

The
Sound of
Summer
Running

Ray Bradbury

Late that night, going home with his mother and father and his brother Tom, Douglas saw the tennis shoes in the bright store window. He glanced quickly away, but his ankles were seized, his feet suspended, then rushed. The earth spun; the shop awnings slammed their canvas wings overhead with the thrust of his body running. His mother and father and brother walked quietly on both sides of him. Douglas walked backward, watching the tennis shoes in the midnight window left behind.

"It was a nice evening," said Mother.

Douglas murmured, "It was…"

It was June and long past time for buying the special shoes that were quiet as a summer rain falling on the walks. June and the earth full of raw power and everything everywhere in motion. The grass was still pouring in from the country, surrounding the sidewalks, stranding the houses. Any moment the town would capsize, go down and leave not a stir in the clover and weeds. And here Douglas stood, trapped on the dead cement and the red-brick streets, hardly able to move.

"Dad!" He blurted it out. "Back there in that window, those Cream-Sponge Para Litefoot Shoes…"

His father didn't even turn. "Suppose you tell me why you need a new pair of sneakers. Can you do that?"

"Well…"

It was because they felt the way it feels every summer when you take off your shoes for the first time and run in the grass. They felt like it feels sticking your feet out of the hot covers in wintertime to let the cold wind from the open window blow on them suddenly and you let them stay out a long time until you pull them back in under the covers again to feel them, like packed snow. The tennis shoes felt like it always feels the first time every year wading in the slow waters of the creek and seeing your feet below, half an inch further downstream, with refraction, than the real part of you above water.

"Dad," said Douglas, "it's hard to explain."

Somehow the people who made tennis shoes knew what boys needed and wanted. They put marshmallows and coiled springs in the soles and they wove the rest out of grasses bleached and fired in the wilderness. Somewhere deep in the soft loam of the shoes the thin hard sinews of the buck deer were hidden. The people that made the shoes must have watched a lot of winds blow the trees and a lot of rivers going down to the lakes. Whatever it was, it was in the shoes, and it was summer.

Douglas tried to get all this in words.

"Yes," said Father, "but what's wrong with last year's sneakers? Why can't you dig *them* out of the closet?"

Well, he felt sorry for

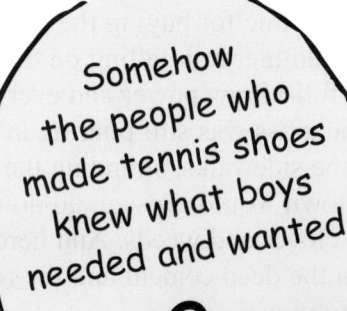

Somehow the people who made tennis shoes knew what boys needed and wanted.

boys who lived in California where they wore tennis shoes all year and never knew what it was to get winter off your feet, peel off the iron leather shoes all full of snow and rain and run barefoot for a day and then lace on the first new tennis shoes of the season, which was better than barefoot. The magic was always in the new pair of shoes. The magic might die by the first of September, but now in late June there was still plenty of magic, and shoes like these could jump you over trees and rivers and houses. And if you wanted, they could jump you over fences and sidewalks and dogs.

"Don't you see?" said Douglas. "I just can't use last year's pair."

For last year's pair were dead inside. They had been fine when he started them out, last year. But by the end of summer, every year, you always found out, you always knew, you couldn't really jump over rivers and trees and houses in them, and they were dead. But this was a new year, and he felt that this time, with this new pair of shoes, he could do anything, anything at all.

They walked up on the steps to their house. "Save your money," said Dad. "In five or six weeks—"

"Summer'll be over!"

Lights out, with Tom asleep, Douglas lay watching his feet, far away down there at the end of the bed in the moonlight, free of the heavy iron shoes, the big chunks of winter fallen away from them.

"Reasons, I've got to think of reasons for the shoes."

Well, as anyone knew, the hills around town were wild with friends putting cows to riot, playing barometer to the atmospheric changes, taking sun, peeling like calendars each day to take more sun. To catch those friends, you must run much faster than foxes or squirrels. As for the town, it steamed with enemies grown irritable with heat, so remembering every winter argument and insult. *Find friends, ditch enemies!* That was the Cream-Sponge Para Litefoot motto. Does the world run too fast? *Want to be alert, stay alert? Litefoot, then! Litefoot!*

He held his coin bank up and heard the faint small tinkling, the airy weight of money there.

Whatever you want, he thought, you got to make your own way. During the night now, let's find that path through the forest…

Downtown, the store lights went out, one by one. A wind blew in the window. It was like a river going downstream and his feet wanting to go with it.

In his dreams he heard a rabbit running running running in the deep warm grass.

Old Mr. Sanderson moved through his shoe store as the proprietor of a pet shop must move through his shop where are kenneled animals from everywhere in the world, touching each one briefly along the way. Mr. Sanderson brushed his hands over the shoes in the window, and some of them were like cats to him and some were like dogs; he touched each pair with concern, adjusting laces, fixing tongues. Then he stood in the exact center of the carpet and looked around, nodding.

There was a sound of growing thunder.

One moment, the door to Sanderson's Shoe Emporium[1] was empty. The next, Douglas Spaulding stood clumsily there, staring down at his leather shoes as if these heavy things could not be pulled up out of the cement. The thunder had stopped when his shoes stopped. Now, with painful slowness, daring to look only at the money in his cupped hand, Douglas moved out of the bright sunlight of Saturday noon. He made careful stacks of nickels, dimes, and quarters on the counter, like someone playing chess and worried if the next move carried him out into sun or deep into shadow.

"Don't say a word!" said Mr. Sanderson.

Douglas froze.

"First, I know just what you want to buy," said Mr. Sanderson. "Second, I see you every afternoon at my window; you think I don't see? You're wrong. Third, to give it its full name, you want the Royal Crown Cream-Sponge Para Litefoot Tennis Shoes: 'like menthol on your feet!' Fourth, you want credit."

"No!" cried Douglas, breathing hard, as if he'd run all night in his dreams. "I got something better than credit to offer!" he gasped. "Before I tell, Mr. Sanderson, you got to do me one small favor. Can you remember when was the last time you yourself wore a pair of Litefoot sneakers, sir?"

---

1. An *emporium* (em POR ee um) is a store, often carrying many different types of merchandise.

Word Bank	**refraction** (ree FRAK shun) *n.*: the bending of a ray of light as it passes from the air through water or glass
	loam (LOAM) *n.*: fertile soil consisting of clay, silt, and sand
	sinews (SIN yooz) *n.*: tendons that connect the muscles with other parts of the body; tendons that have been dressed for use as cords or thread

Mr. Sanderson's face darkened. "Oh, ten, twenty, say, thirty years ago. Why…?"

"Mr. Sanderson, don't you think you owe it to your customers, sir, to at least try the tennis shoes you sell, for just one minute, so you know how they feel? People forget if they don't keep testing things. Candy-store man samples his own stuff, I should think. So…"

"You may have noticed," said the old man, "I'm wearing shoes."

"But not sneakers, sir! How you going to sell sneakers unless you can rave about them and how you going to rave about them unless you know them?"

Mr. Sanderson backed off a little distance from the boy's fever, one hand to his chin. "Well…"

"Mr. Sanderson," said Douglas, "You sell me something and I'll sell you something just as valuable."

"Is it absolutely necessary to the sale that I put on a pair of the sneakers, boy?" said the old man.

"I sure wish you could, sir!"

The old man sighed. A minute later, seated panting quietly, he laced the tennis shoes to his long narrow feet. They looked detached and alien down there next to the dark cuffs of his business suit. Mr. Sanderson stood up.

"How do they *feel*?" asked the boy.

"How do they feel, he asks; they feel fine." He started to sit down.

"Please!" Douglas held out his hand. "Mr. Sanderson, now could you kind of rock back and forth a little, sponge around, bounce kind of, while I tell you the rest? It's this: I give you my money, you give me the shoes, I owe you a dollar. But, Mr. Sanderson, but —soon as I get those shoes on, you know what happens?"

"What?"

"Bang! I deliver your packages, pick up packages, bring you coffee, burn your trash, run to the post office, telegraph office, library! You'll see twelve of me in and out, in and out, every minute. Feel those shoes, Mr. Sanderson, *feel* how fast they'd take me? All those springs inside? Feel all the running inside? Feel how they kind of grab hold and can't let you alone and don't like you just *standing* there? Feel how quick I'd be doing the things you'd rather not bother with? You stay in the nice cool store while I'm jumping all around town! But it's not me really, it's the shoes. They're going like mad down alleys, cutting corners, and back! There they go!"

Mr. Sanderson stood amazed with the rush of words. When the words got going the flow carried him; he began to sink deep in the shoes, to flex his toes, limber his arches, test his ankles. He rocked softly, secretly, back and forth in a small breeze from the open door. The tennis shoes silently hushed themselves deep in the carpet, sank as in a jungle grass, in loam and resilient clay. He gave one solemn bounce of his heels in the yeasty dough, in the yielding and welcoming earth. Emotions hurried over his face as if many colored lights had

Word Bank	**limber** (LIM ber) *v.*: make flexible; loosen up
	resilient (ree ZIL yint) *adj.*: flexible and elastic; able to return to its original shape after being pressed out of shape by some force
	revelation (REV ih lay shun) *n.*: the discovery of something previously unknown; something unexpected that creates surprise
	gazelles (gu ZELZ) *n.*: small, graceful African antelopes

been switched on and off. His mouth hung slightly open. Slowly he gentled and rocked himself to a halt, and the boy's voice faded and they stood there looking at each other in a tremendous and natural silence.

A few people drifted by on the sidewalk outside, in the hot sun.

Still the man and boy stood there, the boy glowing, the man with revelation in his face.

"Boy," said the old man at last, "in five years, how would you like a job selling shoes in this emporium?"

"Gosh, thanks, Mr. Sanderson, but I don't know what I'm going to be yet."

"Anything you want to be, son," said the old man, "you'll be. No one will ever stop you."

The old man walked lightly across the store to the wall of ten thousand boxes, came back with some shoes for the boy, and wrote up a list on some paper while the boy was lacing the shoes on his feet and then standing there, waiting.

The old man held out his list. "A dozen things you got to do for me this afternoon. Finish them, we're even Stephen, and you're fired."

"Thanks, Mr. Sanderson!" Douglas bounded away.

"Stop!" cried the old man.

Douglas pulled up and turned.

Mr. Sanderson leaned forward. "How do they *feel*?"

The boy looked down at his feet deep in the rivers, in the fields of wheat, in the wind that already was rushing him out of town. He looked up at the old man, his eyes burning, his mouth moving, but no sound came out.

"Antelopes?" said the old man, looking from the boy's face to his shoes. "Gazelles?"

The boy thought about it, hesitated, and nodded a quick nod. Almost immediately he vanished. He just spun about with a whisper and went off. The door stood empty. The sounds of the tennis shoes faded in the jungle heat.

Mr. Sanderson stood in the sun-blazed door, listening. From a long time ago, when he dreamed as a boy, he remembered the sound. Beautiful creatures leaping under the sky, gone through brush, under trees, away, and only the soft echo their running left behind.

"Antelopes," said Mr. Sanderson. "Gazelles."

He bent to pick up the boy's abandoned winter shoes, heavy with forgotten rains and long-melted snows. Moving out of the blazing sun, walking softly, lightly, slowly, he headed back toward civilization…

Beautiful creatures gone through brush, under trees, away, and only the soft echo their running left behind.

Studying THE SELECTION

Recalling

1. At what time of year does the story take place?

2. Why does Douglas feel that he needs a new pair of sneakers?

3. What does Douglas make Mr. Sanderson do?

4. What sort of deal does Douglas make with Mr. Sanderson?

Interpreting

5. Why do you think Douglas has so much difficulty telling his father that he needs sneakers?

6. Why had it been so long since Mr. Sanderson had tried on a pair of the sneakers he sold? Why did he resist Douglas's suggestion to try them on?

7. What is the "sound" of summer running?

Concluding

8. Have you ever owned a special outfit or pair of shoes that you felt enabled you to do and feel extraordinary things?

Examining Fiction

In *The Sound of Summer Running*, the theme is conveyed through the events, the behavior and traits of the characters, and by the use of metaphors.

1. Explain what a metaphor is.

2. Explain how a metaphor is different from a simile.

3. Choose one metaphor from the story and write it down.

Thinking About Fiction

In the selection you have just read, the characters anticipate the coming of summer, and the freedom that it brings, in different ways.

1. What was Douglas's reaction?

2. How did his father react?

3. What were Mr. Sanderson's feelings?

Creating and Writing

1. Choose an object that has special meaning to you. On the front of an index card, draw a picture of the object. On the back of the card, name three emotions you feel when you see, touch, smell, or hear this object. Make three such cards. Play a game with your classmates. Show them the "object" side of the card and have everyone write down the three emotions they think you listed on the back of the card. Then read the back of your card aloud. Whoever came closest to what you wrote, earns a point and takes the next turn.

2. Play the game in reverse. Read the emotions you listed on the card to your class. See who can guess what object, sound, smell, or texture causes you to feel this way. The first person to guess the object earns a point and takes the next turn.

Into • *The Circuit*

What would it be like to work all day in the fields instead of going to school? What would it be like if you could hardly express yourself in English? What would it be like if your home was an old garage with a dirt floor, and your furniture was some old boxes? What would it be like if, just as you felt a little hope of escaping this life of poverty, you were pulled away, and sent back to the fields to labor under the hot sun? *The Circuit* tells of the terrible circuit—a circle of poverty, labor, school, hope, poverty, labor—the author experienced as a young boy.

Focus

The Circuit is **semi-autobiographical**. This means that although the story is based on the author's life, the facts have been altered to make the story's plot and theme stronger.

Let us compare a semi-autobiographical story to a diary. A diary records life just as it happened. Some of the diaries of famous people tell what the weather was like, where they went on a given day, and whom they met that day. These diaries are of interest to us because they give us a glimpse into the personal life of the diarist. The authors of semi-autobiographical stories have different goals. They wish to make a point about someone or something. Therefore, they choose only those details that will help them make this point. Although the main characters and general plot are real, some of the dialogue and minor characters may be fictional.

To summarize: In a semi-autobiographical story, the author uses a mixture of real and fictional characters and dialogue to express the main idea of the story.

About the Author

FRANCISCO JIMÉNEZ was born in 1943 in Mexico, and emigrated to the United States with his family in 1947. Jiménez has written works both in English and Spanish. He has said that his ability to express himself bilingually is a great privilege. At ease in both languages and cultures, Jiménez considers bridging the gap between the two cultures his primary goal. The son of a farm laborer, he successfully brings Mexican-American culture to life in his story, *The Circuit*.

Francisco Jimenez[1]

The Circuit

It was that time of the year again. Ito, the strawberry sharecropper,[2] did not smile. It was natural. The peak of the strawberry season was over and the last few days the workers, most of them braceros,[3] were not picking as many boxes as they had during the months of June and July.

As the last days of August disappeared, so did the number of braceros. Sunday, only one—the best picker—came to work. I liked him. Sometimes we talked during our half-hour lunch break. That is how I found out he was from Jalisco,[4] the same state in Mexico my family was from. That Sunday was the last time I saw him.

When the sun had tired and sunk behind the mountains, Ito signaled us that it was time to go home. "Ya esora,"[5] he yelled in his broken Spanish. Those were the words I waited for twelve hours a day, every day, seven days a week, week after week. And the thought of not hearing them again saddened me.

As we drove home Papá did not say a word. With both hands on the wheel, he stared at the dirt road. My older brother, Roberto, was also silent. He leaned his head back and closed his eyes. Once in a while he cleared from his throat the dust that blew in from outside.

Yes, it was that time of year. When I opened the front door of the shack, I stopped. Everything we owned was neatly packed in cardboard boxes. Suddenly I felt even more the weight of hours, days, weeks, and months of

---

1. *Jiménez* (hee MEN ez)
2. A *sharecropper* is a person who farms land they do not own. A part of the harvest is given to the landowners.
3. *Braceros* (brah SAIR ose) is Spanish for farm laborers.
4. *Jalisco* (ha LEESE koe) is a state in west-central Mexico.
5. *Ya esora* (YAH ess OR uh) is another way of saying *es hora,* Spanish for "it's time."

work. I sat down on a box. The thought of having to move to Fresno and knowing what was in store for me there brought tears to my eyes.

That night I could not sleep. I lay in bed thinking about how much I hated this move.

A little before five o'clock in the morning, Papá woke everyone up. A few minutes later, the yelling and screaming of my little brothers and sisters, for whom the move was a great adventure, broke the silence of dawn. Shortly, the barking of the dogs accompanied them.

While we packed the breakfast dishes, Papá went outside to start the "Carcanchita."[6] That was the name Papá gave his old '38 black Plymouth. He bought it in a used-car lot in Santa Rosa in the winter of 1949. Papá was very proud of his little jalopy. He had a right to be proud of it. He spent a lot of time looking at other cars before buying this one. When he finally chose the "Carcanchita," he checked it thoroughly before driving it out of the car lot. He examined every inch of the car. He listened to the motor, tilting his head from side to side like a parrot, trying to detect any noises that spelled car trouble. After being satisfied with the looks and sounds of the car, Papá then insisted on knowing who the original owner was. He never did find out from the car salesman, but he bought the car anyway. Papá figured the original owner must have been an important man because behind the rear seat of the car he found a blue necktie.

Papá parked the car out in front and left the motor running. "Listo," he yelled. Without saying a word, Roberto and I began to carry the boxes out to the car. Roberto carried the two big boxes and I carried the two smaller ones. Papá then threw the mattress on top of the car roof and tied it with ropes to the front and rear bumpers.

Everything was packed except Mamá's pot. It was an old large galvanized pot she had picked up at an army surplus store in Santa María the year I was born. The pot had

---

6. *Carcanchita* (kahr kahn CHEE tuh)

Word Bank

galvanized (GAL vuh nyzd) *v.*: plated with zinc to resist rust

surplus (SIR plus) *n.*: superabundance

many dents and nicks, and the more dents and nicks it acquired the more Mamá liked it. "Mi olla,"[7] she used to say proudly.

I held the front door open as Mamá carefully carried out her pot by both handles, making sure not to spill the cooked beans. When she got to the car, Papá reached out to help her with it. Roberto opened the rear car door and Papá gently placed it on the floor behind the front seat. All of us then climbed in. Papá sighed, wiped the sweat off his forehead with his sleeve, and said wearily: "Es todo."[8]

As we drove away, I felt a lump in my throat. I turned around and looked at our little shack for the last time.

At sunset we drove into a labor camp near Fresno. Since Papá did not speak English, Mamá asked the camp foreman if he needed any more workers. "We don't need no more," said the foreman, scratching his head. "Check with Sullivan down the road. Can't miss him. He lives in a big white house with a fence around it."

When we got there, Mamá walked up to the house. She went through a white gate, past a row of rose bushes, up the stairs to the front door. She rang the doorbell. The porch light went on and a tall husky man came out. They exchanged a few words. After the man went in, Mamá clapped her hands and hurried back to the car. "We have work! Mr. Sullivan said we can stay there the whole season," she said, gasping and pointing to an old garage near the stables.

The garage was worn out by the years. It had no windows. The walls, eaten by termites, strained to support the roof full of holes. The dirt floor, populated by earthworms, looked like a gray road map.

That night, by the light of a kerosene lamp, we unpacked and cleaned our new home. Roberto swept away the loose dirt, leaving the hard ground. Papá plugged the holes in the walls with old newspapers and tin can tops. Mamá fed my little brothers and sisters. Papá and Roberto then brought in the mattress and placed it on the far corner of the garage. "Mamá, you and the little ones sleep on the mattress. Roberto, Panchito, and I will sleep outside under the trees," Papá said.

---

7. *Mi olla* (ME OH yuh) is Spanish for my pot.
8. *Es todo* (ESS TOE thoe) is Spanish for "that's all."

Early next morning Mr. Sullivan showed us where his crop was, and after breakfast, Papá, Roberto, and I headed for the vineyard to pick.

Around nine o'clock the temperature had risen to almost one hundred degrees. I was completely soaked in sweat and my mouth felt as if I had been chewing on a handkerchief. I walked over to the end of the row, picked up the jug of water we had brought, and began drinking. "Don't drink too much; you'll get sick," Roberto shouted. No sooner had he said that than I felt sick to my stomach. I dropped to my knees and let the jug roll off my hands. I remained motionless with my eyes glued on the hot sandy ground. All I could hear was the drone of insects. Slowly I began to recover. I poured water over my face and neck and watched the dirty water run down my arms to the ground.

I still felt a little dizzy when we took a break to eat lunch. It was past two o'clock and we sat underneath a large walnut tree that was on the side of the road. While we ate, Papá jotted down the number of boxes we had picked. Roberto drew designs on the ground with a stick. Suddenly I noticed Papá's face turn pale as he looked down the road. "Here comes the school bus," he whispered loudly in alarm. Instinctively, Roberto and I ran and hid in the vineyards. We did not want to get in trouble for not going to school. The neatly dressed boys about my age got off. They carried books under their arms. After they crossed the street, the bus drove away. Roberto and I came out from hiding and joined Papá. "Tienen que tener cuidado,"⁹ he warned us.

After lunch we went back to work. The sun kept beating down. The buzzing insects, the wet sweat, and the hot dry dust made the afternoon seem to last forever. Finally the mountains around the valley reached out and swallowed the sun. Within an hour it was too dark to continue picking. The vines blanketed the grapes, making it difficult to see the bunches. "Vámonos,"¹⁰ said Papá, signaling to us that it was time to quit work. Papá then took out a pencil and began to figure out how much we had earned our first

_____

9. *Tienen que tener cuidado* (TYEE nen KIH ten AIR kwee THAH thoe) means "You have to be careful" in Spanish.
10. *Vámanos* (VAH mah NOCE) means "Let's go" in Spanish.

day. He wrote down numbers, crossed some out, wrote down some more. "Quince,"[11] he murmured.

When we arrived home, we took a cold shower underneath a waterhose. We then sat down to eat dinner around some wooden crates that served as a table. Mamá had cooked a special meal for us. We had rice and tortillas with "carne con chile,"[12] my favorite dish.

The next morning I could hardly move. My body ached all over. I felt little control over my arms and legs. This feeling went on every morning for days until my muscles finally got used to the work.

It was Monday, the first week of November. The grape season was over and I could now go to school. I woke up early that morning and lay in bed, looking at the stars and savoring the thought of not going to work and of starting sixth grade for the first time that year. Since I could not sleep, I decided to get up and join Papá and Roberto at breakfast. I sat at the table across from Roberto, but I kept my head down. I did not want to look up and face him. I knew he was sad. He was not going to school today. He was not going tomorrow, or next week, or next month. He would not go until the cotton season was over, and that was sometime in February. I rubbed my hands together and watched the dry, acid stained skin fall to the floor in little rolls.

When Papá and Roberto left for work, I felt relief. I walked to the top of a small grade next to the shack and watched the "Carcanchita" disappear in the distance in a cloud of dust.

Two hours later, around eight o'clock, I stood by the side of the road waiting for school bus number twenty. When it arrived I climbed in. Everyone was busy either talking or yelling. I sat in an empty seat in the back.

When the bus stopped in front of the school, I felt very nervous. I looked out the bus window and saw boys and

---

11. *Quince* (KEEN say) is Spanish for fifteen.
12. *Carne con chile* (KAHR nay KAHN CHEE lay) is a dish made of meat, chili peppers, and beans.

Word Bank	**savoring** (SAY vohr ing) *v.*: relishing; enjoying

girls carrying books under their arms. I put my hands in my pant pockets and walked to the principal's office. When I entered I heard a woman's voice say: "May I help you?" I was startled. I had not heard English for months. For a few seconds I remained speechless. I looked at the lady who waited for an answer. My first instinct was to answer her in Spanish; but I held back. Finally, after struggling for English words, I managed to tell her that I wanted to enroll in the sixth grade. After answering many questions, I was led to the classroom.

Mr. Lema, the sixth-grade teacher, greeted me and assigned me to a desk. He then introduced me to the class. I was so nervous and scared at that moment when everyone's eyes were on me that I wished I were with Papa and Roberto picking cotton. After taking roll, Mr. Lema gave the class the assignment for the first hour. "The first thing we have to do this morning is finish reading the story we began yesterday," he said enthusiastically. He walked up to me, handed me an English book, and asked me to read. "We are on page 125," he said politely. When I heard this, I felt my blood rush to my head; I felt dizzy. "Would you like to read?" he asked hesitantly. I opened the book to page 125. My mouth was dry. My eyes began to water. I could not begin. "You can read later," Mr. Lema said understandingly.

For the rest of the reading period I kept getting angrier and angrier with myself. I should have read, I thought to myself.

During recess I went into the restroom and opened my English book to page 125. I began to read in a low voice, pretending I was in class. There were many words I did not know. I closed the book and headed back to the classroom.

Mr. Lema was sitting at his desk correcting papers. When I entered he looked up at me and smiled. I felt better. I walked up to him and asked if he could help me with the new words. "Gladly," he said.

The rest of the month I spent my lunch hours working on English with Mr. Lema, my best friend at school.

One Friday during lunch hour Mr. Lema asked me to take a walk with him to the music room. "Do you like music?" he asked me as we entered the building.

"Yes, I like corridos,"[13] I answered. He then picked up a trumpet, blew on it and handed it to me. The sound gave me goose bumps. I knew that sound. I had heard it in many corridos. "How would you like to learn how to play it?" he asked. He must have read my face because before I could answer, he added: "I'll teach you how to play it during our lunch hours."

That day I could hardly wait to get home to tell Papá and Mamá the great news. As I got off the bus, my little brothers and sisters ran up to meet me. They were yelling and screaming. I thought they were happy to see me, but when I opened the door to our shack, I saw that everything we owned was neatly packed in cardboard boxes.

---

13. *Corridos* (kuh REE dos) are ballads.

Recalling

1.   What saddened the narrator at the beginning of the story?

2.   Which family possessions did the narrator and his brother bring out to Papá's car?

3.   Where does the family finally find a place to work? Where do they have to live?

4.   What causes the father to turn pale?

5.   When does the narrator finally get to go to school? Why does he enjoy school?

Interpreting

6.   Why do you think Mamá's pot was so special to her?

7.   How does the narrator show that he wants a better life for himself?

Concluding

8.   As you have learned, a circuit is a repeated journey from place to place. In this story, the narrator always ends up in the same place he began. Describe the narrator's circuit.

Examining Fiction

In the short story *The Circuit*, all the elements of a short story—plot, character, setting, and theme—come together.

1. **Plot:** How do you know that the narrator yearns for a better life, given the instability and poverty he describes? Include examples of the things he longs for.

2. **Character:** What personal strengths do the parents possess that enable the children to retain a sense of family, in spite of their nomadic life?

3. **Setting:** How does the setting of the story emphasize the hardship of their lives?

4. **Theme:** What message does the author convey about the hardship of migrant life, and the impact it has on those who experience it?

5. **Overall Effect:** What is the impact of the story on you? In your answer, include the separate effect of each element of the story: plot, character, setting, and theme.

Thinking About Fiction

The title of this story indicates a repeated journey over a circular route, in which the traveler always returns to the place where the journey began. The narrator's existence is a circuit, as the family migrates from place to place, depending on the season and the availability of work. Would the narrator's life change if the family were able to stay in one place for an extended period of time? Give sufficient detail in your answer.

Creating and Writing

In *The Circuit*, we briefly glimpse another family, the Sullivans. Their lives contrast greatly with the lives of the migrant workers. Imagine you are one of the children in the Sullivan family.

1. What would your opinion be of migrant workers?

2. Would you notice them at all?

3. Would you wonder why they didn't go to school?

4. Would you try to befriend them?

Write a short story in which you discuss a possible friendship between you and a migrant worker. Remember that the life of a migrant worker is very different from yours, and that migrants stop in one place for only a short time, and then move on to the next job.

Blueprint FOR READING

Into • *Home*

Be it ever so humble, there is no place like home. How would you feel if your family were threatened with eviction from their home? Some people would feel as though a part of themselves were being torn away. The longer people live in a house, the harder it becomes to lose it. In *Home*, a mother and her two daughters sit on their porch—their old, beloved, shabby porch—waiting for the verdict: will they be allowed to stay, or will they be forced to move? They sit and wait for Papa to return. He will have the answer that could change their lives.

Focus

In this short story, you can see how a plot can exist with almost no action; how a conflict can exist with almost no plot; how characterization can be developed with almost no description; and how everyday dialogue can express all sorts of emotions. When you have read the story, you will see that its plot can be summarized in a few short sentences. Yet, the feelings that the story leaves you with are more complicated. This is because the story's descriptions and dialogue are **evocative**. This means they evoke, or bring out, emotions in the reader. As you read the story, think about what images or dialogue evoke feelings of sadness, happiness, anxiety, relief, or nostalgia in you.

About the Author

GWENDOLYN BROOKS was born in 1917. She began writing poetry at the age of seven. By the time she was seventeen, more than seventy five of her poems had been published in the *Chicago Defender*. Brooks has received many awards. In 1950, she became the first African-American to receive the Pulitzer Prize for Literature. In 1977, she was named the Poet Laureate of Illinois. Brooks' style is sensitive and sentimental, as the story *Home* makes clear. She died in 2000.

Gwendolyn Brooks

Home

What had been wanted was this always, this always to last, the talking softly on this porch, with the snake plant in the jardiniere[1] in the southwest corner, and the obstinate slip from Aunt Eppie's magnificent Michigan fern at the left side of the friendly door. Mama, Maud Martha, and Helen rocked slowly in their rocking chairs, and looked at the late afternoon light on the lawn and at the emphatic iron of the fence and at the poplar tree. These things might soon be theirs no longer. Those shafts and pools of light, the tree, the graceful iron, might soon be viewed possessively by different eyes.

Papa was to have gone that noon, during his lunch hour, to the office of the Home Owners' Loan. If he had not succeeded in getting another extension, they would be leaving this house in which they had lived for more than fourteen years. There was little hope. The Home Owners' Loan was hard. They sat, making their plans.

"We'll be moving into a nice flat[2] somewhere," said Mama. "Somewhere on South Park, or Michigan, or in Washington Park Court." Those flats, as the girls and Mama knew well, were burdens on

---

1. A *jardiniere* (zhar din AIR) is a decorative stand for potted plants.
2. *Flat* is another word for apartment.

Word Bank	**obstinate** (AHB stin it) *adj.*: stubborn
	emphatic (em FAT ik) *adj.*: definite; accented
	shafts (SHAFTS) *n.*: sharply defined beams that shine through an opening

wages twice the size of Papa's. This was not mentioned now.

"They're much prettier than this old house," said Helen. "I have friends I'd just as soon not bring here. And I have other friends that wouldn't come down this far for anything, unless they were in a taxi."

Yesterday, Maud Martha would have attacked her. Tomorrow she might. Today she said nothing. She merely gazed at a little hopping robin in the tree, her tree, and tried to keep the fronts of her eyes dry.

"Well, I do know," said Mama, turning her hands over and over, "that I've been getting tireder and tireder of doing that firing.[3] From October to April, there's firing to be done."

"But lately we've been helping, Harry and I," said Maud Martha. "And sometimes in March and April and in October, and even in November, we could build a little fire in the fireplace. Sometimes the weather was just right for that."

She knew, from the way they looked at her, that this had been a mistake. They did not want to cry.

But she felt that the little line of white, sometimes ridged with smoked purple, and all that cream-shot saffron[4] would never drift across any western sky except that in back of this house. The rain would drum with as sweet a dull-ness nowhere but here. The birds on South Park were mechanical birds, no better than the poor caught canaries in those "rich" women's sun parlors.

"It's just going to kill Papa!" burst out Maud Martha. "He loves this house! He lives for this house!"

"He lives for us," said Helen. "It's us he loves. He wouldn't want the house, except for us."

"And he'll have us," added Mama, "wherever."

---

3. *Firing* is starting and tending a coal or wood fire.

4. *Saffron* (SAFF ron) is an orange-yellow color.

"Yes," Maud Martha cracked in, "that's what you always say—that G-d knows best."

Her mother looked at her quickly, decided the statement was not suspect, looked away.

Helen saw Papa coming. "There's Papa," said Helen.

They could not tell a thing from the way Papa was walking. It was that same dear little staccato[5] walk, one shoulder down, then the other, then repeat, and repeat. They watched his progress. He passed the Kennedys', he passed the vacant lot, he passed Mrs. Blakemore's. They wanted to hurl themselves over the fence, into the street, and shake the truth out of his collar. He opened his gate—the gate—and still his stride and face told them nothing.

"Hello," he said.

Mama got up and followed him through the front door. The girls knew better than to go in too.

Presently Mama's head emerged. Her eyes were lamps turned on.

"It's all right," she exclaimed. "He got it. It's all over. Everything is all right."

The door slammed shut. Mama's footsteps hurried away.

"I think," said Helen, rocking rapidly, "I think I'll give a party. I haven't given a party since I was eleven. I'd like some of my friends to just casually see that we're homeowners."

---

5. *Staccato* (stuh KAH toe) is a way of walking with quick, sharp, abrupt steps.

"You know," Helen sighed, "if you want to know the truth, this is a relief. If this hadn't come up, we would have gone on, just dragged on, hanging out here forever."

"It might," allowed Mama, "be an act of G-d. G-d may just have reached down and picked up the reins."

Word Bank	**hurl** (HERL) *v.*: throw forcefully; fling

Recalling

1. Which conflict must the family deal with at the beginning of the story?

2. Where does Papa go, and what does he hope to do, in order to solve their problem?

3. What observations does Maud Martha make about Papa?

4. How does Helen respond to Maud Martha's opinion?

Interpreting

5. What is the family's attitude toward its problem? Have they given up, or have they decided to continue to struggle with their difficulties? Give details from the story to support your answer.

6. Does Papa reveal anything through facial expressions or body language as he approaches the family?

7. What changes Helen's feelings about the house at the end of the story?

Concluding

8. Why is it difficult to move into a new home? What are some circumstances that might make a move pleasurable?

Examining Fiction

The overall effect of a short story depends on the way that plot, character, setting, and theme are interwoven. In the short story *Home*, the characters deeply love their house, and bravely face the possibility of losing it. The setting provides a backdrop against which their feelings are magnified. The theme implies that although the house is very important, family is even more valuable.

- **Plot and Character**: The personalities involved make the internal conflict—that has resulted from their fears for their house—more difficult. Which family character traits intensify the conflict?

- **Setting and Character**: The vivid descriptions of the home help the reader understand why the characters care so much. Name some features of the setting that contribute to the family's strong emotions about their home.

- **Theme and Character**: The author shows that something matters more to the family than their home. How do the characters reveal this in their dialogue and action?

Thinking About Fiction

The total effect of a story is generated by the coming together of all four elements of fiction. This union has an overall impact on the reader. Naturally, this effect varies from story to story. The reader may experience the range of emotions from humor to sadness, depending on the author's mission.

1. What is the overall effect of the story, *Home*?

2. Does any one of the four elements of fiction play a greater role in creating the overall effect than the others?

Creating and Writing

The author, Gwendolyn Brooks, vividly describes Maud Martha's home. Her choice of words stirs the special sentiment we feel towards our homes. Decide which emotions your home stirs within you. Perhaps it is a comfortable feeling, or a sense of security. Maybe it is a feeling of appreciation or confidence. Write a paragraph that describes your feelings. Use vivid adjectives to support the sentiment you want to express.

Blueprint FOR READING

Into • *Child Pioneer*

In the fall of 1844, John appeared at the gate of Dr. Whitman's medical mission...carrying a starving five-month-old baby sister...

Seven children had traveled 500 miles over the Oregon Trail, fighting hunger, thirst, Indians, heat, cold, and a host of other problems. Honoré Willsie Morrow recorded their story in a style that reads more like a history report than a short story. But the tale itself is so gripping, and the character of John Sager, so powerful, that the writer wisely lets the plain facts speak for themselves.

Focus

This is the story of one family, and of one member of that family in particular—John Sager. It is also the story of a certain breed of person, the tough, determined pioneer who conquered the wilderness and settled the vast, wild country that was the American frontier. The story's style is the reverse of dramatic: it is understated. This style mirrors the spirit of the pioneers. Facing danger and deprivation at every turn, they had to be calm and matter-of-fact. Their tone, expression, and language tended to minimize rather than to dramatize the obstacles they faced. As you read the story, ask yourself where John Sager got the strength and purpose that so characterize him. Do you know anyone whom you could call "single-minded"? Do you admire this trait?

About the Author

American novelist **HONORÉ WILLSIE MORROW** was born in 1880. She wrote many works of historical fiction set in the American past. These novels include *With Malice Towards None*, *Mary Todd Lincoln*, *Yonder Sails the Mayflower*, and *We Must March*. The story, *Child Pioneer*, was first published in 1926. It describes the ordeals suffered by the pioneers on the Oregon Trail—a well-known chapter in American history. In her simple and forceful style, Honoré Willsie Morrow brings these historical events to life. Morrow died in 1940 in Connecticut.

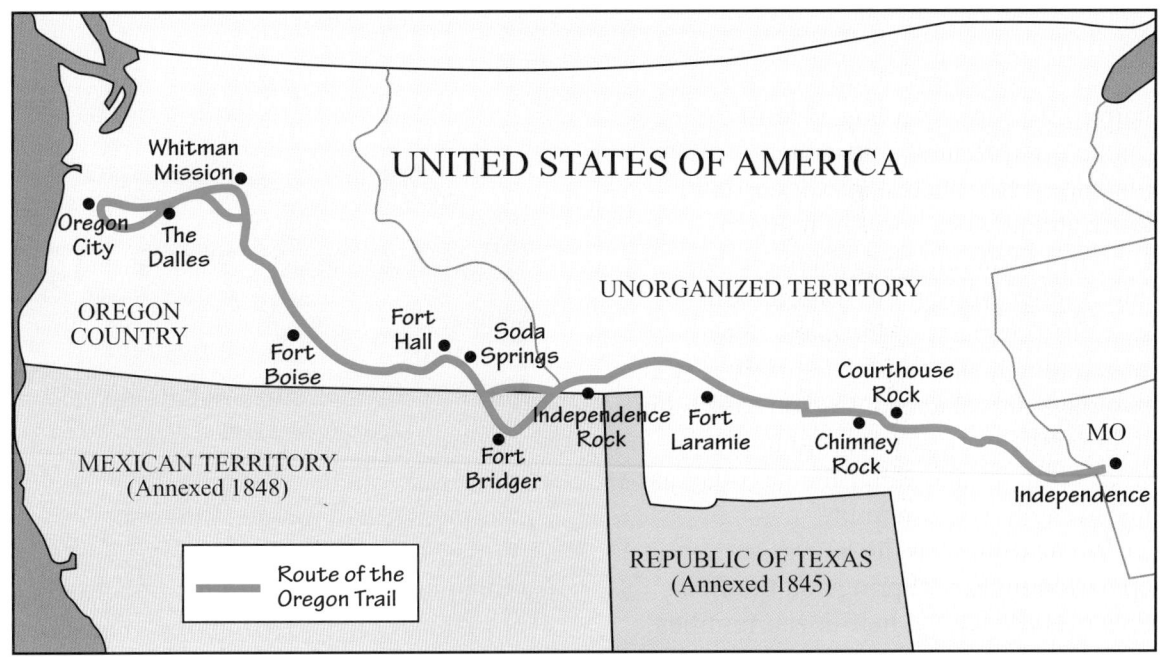

UNITED STATES OF AMERICA

Whitman Mission

Oregon City
The Dalles

OREGON COUNTRY

Fort Boise

Fort Hall

Soda Springs

UNORGANIZED TERRITORY

Independence Rock

Fort Bridger

Fort Laramie

Courthouse Rock

Chimney Rock

Courthouse Rock

MO

Independence

MEXICAN TERRITORY
(Annexed 1848)

REPUBLIC OF TEXAS
(Annexed 1845)

Route of the
Oregon Trail

Child Pioneer

Honoré Willsie Morrow

Let me tell you the epic story of thirteen-year-old John Sager, as I gleaned it from letters and diaries of Oregon pioneers.

In the fall of 1844, John appeared at the gate of Dr. Whitman's medical mission, in what is now the state

The Oregon Trail

of Washington, carrying a starving five-month-old baby sister. He was staggering before an emaciated cow on whose back were perched a sister aged eight, with a broken leg, and a sister of five who helped support the leg. A sister of three and one of seven walked beside his eleven-year-old brother, Francis.

Unaccompanied, John Sager and his five sisters and a brother, all younger than himself, had made their way from Fort Hall, 500 miles to the east, over the Oregon Trail, which was then little more than a horse track.

The trail was visited by unfriendly Indians and was so difficult that the migration of 1844, which John's parents had joined, went to pieces. Some died

en route; others turned southwest into California. But John came through.

The record of this strange children's expedition starts in early July, when Kit Carson came across the Sager's camping place near the Green River Rendezvous in what is today eastern Idaho.

He rode at a gallop into the camp, two fresh scalps hanging at his belt, flung himself from his horse and told John to put out the fire—a band of Sioux was on the warpath. John sent his brother and little sisters scurrying into the Conestoga wagon, kicked out the tiny blaze of buffalo chips, then looked to Carson for further orders.

Word Bank	**epic** (EH pick) *adj.*: heroic; extending beyond the usual in size or scope

gleaned (GLEEND) *v.*: gathered information bit by bit

staggering (STAG er ing) *v.*: having difficulty standing; reeling from side to side

Carson described John as a sandy-haired, freckle-faced boy, clad in a hunter's red flannel shirt which came to his knees. His snakeskin belt carried a knife and powder horn. In reply to Carson's questions, he said his father and mother were in the wagon, both sick. The remnant of the caravan to which they had attached themselves was two days' travel ahead. Carson told John to hitch the oxen at once and move forward all night and as far the next day as his strength would permit.

We next pick up the Sagers approaching Soda Springs on the Bear River. There were a half-dozen families in this camp, and one of the men was a veterinary. On the edge of the camp John halted the oxen and asked for a doctor. He said that for two days his mother had been too sick to nurse the baby and that he couldn't make the infant drink cow's milk. The veterinary climbed into the wagon. He was out in a few moments. Both the Sagers were dead, he told the waiting crowd. John called the doctor a liar and tried to climb into the wagon, but was held back by a dozen pitying hands.

The Sager orphans stayed with the caravan until it reached Fort Hall, a British trading post owned by the Hudson's Bay Company. The factor[1] in charge of the post was trying to prevent American emigrants from entering the Columbia Valley by deflecting them into California. (Great Britain was then beginning her final struggle to retain her hold on Oregon Territory.) He told them that the wagon trail to Oregon, made the year before by Marcus Whitman, the missionary doctor, was impassable. The members of the caravan, already worn and discouraged and terribly afraid of Indian massacre, decided to go down into California.

John Sager, squatting by the camp-fire, listened without a word to the council of elders. His grief for his father

Fort Hall

and mother had merged into one immense desire. Ever since he could remember, he had heard his father talk of making a great farm in the valley of the Columbia, of helping to keep Oregon Territory for America. John determined to go on to the Columbia, to complete his father's life for him.

He would abandon the wagon; the oxen and cow could carry the packs of food and bedding. He had learned from an old woman in the camp how to feed the baby. The next morning he was gone, leaving this note: "I have taken the family back to the States with Kit Carson. He is in a hurry. John Sager." By this false information he made sure he would not be followed and prevented from pushing westward.

Here there is a break of several weeks in the story while John and the rest of the children crept along the valley of the Snake River to Fort Boise[2] nearly 300 miles beyond. The Snake writhes through a tremendous canyon that slashes Idaho from east to west. Barren plains, brutal mountains, scorch-

---

1. A *factor* is an agent.
2. *Boise* (BOY zee) is now the capital of Idaho.

Snake River Falls

ing heat by day and chill by night, a pestilence of mosquitoes and fleas—a heartbreaking test even for seasoned adults. Yet, one September afternoon there crept up to the gates of Fort Boise a boy holding a baby in his arms. The boy was dressed in ragged buckskin pants and still more ragged moccasins. His sun-faded hair fell to his shoulders in tangled profusion.

The factor in this one-man post was accustomed to all kinds of hardships, but when he saw John he uttered an oath of shocked surprise. John asked with fierce eagerness if there was a white woman in the fort. Something had to be done for the baby: she vomited everything she ate. The factor, with increasing horror in his eyes, looked down on the unsavory atom[3] in the boy's arms. There was no white woman, and the factor suggested an Indian mother. John declared that nothing could induce him to allow a squaw to touch the baby. Someone had warned him of the diseases a child would contract through such measures.

At this point Francis came up with the pack-train, and there disembarked such a rabble of wild little girls as the Scotsman had never seen even among Indians. He ordered his cook to feed the youngsters and watched while they devoured the venison[4] stew, gobbling and fighting like puppies. John stood aloof and chewed down a hunk of venison which he held in one hand, support-

ing the baby with the other.

The factor suggested that John leave the baby and the two next sisters at the fort. John shook his head. The baby's one chance, he decided, was to get through to Dr. Whitman's mission with all speed. The factor warned the lad that the baby looked ready to die any minute, anyhow. John's face flamed; he cursed the factor and began to sob.

The Scottish factor afterward set down his feelings in a letter to his mother.

My letters to you have contained many strange tales, but none that twisted me like this. They were a scourge to have about, I assure you, but nothing could lessen the pathos of them. That lad John! How moving was this lad's vicarious[5] fatherhood. Not that he was a gentle guardian! He took no nonsense from any of them. When the girl of eight protested against holding the baby, he jerked the sister across his knees and clouted her until she begged to take the baby. The strain had told on him. He was all nerves and unable to throw off the torture of responsibility. By Jove, he ruled me too, for I sent them on, after a night's sleep, under the care of a pair of good Indians and fresh horses.

---

3. Here, an *atom* is a very small creature.
4. *Venison* (VEN ih sun) is deer meat.
5. *Vicarious* (vy KARE ee uss) means serving instead of someone else.

Word Bank	**pestilence** (PES tih lintz) *n.*: a natural population suddenly and greatly enlarged; epidemic

seasoned (SEE zuhnd) *adj.*: experienced

profusion (pro FYOO zhun) *n.*: a great supply; superabundance

aloof (uh LOOF) *adj.*: reserved; withdrawn

pathos (PATH ose) *n.*: feelings of pity

clouted (CLOW tid) *v.*: struck forcefully, especially with the hand or fist

They may have been good Indians once, but evidently they regarded the job of guiding white papooses across the difficult Blue Mountains as beneath their dignity. A few days out they disappeared, accompanied by the horses.

We have few details of the crossing of the Blue Mountains. The oldest sister slipped under a ponderously moving ox and broke her leg. John used hard-packed snowballs to keep down the swelling. The baby was very low, and John was sometimes not sure she was breathing at all. He had to abandon the starving oxen. The cow, which still yielded a small quantity of milk for the baby and transportation for the oldest sister, must come along. With frosted feet, with festering sores due to dirt and emaciation, the children began the last lap of the journey. They made five or six miles a day, huddling together at night like stricken lambs under the shelter of a rock or backed against a fallen tree, warmed by huge fires. A thousand times during the trip the younger children shrieked that they would go no farther. John forced them to go on.

It would have wrung my heart, but I wish I might have witnessed the last lap of that immortal journey, though after many days with the diaries I can see it as clearly as if I had actually come upon them in those mountain fastnesses.[6]

Now they have topped the last crest, and as they stand gazing into the vast valley to the west, the snow is blood-stained beneath their feet. Behind them is a chaos of range and canyon over which they have crept like snails. Before them, a wide, undulating plain cut by the black and silver ribbon of the Columbia River. A moment to gaze, to shiver, then John moves with fumbling feet down the mountain. His legs are tied in strips of buffalo hide. His long hair is bound back from his eyes by a twist of leather around his forehead. On his back is the three-year-old sister. In his arms the baby, wrapped in a wolf-skin, lies motionless as death.

Staggering back of John moans the cow, her hoofs split to the quick. On her back the eight-year-old girl huddles under a bit of blanket which she shares with the five-year-old. Francis, his gray eyes dull with hunger and exertion, buckskin pants reduced to a mere patch of leather, and flannel shirt only a fluttering decoration across his chest, brings up the rear with the others.

Stumbling, rising, panting, but in a silence more tragic than weeping, they move down into the valley and stand at last before the Whitman mission. Narcissa Whitman gave a little cry when she saw them and held out her arms toward the bundle in John's arms. Her only child, a little girl of two, had been drowned a few years before. She groaned as she turned back the wolfskin and saw what lay beneath.

Dr. Whitman looked with her while the six young derelicts waited in breathless silence. The doctor thought that perhaps the baby was still alive, and Narcissa took her into the house and laid her in a warm bath while her husband herded the others into an outbuilding and began the unsavory job of turning them into human children. All but John. He shook his head on hearing the doctor's order and followed Mrs. Whitman into the house. Bathed, rubbed with warm oil, wrapped in soft wool, the baby showed no sign of life until Narcissa began to drop hot, diluted milk

---

6. *Fastnesses* are objects which are firmly fixed and stable.

Word Bank	derelicts (DEHR uh LIKTS) *n.*: persons abandoned or forgotten

between the blue lips. After several moments of this, the little throat contracted and a whimper, something less than a mouse squeak, came forth. At this sound John dropped to the floor, wrapped his arms around Narcissa's knees, laughed, groaned, and then limped from the room.

All that night Narcissa sat with the baby on her lap. John, washed and in decent garments, slept on a blanket on the floor beside her. The doctor dozed on a cot nearby. What thoughts passed through Narcissa Whitman's mind that night we cannot know. We do know that she was already worn with anxiety and overwork, and the prospect of adding seven more to her household must have been staggering. Toward dawn she roused the doctor and told him that she wanted to keep the children at the mission. The next morning they invited the little orphans to become their adopted children.

And so the heroic odyssey[7] came to an end. Little John Sager had fulfilled his father's dream of making a home for the Sager family in the Columbia Valley, and of helping save Oregon for America.

_____

7. An *odyssey* (AHD ih see) is a long wandering.

Columbia River

Recalling

1. How did the Sager family appear at the beginning of the story? Describe their appearance, using details given by the author.

2. Why did John need to take his siblings to the Oregon Territory all alone?

3. What did John feel he was accomplishing, by leading his family to Columbia?

4. What happened as the family crossed the Blue Mountains?

Interpreting

5. What does John's decision, to take the family on a difficult journey, show about his character?

6. The Scottish factor said that John was not a gentle guardian. Do you think the harsh manner in which John behaved was appropriate? Explain.

Concluding

7. Which character traits did John possess that allowed him to complete his journey with all his siblings?

Examining Fiction

The story, *Child Pioneer*, is written in a natural, matter-of-fact style. Even though the events are dreadful and grim, the author relates them with little emotion. The overall effect is one of harsh realism.

1. The author's plain, factual telling of the story reflects the plain, matter-of-fact way the characters face hardship. Choose three places in the story where some difficulty is described. Copy out the descriptive sentence, then add one or two sentences of your own, that tell about the character's emotions.

2. Is the simple, deadpan tone more powerful than a voice charged with drama? Explain your answer.

Thinking About Fiction

1. Suppose that you were facing the same circumstances as John Sager. Would you continue your journey on the Oregon Trail? Explain your decision.

2. Many thoughts went through Narcissa Whitman's mind the night before she decided to adopt the children. Reconstruct the events of that evening, and explain how Narcissa arrived at her decision.

Creating and Writing

The settling of the western territories of the United States required strength and courage. Thousands of Americans made this treacherous journey, yet little is known about their lives. Write a paragraph in which you discuss the bravery of families such as the Sagers whose persistence transformed the history of the United States, particularly regions west of the Mississippi River.

Into • *The Runner*

Do you like horses? These graceful creatures once ran wild in the Old West. Many hunters tried to capture and sell them and, in the process, the horses were often injured or killed. *The Runner* is the story of a boy named Shadow who cannot bear to see a wild horse captured by a group of unfeeling, greedy men. Shadow is skilled and courageous. He has named the horse The Runner.

A brave boy, a magnificent horse, a mean uncle, some cruel men—this story has all the ingredients of a classic Western. Enjoy!

Focus

In contrast to *Child Pioneer*, this story is clearly a work of fiction. It is an adventure story with a lot of action and a well-defined setting. It is strong in plot and characterization. Like most adventure stories, it requires little analysis or deep thought. The description of the hills and valleys, woods and bogs, create the perfect setting for this tale of a wild horse. As you read the story, ask yourself the following questions: What is the theme? What is the conflict? Where is the story's climax?

About the Authors

JANE ANNIXTER is the pen name for Janet Levington Sturtzel, who was born in 1903 in Detroit, Michigan. **PAUL ANNIXTER**, who was to be her husband, is the pen name for Howard Sturtzel, and was born in 1894 in Minnesota. Together, they co-authored *The Runner*. Jane began writing at the age of nine. She attributes her abilities to her father, who instilled in her a love of the classics, and encouraged her to develop her writing skills. Paul had extensive exposure to the outdoor life. His experience in the wilderness is an element in most of his works, including *The Runner*. Paul died in 1985 and Jane died in 1996.

The Runner

Jane and Paul Annixter

That afternoon, when Shadow took the binoculars to the ridge for his daily check, he saw five strange horsemen in the valley below. There was only one explanation; they were after the wild band.

Shadow sped downgrade at a rocking run. He didn't know what he could do, but he must try to get to The Runner. He paused at intervals, panting, to watch the progress below. With a muffled thunder that filled the lap of the hills, the roan stallion and his band broke for the valley's narrow throat, the first rider pounding close behind. But only for seconds, for the wild ones left the horseman as if he were roped to a tree. When the second man in the cordon[1] broke out of cover with fearsome yips designed to scatter them, the eleven broke about him, passing like a cataract to either side. And so did the third. But the fourth man, breaking cover from the opposite side of the valley, produced a panic in the band which the fifth man was able to utilize as he lanced in with swinging lariat.

The rope snaked through the air and curled about the forelegs of the roan stallion himself. As it went taut, the roper and his mount were flung to the ground. But the stallion had fallen, too, and the other four riders were closing in before he could rise. The Runner and the mares fled on. In a matter of moments, the stallion was trussed and helpless.

Shadow was running downward again, shouting unheard. Inevitably he fell, pitching forward on chest and hands. He rose, breathless and groggy, and plunged on. For now the five men were slowly closing in about the valley head where The Runner and the mares were cornered. Of course it was The Runner they wanted now. Without a leader the mares could easily be caught later.

As he broke out into the open, gasping for breath, Shadow saw that four of

----

1. A *cordon* (KOR dun) is a line of persons or objects enclosing an area to prevent passage.

> **Word Bank**
>
> **roan** (ROAN) *n.*: a brownish-red colored horse
>
> **lariat** (LAIR ee ut) *n.*: a long rope that is used with a noose to catch livestock

the riders were converging through the trees, bent on cutting off The Runner. The fifth man sat his mount in the open with a rifle resting across the pommel of his saddle.

Shadow knew what this meant. They would try the cruel crease shot, most dangerous of all methods for capturing wild horses. The rifleman would try to graze the base of The Runner's neck where it met the spine, stunning him just long enough for capture. At least a hundred horses were killed by the crease shot for every animal captured.

A great cry burst from Shadow as he ran, but no one heard. With the mares wheeling and screaming at the edge of the woods, he saw The Runner chivvied[2] into the open. In the moment that he paused in consternation, the rifleman aimed and fired. The Runner's legs buckled under him and he pitched forward on his nose, then onto his side, to lie motionless and apparently lifeless. Three riders spurred forward.

Shadow's legs had gone out from under him, too. He crouched, sobbing, on the ground. He could not watch now, yet he had to. He saw ropes in the hands of two of the riders. Right in the midst of this the miracle occurred. The luck of the hundredth horse was with The Runner. He had been stunned but came to with a sudden heave and gained his feet. Blood was running down his neck and shoulder. He reared, screamed, and charged. The mounted rifleman in front of him went down, horse and rider knocked to the ground beneath The Runner's slashing forehoofs. Then The Runner was through the cordon and thundering down the valley toward the dense pines, like a wild duck in flight.

Only two riders gave chase. The other two stayed behind, bent over the stricken man and his mount. Still helpless in the legs, with a hollow cave in his chest, Shadow remained where he was. No one, it seemed, had seen him.

After a time he dragged himself over to the shade of some berry bushes and waited, trembling, listening, agonized over the struggle of the roan stallion against his bonds that went on and on to the point of exhaustion, when he simply lay there inert.

A long time passed while the two men who had stayed behind worked over the fallen one. Shadow heard groans and the pained cough of the man's downed horse, which had not risen. Evidently a leg had been broken. When the man on the ground had received first aid, one of the other men knelt by the fallen horse, a hand on its nose, and stroked its neck. When the revolver was slowly drawn from its holster, Shadow turned away.

Dusk was close when the other two men emerged from the woods. They had failed to capture The Runner. Shadow could only hope they had not killed him.

---

2. *Chivvied* (CHIV eed) means to tease or annoy with persistent, petty attacks.

Word Bank	consternation (KAHN ster NAY shin) *n*.: amazement or dismay that hinders or throws into confusion

He crouched where he was while they close-hobbled the roan stallion and hazed[3] him to his feet. Then the invaders left the valley, a mounted man on either side of the stallion, one of the other horses carrying double.

When all was quiet again, Shadow emerged from the thickets and went limping down the valley. They would be expecting him at home, but he could not go until he had found the Runner, no matter how long it took. Probably the men who had caught the stallion would be back tomorrow. Shadow did not know what he could do except find The Runner and stay by him if he were still alive.

He located the coil of rope and the small hand ax he had hidden with it two weeks before; then he entered the woods, following the tracks of The Runner and the two riders who had gone after him. The tracks led in and out through a maze of thickets cut by a swampy, spring-fed creek that later joined the larger stream in the valley bottom. From time to time, Shadow's eyes picked out the slim-hoofed tracks of The Runner from among the deep marks of the heavier horses, but darkness was already falling and he could not follow much longer.

He sought higher ground and a spot to spend the night. On a slope he found a dry hideout beneath the low-sweeping boughs of a spruce. It was not until he sank down on the mat of dry needles that he was aware of how exhausted he was. His weariness was far more than the body's fatigue and the pain of his bad leg; the strength had been wrung from his very heart.

Even if The Runner had escaped vital injury, all his work was undone, for the young stallion would have lost his faith in man. Under the best conditions it would take a long time to win him back. But in this valley, conditions

---

3. *Hazed* (HAYZD) him means they intimidated and harrassed him by physical punishment.

would never be right again. That Shadow knew. All this revolved in his mind in addition to a full sense of the pain and consternation his absence would cause at home.

After he had lain there for a time in silence, there came a soft, nervous nickering of a mare from the darkness far ahead, answered by another. The familiar sounds soothed Shadow to a sense of companionship, and he slept. He was awake many times, uncomfortable and cold. Once he heard coyotes[4] making a rabbit kill in the valley below. A horned owl alighted in the spruce a dozen feet above him and went through its horrid gamut[5] of shrieks and gibbers and booming hoots, as if bent on scaring him into a rout. He pulled his hat down over his face, but it did no good. Finally, he just lay awake, waiting for the first light.

Hunger drove Shadow along the dawn-lit slopes, searching for nuts or berries to eat. His breakfast was a handful of hazelnuts, eatable though not yet ripe, and a few beechnuts. He limped down to the creek for water, then took up the trail again. The way still led along the soggy creek bed. The going grew wetter; water oozed up in his tracks.

Shadow found the place where the two riders had turned back the night before. Their mounts had evidently sunk too deep in the muck to keep on. Farther along, the little stream spread out in a boggy swamp overgrown with tough, reedlike grass and moss. Shadow heard the nickering of mares again. Guarding each step for silence, he pressed on until a sort of blasting snort and the sound of struggle came from a

4. A *coyote* (KY oh tee) is a small wolf living on prairies.
5. *Gamut* (GAM it) means the entire range from one extreme to another.

thickety place ahead.

Through parted bushes Shadow saw where the young roan was fettered belly-deep in the clutch of black, viscous[6] mud. The Runner's wound and the panic of pursuit had evidently robbed him of the inherent judgment of the wild, and he had taken one chance too many. All night he must have struggled against the mud, only to mire himself deeper. Now he was white-eyed with renewed frenzy.

Cautiously and slowly, stepping on the grass tussocks[7] and fallen branches wherever he could, Shadow moved into the open, talking as he had always talked to The Runner, holding out his empty hand. When the roan struggled again, Shadow hummed until he quieted him. Finally he was crouched down close to The Runner's shoulder, running his hand along the straining neck to soothe him.

There was a foam of fever and thirst on the black lips. Not far away Shadow found a pool on the bog's surface. He dipped up a hatful of water and returned. At first The Runner was too terrified to drink, but his great need and the cool smell of water overcame that. Afterward Shadow made six more trips with his dripping hat. Then he set to work to do what he could.

Without this mud, he thought gratefully, he might never have gotten near The Runner again. He tore the bottom of his shirt, soaked it in water, and he cleansed the bullet wound on the roan's crest. It was not deep and had long since ceased to bleed. Shadow unraveled some strands of his rope and tied the cloth over the wound to keep off the gnats and flies. The Runner loosed his pain and fear in blast upon snorting blast through distended red nostrils, but gradually white panic left his liquid eyes. Shadow never stopped talking or humming, and he made all his movements slow and rhythmic.

Later he went to higher ground and gathered a big armful of grass. He found a wide, flat slab of bark to lay it upon, within easy reach of The Runner's nose. He knew the roan would be loath[8] to eat pulled grass with the man-smell upon it, but sooner or later he would be driven to it. Shadow slipped away to forage again for himself. He found some wild blackberries and some more beechnuts. Then he carried several slabs of bark back to the bog and laid them about The Runner for his own footing. Meanwhile he had felt out all the most solid tussocks of grass and moss between the horse and the pool and the horse and the firm bank beyond, for some spots that looked like tussocks were mere traps of mud.

Finally he set to work close to The Runner's mired forelegs, digging with a

---

6. *Viscous* (VISS kuss) means sticky.
7. *Tussocks* (TUSS ocks) are bunches or clumps.
8. *Loath* (LOTHE) means unwilling.

Word Bank	inherent (in HIR int) *adj*.: inborn forage (FOR idj) *v*.: search for food

slab of bark. The wet mud slithered back into the hole almost as fast as he could scoop it out, but flinging it far aside he gradually gained depth. It was slow, killing work. Gnats and mosquitoes whined about him, and he had to stop often to get his breath. The Runner ruckled[9] and tossed his head and whipped his muddied tail.

It was mid-afternoon before Shadow had dug down to the horse's knees. He was trembling and sick with exhaustion, but he was beginning to hope. He ranged through the woods with his short ax, cutting a score of thin saplings to lay in the hole he had dug. Over these he laid many more flat slabs of pine bark.

By this time The Runner sensed he was being helped and whinnied greeting as Shadow returned through the trees, making the exhausted youth so happy he forgot his fatigue and struggled on until dusk. By that time he had cleared enough space for The Runner to move sideways a little and saw, to his great relief, that the horse had sunk as far as he was going to.

Before it was dark, he brought water again, several hatfuls, and gathered another armful of grass. Now he had to think about his own sleeping place. The night would be chill and the evening full of mosquitoes. He should, he knew, sleep on higher, drier ground. With this in mind he gathered a pile of pine knots and cones and left them on the bank beyond the pool. With his hand ax he cut a large pile of dry branches, knowing he would need a good fire before morning. But The Runner was still whinnying wildly from time to time, and he decided to stay as close as possible through the night.

He cut more pine boughs and gathered still more bark and cones and made a platform bed on the soggy ground almost within touch of the young roan's reaching muzzle. Beside this he lit a

smudge[10] of bark and leaves—no fire because that would have startled the horse—to help both of them through the worst of the mosquito time. Then he lay down and gazed up at the brilliant high-country stars. Now that it was dark and still, Shadow could feel how glad the young roan was not to be alone. He was glad, too. How much better it was for both of them than last night. In their day-long struggle and strange night-sharing, a new bond was growing between them that he hoped nothing would ever break.

Shadow roused with a jerk. The smudge had gone out, and the chill, spare wind of midnight was flowing down from the heights. The Runner's frightened snorting told him they were not alone. He sat up and the back of his neck tingled, for in the darkness he made out the slow turning of The Runner's head, the rolling eyes fixed

---

9. *Ruckled* (RUCK eld) is to make a hoarse, rattling sound.
10. A *smudge* is a smoldering mass with no flames.

upon the circle of the spruces. His own eyes tried to follow but could make out nothing. Yet something was happening out there in the blackness, something that only The Runner could interpret. In that moment cold fear seeped through Shadow's blood.

From the glowing, phosphorescent terror in the young stallion's eye, he knew it was one of the ancient enemies of horse out there. That meant cougar or bear. If it was cougar, the danger was slight, for the big cats were too cowardly to attack a man. But a grizzly, for instance, would be a different matter.

Shadow crept over to a place directly in front of The Runner, stepping on the bark slabs he had laid across the mud. He crouched down, facing the bank and the spruces beyond, holding the light ax in his hand. He knew, of course, that the great paw of a grizzly could strike him down before he could ever use his inadequate weapon. But he sat on, talking quietly to The Runner, waiting for what would come. He could light a fire, but there was the wild horse to think of, with his natural terror of flame. Fear-

filled as the roan was, and with many hours of trapped torment behind him, the added shock might break his spirit for all time.

Moments dragged by, blind and black. A sharp sound, the snapping of a sizable branch in the thicket, brought Shadow to his knees, wire-taut. No cat-thing would have been clumsy enough to make that sound. It had been made by a ponderous creature of great weight and with little or no concern for any foe. Hard upon that sound came a vast, windy breath from the darkness. The Runner's nostrils ruckled in sheer terror, and he heaved and struggled in new frenzy. No doubt in Shadow's mind now but that it was a grizzly watching and circling there in the blackness. The bear must have sensed the plight of the horse. Only man's presence here had held him from immediate attack, and probably he was nerving himself to it.

> **Word Bank**
>
> **phosphorescent** (FAHS fer ESS int) *adj.*: glowing that is caused by the absorption of light

An aroused grizzly, Shadow knew, feared nothing at all, not even a magazine rifle, but so far there had been nothing to rouse this one but his own hunger. Fire might hold him at bay without touching off his fury. Shadow would have to light a fire.

Some of the leaves and pine cones he had brought for the smudge had not been used, and there were the bark slabs and pine boughs of his bed. Even so, it seemed an interminable time before flame was started and the needles set ablaze. Shadow feverishly chipped bits of bark to strengthen the flame. At last, in its light, a great boulderlike form took shape from the deeper blackness of the trees less than twenty yards away. It was a grizzly. Even in that flickering light, Shadow saw the small, wrathful eyes burning with a red violence, but the bear was as motionless as a museum piece. Moments passed. Shadow could scarcely tear his eyes from the creature to put another branch on the fire. In the renewed light he looked again. Still no movement, just an unbreathing pause with only the little red eyes alive in the great head.

The Runner, too, was silent in the grip of that prolonged, primeval[11] spell of terror. His was the stillness of the conscious victim awaiting the lethal rush. Shadow, a frail human thing frozen in this ancient tableau between predator[12] and prey, knew the awful truth—that the bear was thinking, figuring, every instant.

Shadow could stand it no longer. He snatched a burning bough and plunged forward a dozen feet, screaming, then flung his brand. That broke it. The grizzly moved slightly aside, head swinging, but only to advance a moment later, the mud sucking beneath the great feet. In the same instant Shadow was back at the fire, building it up again. The Runner, roused from his fearful trance, was heaving and struggling.

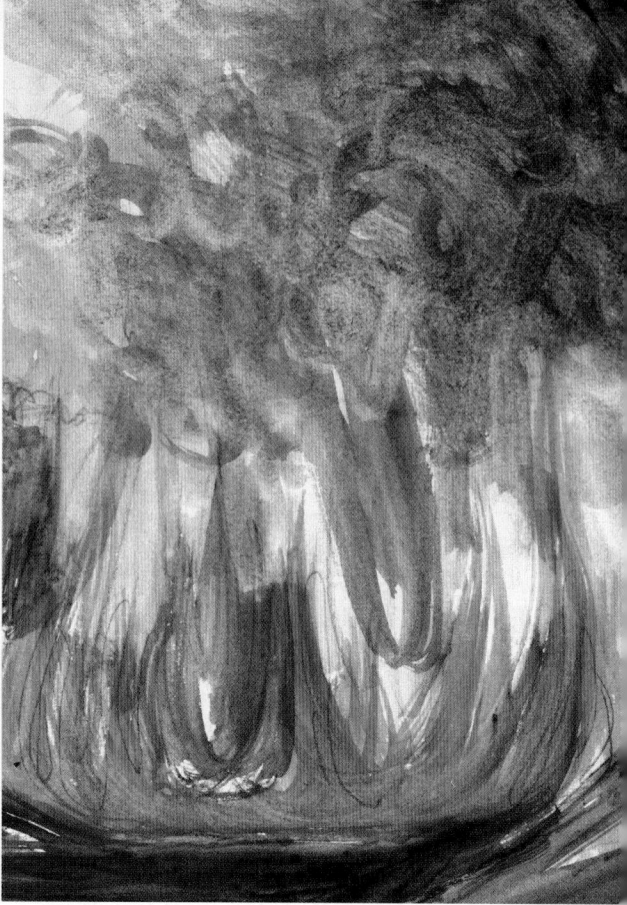

The grizzly advanced to within ten yards, then reared up on his hind legs as if the better to size up the situation, looking vaster than anything Shadow had ever seen. A low, coughing roar came from the open mouth as the fire blazed high with a resinous[13] crackle. Shadow shouted again, an involuntary war cry as old as man. The grizzly moved farther to one side, keeping to the tussocks of grass on the boggy surface.

With two long pieces of bark, Shadow forked a flaming branch in that direction and started a new fire, piling on more bark. The grizzly watched. The swirling smoke was not the least of Shadow's defenses. The enemy showed

---

11. *Primeval* (pry MEE vil) is age-old.
12. A *predator* (PRED uh ter) is one that preys, destroys, or devours.
13. *Resinous* (REZ in uss) means made from tree gums.

no fear but was obviously nonplused. He maneuvered again to the opposite side. Shadow moved to face him, a burning branch in his hand.

The bear stood stolidly, all four great feet ludicrously bunched on a tussock. A spark of inspiration flashed across Shadow's mind. He shouted again and hurled his fiery branch. Momentarily confused, the grizzly floundered aside, to bring up belly-deep in a sucking, viscous hollow. When he roared again, it was a bawl of sheer consternation as he fought with giant swimming strokes toward another grass hummock. For a space his struggles only drove him deeper. Shadow seized the moment to spring from grass bunch to tussock toward the bank, as he had done so many times the day before, and return with more of the dry fuel he had gathered there. He heaped it on his fire and was free to go again, the bear still struggling in the mire.

Systematically now, adding to the growing demoralization of the enemy, Shadow flung his burning brands. One, a flaring pine knot, lit directly on the broad, undulating back, sizzling a minute in the coarse, brown hair before burning through to the hide. A bellow of torment sounded. Shadow continued his barrage of shouts and fire.

When he had once reared out of the mire, the grizzly waited a short time, obviously trying to figure out a fresh attack. Tentatively he moved to the right, then to the left. Abruptly he pivoted on his hind quarters, sloshed to higher ground, and, without once turning, lumbered away into the woods as if it were all a matter of his own decision.

Dawn was not far away. In delayed reaction from the stress of those dark hours, Shadow trembled and sobbed a little. He crouched now close to The

Word Bank	**nonplused** (nahn PLUST) *v.*: puzzled; unsure; at a loss of what to say, think, or do

Runner, sharing the horse's warmth in the predawn chill. The soft nose lifted at times to nudge his neck or shoulder. Together the two had met and bested the most terrible foe the mountain wilderness concealed. The Runner seemed to know this, but Shadow still could not believe. It took the full golden dawn of the September morning to reassure him that the bear was gone.

Even then he could not be sure that the grizzly was not lurking close. Ravenous as he was, he forewent searching the thickets for nuts or berries and set to work immediately clearing the mud away from beneath The Runner's forelegs and belly. The mud was even softer here and progress was very slow. Hours passed before he was able to scrape the mud away. Then he floored the hole he had made with more bark and pine boughs, and was ready for the telling trial.

One of The Runner's forelegs was now quite free, resting upon the floor of bark and branches at the bottom of the excavation. Shadow tied his rope about the stallion's neck in a slipless knot and backed up to solid ground. Then he yipped out an order and pulled on the rope. With a prodigious effort The Runner flung himself upward and forward, gaining a full foot. The inexorable mud still held, but he had practically freed the other foreleg. Two more heaving struggles and both forehoofs rested on the improvised ramp. Half his belly was free.

Shadow let him rest awhile. He talked soothingly, stroking the sweat-damp neck and shoulders, praying in his heart that deliverance was near. Finally he pulled from the bank once more, putting a lilt of encouragement into his yell. With snorting, whistling breath, The Runner put forth all that was in him. Two or three times the forehoofs slipped on the ramp. Bark and saplings bent and snapped beneath him, yet

offered enough solid purchase to raise his weight. With a final, sucking sigh the quag released its prisoner. The stallion scrambled wildly up the solid bank, and there rescuer and rescued stood together, the young roan's chestnut mane falling in a cloud about Shadow's shoulders.

A grizzly will attack as readily in daylight as in darkness, and even now the bear might be lurking anywhere about. When they started moving out of the woods, Shadow kept The Runner to the open places. Also, at any moment the wild blood of the roan might reassert itself. For The Runner's own sake Shadow could not chance that now. The young stallion might elude the bear, but if the horse wranglers returned he was doomed. So Shadow rode The Runner out of the swamp woods, keeping to the stream bed until they came to the meadows where the wild band had fed. Some of the mares were in sight there, feeding by the stream. They

| **Word Bank** | **prodigious** (prah DIDGE iss) *adj.*: immense; extraordinary size |
| | **inexorable** (in EX ser uh bul) *adj.*: unyielding; relentless |

answered The Runner's whinny and circled closer. The stallion reared and trembled, on the verge of bolting, but Shadow knew that he was riding an exhausted horse. Down by the stream he dismounted while The Runner drank, then led the horse into the water and washed the caked mud from his legs and belly. Later, while The Runner grazed, he fashioned a loose hackamore[14] from a piece of his rope. There was the inevitable near frenzy as he slipped it on, but the trust of the long night prevailed and he fastened it loosely into place, allowing for further grazing if The Runner would.

All this time Shadow was mulling over what lay ahead. It was blacker than anything he had ever faced before. For two days and nights without explanation, he had been away from home and job. Considering his uncle's wrath at other times, when he had been away but a few hours, this might end things. Also, Aunt Martha would have worried herself sick and that, too, would be held against him.

The bitless bridle was a final conquest, but Shadow was too hungry, weak, and tired for so much as a quiver of pride as he guided The Runner up out of the wild-horse valley. Thinner than ever, shirtless, mud-caked, slumped above The Runner's wounded crest, he was more a picture of trail's end than victor as they climbed the last steep slope.

It was nearing dusk when he halted The Runner at the gate of his uncle's cow lot. There were no cows there now but the fence was solid and high. Trembling only slightly, The Runner let himself be ridden into the railed enclosure. Talking softly, promising swift return, Shadow barred the gate and limped down toward the house.

---

14. A *hackamore* (HACK uh MORE) is a bridle with a loop that can be tightened around the nose of a horse.

Recalling

1. What were the five strange men after?

2. Why was Shadow so worried about the possible capture of The Runner?

3. What happened to The Runner after he escaped?

4. Where did Shadow spend the first night? Why didn't he go home?

5. Where did Shadow find the horse?

6. Where did Shadow spend the second night? What was he afraid to do, for fear it would frighten The Runner?

7. From what danger does Shadow save the horse?

Interpreting

8. Why was it so important for Shadow to regain the horse's trust?

9. Judging from the way in which Shadow treated the horse, what do you know about his character?

10. What does the boy's battle with the grizzly bear tell you about his character?

Concluding

11. Would you have been able to show such devotion to a horse? What type of upbringing do you think Shadow had, that he was able to show such loyalty to an animal?

Examining Fiction

People in the Old West led very different lives from our own. They faced many dangers and were isolated from other people, because the area was sparsely settled. They had a close relationship with nature and animals, and had to cope with the challenges this presented. Because of this, many characters in Westerns are portrayed as independent and courageous.

1. Compare and contrast Shadow's character with that of an average boy growing up in a big city.

2. How did life in the Old West give meaning and possibility to Shadow's relationship with The Runner?

Thinking About Fiction

In many short stories, the setting affects the way the character develops. For example, in *The Circuit*, the terrible living conditions and the lack of a permanent home gives rise to certain traits in the main character. In *The Runner*, the setting of the Old West fosters other character traits.

1. Write a list of three character traits you find in Shadow. Next to each trait write a sentence explaining how the environment in which Shadow lived fostered that character trait.

2. Visualize a meeting between the main character in *The Circuit* and Shadow. Can you predict whether or not a friendship would form? What would they have in common?

Creating and Writing

Think about Shadow's decision to protect The Runner from all the perils the horse faced. Remember that this decision led to Shadow's disappearance from his uncle's farm for two days. This generated much anxiety and worry. Write a letter to Shadow's uncle, in which you justify Shadow's actions. Use a friendly letter format, and give plenty of reasons for supporting Shadow's decision.

Into • *After Twenty Years*

We usually think of a punch line as the best part of a joke. But a short story can have a punch line (although it may be more than one line), too. O. Henry was master of the short story punch line. His stories are small works of art; the interesting characters, crisp dialogue, and sharply drawn settings draw us in right from the start. The story moves along rapidly until, suddenly, it is over. The ending is usually so good and so unexpected that readers of O. Henry have been known to stand up and applaud!

Focus

Have you ever had just a small amount of money to spend on an outing or at a store? If so, you will remember how you had to make every penny count. O. Henry uses words the way you would use pennies. He makes every one count. Look at how he constructs a setting with a few well-chosen phrases; the dark street, the closed doors, the chilly air—the scene jumps out at you. Look at the dialogue—there are no long speeches, yet, with a few short lines, he outlines the two friends' personalities. Look at the narrative. With a few brief descriptions, he develops the characters and advances the plot. Then, in one small paragraph at the end, he makes the story one you will not forget!

About the Author

O. HENRY is the pen name for William Sidney Porter, who was born in 1862 in North Carolina. O. Henry was employed in many different lines of work. He was sent to prison in 1896 for embezzlement, a crime he may or may not have committed. After his release, he moved to New York, where he became one of America's most prolific writers. For a period of several years, he was producing one story a week. O. Henry is well known for his use of irony and surprise endings. At the time of his death in 1910, he had published over 250 stories.

After twenty years

O. Henry

The policeman on the beat moved up the avenue impressively. The impressiveness was habitual and not for show, for spectators were few. The time was barely ten o'clock at night, but chilly gusts of wind with a taste of rain in them had well nigh[1] depeopled the streets.

Trying doors as he went, twirling his club with many intricate and artful movements, turning now and then to cast his watchful eye down the pacific thoroughfare,[2] the officer, with his stalwart form and slight swagger, made a fine picture of a guardian of the peace. The vicinity was one that kept early hours. Now and then you might see the lights of a cigar store or of an all-night lunch counter; but the majority of the doors belonged to business places that had long since been closed.

When about midway of a certain block, the policeman suddenly slowed his walk. In the doorway of a darkened hardware store a man leaned, with an unlighted cigar in his mouth. As the policeman walked up to him, the man spoke up quickly.

"It's all right, Officer," he said, reassuringly. "I'm just waiting for a friend. It's an appointment made twenty years ago. Sounds a little funny to you, doesn't it? Well, I'll explain if you'd like to make certain it's all straight. About that long ago

there used to be a restaurant where this store stands—'Big Joe' Brady's restaurant."

"Until five years ago," said the policeman. "It was torn down then."

The man in the doorway struck a match and lit his cigar. The light showed a pale, square-jawed face with keen eyes, and a little white scar near his right eyebrow. His scarfpin was a large diamond, oddly set.

"Twenty years ago tonight," said the man, "I dined here at 'Big Joe' Brady's with Jimmy Wells, my best chum, and the finest chap in the world. He and I were raised here in New York, just like two brothers, together. I was eighteen and Jimmy was twenty. The next morning I was to start for the West to make my fortune. You couldn't have dragged

---

1. *Well nigh* (NY) means almost or nearly.
2. *Pacific thoroughfare* (puh SIF ick THUR oh FAIR) means a calm, peaceful street.

Word Bank

spectator (SPEK tay ter) *n.*: one who looks or watches

stalwart (STAHL wert) *adj.*: marked by outstanding strength and vigor of body, mind, or spirit

swagger (SWAG er) *n.*: a walk with an air of overbearing self-confidence

vicinity (vih SIN ih tee) *n.*: a surrounding area or district; neighborhood

Jimmy out of New York, he thought it was the only place on earth. Well, we agreed that night that we would meet here again exactly twenty years from that date and time, no matter what our conditions might be or from what distance we might have to come. We figured that in twenty years each of us ought to have our destiny worked out and our fortunes made, whatever they were going to be."

"It sounds pretty interesting," said the policeman. "Rather a long time between meets, though, it seems to me. Haven't you heard from your friend since you left?"

"Well, yes, for a time we corresponded," said the other. "But after a year or two we lost track of each other. You see, the West is a pretty big proposition, and I kept hustling around over it pretty lively. But I know Jimmy will meet me here if he's still alive, for he always was the truest, staunchest[3] old chap in the world. He'll never forget. I came a thousand miles to stand in this door tonight, and it's worth it if my old partner turns up."

The waiting man pulled out a handsome watch, the lids of it set with small diamonds.

"Three minutes to ten," he announced. "It was exactly ten o'clock when we parted here at the restaurant door."

"Did pretty well out West, didn't you?" asked the policeman.

"You bet! I hope Jimmy has done half as well. He was a kind of plodder, though, good fellow as he was. I've had to compete with some of the sharpest wits going to get my pile. A man gets in

a groove in New York. It takes the West to put a razor-edge on him."

The policeman twirled his club and took a step or two.

"I'll be on my way. Hope your friend comes around all right. Going to call time on him sharp?"

"I should say not!" said the other. "I'll give him half an hour at least. If Jimmy is alive on earth he'll be here by that time. So long, Officer."

"Good-night, sir," said the policeman, passing on along his beat, trying doors as he went.

There was now a fine, cold drizzle falling, and the wind had risen from its uncertain puffs into a steady blow. The few foot passengers astir in that quarter hurried dismally and silently along with coat collars turned high and pocketed hands. And in the door of the hardware store the man who had come a thousand miles to fill an appointment, uncertain almost to absurdity, with the friend of his youth, smoked his cigar and waited.

---

3. *Staunchest* (STAUN chist) means steadfast in loyalty and principle.

About twenty minutes he waited, and then a tall man in a long overcoat, with a collar turned up to his ears, hurried across from the opposite side of the street. He went directly to the waiting man.

"Is that you, Bob?" he asked doubtfully.

"Is that you, Jimmy Wells?" cried the man in the door.

"Bless my heart!" exclaimed the new arrival, grasping both the other's hands with his own. "It's Bob, sure as fate. I was certain I'd find you here if you were still in existence. Well, well, well!—twenty years is a long time. The old restaurant's gone, Bob; I wish it had lasted, so we could have had another dinner there. How has the West treated you, old man?"

"Bully; it has given me everything I asked it for. You've changed lots, Jimmy. I never thought you were so tall by two or three inches."

"Oh, I grew a bit after I was twenty."

"Doing well in New York, Jimmy?"

"Moderately. I have a position in one of the city's departments. Come on, Bob; we'll go around to a place I know of, and have a good long talk about old times."

The two men started up the street, arm in arm. The man from the West, his egotism enlarged by success, was beginning to outline the history of his career. The other, submerged in his overcoat, listened with interest.

At the corner stood a drugstore, brilliant with electric lights. When they came into this glare each of them turned simultaneously to gaze upon the other's face.

The man from the West stopped suddenly and released his arm.

"You're not Jimmy Wells," he snapped. "Twenty years is a long time, but not long enough to change a man's nose from a Roman to a pug."

"It sometimes changes a good man into a bad one," said the tall man. "You've been under arrest for ten minutes, 'Silky' Bob. Chicago thinks you may have dropped over our way and wires us she wants to have a chat with you. Going quietly, are you? That's sensible. Now, before we go to the station here's a note I was asked to hand to you. You may read it here at the window. It's from Patrolman Wells."

The man from the West unfolded the little piece of paper handed him. His hand was steady when he began to read, but it trembled a little by the time he had finished. The note was rather short.

Bob:

I was at the appointed place on time. When you struck the match to light your cigar I saw it was the face of the man wanted in Chicago. Somehow I couldn't do it myself, so I went around and got a plainclothesman to do the job.

Jimmy

Word Bank egotism (EE go TIZ um) *n.*: an exaggerated sense of self-importance

Recalling

1. Whom does the policeman find as he walks down the street? What does the man tell him?

2. Does the Westerner think Jimmy will keep the agreement?

3. According to the Westerner, how can a person's environment influence them?

4. When does the Westerner realize that the person who claims to be Jimmy Wells is really someone else?

5. In actuality, who is the man pretending to be Jimmy Wells and who is the Westerner?

Interpreting

6. Why is 'Silky' Bob an appropriate name for this character? What does the word "silky" tell you about him?

7. Given what you know about Jimmy, would you say it was difficult for him to resolve his internal conflict?

8. Who do you think has been more successful, Jimmy or Bob? Explain your answer.

Concluding

9. Do you think that environment affects people? Explain your answer.

Examining Fiction

The elements of plot, character, setting, and theme all contribute to the **overall effect**, the story's complete impression on the reader. By breaking the story into parts, the reader can analyze it and then clearly see the overall effect.

1. **Plot:** Briefly summarize the story.

2. **Character:** Compare and contrast Jimmy and Bob.

3. **Setting:** Is the setting important to this story?

4. **Theme:** A sentence at the end of the story suggests the theme. Find it and state what the theme is.

5. **Overall Effect:** How does the author achieve the overall effect of this story?

Thinking About Fiction

An author who uses irony focuses on the difference between the way things seem to be, and the way they actually are.

1. At the beginning of the story, what are 'Silky' Bob's expectations? To his surprise, what unanticipated events occur at the end of the story?

2. Go back and reread the story. Can you now find clues to the surprise ending?

Creating and Writing

Picture yourself in Jimmy Wells' position. Would you have written the note? Rewrite the ending to the story with an alternative method for capturing 'Silky' Bob.

poetry

Poets are experts in exposing the beauty and rhythm of language using a small number of words. Poets begin with broad, universal concepts and employ many methods in order to capture the meaning of these concepts and create finely tuned, highly effective poems. They carefully examine every phrase and consider the effectiveness of the words they use.

Most poetry is written in stanzas. Each stanza is composed of several lines. Each line contains well-chosen words effectively arranged. Poets realize that each word in the English language has its own specific sounds, associations, form, and rhythm. Poets analyze these four components and modify words to create the desired effect. Poets may use alliteration (*Sea Shell*), onomatopoeia (*Cat!*), simile (*I Wandered Lonely as a Cloud*), or repetition (*Train Tune*). Visual and auditory images reflect the poems' themes. Poets may use the concrete form of the poem (*Pendulum*) as a way of maximizing the impact of their poetry.

Poets are artists who have created a literary form that is emotional, moving, inspiring, and invigorating. In many ways, poetry is the most graceful and rewarding form of literature.

mini table of contents

Poetic Sound

Poetic Language

Poetic Form

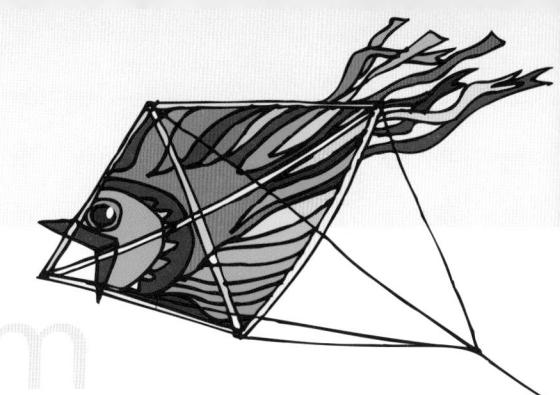

Poetic Theme

Pulling It All Together

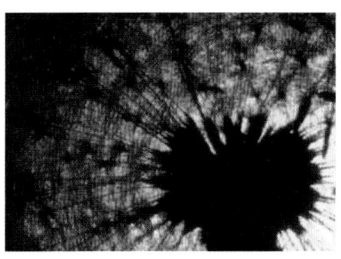

Blueprint FOR READING

Into
- *The Flower-Fed Buffaloes*
- *Train Tune*
- *Voyage*

Sound is one of the elements that draw you to a poem. The poet's choice and combination of sounds can make the poem loud and dramatic, or quiet and still. There are different techniques a poet may use to create the sound desired. The poem may contain repetition of certain words or consonants. It can even repeat full phrases. These methods create a sound that is an essential part of the poem's overall meaning and impact.

Focus

As you read the three poems *The Flower-Fed Buffaloes*, *Train Tune*, and *Voyage*, notice how the poets repeat certain sounds, words, and phrases. How does repetition create the unique sound the poet desires?

About the Authors

American poet **VACHEL LINDSAY** was born in Springfield, Illinois in 1879. Lindsay wrote many works of both poetry and prose. He went on walking tours of different areas of the United States. During his travels, he would recite his poetry, in exchange for food and lodging. His journeys gave him understanding of a broad range of the American public. Lindsay drew on his travel experiences in his writing. Vachel Lindsay died in 1931, in the city of his birth.

LOUISE BOGAN was born in 1897 in Maine. She first published her poems in 1915, in the *Boston University Beacon*. Her first book of poetry appeared in 1923. Bogan served as the Chair of Poetry at the Library of Congress. She was honored by the Academy of American Poets for her contributions to American poetry. A renewed interest in Bogan's work developed after her death in 1970. Since that time, some of her work has been reissued, including her autobiography.

CARMEN TAFOLLA was born in Texas in 1951. Of Mexican-American descent, Tafolla was awarded first prize in the National Chicano Literature Competition in 1987. She has written widely published prose and poetry, and is known for bringing Mexican-American culture to life in her works.

The Flower-Fed Buffaloes

Vachel Lindsay

The flower-fed buffaloes of the spring
In the days of long ago,
Ranged[1] where the locomotives sing
And the prairie flowers lie low—
5   The tossing, blooming, perfumed grass
Is swept away by wheat,
Wheels and wheels and wheels spin by
In the spring that still is sweet,
But the flower-fed buffaloes of the spring
10   Left us long ago.
They gore[2] no more, they bellow[3] no more,

They trundle[4] around the hills no more—
With the Blackfeet, lying low,
With the Pawnees,[5] lying low.
15   Lying low.

---

1. *ranged* (RAINJD): roamed
2. *gore*: stab with horns
3. *bellow* (BELL oh): roar loudly
4. *trundle*: move freely
5. *Blackfeet, Pawnees* (black feet, paw NEEZ): These two tribes of Plains Indians lived in the midwestern United States and once hunted buffalo.

Train
Tune

Back through clouds
Back through clearing
Back through distance
Back through silence

5 Back through groves
Back through garlands[1]
Back by rivers
Back below mountains

Back through lightning
10 Back through cities
Back through stars
Back through hours

Back through plains
Back through flowers
15 Back through birds
Back through rain

Back through smoke
Back through noon
Back along love
20 Back through midnight

1. *garlands* (GAR lundz):
wreaths of flowers and leaves

Louise Bogan

Voyage

Carmen Tafolla

I was the fourth ship
    Behind Niña, Pinta, and Santa Maria,
    Lost at sea while watching a seagull,
    Following the wind and sunset skies,
5   While the others set their charts.

I was the fourth ship.
    Breathing in salt and flying with clouds,
    Sailing moonbreezes and starvision nights,
    Rolling into the wave and savoring its lull,
10   While the others pointed their prows.

I was the fourth ship.
    Playfully in love with the sea,
    Eternally entwined with the sky,
    Forever vowed to my voyage,
15   While the others shouted "Land."

• *The Flower-Fed Buffaloes*

Recalling

1. "In the days of long ago," where did the buffalo live in this country?

2. What happened to the buffalo?

Interpreting

3. Do the words, "flower-fed," affect your image of the buffalo? How?

4. Besides the buffalo's disappearance, what else has vanished from this country?

5. Identify sounds, language, and imagery that enhance the effect of the poem.

6. The phrase "lying low," is repeated three times at the end of the poem. What does the phrase mean? To which three things is it referring?

Concluding

7. In many ways, this country has undergone improvements since the days of the buffalo. However, certain things have been lost as well. What has this country lost, in the name of progress?

Examining Poetry

Sound is an essential element that contributes to the overall meaning of a poem. The poet uses tools such as **alliteration** (the repetition of initial consonant sounds— for example, pious person).

1. Give an example of alliteration in the poem, *The Flower-Fed Buffaloes*.

2. How does sound create the mood? How does it further one's understanding of the meaning of this poem?

Creating and Writing

The thoughtless slaughter of the buffalo by white hunters for "sport" is a sad chapter in American history. Native Americans hunted buffalo with an eye for killing only what they needed for food. They were farsighted enough to understand where the white man's destruction would lead. Imagine you lived at the time the buffalo roamed the Great Plains. You are aware of the consequences of the needless destruction of these animals. Write a persuasive letter to the editor of a newspaper arguing against the slaughter of the buffalo.

• *Train Tune*

Recalling

1. The train travels through a series of locales. Where else does the train go?

2. Which emotion does Bogan mention in this poem? Instead of using the word "through" when she refers to this emotion, which word does she use?

Interpreting

3. Describe the repetition used in *Train Tune*. Which word is repeated in every line?

4. Could this poem be put to music, as words for a song? Would the poem still make sense, if it had a different title? Why or why not?

Concluding

5. At first glance, this appears to be a simple poem. However, what is the serious message the poet conveys about trains and time?

Examining Poetry

A poet may use different kinds of repetition for effect. The poet may repeat sounds, words, or phrases. The type of repetition used has an effect that is more subtle or more dramatic.

1. What is the effect of the repetition in *Train Tune*?

2. Is the effect more subtle or dramatic than the repetition in *The Flower-Fed Buffaloes*?

3. Does the repetition correspond with the theme of the poem?

Creating and Writing

Choose a subject for a poem. Which type of repetition will lend itself to the mood you wish to create? Does the subject of your poem soothe you or excite you? Now, write the poem.

• *The Voyage*

Recalling

1. What is the subject of the poem?

2. What happened to the fourth ship? Why?

3. What was the third and most important action taken by those who piloted the Niña, the Pinta, and the Santa Maria?

4. Which three actions did the fourth ship take, while it sailed behind the others?

Interpreting

5. Using examples from the poem, explain why the fourth ship was lost at sea.

6. Contrast the feelings and mission that propel the fourth ship, with that of the Niña, the Pinta, and the Santa Maria.

7. What sort of people does the fourth ship represent? What types of people are represented by the Niña, the Pinta, and the Santa Maria?

Concluding

8. What are the advantages of taking time to look at the world around you, in all its beauty and pleasure? Are there any disadvantages?

Examining Poetry

Repetition helps create the unique sound that adds to the meaning and effect of a poem. In *Voyage*, the technique of repetition is used by repeating a whole phrase several times.

1. Which phrase does the poet repeat in *Voyage*? How often?

2. Why does the poet repeat the whole phrase?

3. What mood is created?

Creating and Writing

There are many different kinds of people in the world. Some people have more definite goals, while others are dreamers. Both types are represented in *Voyage*. Which type of person do you think the poet admires, given her description of the fourth ship? Are you similar to the poet, or do you have more in common with the people on the Niña, Pinta, and Santa Maria? Write a paragraph indicating with whom you identify most.

Into • *The Magnificent Bull*

Many cultures have, or have had, oral tradition. The words and stories often were what we call "poetry." This poetry was not written down, and its recitation was often chanted. The poems were passed down orally, from generation to generation. Tribal poets used many techniques for remembering poems. Sometimes they would repeat words to make memorization an easier task.

Focus

The Dinka are Nomadic tribe people, who live west of the Nile River in the southern Sudan. As you read this poem, notice that the word "like" is repeated in every line. This made memorization easier for the tribal poet.

THE MAGNIFICENT BULL

DINKA TRADITIONAL

My bull is white like the silver fish in the river
white like the shimmering crane bird on the river bank
white like fresh milk!
His roar is like the thunder to the Turkish cannon[1] on the steep shore.
5   My bull is dark like the raincloud in the storm.
He is like summer and winter.
Half of him is dark like the storm cloud,
half of him is light like sunshine.
His back shines like the morning star.
10 His brow is red like the beak of the Hornbill.[2]
His forehead is like a flag, calling people from a distance,
He resembles the rainbow.

I will water him at the river,
With my spear I shall drive my enemies.
15 Let them water their herds at the well;
the river belongs to me and my bull.
Drink, my bull, from the river; I am here
to guard you with my spear.

---

1. *Turkish cannon*: a large, powerful cannon used by the Turkish army
2. *Hornbill*: a tropical bird with a bright, curved bill

- *The Magnificent Bull*

Recalling

1. A **simile** is a figure of speech, in which two distinct things are compared, using the word "like" or "as," as in "my bull is white like the silver fish…" Reread the poem, and list as many similes as you can find.

Interpreting

2. This poem was written by a nomadic Dinka tribesman. The Dinkas were herders and hunters. How do they feel about their "magnificent bull"?

Concluding

3. We often read stories and poems in which an animal is the main character. Why are animals popular subjects for writers?

Examining Poetry

Poetry and song are closely related. Long ago, poems were chanted, not just recited. Poets would repeat certain lines or words, in order to help keep the oral tradition alive.

- Which words are repeated in *The Magnificent Bull*? Make a list of these words.

- Which stanzas contribute to the poem's hypnotic quality? Finally, at which point does the repetition cease?

Creating and Writing

Imagine you live in a time or culture where poems are recited, not written. Choose a subject that expresses a special interest—your family's or your own. Create a poem about this subject. How will you make the poem easy to remember? Perhaps you can repeat certain words, as the Dinkas did in their song, *The Magnificent Bull*. Memorize your poem and share your work with your classmates.

Into
- *Sea Shell*
- *Cat!*

There are many different sound effects a poet may use when composing a poem. The repetition of initial consonant sounds is called **alliteration**. A figure of speech a poet may use is **onomatopoeia**. An onomatopoeic word actually imitates or suggests the action, sound, or creature it describes, for example, "sizzle," "cuckoo," or "boom."

Focus

Notice how the author uses alliteration in the poem, *Sea Shell*. The use of alliteration, here, suggests a sea shell actually singing. In the poem, *Cat!*, the poet uses onomatopoeia to mimic the sounds she wishes to capture. As you read each of these poems, consider how alliteration and onomatopoeia contribute to the effectiveness of each poem.

About the Authors

American poet **AMY LOWELL** was born in 1874 to a wealthy, aristocratic family. She grew up on her family's estate in Brookline, Massachusetts. Not until the age of 28 was Lowell inspired to write poetry. She began to study the works of other poets, and published her first work in 1910. Lowell became a famous and accomplished writer. She died at the age of 51, in 1925.

English author **ELEANOR FARJEON** was born in 1881 in London. Farjeon lived most of her life in Hampstead, England, except for a short stay in the United States after her father's death in 1903. Her father was a novelist known for a special approach to education. He had a strong influence on her life. Farjeon was largely self-educated, and read widely. She is said to have read more than 8,000 books. Farjeon is known for producing excellent children's literature, and was the first recipient of the International Hans Christian Anderson Award. She died in 1965.

Sea Shell

Amy Lowell

Sea Shell, Sea Shell,
  Sing me a song, O please!
A song of ships and sailor men,
  And parrots and tropical trees,

5   Of islands lost in the Spanish Main
Which no man may ever find again,
Of fishes and corals under the waves,
And sea horses stabled in great green caves.

Sea Shell, Sea Shell,
10   Sing of the things you know so well.

Cat!

Eleanor Farjeon

    Cat!
    Scat!
After her, after her,
Sleeky[1] flatterer,
5 Spitfire[2] chatterer,
Scatter her, scatter her
    Off her mat!
    Wuff!
    Wuff!
10   Treat her rough!
Git her, git her,
Whiskery spitter!
Catch her, catch her,
Green-eyed scratcher!
15 Slathery[3]
    Slithery[4]
    Hisser,
    Don't miss her!
Run till you're dithery,[5]
20   Hithery
    Thithery[6]
    Pftts! pftts!
    How she spits!
    Spitch! Spatch!
25   Can't she scratch!
Scritching the bark
Of the sycamore tree,
She's reached her ark
And's hissing at me
30   *Pftts! pftts!*
   Wuff! wuff!
   Scat,
   Cat!
   That's
35   *That!*

---

1. *sleeky*: smooth; glossy
2. *spitfire*: easily angered
3. *slathery*: the ability to spread quickly
4. *slithery*: slippery; slick
5. *dithery*: nervousness
6. *hithery/thithery*: running this way and that way

Sea Shell

Recalling

1. What does the poet ask the shell to sing about?

2. Are all of these familiar to the sea shell?

Interpreting

3. Are all of the details of the poem actually found in the real world? Which are from the poet's imagination?

4. Which line of the poem is used as the refrain?

Concluding

5. What images or mental pictures were brought to mind by *Sea Shell*?

Examining Poetry

In *Sea Shell*, the poet repeats certain initial consonants. When a poet uses alliteration, it increases the musical quality of the poem; alliteration may also bring greater power or humor, depending on the nature of the work.

1. Find three examples of alliteration in the poem.

2. How does the alliteration enhance the power of the poem?

Creating and Writing

In this poem, Amy Lowell attributes knowledge and vision to an ordinary sea shell. Where are sea shells found? See what you can find out about sea shells. Perhaps you know someone who has a collection. Share your information with your classmates.

- *Cat!*

Recalling

1. Find two references from the poem that tell you where the cat was.

Interpreting

2. Why does the poet refer to the cat as a "sleeky flatterer"?

3. Why is "spitfire chatterer" a good description for a cat?

4. Based on the poet's choice of words, how would you describe this cat's personality?

Examining Poetry

Onomatopoeia is the use of words that sound like what they are. For example, the word "purr" sounds exactly like the contented sound a cat makes. Words that mimic real sounds make a poem more enjoyable to read and to listen to.

- Give examples of four or five onomatopoeic words used in this poem.

- Can you think of any not used in the poem?

Creating and Writing

In *Cat!*, the poet talks about an animal and its special characteristics.

1. Choose any animal and list six to eight of its personality traits.

2. Now use your list of traits to help you write a six to eight line poem. Try to express the unique nature of this animal. If the animal makes a distinct sound, see if you can use onomatopoeia and include that sound in your poem.

Into
- *When the Frost Is on the Punkin*
- *Smells*

Rhyme enhances the sound and the "beat" of a poem. Though not a necessity, rhyme is commonly used in poetry. When a poet uses a **rhyme**, they repeat identical sounds, or sounds that are alike, in words that appear near each other. Many times the rhyme appears at the end of a line. These rhymes are called **end rhyme**. Words do not have to be spelled alike in order to rhyme. For example, "neighbor" and "labor" rhyme, but the internal vowel sound ("eigh" and "a") in the first syllable is spelled differently.

Focus

When you read the following two poems, notice how and where they rhyme. Does the poet use end rhyme, or is the rhyme contained within the lines of the poem? Are the rhyming words spelled alike?

About the Authors

JAMES WHITCOMB RILEY was born in 1849 in Indiana. His native state holds him in such high esteem that Riley's birthday is a state holiday in Indiana. His residence in Indianapolis and the Greenfield house where he was born are both public memorials. Early in life, Riley worked as a sign painter and a traveling musician. A natural with languages and an avid reader of the classics, Riley was a well-known American poet. He died in 1916. In the poem, *When the Frost Is on the Punkin*, Riley writes in the rural dialect of his native Indiana.

CHRISTOPHER MORLEY was born in 1890 in Pennsylvania. Morley is known primarily for his novels. A Rhodes Scholar, he published more than fifty books in his lifetime. He was also a poet, editor, playwright, and author of essays. He began his career as an editor and writer for many well-known periodicals. He was one of the founders of the *Saturday Review of Literature*. Morley was a resident of New York and died in 1957.

When the Frost Is on the Punkin

James Whitcomb Riley

When the frost is on the punkin and the fodder's in the shock,[1]
And you hear the kyouck and gobble of the struttin' turkey cock,
And the clackin' of the guineys,[2] and the cluckin' of the hens,
And the rooster's hallylooyer as he tiptoes on the fence;
5 O, it's then's the time a feller is a-feelin' at his best,
With the risin' sun to greet him from a night of peaceful rest,
As he leaves the house, bareheaded, and goes out to feed the stock,[3]
When the frost is on the punkin and the fodder's in the shock.

They's something kindo' harty-like about the atmusfere
10 When the heat of summer's over and the coolin' fall is here—
Of course we miss the flowers, and the blossums on the trees,
And the mumble of the hummin' birds and buzzin' of the bees;
But the air's so appetizin'; and the landscape through the haze
Of a crisp and sunny morning of the airly autumn days
15 Is a pictur' that no painter has the colorin' to mock[4]—
When the frost is on the punkin and the fodder's in the shock.

The husky, rusty russel of the tossels[5] of the corn,
And the raspin' of the tangled leaves, as golden as the morn;
The stubble in the furries[6]—kindo' lonesome-like, but still
20 A-preachin' sermuns to us of the barns they growed to fill;
The strawstack in the medder,[7] and the reaper in the shed;
The hosses in theyr stalls below—the clover overhead!—
O, it sets my hart a-clickin' like the tickin' of a clock,
When the frost is on the punkin and the fodder's in the shock!

25 Then your apples all is gethered, and the ones a feller keeps
Is poured around the celler floor in red and yeller heaps;
And your cider makin's over, and your wimmern[8] folks is through
With theyr mince[9] and apple butter, and theyr souse[10] and sausage, too!
I don't know how to tell it—but ef sich a thing could be
30 As the Angels wantin' boardin', and they'd call around on me—
I'd want to 'commodate[11] 'em—all the whole indurin' flock—
When the frost is on the punkin and the fodder's in the shock!

---

1. *fodder* (FAHD ur)...*shock* (SHAHK): coarse food for farm animals tied in a bundle (shock)
2. *guineys* (GIN eez): bird similar to the pheasant
3. *stock*: farm animals
4. *mock* (MAHK): imitate
5. *tossels* (TAH silz): tassels: refers to silky-like flowers at the top of cornstalks
6. *furries*: furrows: grooves made by a plow
7. *medder* (MED ur): meadow
8. *wimmern* (WIM urn): women
9. *mince*: mixture of fruit and spices used as pie filling
10. *souse* (SOUSE): pickled foods
11. *'commodate*: accommodate: to provide for

Smells

Christopher Morley

Why is it that the poets tell
So little of the sense of smell?
These are the odors I love well:

The smell of coffee freshly ground;
5 Or rich plum pudding, holly-crowned;
Or onions fried and deeply browned.

The fragrance of a fumy¹ pipe;
The smell of apples, newly ripe;
And printer's ink on leaden type.

10 Woods by moonlight in September
Breathe most sweet; and I remember
Many a smoky campfire ember.

Camphor,² turpentine,³ and tea,
The balsam⁴ of a tree,
15 These are whiffs of gramarye⁵…
A ship smells best of all to me!

---

1. *fumy* (FYOO mee): smoky
2. *camphor* (KAM fur): a substance with a strong
odor that comes from the wood of the camphor tree
3. *turpentine* (TURP in TYN): liquid produced by
pine trees, used as paint thinner
4. *balsam* (BALL sum): an aromatic oil that
comes from a kind of evergreen tree
5. *gramarye* (GRAM uh REE): magic

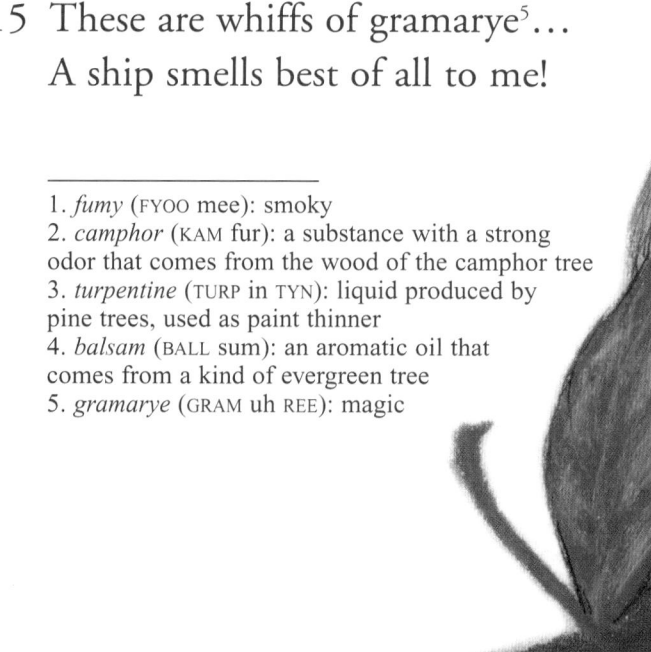

- *When the Frost Is on the Punkin*

Recalling

1. When is the time "a feller is a-feelin' at his best"?

2. How does the poet describe the air and the landscape of the "airly autumn days"?

3. What sets the poet's heart "a-clickin'" in the third stanza? Can you describe this in your own words?

Interpreting

4. What are the poet's feelings about fall?

5. Refer back to the second question. In your own words, translate the poet's description of the air and the landscape in autumn.

6. The poem is written in dialect. What effect do you think this has? Would the poem be the same if it were written in standard English?

Concluding

7. The setting of this poem is rural Indiana, yet it appeals to readers all over the country. Why do you think this poem has universal appeal?

Examining Poetry

Rhyme is a common element of poetry. The technique of repeating identical sounds that rhyme at the end of a line gives the poem a beat, or rhythm, as in music. This type of rhyme is called **end rhyme**. These words do not need to be spelled alike as long as they sound alike. The poet uses end rhymes throughout this poem.

1. Write down five examples of end rhymes in this poem.

2. Are the words spelled alike? Give a few examples of end rhymes that are not spelled alike.

Creating and Writing

Writing a poem that rhymes is a challenge, but the result makes the effort worthwhile. Many poets have used rhyme in creating some of their most famous works. Try writing a poem that rhymes, about any topic. Remember that in order to rhyme, words need only to sound alike, not necessarily to be spelled alike.

Recalling

1. What is the poet's question? What does he then go on to do?

2. List three of the smells the poet writes about.

3. What is the poet's favorite smell?

Interpreting

4. Which smells does Morley describe? What can you infer from his choice of descriptions? Do they suggest anything about the life he lives?

5. What are the magical smells for the poet?

Concluding

6. What is your favorite aroma? Why?

7. In the poem *Smells*, the images appeal to all the senses. List the image and the corresponding sense that each appeals to, besides the sense of smell.

Examining Poetry

Rhyme keeps the reader's interest in a poem. A poet may choose to use words that sound alike after the first consonant. These are called **perfect rhymes**. Other times, a poet may use words that sound similar but not exactly alike.

1. In *Smells*, does the author use perfect rhymes at the end of each line?

2. How many lines are included in each stanza?

3. Which stanza uses a different number of lines?

4. Why do you think the poet changes the pattern?

Creating and Writing

Through our five senses, we have amazing capabilities for appreciating the world around us. In the poem, the author writes about one of these senses. Notice the many adjectives he uses, to show the pleasures of smell and the images it brings to mind. In fact, smell is significantly linked to memory! Write a short poem about one of the five senses. The poem need not rhyme—although it may rhyme if you like! Use vivid descriptive words, to bring the sense you write about to life.

Blueprint FOR READING

Into
- *Laughing Song*
- *The Children's Hour*

A poet may use **literal** or **figurative** language. **Literal language** can be understood from its obvious meaning. In poetry, often the meaning is masked. The poet can use beautiful, dreamlike language to express ideas. This is called **figurative language**. A poet uses figurative language to create striking images in the reader's mind.

Focus

Notice the figurative language in *Laughing Song*, and the combination of both figurative and literal language in *The Children's Hour*. Which phrases enable us to actually see the scenes the poets have created?

About the Authors

WILLIAM BLAKE was born in 1757 in London, England. Blake studied art until the age of fourteen. When his family could no longer afford his art lessons, he became an apprentice engraver. Blake was extraordinarily gifted. He became a book illustrator, and developed a new method of printing. A writer and artist, Blake's works contain many of his own illustrations. He was brilliant and original; therefore, his works are not always easy to understand and interpret. Blake died in 1827.

HENRY WADSWORTH LONGFELLOW was born in 1807. He is one of America's most famous and beloved poets. Born in Maine to a prominent lawyer, Longfellow eventually became a professor of language at Harvard University. Many of his works are expressions of United States culture and events in the 19th century. Longfellow died in 1882. Another of his poems included in this anthology is *Paul Revere's Ride*.

Laughing Song

When the green woods laugh with the voice of joy,
And the dimpling stream runs laughing by;
When the air does laugh with our merry wit,
And the green hill laughs with the noise of it;

5   When the meadows laugh with lively green,
And the grasshopper laughs in the merry scene;
When Mary and Susan and Emily
With their sweet round mouths sing, "Ha ha he!"

When the painted birds laugh in the shade,
10   When our table with cherries and nuts is spread;
Come live, and be merry, and join with me,
To sing the sweet chorus of "Ha ha he!"

William Blake

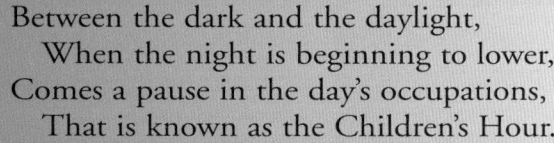

The CHILDREN'S HOUR

HENRY WADSWORTH LONGFELLOW

Between the dark and the daylight,
    When the night is beginning to lower,
Comes a pause in the day's occupations,
    That is known as the Children's Hour.

5   I hear in the chamber[1] above me
      The patter of little feet,
The sound of a door that is opened,
    And voices soft and sweet.

From my study I see in the lamplight,
10   Descending the broad hall stair,
Grave Alice, and laughing Allegra,[2]
    And Edith with golden hair.

A whisper, and then a silence:
　　Yet I know by their merry eyes
15　They are plotting and planning together
　　To take me by surprise.

A sudden rush from the stairway,
　　A sudden raid from the hall!
By three doors left unguarded
20　　They enter my castle wall!

They climb up into my turret[3]
　　O'er the arms and back of my chair;
If I try to escape, they surround me;
　　They seem to be everywhere.

25　They almost devour[4] me with kisses,
　　Their arms about me entwine,
Till I think of the Bishop of Bingen[5]
　　In his Mouse Tower on the Rhine!

Do you think, O blue-eyed banditti,[6]
30　　Because you have scaled[7] the wall,
Such an old mustache as I am
　　Is not a match for you all!

I have you fast in my fortress,
　　And will not let you depart,
35　But put you down into the dungeon
　　In the round tower of my heart.

And there I will keep you forever,
　　Yes, forever and a day,
Till the walls shall crumble to ruin,
40　　And molder[8] in dust away.

---

1. *chamber* (CHAYM bur): a room
2. *Allegra* (ah LAY gruh)
3. *turret* (TUR it): a small tower
4. *devour* (dih VOW ur): eat eagerly
5. *Bishop of Bingen*: In an old legend, the Bishop of Bingen is a man who was devoured by mice as punishment for refusing to share his food. The poet feels just like the Bishop.
6. *banditti* (bahn DEE tee): Italian for bandits
7. *scaled* (SKAY uld): climbed
8. *molder* (MOLE dur): decay

- *Laughing Song*

Recalling

1. Who (not what) is laughing in the poem?

2. What has William Blake invited you to come and do?

Interpreting

3. Why do you think the poet chose the word "dimpling" to describe the stream? Why is "dimpling" an appropriate word for the first stanza?

4. As you read the poem, did it cheer you? Why?

Concluding

5. List the people, creatures, places, and things that "laugh" in the poem. Do they actually laugh, or might Blake be using the word figuratively or symbolically?

Examining Poetry

Many of the phrases and words that Blake uses in *Laughing Song* are not meant to be taken literally. Using figurative language, Blake creates a lighthearted and picturesque scene. Blake uses ordinary, unsophisticated language for this poem.

1. List five examples of figurative language in *Laughing Song*.

2. Rewrite the five examples using literal language.

3. Would the poem be as effective with literal language? Explain your answer.

Creating and Writing

Blake has also used rhythm in this poem, to create a lighthearted scene. **Rhythm** is the beat a writer or composer uses. By stressing certain syllables and leaving others unstressed, a rhythm is created. It is the use of rhythm that makes poetry so musical.

If you were a composer, and you were asked to set this poetry to music, what type of music would you choose? Would the tempo be fast or slow? Which instrument would you use? Write a paragraph in which you answer these questions and explain how you arrived at your answers. While you select the mood of your musical style, instrument, and tempo, remember that you want to preserve the mood of *Laughing Song*.

Recalling

1. What is the setting of *The Children's Hour*?

2. What does the speaker in the poem hear from above?

3. What are the three girls planning?

4. List three things the girls do.

Interpreting

5. The stanzas at the beginning of the poem illustrate a cheerful scene. Which words does Longfellow use that make the scene a happy one?

6. What do you think "my castle wall" is?

7. Who are the "blue-eyed banditti," and why does the speaker describe them this way?

Concluding

8. By the end of the poem who has been captured? Where will the captives be held?

Examining Poetry

Longfellow uses both literal and figurative language in *The Children's Hour*. At times he expresses himself **literally**—in a matter-of-fact way. He also expresses himself **figuratively**—using poetic language that is more image-like.

1. Choose three phrases that are literal descriptions.

2. Give examples of three phrases that are written figuratively.

3. Why do you think the poet wrote both literally and figuratively when creating this poem?

Creating and Writing

The Children's Hour depicts a family that lived more than a century ago. Clearly some of the characteristics of family life that are in this poem are universal. Write a paragraph explaining how the father's feelings towards the three daughters are conveyed in the poem. Indicate how these values are shared by most families.

Into • *I Wandered Lonely as a Cloud*

A poet may use many devices to make a poem vivid and real, and to stir our feelings. The element of language called **figurative language** is used when the poet's words are not meant to be understood precisely. The different types of figurative language are known as **figures of speech**.

When a poet compares two seemingly unlike things and uses the words "like" or "as," they are creating a **simile**. Writers use similes in order to bring to mind vivid images, and because similes reveal our sense of "likeness" about seemingly unlike things.

Focus

As you read *I Wandered Lonely as a Cloud*, what do you see? Notice how the poet uses the figure of speech of simile to create a picture in the reader's mind.

About the Author

WILLIAM WORDSWORTH was born in 1770. He is among England's greatest poets. As a young man, Wordsworth participated in the French Revolution. Upon his return to England, he developed a friendship with another English poet, Samuel Taylor Coleridge. Together, they composed a famous book of poetry, *Lyric Ballads*. Wordsworth wrote more than 523 sonnets in his lifetime. In 1843, he was named the Poet Laureate of England. He died in 1850, but his works are as much admired today as they were in his lifetime.

I WANDERED LONELY AS A CLOUD

WILLIAM WORDSWORTH

I wandered lonely as a cloud
  That floats on high o'er vales[1] and hills,
When all at once I saw a crowd,
A host, of golden daffodils;
5   Beside the lake, beneath the trees,
Fluttering and dancing in the breeze.

Continuous as the stars that shine
And twinkle on the milky way,
They stretched in never-ending line
10 Along the margin of a bay;
Ten thousand saw I at a glance,
Tossing their heads in sprightly dance.

The waves beside them danced; but they
Outdid the sparkling waves in glee;
15 A poet could not but be gay,
In such a jocund[2] company;
I gazed—and gazed—but little thought
What wealth the show to me had brought:

For oft, when on my couch I lie
20 In vacant or in pensive[3] mood,
They flash upon that inward eye
Which is the bliss of solitude;
And then my heart with pleasure fills,
And dances with the daffodils.

---

1. *vales* (VAY ils): valleys
2. *jocund* (JAHK und): merry
3. *pensive* (PEN siv): thoughtful

• *I Wandered Lonely as a Cloud*

Recalling

1. What is the poet doing at the beginning of this poem?

2. What does the speaker suddenly see? With what does the speaker compare them?

3. What does the poet imagine, when he lies on the couch feeling pensive?

Interpreting

4. Describe the scene you see as the poem unfolds.

5. What does the speaker mean when he says, "What wealth the show to me had brought"?

6. What is the main idea of the last stanza?

7. What do you think is the "inward eye"?

Concluding

8. What is the overall mood or atmosphere of this poem? Which words or phrases does Wordsworth use that intensify this mood?

Examining Poetry

When two subjects are compared using the words "like" or "as," the poet is employing a figure of speech called a **simile**. Even though the things compared are different from each other, they may share certain characteristics.

1. Identify two similes in *I Wandered Lonely as a Cloud.*

2. In each of the two similes, which characteristics do the two elements being compared have in common?

3. How do the similes help convey the images and feeling of the poem?

Creating and Writing

The beauty of nature is a common theme in poetry. The poet may describe the natural world as peaceful and serene, or a poem may express the violent and destructive forces of nature. Choose an element of nature that you would like to write a poem about. Write a poem using at least two similes, in order to help the reader appreciate the feelings you are trying to communicate.

Into • *Fog*

The language of poetry (and often prose) employs different types of figurative language called **figures of speech**. At times, a poet will create a stronger image by comparing two seemingly different things. When the poet compares two unlike things, and does not use the words "like" or "as," the figure of speech is called a **metaphor**. Examples of a metaphor are the phrases "mountains laughing" or "dimpled stream." With a metaphor, the comparison is not stated as directly or clearly as with a **simile**.

Focus

In the poem *Fog*, Carl Sandburg describes this element of nature vividly. As you read *Fog*, notice the poet's very effective use of a metaphor throughout the poem, in order to create a true-to-life image of fog.

About the Author

CARL SANDBURG was born in Illinois in 1876. He is often referred to as America's National Poet. As a young man he worked at many odd jobs; he worked both as a milk delivery boy and a fireman. Sandburg eventually became a respected journalist. He was awarded the Pulitzer Prize for Writing both in History (1939) and Literature (1951). Sandburg died in 1967 in North Carolina.

Fog

Carl Sandburg

The fog comes
on little cat feet.

It sits looking
over harbor and city
5   on silent haunches[1]
and then moves on

1. *haunches* (HAWN chiz): thickest
part of the thigh

- *Fog*

Recalling

1. Using references from the poem, describe in your own words what fog does.

Interpreting

2. What was your reaction to reading the poem?

3. How does the length of the poem's lines compare to "little cat feet"?

Concluding

4. There have been many poems written about fog. Why do you think fog is a good topic for a poem?

Examining Poetry

Similes and metaphors compare one thing to another that is seemingly different. In a **simile**, the poet uses the words "like" or "as," in order to make a direct comparison. With a **metaphor**, the comparison is more subtle. The writer does not use the words "like" or "as."

When metaphors and similes are used, the ideas or things being compared must be different in their nature. For example, you would not compare two different fruits; you could compare a fruit with an animal.

1. With what is the fog compared?

2. Which characteristics of fog are represented through the writer's comparison?

Creating and Writing

Use your imagination to create a metaphor for fog with yet another animal. Using this metaphor, write a poem. Which characteristics are shared by the animal and the fog? Make sure that the metaphor is carried through the length of the poem.

Into • from *The Cloud*

Another figure of speech that poets frequently use is personification. **Personification** means giving human characteristics to something not human: an animal, an object, or a concept. By personifying the object, the writer helps the reader view that object in an imaginative and vivid way.

Focus

The piece that follows is an excerpt from the poem, *The Cloud*, by Percy Bysshe Shelley. Shelley gives a cloud human characteristics. As you read, notice the phrases Shelley uses to enhance his description of the natural world.

About the Author

PERCY BYSSHE SHELLEY was born in Sussex, England in 1792. He is one of England's most famous poets. Shelley was the son of a country squire. He was educated both at Eton and Oxford Universities. Shelley spent the last years of his life in Italy. He died in 1822 in a sailing accident off the shore of Italy.

From THE CLOUD

PERCY BYSSHE SHELLEY

I bring fresh showers for the thirsting flowers,
  From the seas and the streams;
I bear light shade for the leaves when laid
  In their noonday dreams.
5 From my wings are shaken the dews that waken
  The sweet buds every one,
When rocked to rest on their Mother's breast,
  As she dances about the sun.
I wield the flail[1] of the lashing hail,
10 And whiten the green plains under,
And then again dissolve it in rain,
  And laugh as I pass in thunder.

---

1. *flail* (FLAY ul): a tool used to thresh grain by hand

• *The Cloud*

Recalling

1. What does the cloud give to the world at large?

2. When does the cloud laugh?

Interpreting

3. Explain lines 3 and 4.

4. Why does the cloud laugh in the last line of the poem?

Concluding

5. Why is Shelley's use of personification so effective? In what ways does personification make this poem more enjoyable?

Examining Poetry

In the poems we just read—*I Wandered Lonely as a Cloud*, *Fog*, and *The Cloud*—we have identified several figures of speech commonly used. They are the **simile**, the **metaphor**, and **personification**.

1. Define each of these figures of speech.

2. Give an example, from the poems you have just read, that illustrates each of these three figures of speech.

Creating and Writing

Shelley wrote *The Cloud* after watching a passing cloud in the sky. He was filled with wonder at the beauty of the world and nature. Choose one of the subjects below, and write a six-line poem describing its unique characteristics. Try to include a simile, a metaphor, or personification to show the reader what you feel or see or think about your subject. It may be helpful to say to yourself, "What does a rainstorm [or a butterfly, or an orange, etc.] remind me of? How does it make me feel?"

Select one of the following:

a rainstorm   a tree

a butterfly   a sunset

a flower bouquet   an orange

Into • *Seagulls*

Poets draw vivid pictures with words. These pictures are called **images**. The language of good poetry appeals to all of our senses, and the poet's images create a drama in which the subject of the poem plays the central role.

Focus

As you read Robert Francis' *Seagulls*, let yourself *see* the image the poet has drawn. Notice how effectively specific words create clear pictures for the reader or listener.

About the Author

American poet **ROBERT FRANCIS** was born in 1901 in Pennsylvania. Francis is not well known, but many of those who are aware of his work hold him in high regard. Robert Francis was also an educator. He directed many writers' conferences and workshops. In 1974, the Juniper Award of the University of Massachusetts was established in his honor. He also received the Academy of American Fellowship Award in 1984. Francis died in 1987 in Massachusetts.

Robert Francis
Seagulls

Between the under and the upper blue
All day the seagulls climb and swerve and soar,
Arc intersecting arc, curve over curve.

And you may watch them weaving a long time
5   And never see their pattern twice the same
And never see their pattern once imperfect.

Take any moment they are in the air—
If you could change them, if you had the power
How would you place them other than they are?

10 What we have labored all our lives to have
And failed, these birds effortlessly achieve:
Freedom that flows in form and still is free.

- *Seagulls*

Recalling

1. What do the seagulls do all day?

2. What is never seen twice?

Interpreting

3. "What [have we] labored all our lives to have"?

4. Rewrite the last line of the poem in your own words.

Concluding

5. According to the poet, what advantage(s) do some creatures of nature have over human beings?

Examining Poetry

A word or phrase that brings a picture to the mind's eye creates an **image**. A poet uses particular adjectives, verbs, and nouns to create images. A poem may be short or long, but the poet must create images quickly and clearly, to communicate effectively and capture the reader's attention. In *Seagulls*, the poet has created an image.

a. What is the image?

b. List three phrases that help you see the seagulls.

Creating and Writing

Using pastels, paints, or pen and ink, draw, paint, or sketch the image you see in your mind when you read *Seagulls*.

Into • *Miracles*

A poet uses poetic images to bring to mind the memory of the way things look, sound, feel, smell, and taste to us. The poet brings to life the world of our senses through **sensory language**—also called **imagery.**

Focus

Walt Whitman is well known for his use of imagery. In the poem *Miracles*, notice how Whitman engages the senses, in appreciation of the beauty of the world around us.

About the Author

WALT WHITMAN was born in New York in 1819; he has been called the father of modern poetry. Whitman began his career as a printer, then he became a journalist, and ultimately, one of America's most renowned poets. Whitman published his first work, *Leaves of Grass*, in 1855, a long poem celebrating his love for his country. He participated in the Civil War, not in combat, but nursing wounded soldiers. Whitman died in 1892 in New Jersey.

Miracles

WALT WHITMAN

Why, who makes much of a miracle?
As to me I know of nothing else but miracles,
Whether I walk the streets of Manhattan,
Or dart my sight over the roofs of houses toward the sky,
5   Or wade with naked feet along the beach just in the edge of the water,
Or stand under trees in the woods,
Or talk by day with any one I love…
Or sit at table at dinner with the rest,
Or look at strangers opposite me riding in the car.
10 Or watch honey-bees busy around the hive of a summer forenoon,
Or animals feeding in the fields,
Or birds, or the wonderfulness of the sundown, or of stars
   shining so quiet and bright,
Or the exquisite delicate thin curve of the new moon in spring;
These with the rest, one and all, are to me miracles,
15 The whole referring, yet each distinct and in its place.

To me every hour of the light and dark is a miracle,
Every cubic inch of space is a miracle,
Every square yard of the surface of the earth is spread with the same,
Every foot of the interior swarms with the same.

20 To me the sea is a continual miracle,
The fishes that swim—the rocks—the motion of the waves—the
   ships with men in them,
What stranger miracles are there?

• *Miracles*

Recalling

1. List several everyday occurrences that the poet feels are miracles.

2. According to the poet, what is a "continual miracle"?

3. What question does the speaker ask at the end of the poem?

Interpreting

4. What does the poet mean, when he says, "...every hour of the light and dark is a miracle"?

5. How is the theme of this poem implied? Use examples to support your observation.

Concluding

6. Does Whitman fail to mention any "miracles" you would have included? Give your own examples.

Examining Poetry

In a poem, the writer can create images that appeal to the senses. This is called **imagery**. Imagery that appeals to the senses is also called **sensory language**. In *Miracles*, Whitman uses imagery to engage our senses in appreciation of the world around us.

1. Make a chart of the five senses.

2. Check off which of the senses Whitman engaged through the use of imagery.

3. Write an example showing which words from the poem engage that sense. For example: touch: ✓ "wade with naked feet along the beach"

Creating and Writing

Many times we take the simple things in life for granted. More often, we should stop and appreciate the beauty of the world around us. Decide what it is that you see and experience on an ordinary day that is really extraordinary. Write a brief paragraph in which you discuss why these experiences should not be taken for granted.

Blueprint FOR READING

Into • *The Listeners*

At times, a poet uses very precise verbs to create a clear image. For example, the poet Walter de la Mare says the Traveler "smote upon the door," instead of "knocked upon the door." "Smote," which means "struck hard" tells us more than if de la Mare had written "knocked." This choice of verb creates an exact and vivid image.

Focus

As you read *The Listeners*, notice the words the poet uses for actions. How do these words create a more vivid image of the action?

About the Author

English poet **WALTER DE LA MARE** was born in 1873. *The Listeners* is typical of de la Mare's special style, which is known to border on fantasy. His poems are extremely puzzling and have a visionary quality. *The Listeners*, for example, seems part dream. Walter de la Mare spent most of his life in England, near the city of London, where he died in 1956.

The Listeners

Walter de la Mare

"Is there anybody there?" said the Traveler,
   Knocking on the moonlit door;
And his horse in the silence champed the grasses
   Of the forest's ferny[1] floor:
5   And a bird flew up out of the turret,[2]
   Above the Traveler's head:
And he smote[3] upon the door again a second time;
   "Is there anybody there?" he said.
But no one descended to the Traveler;
10   No head from the leaf-fringed sill
Leaned over and looked into his gray eyes,
   Where he stood perplexed and still.
But only a host of phantom[4] listeners
   That dwelt in the lone house then
15   Stood listening in the quiet of the moonlight
   To that voice from the world of men:
Stood thronging the faint moonbeams on the dark stair
   That goes down to the empty hall,
Hearkening[5] in an air stirred and shaken
20 By the lonely Traveler's call.
And he felt in his heart their strangeness,
   Their stillness answering his cry,
While his horse moved, cropping the dark turf,[6]
   'Neath the starred and leafy sky;
25   For he suddenly smote on the door, even
   Louder, and lifted his head—
"Tell them I came, and no one answered,
   That I kept my word," he said.
Never the least stir made the listeners,
30 Though every word he spake[7]
Fell echoing through the shadowiness of the still house
   From the one man left awake:
Aye, they heard his foot upon the stirrup,
   And the sound of iron on stone,
35   And how the silence surged softly backward,
   When the plunging hoofs were gone.

1. *ferny* (FUR nee): full of shrubby plants
2. *turret* (TUR it): a small tower projecting from a building
3. *smote* (SMOAT): hit with force
4. *phantom* (FAN tum): ghostly
5. *Hearkening*: listening
6. *cropping...turf*: eating the grass
7. *spake* (SPAYK): spoke

• *The Listeners*

Recalling

1. The Traveler asked an important question two times. What was the question?

2. Was anyone listening "to that voice from the world of men"? If so, who?

3. Who or what was the Traveler expecting to find inside?

Interpreting

4. The poet does not tell us where or when the action of the poem occurs. What do you conclude about the setting of the poem?

5. Because the poet leaves out many basic details of the story, the reader must draw their own conclusions. How did you feel after reading the poem?

Concluding

6. Briefly tell the story of the poem. Why did the Traveler return? Where and when does the story take place? Who are the listeners and what happened to them? Make educated guesses, based on what is included in the original poem. Use your imagination to fill in details that the poem either omits or only suggests.

Examining Poetry

Poets use vivid and specific words to create an image in the reader's mind. The image the poet creates in *The Listeners* makes the poem eerie and mysterious.

1. Indicate three phrases that contribute to the imagery of the poem.

2. In the following sentences, fill in the blanks with descriptive words that create an eerie and mysterious atmosphere.
   a. The ___ house stood alone in the ___ forest.
   b. The ___ woman ___ along the ___ hallway.
   c. The storm ___ across the ___ plain.

Creating and Writing

If you find a poem difficult to understand, it helps to read the poem aloud several times and then to restate the poem in your own words. Your rephrasing of the poem will make its language less beautiful, but will help you interpret it. When we rewrite something in our own words it is called **paraphrasing**. Choose one of the poems that you have read. Paraphrase it in your own words. Why is the language of the original poem more descriptive and substantial than the prose used in the paraphrasing?

Blueprint FOR READING

Into
- *This Land Is Your Land*
- *The Pasture*

When a poet places a poem on paper, a visual pattern is created. This overall pattern is the **form** of a poem. A poet produces the form with several techniques: varying the length of line, or keeping them uniform; grouping the lines to create a pattern; or even shaping the lines of the poem into a likeness. A poet may divide the poem in stanzas, to create order and balance, both in form and meaning. A **stanza** is a group of lines forming the division of a poem. There is a space above and a space below each stanza which separates the stanzas from each other. When the poem has a **refrain**, a line or group of lines is repeated after each stanza.

Focus

As you read the following poems, notice how the stanzas of a poem are almost like mini chapters of a book or paragraph of prose.

About the Authors

American songwriter **WOODY GUTHRIE** was born in 1927. He was a well-known folksinger, whose music delighted the American public for years. Most of Guthrie's music was about the people and the land of the United States. Guthrie spent much of his life traveling across America. From his travels, he gathered material for the compositions he wrote and performed. One of Guthrie's most famous pieces is the song *This Land Is Your Land*. His experiences and positive feelings come across loud and clear in this popular folk song. He died in 1967.

ROBERT FROST, whose poems reflect the wholesome, country culture of picturesque New England, was actually born in San Francisco in 1875. With the death of his father, Frost returned to his family's original home of New England. He worked there as a farmer and part-time teacher, but his goal was to become a poet. Robert Frost won four Pulitzer Prizes for his work. He was nominated for the Nobel Prize and received a Congressional Medal of Honor for his poetry. Robert Frost was honored by John F. Kennedy who requested that he read his poetry at Kennedy's presidential inauguration. Frost died two years later in 1963.

This Land Is Your Land

Woody Guthrie

Refrain
This land is your land, this land is my land
From California to the New York island;
From the redwood forest to the Gulf Stream waters;
This land was made for you and me.

5   As I was walking that ribbon of highway,
I saw above me that endless skyway.
I saw below me that golden valley,
This land was made for you and me.

I've roamed and rambled and I followed my footsteps
10   To the sparkling sands of her diamond deserts,
And all around me a voice was sounding,
"This land was made for you and me."

When the sun comes shining and I was strolling
And the wheat fields waving and the dust clouds rolling,
15   As the fog was lifting a voice was chanting,
"This land was made for you and me."

The Pasture

Robert Frost

I'm going out to clean the pasture spring;
I'll only stop to rake the leaves away
(And wait to watch the water clear, I may):
I sha'n't be gone long.—You come too.

I'm going out to fetch the little calf
That's standing by the mother. It's so young
It totters when she licks it with her tongue.
I sha'n't be gone long.—You come too.

• *This Land Is Your Land*

Recalling

1. What is the subject of this poem? What belongs to you and me?

2. Guthrie says "roamed," "rambled," and "followed my footsteps." What does this suggest about the way he traveled across the United States?

Interpreting

3. Why does Guthrie use "ribbon" to describe a highway?

4. What is the effect of such phrases as "wheat fields waving," "sparkling sands," and "diamond deserts"?

Concluding

5. Guthrie wrote *This Land Is Your Land* as a song, rather than as a poem to be read aloud or silently. Do you think it is more effective performed as a piece of music?

Examining Poetry

This Land Is Your Land is an example of a work written in **stanza** form. When a poet writes a poem in stanzas, the work is grouped into lines forming the division of a poem. There is a space before and after each stanza. Each stanza has its own topic similar to a paragraph in prose.

The first stanza of this song is called a **refrain** because it is repeated after every stanza that follows. The purpose of a refrain is to emphasize the main feeling or idea of the song or poem.

1. How many lines comprise each stanza in *This Land Is Your Land*?

2. What is the theme of each stanza?

3. What does the refrain express? How does the refrain make the song more effective?

Creating and Writing

This Land Is Your Land expresses the love Guthrie had towards his country. Similar thoughts could be written in prose.

1. Write a prose essay expressing your positive feelings about the United States.

2. Reread the essay. Using your essay as a starting point, write a poem that expresses the same feelings.

• *The Pasture*

Recalling

1. For which chores is the speaker going out to the pasture?

2. What is the speaker going to do on the way?

3. Where is there repetition in the poem?

Interpreting

4. How would you describe the speaker of the poem? Include physical features, age, gender, and occupation.

5. Why did the poet put Line 3 in parentheses?

6. How does the poet's language make the chores seem less like work and more like fun?

Concluding

7. What do you learn about a positive attitude toward work from *The Pasture*? Which chores do you do that give you a sense of purpose and fulfillment?

Examining Poetry

A poet may choose to use an arrangement of lines to give a poem visual **form** and to help organize the poem's topics. When a poet organizes the lines in stanzas, it creates order and balance. The form of the poem can also be shaped by the length of the lines. The lines may be uniformly long, uniformly short, or of alternating size.

1. Are the lines in *The Pasture* uniform?

2. How does this contribute to the sense and balance of the poem?

Creating and Writing

Some poems are written in a less structured manner. Sometimes poets choose to express themselves more freely; they do not want to restrict themselves to a form that is confining. Which type of poetry do you prefer to read? To write yourself? Write a paragraph expressing your preference. Explain which form of poetry is easier to understand. Which form is easier to write? Refer to some of the poems we have read to support your reasoning.

Into • *The Vagabond*

In a poem, a thought may be complete at the end of a line (an **end-stopped line**), or where there is punctuation within a line (a **run-on line**). *The Vagabond* uses end-stopped lines. The next poem, *The River Is a Piece of Sky*, uses run-on lines.

When the poet uses end-stopped lines, there are two kinds of pauses at the end of the line: a complete stop or a brief one. If the poet desires the reader to stop completely, the end of the line is punctuated with a colon, period, question mark, or exclamation point. If the poet wishes the reader to pause for a brief time, the end of the line is punctuated with a comma, semi-colon, or long dash.

Focus

As you read *The Vagabond*, notice that the poet wishes you to pause at the end of each line. Pay close attention to the punctuation Stevenson uses. After the end of which lines does he want the reader to stop completely? When should the reader stop for only a brief moment?

About the Author

ROBERT LOUIS STEVENSON was born in Scotland in 1850. Stevenson was a famous novelist and poet who also wrote essays and travel books. His love of adventure, which led him to many different areas of the world, combined with his writing talent, enabled him to produce such wonderful books as *Treasure Island* and *Kidnapped*. One of Stevenson's most beloved works is *A Child's Garden of Verse*, a collection of poetry written for children. Stevenson spent the last years of his life in the Pacific island of Samoa, where he died in 1894.

The Vagabond[1]

Give to me the life I love,
Let the lave[2] go by me,
Give the jolly heaven above,
And the byway nigh me,
5   Bed in the bush with stars to see,
Bread to dip in the river,
There's the life for a man like me,
There's the life forever.

Robert Louis Stevenson

Let the blow fall soon or late,
10 Let what will be o'er me,
Give the face of earth around,
And the road before me.
Wealth I seek not, hope nor
love,
Not a friend to know me;
15 All I seek, the heaven above
And the road below me.

Or let Autumn fall on me,
Where afield I linger,
Silencing the bird on tree,
20 Biting the blue finger,
White as meal the frosty field,
Warm the fireside haven,
Not to Autumn will I yield,
Not to Winter even.

25 Let the blow fall soon or late,
Let what will be o'er me;
Give the face of earth around,
And the road before me.
Wealth I ask not, hope nor love,
30 Not a friend to know me,
All I ask, the heaven above
And the road below me.

_____

1. *vagabond* (VAAG uh BOND): a wanderer
2. *lave* (LAYF): the remainder

• *The Vagabond*

Recalling

1. What kind of life does the speaker of the poem live?

2. What wishes does the speaker have? What does he not want?

3. Which two seasons are mentioned in the poem?

Interpreting

4. Why do you think all the poet seeks is "the road below me" without "a friend to know me"?

5. What do you think the poet means when he says, "Not to Autumn will I yield, Not to Winter even"?

6. If you were to live the life of a vagabond, would you want to do so for a short period of time or for a lifetime? Why do you feel this way?

Concluding

7. In *The Vagabond*, as many people might see it, the speaker leads an unusual life. He has many interesting likes and dislikes. Describe the likes and dislikes that make you unique.

Examining Poetry

When a poet wishes the reader to pause naturally at the end of a line, the line is called an **end-stopped line**. A full stop is punctuated with a colon, question mark, exclamation mark, or period. A brief pause uses a comma, semi-colon, or long dash. The punctuation makes the meaning of the poem clearer.

1. Choose a stanza from *The Vagabond* and copy it on a piece of paper.

2. Highlight the punctuation at the end of each line.

3. How does the punctuation aid the reader in understanding the poem?

Creating and Writing

In this poem, the speaker expresses his desire to roam and enjoy nature. Some people enjoy the freedom of this lifestyle, whereas others would be frightened by what they saw as the lack of stability. Imagine Stevenson wrote you a letter expressing his desire to wander like a vagabond. In your reply, write which you would prefer, a stable life or a vagabond's life. Give your reasons for your feelings.

Into • *The River Is a Piece of Sky*

A poet may choose not to use **end-stopped lines**. The poet may want the reader to keep on reading, past the end of each line, until the reader reaches a punctuation mark. When there is no punctuation at the end of the line, we are looking at a **run-on line**. A poet uses run-on lines to indicate that the thought is not complete until the reader comes to the punctuation in one of the next lines.

Focus

As you read the following poem, notice that the thoughts expressed are not contained within one line, but rather continue into the next line or the next several lines. Pay close attention to the number of sentences in the poem. How many complete statements are made?

About the Author

JOHN CIARDI was born in Boston in 1916. The son of Italian immigrants, Ciardi became a well-known poet. Admired for his clever use of imagery, John Ciardi is the author of many poems, including a collection written especially for children. He received many honors and awards for his work, and served as a judge in the Children's Literature section of the National Book Awards. Ciardi died in Edison, New Jersey in 1986.

The River Is a Piece of Sky

John Ciardi

From the top of a bridge
The river below
Is a piece of sky—

 —Until you throw
5 —A penny in
 —Or a cockleshell[1]
 —Or a pebble or two
 —Or a bicycle bell
 —Or a cobblestone
10 —Or a fat man's cane—

And then you can see
It's a river again.

The difference you'll see
When you drop your penny:
15 The river has splashes,
The sky hasn't any.

---

1. *cockleshell* (KAHK ul SHELL): the shell of a cockle; it is shaped like a heart and has two parts

The River Is a Piece of Sky

Recalling

1. Where is the speaker standing while describing the river?

2. When you drop a penny into the river, what is the difference between the river and the sky?

Interpreting

3. What are some similarities between a river and the sky?

4. Why did the poet choose such different objects to throw in the river?

Concluding

5. Describe some other elements of nature that share similar characteristics.

Examining Poetry

In many of these poems a punctuation mark generally appears at the end of the lines. In a poem with run-on lines, this is not the case. A poet uses run-on lines when several ideas are expressed, or when the style of the poem is less formal.

In Lines 4-10, Ciardi lists a variety of items. Reread the poem and develop your own list of objects to throw into a river. Why did you choose these items?

Creating and Writing

Try writing a poem in which you compare two different things to each other. For instance, you might compare a budding flower to a sweet baby, a book to a garden, or a storm to your feelings. In order to compare two things, they must be different, yet still have something in common as you see it. In your poem, try using similes, metaphors, onomatopoeia, and alliteration.

Into • *in Just—*

Some modern poets write in free verse. **Free verse** has no rhythmic pattern and the words do not rhyme. Free verse is usually not set in any specific form such as stanzas. When reading free verse, the poem is recited just as we speak, although certainly emphasis and a dramatic tone are used when appropriate.

Focus

E. E. Cummings is a modern poet, well known for his use of free verse. There is a visual pattern in the way the words have been put on the page. Also notice that only two words are capitalized; words normally capitalized are all lower case. How do you think the visual and printed style add to the meaning and the mood of the poem?

About the Author

E. E. CUMMINGS was born in 1894 in Massachusetts, where he grew up, studied, and graduated from Harvard College. While serving his country in World War I, he was mistakenly jailed for six months in a French prison. This experience became the basis for his first book, *The Enormous Room*. Cummings was known both as an artist and a poet. He is known for his unusual usage of punctuation and the absence of capitalization in his poems. Cummings, who died in 1962, was regarded by critics as an "authentic voice of the twentieth century."

in Just—

E. E. Cummings

in Just—
spring   when the world is mud-
luscious the little
lame balloonman

5 whistles   far   and wee

and eddieandbill come
running from marbles and
piracies[1] and it's
spring

10 when the world is puddle-wonderful

the queer
old balloonman whistles
far   and   wee
and bettyandisbel come dancing

15 from hopscotch and jump rope and
it's
spring
and
    the

20   goat-footed
balloonMan   whistles
far
and
wee

---

1. *piracies* (PY ruh SEEZ): the act of robbing ships

• *in Just—*

Recalling

1. What is happening in the poem?

2. Who is whistling?

Interpreting

3. Is this poem told from a child's point of view or an adult's? Which words in the poem make you come to this conclusion?

4. Why does the poet run the boys' and girls' names together with no capitalization or the usual spaces?

5. What sort of feelings does the poem *in Just—* express, in connection with the coming of spring?

6. Why does the poet place the words and the lines as he does? Does this affect your interpretation of the poem?

Concluding

7. Why do people call the feeling we get in the springtime spring fever?

Examining Poetry

The poem *in Just—* is written in free verse. When you read the poem aloud, it is almost like just talking. However, the poem does present itself with a rush of words that are more like the words in our mind, the words of our feelings, than the way we speak. Free verse has been used by modern poets since the early-20th century. What are the advantages of this poetic style?

Creating and Writing

Notice how Cummings creates his own vocabulary with marvelous words such as "mud-luscious" and "puddle-wonderful."

1. Think of two or three ideas for a free verse poem.

2. List five self-created sensory words, in the style of E. E. Cummings.

3. Using your ideas and your words, write a free verse poem.

Blueprint FOR READING

Into
- *Bamboo Grove*
- *The New and the Old*
- *A Balmy Spring Wind*

Haiku is a 600-year-old form of Japanese poetry. A standard **haiku** contains only three lines with five syllables in the first line, seven syllables in the second line, and five syllables in the third line. Therefore, the poet must choose words carefully. The purpose of many haiku is to create a visual image, often drawing on the elements of nature.

Focus

As you read the following haiku, look carefully at their form and shape. In your mind, try to see the picture the poet is painting.

About the Authors

BASHO was born in 1644. He was a well-known Japanese poet, teacher of poetry, and author of many poetic works. Basho was exceptionally gifted with the special form of Japanese poetry called haiku. Basho's devotion to creating poetry was demonstrated at the end of his life when he gathered his students together and spent his final moments reciting his last poem to them.

Japanese poet **SHIKI** was born in 1867. Shiki lived during the age of Imperialism, a time when Japan was being more intensely exposed to European culture. His concern over this resulted in his lifelong work to preserve Japanese tradition. He lived nearly two centuries after the death of Basho, and was also renowned for writing haiku. His poems are a reflection of his love for his country and its traditions. Shiki died in 1902.

African-American poet and novelist **RICHARD WRIGHT** suffered an impoverished childhood. In spite of the difficulties he faced, he graduated as valedictorian of his high school class in 1925. Wright's most famous novel, *Native Son*, was the first national bestseller written by an African-American author. In 1947, Wright moved to France. He died there in 1960. In the poem, *A Balmy Spring Wind*, Wright uses the Japanese style of poetry, haiku.

Bamboo Grove

Basho

Song of the cuckoo:
 in the grove of great bamboos,
  moonlight seeping through.

The New and the Old

Shiki

Railroad tracks; a flight
 of wild geese close above them
  in the moonlit night.

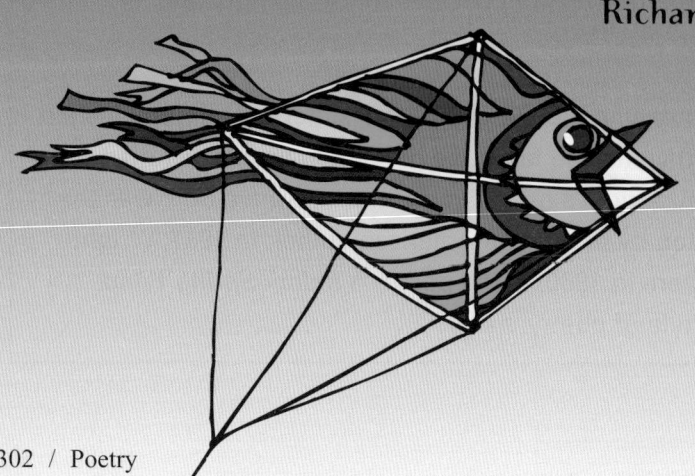

A Balmy Spring Wind

Richard Wright

A balmy spring wind
Reminding me of something
I cannot recall

• *Haiku*

Recalling

1. What is the setting of Basho's poem?

2. What are the subjects of Shiki's poem?

3. What does Wright's "balmy spring wind" recall?

Interpreting

4. What image do you see, when you read *Bamboo Grove*? Was Basho's choice of words effective?

5. Why do you think Shiki chose to set his poem on a moonlit night?

Concluding

6. If you were to write haiku, what would your subject be?

Examining Poetry

The Japanese verse haiku is a compact word-picture. The three poems you have read are classic examples of this poetic form.

1. Why is the poem by Basho an example of haiku?

2. Can you find any differences between the haiku by the American writer Richard Wright and the haiku of the traditional Japanese poets?

Creating and Writing

Writing haiku can be a creative and pleasurable challenge.

1. Make a list of subjects, drawing from nature and your surroundings.

2. Choose from your list of ideas and write a haiku.

3. Remember: line one = 5 syllables

               line two = 7 syllables

               line three = 5 syllables

Here is a model to get you started:

A chirping blue jay

Sat on the telephone wire

That I dared not touch

Into • *Pendulum*

When a poet shapes a poem to look like its subject, it is called a **concrete poem**. In concrete poetry, the poet shapes the poem by placing words, letters, lines, and even punctuation marks in such a way that there is an actual physical image or likeness.

Focus

The poem, *Pendulum*, by John Updike, is an example of a concrete poem. Notice how Updike places his lines to imitate a swinging pendulum. How does writing the poem in a concrete form add to its interest and effectiveness?

About the Author

JOHN UPDIKE was born in Shillington, Pennsylvania in 1932. He received his formal education at Harvard College and Oxford University. In the mid-1950s he began working for the *New Yorker*, a well-known, respected magazine. After Updike left the magazine, he devoted himself to becoming a full-time writer, becoming one of the most widely published authors of his time. Updike has published over thirty books since he began writing full time, including essays, poetry, and fiction, which is considered the area of his greatest talent. Updike has received a National Book Award, a Pulitzer Prize, and an American Book Award.

Pendulum
John Updike

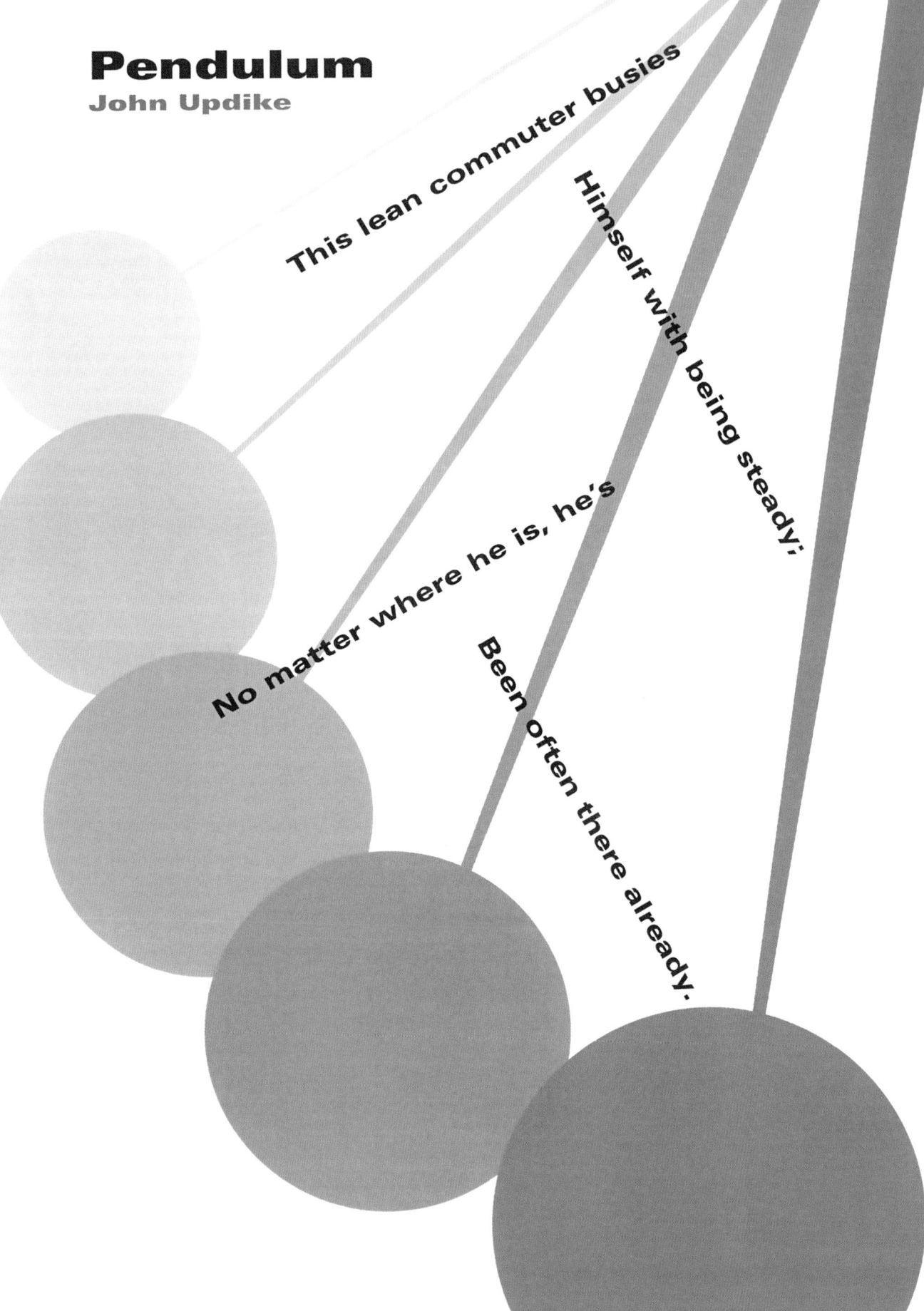

This lean commuter busies

Himself with being steady;

No matter where he is, he's

Been often there already.

• *Pendulum*

Recalling

1. What is a commuter?

2. How is the commuter described in the poem?

3. What keeps the commuter busy?

Interpreting

4. Why does the commuter busy "Himself with being steady"?

5. Which words rhyme? How does rhyming end words in alternate lines add to the overall effect?

6. How does the placement of the words enhance the effect of the poem?

Concluding

7. What is a pendulum? Is this a good title for the poem? Explain your answer. Can you think of another possible title? If so, what is it?

Examining Poetry

In *Pendulum*, the poet places the lines of his poem in such a way as to create a specific image. This is an example of a concrete poem. The arrangement of letters, words, lines, and punctuation create an image of the poet's subject.

1. How does the line form Updike uses here suit the subject of his poem?

2. Does writing the poem in concrete form add to the impact of the poem?

3. Do you think you could more easily understand and enjoy poetry, if more of it were written as concrete poetry?

Creating and Writing

Write a concrete poem. Make sure that your choice of form, and the way you choose to place your words on the page, clearly bring to mind the poem's subject. Your choices are limitless. You can choose an unusual object, a common household item like a chair, or an activity you enjoy.

Into • *The Bearded Man*
A Mouse in Her Room
There Was an Old Man of Peru

A **limerick** is an amusing five-line poem that follows an exact form and rhyme pattern. Lines one and two each have eight syllables. Lines three and four each have five syllables. Line five has eight syllables, like the first two lines.

Focus

The following limericks are humorous and entertaining. Notice how the choice of words, the length of the lines, the rhythm, and the rhyme, work together to heighten the effect. Also, remember that limericks should be read aloud, rather than silently, to fully bring their whimsy and fun alive.

About the Author

English poet **EDWARD LEAR** was born in 1812. He is famous for popularizing the limerick. A talented artist, Lear illustrated his own books of poetry. He gave art lessons to many students, including Queen Victoria! Lear's most famous work, *The Book of Nonsense*, was published in 1845 under the pen name of Derry Down Derry. Lear's talents brought joy and laughter to the children of his generation. His work is just as entertaining for children and adults today. Lear died in 1888 in Italy.

The Bearded Man
Edward Lear

There was an old man with a beard,
Who said, "It is just as I feared!
 Two owls and a hen,
 Four larks and a wren
Have all built their nests in my beard."

A Mouse in Her Room
Anonymous

A mouse in her room woke Miss Dowd;
She was frightened and screamed very loud,
 Then a happy thought hit her—
 To scare off the critter,
She sat up in bed and meowed.

There Was an Old Man of Peru
Anonymous

There was an old man of Peru
Who dreamed he was eating a shoe.
 He awoke in the night
 With a terrible fright
And found it was perfectly true!

• *Limericks*

Recalling

1. In *The Bearded Man*, what became of the old man's beard?

2. What woke Miss Dowd in *A Mouse in Her Room*? What was her reaction? How did she get rid of the intruder?

3. What did the old man dream about in *There Was an Old Man of Peru*? What was so surprising about his dream?

Interpreting

4. Why are all three of these limericks funny? Which one is your favorite? Why?

Concluding

5. If you were to write a limerick, what would you write about? List at least three possible topics.

Creating and Writing

Write your own limerick.

Write the line, "There was a young boy/girl named ____."
Fill in the blank with a two-syllable name that is easy to rhyme.

- Lines 2 and 5 will end with a word that rhymes with the name you have chosen.

- Lines 2 and 5 should also have eight syllables.

- Lines 3 and 4 should be only five syllables, and should end rhyme with each other.

- The success of your limerick depends on the humor of your subject matter and the wit of the words you choose.

Into • *The Road Not Taken*

In reading poetry, the reader's biggest challenge may be understanding the poet's reason for writing the poem. The poet's purpose gives the poem its theme. Therefore, the poet always shares feelings and ideas that are inspiring, and to which the poet must give voice. It is this central message that is the **main idea**, or **theme**, of the poem. Without it, the poem would lack a reason to be.

Focus

The Road Not Taken, by Robert Frost, is one of the best known and most beloved pieces of modern American poetry. The poem's popularity is surely because of Frost's skill, but its theme, which is slowly revealed to the reader, speaks to our hearts and minds. By the end of this important poem, hopefully you will grasp its meaning, and Frost's need to write the poem.

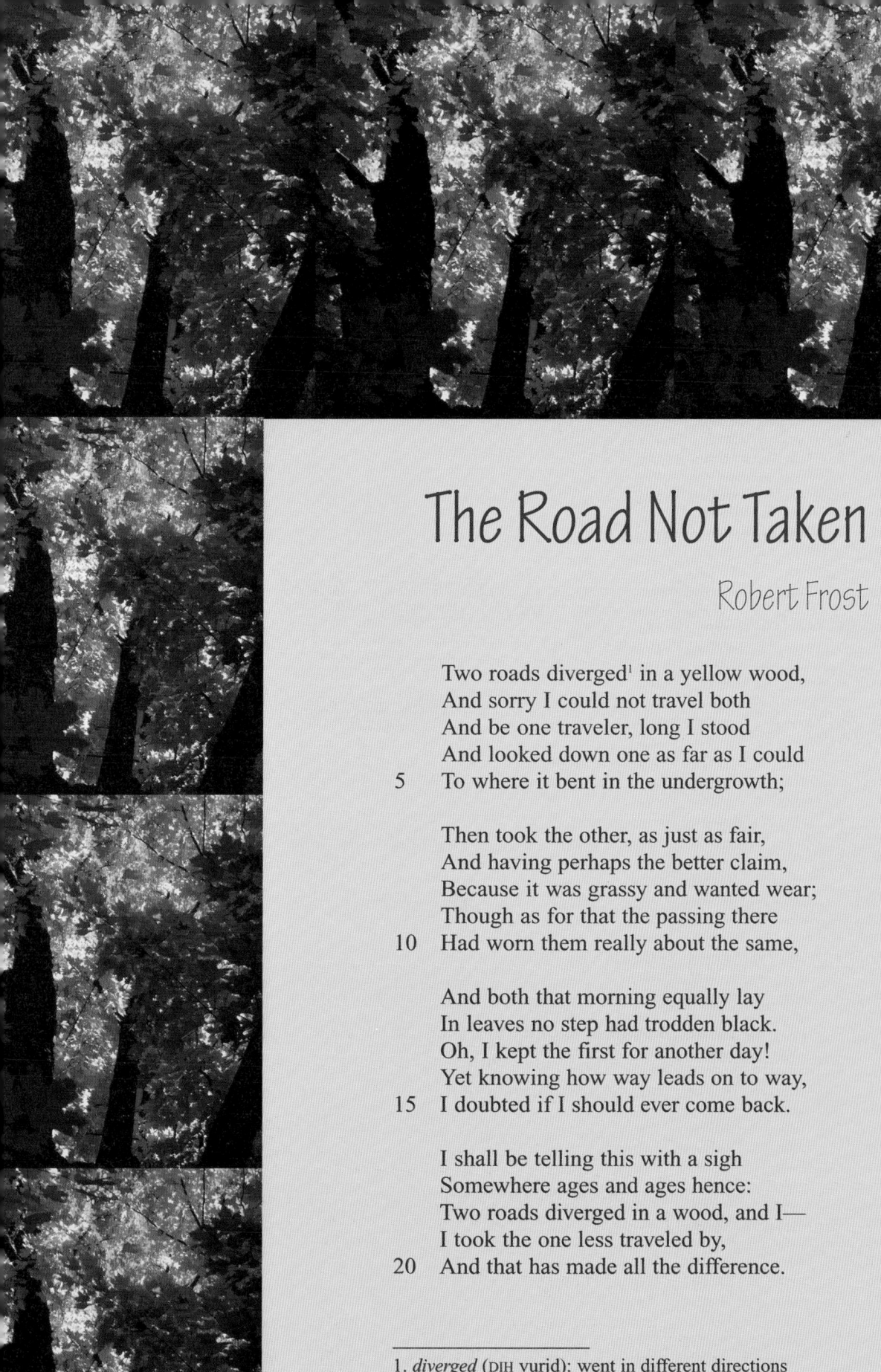

The Road Not Taken

Robert Frost

Two roads diverged[1] in a yellow wood,
And sorry I could not travel both
And be one traveler, long I stood
And looked down one as far as I could
5   To where it bent in the undergrowth;

Then took the other, as just as fair,
And having perhaps the better claim,
Because it was grassy and wanted wear;
Though as for that the passing there
10   Had worn them really about the same,

And both that morning equally lay
In leaves no step had trodden black.
Oh, I kept the first for another day!
Yet knowing how way leads on to way,
15   I doubted if I should ever come back.

I shall be telling this with a sigh
Somewhere ages and ages hence:
Two roads diverged in a wood, and I—
I took the one less traveled by,
20   And that has made all the difference.

---

1. *diverged* (DIH vurjd): went in different directions

Recalling

1. Describe the setting of the poem.

2. What decision was the speaker faced with?

3. Which road does the speaker choose?

4. What is the meaning of the speaker's final statement?

Interpreting

5. Why did the speaker choose one road and not the other? Explain what the speaker means.

6. What does Frost mean in Lines 13-15?

7. What do the two roads symbolize? What is the theme of the poem?

Concluding

8. Have you ever had to make a difficult choice? What did your decision concern? Why did you make the choice you did?

Examining Poetry

Reread the Frost selection, and concentrate on the symbolism in the poem. Remember, a **symbol** is one thing that represents something else. For example, the American flag is a symbol of national pride and patriotism. In literature the appearance of dark clouds, lightning, and thunder is often used as an indication that something bad is about to happen. Symbols may be suggestive of future events.

What was symbolic about the speaker taking the road that "was grassy and wanted wear"?

Creating and Writing

Look back at your answer to question 8. Think again about the choice you made. Now think about the choice that the speaker made in *The Road Not Taken*. Try to write your own poem about important choices.

Into • *Robin Hood and Little John*

A **narrative poem** tells a story and is often action-packed. The story, also called a **ballad**, is told in verse and is usually in chronological order. Many times narrative poetry contains all the elements of short stories: plot, character, setting, and theme.

Focus

As you read the following narrative poem, identify the different elements of plot. Pay close attention to the setting, characterization, and conflict. How does the poet develop these elements as the poem unfolds?

Robin Hood and Little John

AN OLD ENGLISH BALLAD

When Robin Hood was twenty years old,
   He happened to meet Little John,
A jolly, brisk blade, right fit for the trade,
   For he was a lusty young man.

5   Though he was called Little, his limbs they were large,
   And his length it was seven foot high;
Whenever he came, they quaked at his name,
   For soon he would make them all fly.

How they came acquainted, I'll tell you in brief,
10   If you will listen awhile.
For this very jest, among all the rest,
   I think it may cause you to smile.

They happened to meet on a long narrow bridge,
    And neither of them would give way.
15   Then spoke Robin Hood as he sturdily stood,
    "I'll show thee right Nottingham[1] play."

"The name of a coward," said Robin, "I scorn,
    Wherefore my longbow I'll lay by;
And now, for thy sake, a staff will I take,
20   The strength of thy manhood to try."

Then Robin Hood stepped to a thicket of trees,
    And broke off a bough of ground oak;
Now this being done, away did he run
    To the stranger, and merrily spoke:

25   "My staff it is trusty and lusty and tough,
    Now here on the bridge we will play;
Whoever falls in, the other shall win
    The battle, and so we'll away."

"With all of my heart," the stranger replied;
30   "I scorn in the least to give out."
This said, they fell to it without more dispute,
    And their staffs they did flourish about.

And first Robin Hood gave the stranger a bang,
    So hard that it made his bones ring;
35   The stranger he said, "This must be repaid;
    I'll give thee as good as thou bring.

"So long as I'm able to handle a staff,
    To die in thy debt, friend, I scorn."
Then to it each goes, and followed their blows,
40   As if they'd been threshing the corn.

The stranger gave Robin a crack on the crown,
    Which caused the red blood to appear;
Then Robin, enraged, more fiercely engaged,
    And followed with blows more severe.

45 Oh, then into fury the stranger he grew,
  And gave him a furious look,
 And with it a blow that laid him full low,
  And tumbled him into the brook.

 "I prithee, good fellow, oh, where art thou now?"
50 The stranger, in laughter, he cried.
 Quoth bold Robin Hood, "Good faith, in the flood,
  And floating along with the tide.

 "I needs must acknowledge thou art a brave soul,
  With thee I'll no longer contend;
55 For needs must I say, thou hast won the day;
  Our battle shall be at an end."

 Then unto the bank he did presently wade,
  And pulled himself out by a thorn;
 Which done, at the last he blew a loud blast
60 Straightway on his fine bugle horn.

 The echo of this through the valleys did fly,
  At which his stout bowmen appeared,
 All clothed in green, most gay to be seen;
  So up to their master they steered.

65 "Oh what is the matter?" quoth William Stutly;
  "Good master, you're wet to the skin."
 "No matter," quoth he, "the lad which you see
  In fighting hath tumbled me in."

 "He'll not go scot-free," the other replied;
70 So straight they were seizing him there,
 To duck him likewise; but Robin Hood cried,
  "This man's a stout fellow. Forbear!

 "There's no one shall wrong thee, my big little friend;
  These bowmen upon me do wait;
75 There's threescore and nine. If thou wilt be mine,
  Thou shalt wear my own livery[2] straight."

"Oh, here is my hand," the stranger replied,
   "I'll serve thee with all my heart;
My name is John Little, a man of good mettle;
80   Ne'er doubt me, for I'll play my part."

"His name shall be altered," quoth William Stutly,
   "And I will his g-dfather be:
Prepare then a feast, and none of the least,
   For we will be merry," quoth he.

85 With all his bowmen, which stood in a ring,
   And were of the Nottingham breed;
Brave Stutly came then, with seven yeomen,[3]
   And did in this manner proceed:

"This infant was called John Little," quoth he,
90   "Which name shall be changed anon;
The words we'll transpose,[4] so wherever he goes,
   His name shall be called Little John."

Then Robin he took the handsome young man,
   And clothed him from top to his toe
95 In garments of green, most gay to be seen,
   And gave him a mighty longbow.

Then music and dancing did finish the day;
   At length, when the sunlight sank low,
Then with all of their goods, they left the greenwoods,
100   And unto their caves they did go.

And so, ever after, as long as he lived,
   Although he was tall evermore,
Yet, nevertheless, the truth to express
   Little John was the name that he bore.

---

1. *Nottingham* (NAHT ing um): the county in
England in which Sherwood forest is located
2. *livery* (LIV ur ee): a uniform
3. *yeomen* (YO men): foot soldiers
4. *transpose* (TRANZ poze): to reverse the places of
two words; to transfer

Robin Hood and Little John

Recalling

1. Describe Little John's physical appearance.

2. How did Robin Hood and Little John become acquainted?

3. What "deal" does Robin Hood make with Little John in the seventh stanza?

4. What happened to Robin Hood after he and Little John made their deal?

Interpreting

5. What did Robin Hood do when he came out of the water?

6. What did Robin Hood tell his followers about how to treat Little John?

7. What did Robin Hood give Little John near the end of the ballad?

8. What was the contradiction between Little John's name and his appearance? Why did Stutly change John Little's name? What did his new name tell you about his relationship with Robin Hood? For what other reason might Robin Hood and his followers want to change their names?

Concluding

9. What is it about fictional heroes, such as Robin Hood, that appeals to so many generations of readers?

Examining Poetry

In **narrative** poetry, a story is told as the poem unfolds. The poem is written in verse and the events take place in the sequence in which they occur. Many times narrative poetry contains all the elements of short stories: plot, character, setting, and theme.

Where does the action of the poem occur? Who are the main characters? At which point is the climax? When does the climax come to resolution?

Creating and Writing

The unit you read on short stories included many exciting works. Could one of those stories be rewritten in the form of a narrative poem? Choose the story you feel would be most suitable to adapt. Remember plot, setting, and theme as you set the story to verse. Retell it, in chronological order, in the form of a narrative poem.

Into • *Paul Revere's Ride*

A **narrative poem** tells a story and has a plot, setting, characters, and a conflict. Unlike a short story, a narrative poem does all of this in verse, rather than prose. A narrative poem also has a theme, which can either be directly stated or implied. A **stated theme** is clearly indicated to the reader, whereas an **implied theme** is gradually revealed to the reader, who must infer it from the action, dialogue, and outcome of the poem.

Focus

As you read *Paul Revere's Ride*, pay close attention to the way the plot unfolds. Try to determine at what point the poet makes a statement of theme.

Paul Revere's Ride

HENRY WADSWORTH LONGFELLOW

Listen, my children, and you shall hear
Of the midnight ride of Paul Revere,
On the eighteenth of April, in Seventy-Five;
Hardly a man is now alive
5   Who remembers that famous day and year.

He said to his friend, "If the British march
By land or sea from the town tonight,
Hang a lantern aloft in the belfry[1] arch
Of the North Church tower as a signal light—
10   One, if by land, and two, if by sea;
And I on the opposite shore will be,

Ready to ride and spread the alarm
Through every Middlesex village and farm,
For the country folk to be up and to arm."

15 Then he said, "Good night!" and with muffled oar
Silently rowed to the Charlestown shore,
Just as the moon rose over the bay,
Where swinging wide at her moorings² lay
The Somerset, British man-of-war;
20 A phantom³ ship, with each mast and spar
Across the moon like a prison bar,
And a huge black hulk, that was magnified
By its own reflection in the tide.

Meanwhile, his friend, through alley and street,
25 Wanders and watches with eager ears,
Till in the silence around him he hears
The muster of men at the barrack door,
The sound of arms, and the tramp of feet,
And the measured tread of the grenadiers,⁴
30 Marching down to their boats on the shore.
Then he climbed the tower of the Old North Church,
By the wooden stairs, with stealthy⁵ tread,
To the belfry chamber overhead,
And startled the pigeons from their perch
35 On the somber rafters, that round him made
Masses and moving shapes of shade—
By the trembling ladder, steep and tall,
To the highest window in the wall,
Where he paused to listen and look down
40 A moment on the roofs of the town,
And the moonlight flowing over all.

Beneath, in the churchyard, lay the dead,
In their night encampment on the hill,
Wrapped in silence so deep and still
45 That he could hear, like a sentinel's⁶ tread,
The watchful night wind, as it went
Creeping along from tent to tent,
And seeming to whisper, "All is well!"
A moment only he feels the spell
50 Of the place and the hour, and the secret dread
Of the lonely belfry and the dead;
For suddenly all his thoughts are bent
On a shadowy something far away,

Where the river widens to meet the bay—
55 A line of black that bends and floats
On the rising tide, like a bridge of boats.

Meanwhile, impatient to mount and ride,
Booted and spurred, with a heavy stride
On the opposite shore walked Paul Revere.
60 Now he patted his horse's side,
Now gazed at the landscape far and near,
Then, impetuous,[7] stamped the earth,
And turned and tightened his saddle girth;
But mostly he watched with eager search
65 The belfry tower of the Old North Church,
As it rose above the graves on the hill,
Lonely and spectral[8] and somber and still.
And lo! as he looks, on the belfry's height
A glimmer, and then a gleam of light!
70 He springs to the saddle, the bridle he turns,
But lingers and gazes till full on his sight
A second lamp in the belfry burns!

A hurry of hoofs in a village street,
A shape in the moonlight, a bulk in the dark,
75 And beneath, from the pebbles, in passing, a spark
Struck out by a steed flying fearless and fleet:
That was all! And yet, through the gloom and the light,
The fate of a nation was riding that night;
And the spark struck out by that steed, in his flight,
80 Kindled the land into flame with its heat.
He has left the village and mounted the steep,
And beneath him, tranquil and broad and deep,
Is the Mystic, meeting the ocean tides;
And under the alders[9] that skirt its edge,
85 Now soft on the sand, now loud on the ledge,
Is heard the tramp of his steed as he rides.

It was twelve by the village clock,
When he crossed the bridge into Medford town.
He heard the crowing of the cock,
90 And the barking of the farmer's dog,
And felt the damp of the river fog,
That rises after the sun goes down.

It was one by the village clock,
When he galloped into Lexington.
95 He saw the gilded weathercock
Swim in the moonlight as he passed,

And the meetinghouse windows, blank and bare,
Gaze at him with a spectral glare,
As if they already stood aghast
100 At the bloody work they would look upon.

It was two by the village clock,
When he came to the bridge in Concord town.
He heard the bleating of the flock,
And the twitter of birds among the trees,
105 And felt the breath of the morning breeze
Blowing over the meadows brown.
And one was safe and asleep in his bed
Who at the bridge would be first to fall,
Who that day would be lying dead,
110 Pierced by a British musket ball.

You know the rest. In the books you have read,
How the British Regulars fired and fled—
How the farmers gave them ball for ball,
From behind each fence and farmyard wall,
115 Chasing the redcoats down the lane,
Then crossing the fields to emerge again
Under the trees at the turn of the road,
And only pausing to fire and load.

So through the night rode Paul Revere;
120 And so through the night went his cry of alarm
To every Middlesex village and farm—
A cry of defiance[10] and not of fear,
A voice in the darkness, a knock at the door,
And a word that shall echo forevermore!
125 For, borne on the nightwind of the Past,
Through all our history, to the last,
In the hour of darkness and peril and need,
The people will waken and listen to hear
The hurrying hoofbeats of that steed,
130 And the midnight message of Paul Revere.

---

1. *belfry* (BELL free): a bell tower
2. *mooring* (MOOR ing): place where a ship is secured
3. *phantom* (FAN tum): ghostlike
4. *grenadiers* (GREN uh DEERZ): special group in an army
5. *stealthy* (STELL thee): secret
6. *sentinel* (SENT ih nil): person who guards an army against surprise attacks
7. *impetuous* (im PET you iss): hasty in action
8. *spectral* (SPEK tril): ghostlike
9. *alder* (ALL dur): a type of tree
10. *defiance* (dih FY intz): the act of challenging

• *Paul Revere's Ride*

Recalling

1. When and where do the events of the poem occur?

2. What signal did Paul Revere await?

3. What was Paul Revere's assignment after seeing the signal?

4. After the two men agreed on the signal, where did each of them go?

5. What time was it when Paul Revere reached Medford? Lexington? Concord?

6. What will people waken and hear, "In the hour of darkness and peril and need"?

Interpreting

7. "The fate of a nation was riding that night" (Line 78). What does this mean?

8. Why is Paul Revere's cry "A cry of defiance and not of fear"?

Concluding

9. Why do you think that in times of peril and need, "people will waken and listen to hear...the midnight message of Paul Revere"?

Examining Poetry

Longfellow's poem *Paul Revere's Ride* is a unique work of poetry. Some of the lines rhyme whereas others do not. Each stanza has a different number of lines. The reader must also pay attention to the theme as it unfolds. Reread the poem and list the lines that are key to understanding theme.

Creating and Writing

The poem, *Paul Revere's Ride*, is considered by some one of the most enjoyable works of American poetry. It tells of the legendary ride of Paul Revere, at the beginning of the American Revolutionary War. Choose a hero famous in your country. Write a poem about their heroic deeds. Your poem does not have to rhyme, but it should contain a distinct rhythm, similar to *Paul Revere's Ride*.

Into • *Abraham Lincoln Walks at Midnight*

Frequently, the theme of a poem is **implied** rather than directly revealed to the reader. After reading through the poem several times (sometimes reading it aloud or writing or typing it out can be helpful), the reader can make inferences about the theme, and discover what the plot is trying to convey.

Focus

In *Abraham Lincoln Walks at Midnight*, Vachel Lindsay never directly tells the reader the main idea of the poem. However, by the end of a careful reading, you should be able to draw your own conclusions about the theme. The poem is a tragic memorial to President Abraham Lincoln.

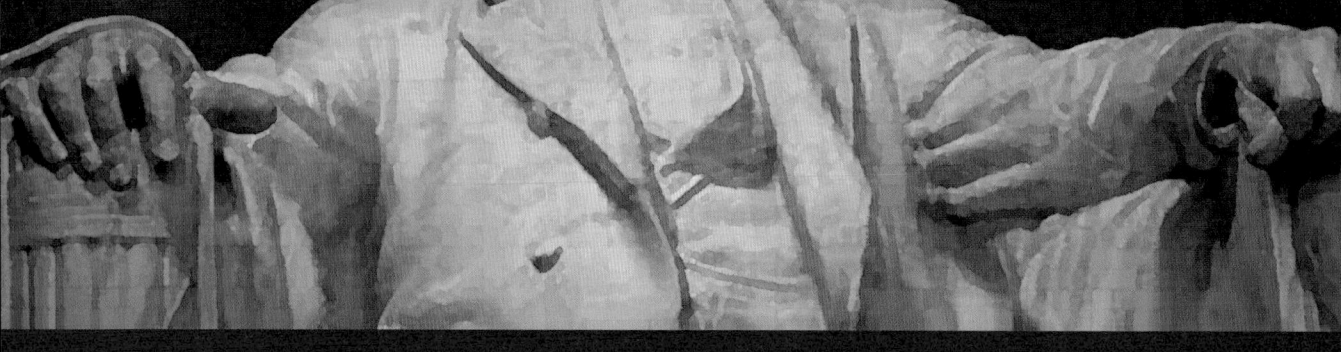

It is portentous,[1] and a thing of state
That here at midnight, in our little town
A mourning figure walks, and will not rest,
Near the old courthouse pacing up and down

5   Or by his homestead, or in shadowed yards
He lingers[2] where his children used to play,
Or through the market, on the well-worn stones
He stalks until the dawn-stars burn away.

A bronzed, lank[3] man! His suit of ancient black,
10   A famous high top hat and plain worn shawl
Make him the quaint[4] great figure that men love,
The prairie lawyer, master of us all.

WALKS AT MIDNIGHT
(IN SPRINGFIELD, ILLINOIS)

He cannot sleep upon his hillside now.
He is among us:—as in times before!
15 And we who toss and lie awake for long
Breathe deep, and start, to see him pass the door.

His head is bowed. He thinks on men and kings.
Yea, when the sick world cries, how can he sleep?
Too many peasants fight, they know not why,
20 Too many homesteads in black terror weep.

The sins of all the wall lords burn his heart.
He sees the dreadnaughts[5] scouring every main.[6]
He carries on his shawl-wrapped shoulders now
The bitterness, the folly and the pain.

25 He cannot rest until a spirit-dawn
Shall come;—the shining hope of Europe free:
The league of sober folk, the Workers' Earth,
Bringing long peace to Cornland, Alp and Sea.

It breaks his heart that kings must murder still,
30 That all his hours of travail[7] here for men
Seem yet in vain. And who will bring white peace
That he may sleep upon his hill again?

---

1. *portentous* (pour TEN tiss): an omen
2. *lingers* (LIN gerz): stays
3. *lank* (LAYNK): tall and thin
4. *quaint* (KWAYNT): old and unusual
5. *dreadnaughts* (DRED NAHTZ): large battleships
6. *main*: the ocean
7. *travail* (truh VAY il): hard labor

• *Abraham Lincoln Walks at Midnight*

Recalling

1. When and where does the mourning figure walk?

2. Describe the mourning figure.

3. What are Abraham Lincoln's thoughts? Why can he not rest peacefully?

4. What breaks Lincoln's heart?

Interpreting

5. Explain Line 14: "He is among us:—as in times before!"

6. What contributes to "The bitterness, the folly and the pain" that Lincoln carries on his shoulders?

7. What does the poet mean by "white peace" (Line 31)?

Concluding

8. This poem was written 49 years after Lincoln's death. Why would it have been appropriate to write such a poem in 1914?

Examining Poetry

In poetry, the theme is revealed by the examples the poet uses to illustrate ideas. The first step in finding the theme of a poem is to ask why it was written and what the poet was trying to say. Then, try to express the poem's main idea, or theme, in one sentence. Finally, check that all the examples given in the poem and the supporting details fit your conclusions about the theme.

1. What is the theme of *Abraham Lincoln Walks at Midnight*?

2. How is the theme stated indirectly? Use examples from the poem to support your answer.

Creating and Writing

The poem we have just read deals with a past president—Abraham Lincoln. To find out more about Lincoln, do some research and answer the following questions.

1. When and where was the President born? When and where did he die?

2. In what year was he elected to the presidency?

3. What were some major accomplishments of his term in office?

4. What were his feelings about slavery?

5. What is his most famous speech, and why is it so powerful and moving?

Into • *The Courage That My Mother Had*

The theme of a poem is often stated directly by the poet in a line from the poem, in the poem's title, or even represented by the action or dialogue. When the poet chooses to make the theme obvious to the reader, we have a **stated theme**.

Focus

Edna St. Vincent Millay chose to directly state the theme in *The Courage That My Mother Had*. Look for the point in the poem where the poet shares the theme with the reader. Think about Millay's reason for writing this poem.

About the Author

EDNA ST. VINCENT MILLAY was born in Maine in 1892. She published her first collection of poetry at the age of nineteen, and was known for the intense emotions evoked by her poetry. Many of her later works reflect her concern for the problems of society. In 1923, Edna St. Vincent Millay became the first woman to receive a Pulitzer Prize. Millay died in 1950 in New York.

The Courage That My Mother Had

Edna St. Vincent Millay

The courage that my mother had
Went with her, and is with her still:
Rock from New England quarried;
Now granite in a granite hill.

5   The golden brooch¹ my mother wore
She left behind for me to wear;
I have no thing I treasure more:
Yet, it is something I could spare.

Oh, if instead she'd left to me
10 The thing she took into the grave!—
That courage like a rock, which she
Has no more need of, and I have.

---

1. *brooch* (BROACH): ornamental pin

● *The Courage That My Mother Had*

Recalling

1. Where was the poet's mother at the time the poem was written?

2. What did the poet's mother take with her to this place?

Interpreting

3. The author uses rock and granite as metaphors for her mother's courage. What are two other words she could have used?

Concluding

4. According to the poet, courage is an important attribute; can it be acquired or gained?

Examining Poetry

When a poet writes a poem, a statement is being made that expresses an attitude towards life. When this statement, or theme, is made directly it is a **stated theme**. Follow the steps below, to figure out the theme of *The Courage That My Mother Had*.

1. Ask yourself why you think the poet wrote this poem. Why did the poet have a compelling need to speak?

2. Write the poet's main idea in a single sentence.

3. Support your sentence with examples and details from the poem.

Creating and Writing

What feelings and thoughts do you want to express? Think of a belief or an experience that has been especially meaningful to you. You may want to write about friendship, the environment, a personal hero, or any other topic about which you have strong feelings. Think of the reasons you have for feeling as you do. These are the examples that will support your theme.

Write a poem that directly states your theme in the text of the poem or in the title. Make sure to add the details and examples that will enrich the reader's understanding.

Into • *I'm Nobody! Who Are You?*

A **lyric poem** is a brief expression of the poet's feelings and emotions. The language used in a **lyric poem** is usually moving and musical. When writing a lyric poem, the poet uses vivid images, metaphors, and similes. One hundred years ago, poets often sung their verses to the accompaniment of a guitar-like instrument called a lyre. This is the basis for the word "lyric."

Focus

When you read Emily Dickinson's poem, *I'm Nobody! Who Are You?*, pay close attention to its lyric qualities.

About the Author

EMILY DICKINSON was born in Massachusetts in 1830. One of America's finest lyric poets, Dickinson was a recluse and her poetry was unknown in her lifetime. Without her permission, seven of her poems were published anonymously while she was alive. After her death in 1886, her family discovered over 1700 poems that she had written. Published posthumously (after her death), these poems brought Dickinson to the forefront of American poetry.

I'M NOBODY!
Who Are You?

Emily Dickinson

I'm nobody! Who are you?
   Are you nobody, too?
Then there's a pair of us—don't tell!
   They'd banish[1] us, you know.

5   How dreary to be somebody!
   How public like a frog
To tell your name the livelong day
   To an admiring bog![2]

---

1. *banish* (BAN ish): send away
2. *bog* (BAHG): swamp

• *I'm Nobody! Who Are You?*

Recalling

1. What does the poet say will happen to people who are "nobodies"?

2. Which pond creature and its sound does the poet think is too "public"?

Interpreting

3. Which figure of speech does the poet use in Line 6?

4. What is the poet's attitude towards people who want to be "somebodies"? What does she say is the downside of being a "somebody"?

Concluding

5. What are some of Emily Dickinson's feelings about being a "nobody"? Do you agree with her? Explain your answer.

Examining Poetry

There is no standard form for a lyric poem. The rhyme and rhythm vary from poem to poem. One element that makes a poem qualify as a lyric poem is the poet's expressing feelings in a striking manner. The words and punctuation also give the poem the quality of going up and down a musical scale.

1. List two characteristics that make *I'm Nobody! Who Are You?* a lyric poem.

2. Find another example of a lyric poem in the poetry we have previously read.

3. Why is that poem an example of lyric poetry?

Creating and Writing

Emily Dickinson was an American poet whose poetry was unknown in her lifetime. She was a recluse, who rarely traveled outside of her home. She became famous after her death, when the majority of her works were found and published. Imagine Dickinson's reaction to finding out that she has become one of America's most beloved poets. Suppose you could go back in time and tell Emily Dickinson about her fame. How might she react? Write a short story describing your meeting. Try to include some of the following: How did you travel back in time? What is Dickinson's reaction to a person from the future? Does she find you believable? How do you prove to her that in the future she will be famous? Is she pleased or displeased about her fame? Why or why not?

Into • *Sarah Cynthia Sylvia Stout Would Not Take the Garbage Out*

A poet can compose a humorous poem by utilizing many different elements. The poet may magnify situations or connect two seemingly different topics. Two of the most important elements in humorous poetry are rhyme and rhythm. Their skillful use makes the poem very funny.

Focus

Sarah Cynthia Sylvia Stout Would Not Take the Garbage Out is a very funny poem by Shel Silverstein. It is filled with exaggeration and overstatement. How does Silverstein use rhyme and rhythm to make this comical poem?

About the Author

Cartoonist, poet, and author **SHEL SILVERSTEIN** was born in Chicago, Illinois in 1932. He demonstrated his artistic and poetic abilities as a very young man. In the 1950s he served in the United States Army in Korea and Japan, where he became the cartoonist for a military newspaper, *Stars and Stripes*. Many of Silverstein's works were written under a pen name, "Uncle Shelby." While many of his poems were written for children, his humor is appreciated by adults as well. Silverstein died in May 1999 in Key West, Florida.

Shel Silverstein

Sarah Cynthia Sylvia Stout Would NOT Take the GARBAGE OUT

Sarah Cynthia Sylvia Stout
Would not take the garbage out!
She'd scour the pots and scrape the pans,
Candy the yams and spice the hams,
5   And though her daddy would scream and shout,
She simply would not take the garbage out.
And so it piled up to the ceilings:
Coffee grounds, potato peelings,
Brown bananas, rotten peas,
10   Chunks of sour cottage cheese.
It filled the can, it covered the floor,
It cracked the window and blocked the door
With bacon rinds and chicken bones,
Drippy ends of ice cream cones,
15   Prune pits, peach pits, orange peel,
Gloppy glumps of cold oatmeal,
Pizza crusts and withered greens,
Soggy beans and tangerines,
Crusts of black burned buttered toast,
20   Gristly bits of beefy roasts...

The garbage rolled on down the hall,
It raised the roof, it broke the wall...
Greasy napkins, cookie crumbs,
Globs of gooey bubblegum,
25 Cellophane from green baloney,
Rubbery blubbery macaroni,
Peanut butter, caked and dry,
Curdled milk and crusts of pie,
Moldy melons, dried up mustard,
30 Eggshells mixed with lemon custard,
Cold french fries and rancid meat,
Yellow lumps of Cream of Wheat.
At last the garbage reached so high
That finally it touched the sky.
35 And all the neighbors moved away,
And none of her friends would come to play.
And finally Sarah Cynthia Stout said,
"OK, I'll take the garbage out!"
But then, of course, it was too late
40 The garbage reached across the state,
From New York to the Golden Gate
And there, in the garbage she did hate,
Poor Sarah met an awful fate,
That I cannot right now relate
45 Because the hour is much too late.
But children, remember Sarah Stout
And always take the garbage out!

- *Sarah Cynthia Sylvia Stout Would Not Take the Garbage Out*

Recalling

1. What was Sarah Cynthia Sylvia Stout's household chore?

2. How does she react to taking out the garbage?

3. What do Sarah's friends and neighbors do?

Interpreting

4. At which point does the poet begin to exaggerate? How does this affect you as you read the poem?

5. The poet concludes the poem with a message or lesson to all children. What does the speaker of the poem tell his readers to remember and to do? Do you think he succeeds in his lesson? Explain.

Concluding

6. Do you think Silverstein wants his readers to take him and his "lesson" seriously?

Examining Poetry

Exaggeration makes a poem humorous. Someone's not taking out the garbage is not funny in its normal context. But exaggerating the circumstances in which Sarah Cynthia Sylvia Stout finds herself—especially when the garbage extends "from New York to the Golden Gate"—makes the situation comical, indeed.

1. List four instances of exaggeration in the poem.

2. If the verses did not rhyme or contain specific rhythm patterns, would the poem still be as funny? Explain your answer.

Creating and Writing

This is a humorous poem about a girl who refuses to take out the trash. The garbage piles up to unmanageable proportions. Can you think of another common household task that, if not done consistently, could get out of hand? For example, what would happen if you did not wash the dishes for a month or do the laundry for a year? Create a humorous poem about the household task you have selected. Remember, the elements of exaggeration and overstatement add to the amusement of a poem. Use rhyme and rhythm to make the poem more humorous.

Into • *Roadways*
• *Something Told the Wild Geese*

In order to fully appreciate poetry, one must consider all the poetic elements we have discussed in this unit. Consider the sound, language, form, and theme that create an **overall effect**. Read a poem several times aloud and to yourself until it is clear to you how the poet works with each of these components.

Focus

As you read the next two poems, ask yourself the following questions: Which devices does the poet use that affect the poem's sound? Is the language literal or figurative? In what form is the poem set? Then, ask yourself what the poet is saying about life. After you have thought about all of these questions, you will be able to better appreciate the poems.

About the Authors

English poet **JOHN MASEFIELD** was born in 1878. Multi-talented, he published over one hundred books of poetry, prose, and drama. Masefield was appointed Poet Laureate of England in 1930, a position he held until his death in 1967, the longest tenure of this position in England's history. As a youth, Masefield served as an apprentice seaman for four years. This time at sea influenced his poetry as reflected in *Roadways*.

RACHEL FIELD, author of novels, plays, and poetry, was born in New York City in 1894. Her love of New England where she was raised is apparent in her writings. Field worked for many years as an editor before focusing on her personal writing career. Many of her works were written for children. Field was the first woman to be presented with the Newbery Medal, an honor awarded yearly to the best piece of fiction written for children. She died in 1942 in California.

Roadways

John Masefield

One road leads to London,
   One road runs to Wales,
My road leads me seawards
   To the white dipping sails.

5 One road leads to the river,
   As it goes singing slow;
My road leads to shipping
   Where the bronzed sailors go.

Leads me, lures me, calls me
10   To salt green tossing sea;
A road without earth's road dust
   Is the right road for me.

A wet road heaving, shining
   And wild with seagull's cries,
15 A mad salt sea-wind blowing
   The salt spray in my eyes.

My road calls me, lures me
   West, east, south, and north;
Most roads lead men homewards,
20   My road leads me forth.

To add more miles to the tally
   Of grey miles left behind,
In quest of that one beauty
   G-d put me here to find.

Something Told the Wild Geese

Rachel Field

Something told the wild geese
    It was time to go.
Though the fields lay golden
    Something whispered,—"Snow."
5 Leaves were green and stirring,
    Berries, luster-glossed,
But beneath warm feathers
    Something cautioned,—"Frost."
All the sagging orchards
10   Steamed with amber[1] spice,
But each wild breast stiffened
    At remembered ice.
Something told the wild geese
    It was time to fly,—
15 Summer sun was on their wings,
    Winter in their cry.

---

1. *amber* (AM bur): golden

• *Roadways*

Recalling

1. In *Roadways*, where do the "bronzed sailors" go?

2. Where is the speaker being lead, lured, and called?

3. Instead of going home, where is the speaker going, in Line 20?

Interpreting

4. Why do you think the poet used the words, "A road without earth's road dust," instead of just saying "the sea"?

5. What could the roads symbolize?

Concluding

6. Have you ever noticed any "roads" or "pathways" in your own life? Where do they seem to lead you?

• *Something Told the Wild Geese*

Recalling

1. In *Something Told the Wild Geese*, what did "something" whisper? What did "something" caution?

2. What do the geese remember? How do they react to their recollection?

3. Describe the setting of the poem. Be specific.

Interpreting

4. What is the "something" that tells the wild geese to go?

5. How do you know that the events in this poem occur at the end of the summer or the beginning of autumn? Support your answer with details from the poem.

6. What do you think compels the geese to go?

Concluding

7. How and why do some wild animals change their habitat with the change of the season?

Examining Poetry

There are many different elements a poet uses in order to create a poem. The sound, language, form, and theme all contribute to its **overall effect**. Sometimes it takes a few readings in order to appreciate a poem thoroughly. Compare the overall effects of the two poems, *Roadways* and *Something Told the Wild Geese*. Make a chart to help you compare the sound, language, form, and theme (meaning) of each of these poems.

Creating and Writing

Roadways uses an ordered and balanced form. What theme is the poet trying to suggest? Now, create a poem that expresses the same message, but in a different form. Perhaps you could try the concrete form that John Updike uses in *Pendulum*. Maybe you would like to write a haiku. Does changing the form of the poem change its overall effect? How? Why? Explain your answer.

Sound, language, form, and theme all contribute to the **overall effect** of a poem. Another important element is personal interpretation. Readers bring their own experiences and knowledge to their reading of a poem. Therefore, the overall effect of a poem varies from individual to individual.

Focus

As you read *The Wind* by Robert Louis Stevenson and *The Sloth* by Theodore Roethke, pay close attention to the way each poem affects you. What is each poet saying? Do you find the messages personally important?

About the Author

THEODORE ROETHKE was born in 1908 in Michigan. His love of nature becomes apparent when you read his poem, *The Sloth*. Roethke became well known for his poetry in the late 1940s and received the Pulitzer Prize and the National Book Award for his writings. Roethke died in 1963 in Washington.

● Studying THE SELECTION

• *The Wind*

Recalling

1. How does Robert Louis Stevenson describe the wind? What did the wind do?
2. What did the poet feel and hear the wind do?
3. Which questions does the speaker ask the wind?

Interpreting

4. Explain how the wind is "Like ladies' skirts across the grass."

5. From whose point of view is this poem told?

6. In Line 7, Stevenson writes, "I saw the different things you did..." Then in Line 10, "I could not see yourself at all—" These lines appear to contradict each other. Why is there really no contradiction?

Concluding

7. Describe a natural force (other than wind) that you experience often, but which is still somewhat mysterious to you.

Robert Louis Stevenson

THE WIND

I saw you toss the kites on high
And blow the birds about the sky;
And all around I hear you pass,
Like ladies' skirts across the grass—
5   O wind, a-blowing all day long,
     O wind, that sings so loud a song!

I saw the different things you did,
But always you yourself you hid.
I felt you push, I heard you call,
10 I could not see yourself at all—
     O wind, a-blowing all day long,
     O wind, that sings so loud a song!
O you that are so strong and cold,
O blower, are you young or old?

15 Are you a beast of field and tree,
    Or just a stronger child than me?
     O wind, a-blowing all day long,
     O wind, that sings so loud a song!

THE SLOTH

THEODORE ROETHKE

In moving-slow he has no peer.
You ask him something in his ear;
He thinks about it for a Year;

And then, before he says a Word
5   There, upside down (unlike a bird)
He will assume that you have heard—

A most EX-as-per-at-ing Lug.
But should you call his manner Smug,
He'll sigh and give his branch a Hug;

10   Then off again to Sleep he goes,
Still swaying gently by his Toes,
And you just know he knows he knows.

- *The Sloth*

Recalling

1. Judging from Line 1, how quickly does a sloth move?

2. What does the sloth do when asked a question?

Interpreting

3. The word "exasperating" is divided into separate syllables. Why did the poet use this technique?

4. Why do you think the poet chose to capitalize certain words throughout the poem, for example "Lug," "Hug," and "Sleep"?

Concluding

5. Have you ever observed an animal that has unusual habits for its species? Describe the attributes you consider unusual.

Examining Poetry

The overall effect of a poem will vary from person to person. Though sound, language, form, and theme contribute to the overall effect, another telling element is the reader's own reaction. The reader's experiences, ideas, and outlook will affect how they interpret the poem. Choose one of the poems you have just read. Answer the following questions:

1. What is the meaning of the poem?

2. Do you agree with the statement the poet is making? Explain.

3. Compare your answers with a friend's.

4. Are your answers similar or do they differ?

5. How do your own experiences influence your reaction to the poem?

Creating and Writing

In this unit, you have studied many different aspects of poetry. Is poetry as effective as prose in conveying a message? Perhaps you feel it is a more effective way to communicate. Compare the advantages and disadvantages of writing poetry to those of writing prose. Decide which you prefer. Write an essay supporting your opinion.

nonfiction

Nonfiction is a literary form based on fact that strives to be as accurate and realistic as possible. The nonfiction writer creates truthful accounts of events that occurred and people who existed. By studying primary sources and interviewing actual participants in events, authors develop their nonfiction stories.

Nonfiction literature may be divided into human-interest stories (*Cat on the Go*), biographies (*Roberto Clemente: A Bittersweet Memoir*), historical essays (*Florence Nightingale*), and autobiographies (*Barrio Boy*). Human-interest stories are about ordinary people; historical essays provide accounts of actual events; biographies usually concern the lives and accomplishments of well-known people; and autobiographies are the stories of their authors' own lives. These literary works can provide a door to the past or a window into someone else's world. Well-crafted nonfiction can transport the reader to a different era. The reader will be challenged, intellectually and imaginatively, to think about the events described. Nonfiction can provide insight into the lives of intriguing people whose adventures, accomplishments, and triumphs touch us.

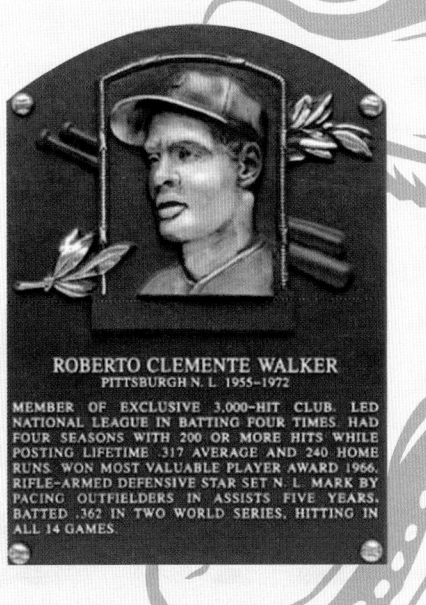

ROBERTO CLEMENTE WALKER
PITTSBURGH N. L. 1955-1972

MEMBER OF EXCLUSIVE 3,000-HIT CLUB. LED NATIONAL LEAGUE IN BATTING FOUR TIMES. HAD FOUR SEASONS WITH 200 OR MORE HITS WHILE POSTING LIFETIME .317 AVERAGE AND 240 HOME RUNS. WON MOST VALUABLE PLAYER AWARD 1966. RIFLE-ARMED DEFENSIVE STAR SET N. L. MARK BY PACING OUTFIELDERS IN ASSISTS FIVE YEARS. BATTED .362 IN TWO WORLD SERIES, HITTING IN ALL 14 GAMES.

mini table of contents

human interest

biographies and autobiographies

historical essays

adventure essays

Into • *Cat on the Go*

Human-interest stories are stories that deal with the challenges and joys of coping with the problems of everyday life. Human-interest stories deal with birth, the joy and pain of growing up, loneliness and popularity, poverty and riches, and illness and death.

Cat on the Go is an example of a story that portrays the human emotions of kindness, loyalty, and generosity. Though its main character seems to be a spirited cat, in reality this story deals with the people who are touched and changed by coming into contact with this lively animal.

Focus

When you read *Cat on the Go*, you will find that every single character is a giving person. As you meet each character—even a minor one—ask yourself what form this quality of "giving" takes in that person. "Giving" can include something as great as performing hours of surgery to save a cat's life or as small as welcoming someone with a smile and a cup of tea. What does the cat give to the humans who love him?

About the Author

Scottish author **JAMES HERRIOT** was actually a veterinarian named James Alfred Wight. Wight served the Yorkshire countryside for over fifty years. He began to write about his experiences under the pen name of James Herriot as an older adult. Herriot recounted his memoirs as if he were telling a story to a friend. In his work, he captured the strength and unpretentious life of the Yorkshire people. At the time of his death in 1995, Herriot was an established author appreciated by readers of all ages.

Cat on the Go

James Herriot

One winter evening Tristan shouted up the stairs from the passage far below.

"Jim! Jim!"

I went out and stuck my head over the bannisters. "What is it, Triss?"

"Sorry to bother you, Jim, but could you come down for a minute?" The upturned face had an anxious look.

I went down the long flights of steps two at a time and when I arrived slightly breathless on the ground floor Tristan beckoned me through to the consulting room at the back of the house. A teenage girl was standing by the table, her hand resting on a stained roll of blanket.

"It's a cat," Tristan said. He pulled back a fold of the blanket and I looked down at a large, deeply striped tabby. At least he would have been large if he had had any flesh on his bones, but ribs and pelvis stood out painfully through the fur and as I passed my hand over the motionless body I could feel only a thin covering of skin.

Tristan cleared his throat. "There's something else, Jim."

I looked at him curiously. For once he didn't seem to have a joke in him. I watched as he gently lifted one of the cat's hind legs and rolled the abdomen into view. There was a gash on the ventral[1] surface through which a coiled cluster of intestines spilled grotesquely onto the cloth. I was still shocked and staring when the girl spoke.

"I saw this cat sittin' in the dark, down Brown's yard. I thought 'e looked skinny, like, and a bit quiet and I bent down to give 'im a pat. Then I saw 'e was badly hurt and I went home for a blanket and brought 'im round to you."

"That was kind of you," I said. "Have you any idea who he belongs to?"

The girl shook her head. "No, he looks like a stray to me."

"He does indeed." I dragged my eyes away from the terrible wound. "You're Marjorie Simpson, aren't you?"

"Yes."

"I know your Dad well. He's our postman."

"That's right." She gave a half smile then her lips trembled.

---

1. The *ventral* (VEN tril) *surface* is the surface near or on the belly.

Word Bank	**gash** (GASH) *n.*: cut or wound

"Well, I reckon I'd better leave 'im with you. You'll be going to put him out of his misery. There's nothing anybody can do about…about that?"

I shrugged and shook my head. The girl's eyes filled with tears, she stretched out a hand and touched the emaciated animal then turned and walked quickly to the door.

"Thanks again, Marjorie," I called after the retreating back. "And don't worry—we'll look after him."

In the silence that followed, Tristan and I looked down at the shattered animal. Under the surgery lamp it was all too easy to see. He had almost been disemboweled[2] and the pile of intestines was covered in dirt and mud.

"What d'you think did this?" Tristan said at length. "Has he been run over?"

"Maybe," I replied. "Could be anything. An attack by a big dog or somebody could have kicked him or struck him." All things were possible with cats because some people seemed to regard them as fair game for any cruelty.

Tristan nodded. "Anyway, whatever happened, he must have been on the verge of starvation. He's a skeleton. I bet he's wandered miles from home."

"Ah well," I sighed. "There's only one thing to do. Those guts are perforated in several places. It's hopeless."

Tristan didn't say anything but he whistled under his breath and drew the tip of his forefinger again and again across the furry cheek. And, unbelievably, from somewhere in the scraggy chest a gentle purring arose.

The young man looked at me, round eyed. "My G-d, do you hear that?"

"Yes…amazing in that condition. He's a good-natured cat."

Tristan, head bowed, continued his stroking. I knew how he felt because, although he preserved a cheerfully hard-boiled attitude to our patients he couldn't kid me about one thing; he had a soft spot for cats. Even now, when we are both around the sixty mark, he often talks to me about the cat he has had for many years. It is a typical relationship—they tease each other unmercifully—but it is based on real affection.

"It's no good, Triss," I said gently. "It's got to be done." I reached for the syringe but something in me rebelled against plunging a needle into that mutilated body. Instead I pulled a fold of the blanket over the cat's head.

"Pour a little ether onto the cloth," I said. "He'll just sleep away."

Wordlessly, Tristan unscrewed the cap of the ether bottle and poised it above the head. Then from under the shapeless heap of blanket we heard it again; the deep purring which increased in volume till it boomed in our ears like a distant motorcycle.

Tristan was like a man turned to stone, hand gripping the bottle rigidly, eyes staring down at the mound of cloth from which the purring rose in waves of warm friendly sound.

At last he looked up at me and gulped. "I don't fancy this much, Jim. Can't we do something?"

"You mean, put that lot back?"

"Yes."

"But the bowels are damaged—they're like a sieve in parts."

"We could stitch them, couldn't we?"

I lifted the blanket and looked again. "Honestly, Triss, I wouldn't know where to start. And the whole thing is filthy."

He didn't say anything, but continued to look at me steadily. And I

---

2. *Disemboweled* (DISS im BOU ild) means that he had no intestines.

| **Word Bank** | emaciated (ih MAY shee AYT id) *adj.*: wasted away physically; malnourished |

didn't need much persuading. I had no more desire to pour ether onto that comradely purring than he had.

"Come on, then," I said. "We'll have a go."

With the oxygen bubbling and the cat's head in the anesthetic mask we washed the whole prolapse[3] with warm saline.[4] We did it again and again but it was impossible to remove every fragment of caked dirt. Then we started the painfully slow business of stitching the many holes in the tiny intestines, and here I was glad of Tristan's nimble fingers which seemed better able to manipulate the small round-bodied needles than mine.

Two hours and yards of catgut[5] later, we dusted the patched up peritoneal[6] surface with sulfanilamide[7] and pushed the entire mass back into the abdomen. When I had sutured muscle layers and skin everything looked tidy but I had a nasty feeling of sweeping undesirable things under the carpet. The extensive damage, all that contamination— peritonitis[8] was inevitable.

"He's alive, anyway, Triss," I said as we began to wash the instruments. "We'll put him onto sulfapyridine and hope for the best." There were still no antibiotics at that time but the new drug was a big advance.

The door opened and Helen came in. "You've been a long time, Jim." She walked over to the table and looked down at the sleeping cat. "What a poor skinny little thing. He's all bones."

"You should have seen him when he came in." Tristan switched off the sterilizer and screwed shut the valve on the anesthetic machine. "He looks a lot better now."

She stroked the little animal for a moment. "Is he badly injured?"

"I'm afraid so, Helen," I said. "We've done our best for him but I honestly don't think he has much chance."

"What a shame. And he's pretty, too. Four white feet and all those unusual colors." With her finger she traced the faint bands of auburn and copper-gold among the gray and black.

Tristan laughed. "Yes, I think that chap has a ginger Tom somewhere in his ancestry."

Helen smiled, too, but absently, and I noticed a broody look about her. She hurried out to the stock room and returned with an empty box.

"Yes…yes…" she said thoughtfully. "I can make a bed in this box for him and he'll sleep in our room, Jim."

"He will?"

"Yes, he must be warm, mustn't he?"

"Of course."

Later, in the darkness of our bed-sitter,[9] I looked from my pillow at a cozy scene. Sam in his basket on one side of the flickering fire and the cat cushioned and blanketed in his box on the other.

As I floated off into sleep it was good to know that my patient was so comfortable, but I wondered if he would be alive in the morning…

I knew he was alive at 7:30 a.m. because my wife was already up and talking to him. I trailed across the room in my pajamas and the cat and I looked

---

3. *Prolapse* (PRO laps) is an internal organ that has fallen out.
4. *Saline* (SAY leen) is a salt solution.
5. *Catgut* (KAT GUT) is a strong thread used in surgery.
6. *Peritoneal* (PAIR it un EE ul) means concerning the membrane that lines the abdomen.
7. *Sulfanilamide* (SUL fuh NIL uh MYD) is a sulfa drug that was used to treat infections before penicillin was discovered.
8. *Peritonitis* (PAIR it un IYT ess) is an infection of the internal organs.
9. A *bed-sitter* is a one-room apartment.

Word Bank   inevitable (in EV it uh bul) *adj.*: unavoidable

at each other. I rubbed him under the chin and he opened his mouth in a rusty miaow. But he didn't try to move.

"Helen," I said. "This little thing is tied together inside with catgut. He'll have to live on fluids for a week and even then he probably won't make it. If he stays up here you'll be spooning milk into him umpteen times a day."

"Okay, okay." She had that broody look again.

It wasn't only milk she spooned into him over the next few days. Beef essence, strained broth and a succession of sophisticated baby foods found their way down his throat at regular intervals. One lunch time I found Helen kneeling by the box.

"We shall call him Oscar," she said.

"You mean we're keeping him?"

"Yes."

I am fond of cats but we already had a dog in our cramped quarters and I could see difficulties. Still I decided to let it go.

"Why Oscar?"

"I don't know." Helen tipped a few drops of chop gravy onto the little red tongue and watched intently as he swallowed.

I was pleased at the way things were going. I had been giving the sulfapyridine every six hours and taking the temperature night and morning, expecting all the time to encounter the roaring fever, the vomiting and the tense abdomen of peritonitis. But it never happened.

It was as though Oscar's animal instinct told him he had to move as little as possible because he lay absolutely still day after day and looked up at us— and purred.

His purr became part of our lives and when he eventually left his bed, sauntered through to our kitchen and began to sample Sam's dinner of meat and biscuit it was a moment of triumph. And I didn't spoil it by wondering if he

was ready for solid food; I felt he knew.

From then on it was sheer joy to watch the furry scarecrow fill out and grow strong, and as he ate and ate the flesh spread over his bones. The true beauty of his coat showed in the glossy medley of auburn, black and gold. We had a handsome cat on our hands.

Once Oscar had fully recovered, Tristan was a regular visitor.

He probably felt, and rightly, that he, more than I, had saved Oscar's life in the first place and he used to play with him for long periods. His favorite ploy was to push his leg round the corner of the table and withdraw it repeatedly just as the cat pawed at it.

Oscar was justifiably irritated by this teasing but showed his character by lying in wait for Tristan one night and biting him smartly[10] in the ankle before he could start his tricks.

From my own point of view Oscar added many things to our menage.[11] Sam was delighted with him and the two soon became firm friends, Helen adored him and each evening I thought afresh that a nice cat washing his face by the hearth gave extra comfort to a room.

Oscar had been established as one of the family for several weeks when I came in from a late call to find Helen waiting for me with a stricken face.

"What's happened?" I asked.

"It's Oscar—he's gone!"

"Gone? What do you mean?"

"Oh, Jim, I think he's run away."

I stared at her. "He wouldn't do that. He often goes down to the garden at night. Are you sure he isn't there?"

"Absolutely. I've searched right into

---

10. Here, *smartly* means forcefully.
11. A *menage* (muh NAAZH) is a household.

Word Bank	**ploy** (PLOY) *n.*: a playful game; a plan or tactic that is different from ordinary contact

the yard. I've even had a walk round the town. And remember." Her chin quivered. "He…he ran away from somewhere before."

I looked at my watch. "Ten o'clock. Yes, that is strange. He shouldn't be out at this time."

As I spoke the front door bell jangled. I galloped down the stairs and as I rounded the corner in the passage I could see Mrs. Heslington, the vicar's wife, through the glass. I threw open the door. She was holding Oscar in her arms.

"I believe this is your cat, Mr. Herriot," she said.

"It is indeed, Mrs. Heslington. Where did you find him?"

She smiled. "Well it was rather odd. We were having a meeting of the Mothers' Union at the house and we noticed the cat sitting there in the room."

"Just sitting…?"

"Yes, as though he were listening to what we were saying and enjoying it all. It was unusual. When the meeting

ended I thought I'd better bring him along to you."

"I'm most grateful, Mrs. Heslington." I snatched Oscar and tucked him under my arm. "My wife is distraught—she thought he was lost."

It was a little mystery. Why should he suddenly take off like that? But since he showed no change in his manner over the ensuing week we put it out of our minds.

Then one evening a man brought in a dog for a distemper[12] inoculation and left the front door open. When I went up to our flat I found that Oscar had disappeared again. This time Helen and I scoured the marketplace and side alleys

---

12. *Distemper* (diss TEM pur) is an infectious virus disease.

Word Bank	inoculation (in OCK yoo LAY shun) *n.*: vaccination

"Aye, he were there, all right. Sitting among t'lads. Shpent t'whole evenin' with us."

"Just sat there, eh?"

"That 'e did." Jack giggled reminiscently. "My 'e enjoyed 'isself. Ah gave 'em a drop out of me own glass and once or twice ah thought 'e was going to have a go at chuckin' a dart. He's some cat." He laughed again.

As I bore Oscar upstairs I was deep in thought. What was going on here? These sudden desertions were upsetting Helen and I felt they could get on my nerves in time.

I didn't have long to wait till the next one. Three nights later he was missing again. This time Helen and I didn't bother to search—we just waited.

He was back earlier than usual. I heard the doorbell at nine o'clock. It was the elderly Miss Simpson peering through the glass. And she wasn't holding Oscar—he was prowling on the mat waiting to come in.

Miss Simpson watched with interest as the cat stalked inside and made for the stairs. "Ah, good, I'm so glad he's come home safely. I knew he was your cat and I've been intrigued by his behavior all evening."

"Where…may I ask?"

"Oh, at the Women's Institute. He came in shortly after we started and stayed there till the end."

"Really? What exactly was your program, Miss Simpson?"

"Well, there was a bit of committee stuff, then a short talk with lantern

in vain and when we returned at half past nine we were both despondent. It was nearly eleven and we were thinking of bed when the doorbell rang.

It was Oscar again, this time resting on the ample stomach of Jack Newbould. Jack was a gardener at one of the big houses. He hiccuped gently and gave me a huge benevolent smile. "Brought your cat, Mr. Herriot."

"Gosh, thanks, Jack!" I said, scooping up Oscar gratefully. "Where the devil did you find him?"

"Well, s'matter o' fact 'e sort of found me."

"What do you mean?"

Jack closed his eyes for a few moments before articulating carefully. "Thish is a big night, tha knows, Mr. Herriot. Darts championship. Lots of t'lads round at t'Dog and Gun—lotsh and lotsh of 'em. Big gatherin'."

"And our cat was there?"

| **Word Bank** | **benevolent** (ben EV uh lint) *adj.*: kind and generous; inclined to doing good |
| | **articulating** (AR tick yoo LAYT ing) *v.*: pronouncing clearly |

slides by Mr. Walters from the water company and we finished with a cake-making competition."

"Yes…yes…and what did Oscar do?"

She laughed. "Mixed with the company, apparently enjoyed the slides and showed great interest in the cakes."

"I see. And you didn't bring him home?"

"No, he made his own way here. As you know, I have to pass your house and I merely rang your bell to make sure you knew he had arrived."

"I'm obliged to you, Miss Simpson. We were a little worried."

I mounted the stairs in record time. Helen was sitting with the cat on her knee and she looked up as I burst in.

"I know about Oscar now," I said.

"Know what?"

"Why he goes on these nightly outings. He's not running away—he's visiting."

"Visiting?"

"Yes," I said. "Don't you see? He likes getting around, he loves people, especially in groups, and he's interested in what they do. He's a natural mixer."

Helen looked down at the attractive mound of fur curled on her lap. "Of course…that's it…he's a socialite!"

"Exactly, a high stepper!"

"A cat-about-town!"

It all afforded us some innocent laughter and Oscar sat up and looked at us with evident pleasure, adding his own throbbing purr to the merriment. But for Helen and me there was a lot of relief behind it; ever since our cat had started his excursions there had been the gnawing fear that we would lose him, and now we felt secure.

From that night our delight in him increased. There was endless joy in watching this facet of his character unfolding. He did the social round meticulously, taking in most of the activities of the town. He became a

familiar figure at whist drives,[13] jumble sales,[14] school concerts and scout bazaars. Most of the time he was made welcome, but was twice ejected from meetings of the Rural District Council who did not seem to relish the idea of a cat sitting in on their deliberations.

At first I was apprehensive about his making his way through the streets but I watched him once or twice and saw that he looked both ways before tripping daintily across. Clearly he had excellent traffic sense and this made me feel that his original injury had not been caused by a car.

13. *Whist drives* are attempts to raise money by playing whist, a card game.
14. *Jumble sales* are sales of donated articles to raise money for charity.

Word Bank

excursions (ex CER zhuns) *n.*: brief, pleasure trips

meticulously (meh TICK yoo lus lee) *adv.*: extremely careful in the treatment of details

apprehensive (APP re HEN siv) *adj.*: uneasy; concerned; viewing the future with anxiety or alarm

Taking it all in all, Helen and I felt that it was a kind stroke of fortune which had brought Oscar to us. He was a warm and cherished part of our home life. He added to our happiness.

When the blow fell it was totally unexpected.

I was finishing the evening surgery.[15] I looked round the door and saw only a man and two little boys.

"Next, please," I said.

The man stood up. He had no animal with him. He was middle-aged, with the rough weathered face of a farm worker. He twirled a cloth cap nervously in his hands.

"Mr. Herriot?" he said.

"Yes, what can I do for you?"

He swallowed and looked me straight in the eyes. "Ah think you've got ma cat."

"What?"

"Ah lost ma cat a bit since." He cleared his throat. "We used to live at Missdon but ah got a job as plowman to Mr. Horne of Wederly. It was after we moved to Wederly that t'cat went missin'. Ah reckon he was tryin to find 'is way back to his old home."

"Wederly? That's on the other side of Brawton—over thirty miles away."

"Aye, ah knaw, but cats is funny things."

"But what makes you think I've got him?"

He twisted the cap around a bit more. "There's a cousin o' mine lives in Darrowby and ah heard tell from 'im about this cat that goes around to meetin's. I 'ad to come. We've been huntin' everywhere."

"Tell me," I said. "This cat you lost. What did he look like?"

"Gray and black and sort o' gingery. Right bonny[16] 'e was. And 'e was allus goin' out to gatherin's."

A cold hand clutched my heart. "You'd better come upstairs. Bring the boys with you."

Helen was putting some coal on the fire of the bed-sitter.

"Helen," I said. "This is Mr.—er—I'm sorry, I don't know your name."

"Gibbons, Sep Gibbons. They called me Septimus because ah was the seventh in family and it looks like ah'm goin' t'same way 'cause we've got six already. These are our two youngest." The two boys, obvious twins of about eight, looked up at us solemnly.

I wished my heart would stop hammering. "Mr. Gibbons thinks Oscar is his. He lost his cat some time ago."

My wife put down her little shovel. "Oh…Oh…I see." She stood very still for a moment then smiled faintly. "Do sit down, Oscar's in the kitchen. I'll bring him through."

She went out and reappeared with the cat in her arms. She hadn't got through the door before the little boys gave tongue.

"Tiger!" they cried. "Oh, Tiger, Tiger!"

The man's face seemed lit from within. He walked quickly across the floor and ran his big work-roughened hand along the fur.

"Hullo, awd lad," he said, and turned to me with a radiant smile. "It's 'im, Mr. Herriot. It's 'im awright, and don't 'e look well!"

"You call him Tiger, eh?" I said.

"Aye," he replied happily. "It's them gingery stripes. The kids called 'im that. They were brokenhearted when we lost 'im."

As the two little boys rolled on the floor our Oscar rolled with them, pawing playfully, purring with delight.

Sep Gibbons sat down again. "That's the way 'e allus wen on wi' the family. They used to play with 'im for hours. We did miss 'im. He were a right favorite."

---

15. *Surgery* means the work done by a surgeon.
16. *Bonny* (BAHN ee) is a British term for attractive.

I looked at the broken nails on the edge of the cap, at the decent, honest, uncomplicated Yorkshire[17] face so like the many I had grown to like and respect. Farm men like him got thirty shillings a week in those days and it was reflected in the threadbare jacket, the cracked, shiny boots and the obvious hand-me-downs of the boys.

But all three were scrubbed and tidy, the man's face like a red beacon, the children's knees gleaming and their hair carefully slicked across their foreheads. They looked like nice people to me. I didn't know what to say.

Helen said it for me. "Well, Mr. Gibbons." Her tone had an unnatural brightness. "You'd better take him."

The man hesitated. "Now then, are ye sure, Missis Herriot?"

"Yes…yes. I'm sure. He was your cat first."

"Aye, but some folks 'ud say finders keepers or summat like that. Ah didn't come 'ere to demand 'im back or owt of t'sort."

"I know you didn't, Mr. Gibbons, but you've had him all those years and you've searched for him so hard. We couldn't possibly keep him from you."

He nodded quickly. "Well, that's right good of ye." He paused for a moment, his face serious, then he stooped and picked Oscar up. "We'll have to be off if we're goin' to catch the eight o'clock bus."

Helen reached forward, cupped the cat's head in her hands and looked at him steadily for a few seconds. Then she patted the boys' heads. "You'll take good care of him, won't you?"

"Aye, missis, thank ye, we will that." The two small faces looked up at her and smiled.

"I'll see you down the stairs, Mr. Gibbons," I said.

On the descent I tickled the furry cheek resting on the man's shoulder and heard for the last time the rich purring.

On the front door step we shook hands and they set off down the street. As they rounded the corner of Trengate they stopped and waved and I waved back at the man, the two children and the cat's head looking back at me over the shoulder.

It was my habit at that time in my life to mount the stairs two or three at a time but on this occasion I trailed upward like an old man, slightly breathless, throat tight, eyes prickling.

I cursed myself for a sentimental fool but as I reached our door I found a flash of consolation. Helen had taken it remarkably well. She had nursed that cat and grown deeply attached to him, and I'd have thought an unforeseen calamity like this would have upset her terribly. But no, she had behaved calmly and rationally.

It was up to me to do as well. I adjusted my features into the semblance of a cheerful smile and marched into the room.

Helen had pulled a chair close to the table and was slumped face down against the wood. One arm cradled her head while the other was stretched in front of her as her body shook with an utterly abandoned weeping.

I had never seen her like this and I was appalled. I tried to say something comforting but nothing stemmed the flow of racking sobs.

Feeling helpless and inadequate I could only sit close to her and stroke the back of her head. Maybe I could have said something if I hadn't felt just about as bad myself.

You get over these things in time.

---

17. *Yorkshire* (YORK sheer) is a county in England.

Word Bank	**sentimental** (SENT im EN tul) *adj.*: having or showing tender feelings

After all, we told ourselves, it wasn't as though Oscar had died or got lost again—he had gone to a good family who would look after him. In fact he had really gone home.

And of course, we still had our much-loved Sam, although he didn't help in the early stages by sniffing disconsolately where Oscar's bed used to lie then collapsing on the rug with a long lugubrious sigh.

There was one other thing, too. I had a little notion forming in my mind, an idea which I would spring on Helen when the time was right. It was about a month after that shattering night and we were coming out of the concert at Brawton at the end of our half day. I looked at my watch.

"Only eight o'clock," I said. "How about going to see Oscar?"

Helen looked at me in surprise. "You mean—drive on to Wederly?"

"Yes, it's only about five miles."

A smile crept slowly across her face. "That would be lovely. But do you think they would mind?"

"The Gibbons? No. I'm sure they wouldn't. Let's go."

Wederly was a big village and the plowman's cottage was at the far end. I pushed open the garden gate and we walked down the path.

A busy-looking little woman answered my knock. She was drying her hands on a striped towel.

"Mrs. Gibbons?" I said.

"Aye, that's me."

"I'm James Herriot—and this is my wife."

Her eyes widened uncomprehendingly. Clearly the name meant nothing to her.

"We had your cat for a while," I added.

Suddenly she grinned and waved her towel at us. "Oh aye, ah remember now.

Sep told me about you. Come in, come in!"

The big kitchen-living room was a tableau[19] of life with six children and thirty shillings a week. Battered furniture, rows of much-mended washing on a pulley, black cooking range and a general air of chaos.

Sep got up from his place by the fire, put down his newspaper, took off a pair of steel-rimmed spectacles and shook hands.

He waved Helen to a sagging armchair. "Well, it's right nice to see you. Ah've often spoke of ye to t'missis."

His wife hung up her towel. "Yes, and I'm glad to meet ye both. I'll get some tea in a minnit."

She laughed and dragged a bucket of muddy water into a corner. "I've been washin' football jerseys. Them lads just handed them to me tonight—as if I haven't enough to do."

As she ran the water into the kettle I peeped surreptitiously around me and I noticed Helen doing the same. But we searched in vain. There was no sign of a cat. Surely he couldn't have run away again? With a growing feeling of dismay I realized that my little scheme could backfire devastatingly.

It wasn't until the tea had been made and poured that I dared to raise the subject.

"How—" I asked diffidently. "How is—er—Tiger?"

"Oh, he's grand," the little woman replied briskly. She glanced at the clock on the mantelpiece. "He should be back

_____

18. A *tableau* (TAB loe) is a dramatic scene.

Word Bank	**uncomprehendingly** (un CAHM pre HEND ing lee) *adv.*: without understanding

any time now, then you'll be able to see 'im."

As she spoke, Sep raised a finger. "Ah think ah can hear 'im now."

He walked over and opened the door and our Oscar strode in with all his old grace and majesty. He took one look at Helen and leaped onto her lap. With a cry of delight she put down her cup and stroked the beautiful fur as the cat arched himself against her hand and the familiar purr echoed round the room.

"He knows me," she murmured. "He knows me."

Sep nodded and smiled. "He does that. You were good to 'im. He'll never forget ye, and we won't either, will we mother?"

"No, we won't, Mrs. Herriot," his wife said as she applied butter to a slice of gingerbread. "That was a kind thing ye did for us and I 'ope you'll come and see us all whenever you're near."

"Well, thank you," I said. "We'd love to—we're often in Brawton."

I went over and tickled Oscar's chin, then I turned again to Mrs. Gibbons. "By the way, it's after nine o'clock. Where has he been till now?"

She poised her butter knife and looked into space.

"Let's see, now," she said. "It's Thursday, isn't it? Ah yes, it's 'is night for the Yoga class."

Recalling

1. Why did Tristan want to save the cat even though it was badly injured?

2. What did Helen do to help the cat recover from his injuries?

3. How did the cat's original owners find out where the cat was?

Interpreting

4. Why did Herriot decide to attempt to save the cat's life? Was it a reaction to something the cat did, or was it connected to his friendship with Tristan?

5. What was special about the cat? Give two examples of how he displayed this extraordinary trait.

6. Why was it hard for Herriot and Helen to return the cat to its rightful owners? What did Herriot and Helen do to ease this adjustment?

Concluding

7. Why did Herriot and his wife become so emotionally attached to this cat?

8. Do you think they will continue visiting the cat? If you feel their visits will end, when do you think they will stop?

Examining Nonfiction

Human-interest stories deal with people's reactions to a real-life crisis. In this story, the arrival of the cat in Herriot's office forced him to consider his responsibility to care for a severely injured animal. Herriot felt an obligation to assure this animal's recovery.

1. Were other characters in this story affected by the cat's personality? How?

2. Were the cat's original owners changed by the cat's disappearance and later reappearance?

3. How did the relationship between Herriot, his wife, and the cat's original owners develop in this story?

Thinking About Nonfiction

One of the challenges of writing stories about animals is the need to make them seem realistic. The author must create a personality for the animal that is true to its nature, yet is still interesting enough for the reader to consider appealing. Somehow the author must make the animal attractive without being unrealistic. It has to appear real both to animal lovers and to readers who are not familiar with the habits of the animals involved. Do you think Herriot's portrait of the cat is realistic in comparison to other stories you have read about cats and other small animals?

Creating and Writing

One of the outcomes of this story is the opportunity that Herriot and Helen received when they developed a friendship with the Gibbons family. Try to imagine a situation where you or a friend find a lost pet. Imagine the steps you would take to return this pet to its rightful owners.

1. Do you think your life might be changed as you attempt to find the people who lost this pet?

2. How would you describe your meeting with the pet's original owners?

As an alternative assignment, imagine finding a lost item.

1. What steps would you take to return this item?

2. How would the search for the item's rightful owner change your life?

3. How would you describe your meeting with the rightful owner of the lost item?

4. What could happen as a result of this meeting?

Into • *The Night the Bed Fell*

Just a typical night at the Thurber home: Father had gone to the attic to "think" ...Grandfather had disappeared to parts unknown to relive the Civil War...cousin Briggs Beall had gone to bed convinced that he would stop breathing while asleep...and that's only part of the family! Is this a human-interest story? It most certainly is, for, as we shall see, nothing is more interesting to humans than humans!

Focus

Human-interest stories can be sad, frightening, moving, happy or, as in this case, comical. James Thurber's clever look at his assortment of odd relatives is funny for a variety of reasons. One reason is Thurber's style of writing. As you read the opening descriptions of his parents, aunts, and cousin, you will see that the tone is very matter-of-fact, as if to say, "doesn't everybody keep their shoes in a pile next to their bed?" Thurber's way of reporting eccentric behavior as though it were perfectly normal adds to the story's humor.

A second reason the story is humorous is that the characters are all described in an affectionate way. Although the author could have been critical of his relatives, and written a complaining, negative story about them, he chooses to laugh at their eccentricities and invites the reader to laugh with him.

A third reason the story is funny is that Thurber, after introducing a whole series of odd characters with strange ideas, skillfully throws them together into one mad scene. As you read *The Night the Bed Fell*, note the short accounts that Thurber uses to introduce each family member. Why do you need all that information in order to understand what happened on the night of the incident?

About the Author

American author **JAMES THURBER** was born in 1894. Memories of his unpredictable family contributed to his humorous outlook on life. This was the basis for many of his essays for adults and children. His accounts of life in the 1940s and 1950s are very popular to this day. Thurber joined the staff of the *New Yorker* where his entertaining contributions enhanced the quality of this widely read magazine. James Thurber received many honors for his work including the Caldecott Medal in 1944. He died in 1961.

The Night the Bed Fell

James Thurber

I suppose that the high-water mark of my youth in Columbus, Ohio, was the night the bed fell on my father. It makes a better recitation[1] (unless, as some friends of mine have said, one has heard it five or six times) than it does a piece of writing, for it is almost necessary to throw furniture around, shake doors, and bark like a dog, to lend the proper atmosphere and verisimilitude[2] to what is admittedly a somewhat incredible tale. Still, it did take place.

It happened, then, that my father had decided to sleep in the attic one night, to be away where he could think. My mother opposed the notion strongly because, she said, the old wooden bed up there was unsafe; it was wobbly, and the heavy headboard would crash down on Father's head in case the bed fell, and kill him. There was no dissuading him, however, and at a quarter past ten he closed the attic door behind him and went up the narrow twisting stairs. We later heard ominous creakings as he crawled into bed. Grandfather, who usually slept in the attic bed when he was with us, had disappeared some days before. (On these occasions he was usually gone six or eight days and returned growling and out of temper, with the news that the Federal Union[3] was run by a passel of blockheads and that the Army of the Potomac[4] didn't have a chance.)

We had visiting us at this time a nervous first cousin of mine named Briggs Beall, who believed that he was likely to cease breathing when he was asleep. It was his feeling that if he were not awakened every hour during the night, he might die of suffocation. He had been accustomed to setting an alarm clock to ring at intervals until morning, but I persuaded him to abandon this. He slept in my room and I told him that I was such a light sleeper that if anybody quit breathing in the same room with me, I would wake instantly. He tested me the first night—which I had suspected he would—by holding his breath after my regular breathing had convinced him I was asleep. I was not asleep, however, and called to him. This seemed to allay his fears a little, but he took the precaution of putting a glass of spirits of camphor[5] on a little table at the head of his bed. In case I didn't arouse him until he was almost gone, he said, he would sniff the camphor, a powerful reviver.

Briggs was not the only member of his family who had his crotchets.[6] Old Aunt Melissa Beall (who could whistle like a man, with two fingers in her mouth)

Word Bank	**notion** (NO shun) *n.*: idea
	ominous (AHM in us) *adj.*: threatening; foreshadows evil or disaster

---

1. A *recitation* (RESS ih TAY shun) is a piece memorized and performed in public.
2. *Verisimilitude* (VAIR ih sih MILL ih tood) means having the appearance of truth.
3. *The Federal Union* was another name for the Northern side in the Civil War.
4. *The Army of the Potomac* (puh TOME ik) was a major division of the Union army that fought in the Civil War.
5. *Spirits of camphor* (KAM fur) is a powerful-smelling solution.
6. *Crotchets* (KROTCH its) are peculiar ideas.

suffered under the premonition that she was destined to die on South High Street because she had been born on South High Street and married on South High Street. Then there was Aunt Sarah Shoaf, who never went to bed at night without the fear that a burglar was going to get in and blow chloroform[7] under her door through a tube. To avert this calamity—for she was in greater dread of anesthetics than of losing her household goods—she always piled her money, silverware, and other valuables in a neat stack just outside her bedroom, with a note reading "This is all I have. Please take it and do not use your chloroform, as this is all I have." Aunt Gracie Shoaf also had a burglar phobia, but she met it with more fortitude. She was confident that burglars had been getting into her house every night for forty years. The fact that she never missed anything was to her no proof to the contrary. She always claimed that she scared them off before they could take anything, by throwing shoes down the hallway. When she went to bed, she piled, where she could get at them handily, all the shoes there were about her house. Five minutes after she had turned off the light, she would sit up in bed and say "Hark!" Her husband, who had learned to ignore the whole situation as long ago as 1903, would either be sound asleep or pretend to be sound asleep. In either case he would not respond to her tugging and pulling, so that presently she would arise, tiptoe to the door, open it slightly, and heave a shoe down the hall in one direction and its mate down the hall in the other direction. Some nights she threw them all, some nights only a couple of pairs.

But I am straying from the remarkable incidents that took place during the night that the bed fell on Father. By midnight

we were all in bed. The layout of the rooms and the disposition[8] of their occupants is important to an understanding of what later occurred. In the front room upstairs (just under Father's attic bedroom) were my mother and my brother Herman, who sometimes sang in his sleep, usually "Marching Through Georgia." Briggs Beall and myself were in a room adjoining this one. My brother Roy was in a room across the hall from ours. Our bull terrier, Rex, slept in the hall.

My bed was an army cot, one of those affairs which are made wide enough to sleep on comfortably only by putting up, flat with the middle section, the two sides which ordinarily hang down like the sideboards of a drop-leaf table. When these sides are up, it is perilous to roll too far toward the edge, for then the cot is likely to tip completely over, bringing the whole bed down on top of one, with a tremendous banging crash. This, in fact, is precisely what happened about two o'clock in the morning. (It was my mother who, in recalling the scene later, first referred to it as "the night the bed fell on your father.")

Always a deep sleeper, slow to arouse (I had lied to Briggs), I was at first unconscious of what had happened when the iron cot rolled me onto the floor and toppled over on me. It left me still warmly bundled up and unhurt, for the bed rested above me like a canopy. Hence I did not wake up, only reached the edge of consciousness and went back. The racket, however, instantly awakened my mother, in the next room, who came to the immediate conclusion that her worst dread was realized: the big wooden bed upstairs had fallen on Father. She therefore screamed, "Let's go to your poor father!"

---

7. *Chloroform* (KLOR uh FORM) is a type of anesthetic, used to cause sleep.
8. Here, *disposition* (DISS puh ZISH un) means arrangement.

It was this shout, rather than the noise of my cot falling, that awakened Herman, in the same room with her. He thought that Mother had become, for no apparent reason, hysterical. "You're all right, Mamma!" he shouted, trying to calm her. They exchanged shout for shout for perhaps ten seconds: "Let's go to your poor father!" and "You're all right!" That woke up Briggs. By this time I was conscious of what was going on, in a vague way, but did not yet realize that I was under my bed instead of on it. Briggs, awakening in the midst of loud shouts of fear and apprehension, came to the quick conclusion that he was suffocating and that we were all trying to "bring him out." With a low moan, he grasped the glass of camphor at the head of his bed and instead of sniffing it poured it over himself. The room reeked of camphor. "Ugf, ahfg," choked Briggs, like a drowning man, for he had almost succeeded in stopping his breath under the deluge of pungent spirits. He leaped out of bed and groped toward the open window but he came up against one that was closed. With his hand, he beat out the glass, and I could hear it crash and tinkle on the alleyway below. It was at this juncture that I, in trying to get up, had the uncanny sensation of feeling my bed above me! Foggy with sleep, I now suspected, in my turn, that the whole uproar was being made in a frantic endeavor to extricate me from what must be an unheard-of and perilous situation. "Get me out of this!" I bawled. "Get me out!" I think I had the nightmarish belief that I was entombed in a mine. "Gugh," gasped Briggs, floundering in his camphor.

By this time my mother, still shouting, pursued by Herman, still shouting, was trying to open the door to the attic, in order to go up and get my father's body out of the wreckage. The door was stuck, however, and wouldn't yield. Her frantic pulls on it only added to the general banging and confusion. Roy and the dog were now up, the one shouting questions, the other barking.

Father, farthest away and soundest sleeper of all, had by this time been awakened by the battering on the attic door. He decided that the house was on fire. "I'm coming, I'm coming!" he wailed in a slow, sleepy voice—it took him many minutes to regain full consciousness. My mother, still believing he was caught under the bed, detected in his "I'm coming!" the mournful, resigned note of one who is preparing to meet his Maker. "He's dying!" she shouted.

"I'm all right!" Briggs yelled to reassure her. "I'm all right!" He still believed that it was his own closeness to death that was worrying Mother. I found at last the light switch in my room, unlocked the door, and Briggs and I joined the others at the attic door. The dog, who never did like Briggs, jumped for him—assuming that he was the culprit in whatever was going on—and Roy had to throw Rex and hold him. We could hear Father crawling out of bed upstairs. Roy pulled the attic door open with a mighty jerk, and Father came down the stairs, sleepy and irritable but safe and sound. My mother began to weep when she saw him. Rex began to howl. "What in the name of heaven is going on here?" asked Father.

The situation was finally put together like a gigantic jigsaw puzzle. Father caught a cold from prowling around in his bare feet, but there were no other bad results. "I'm glad," said Mother, who always looked on the bright side of things, "that your grandfather wasn't here."

Word Bank

vague (VAYG) *adj.*: unclear

juncture (JUNK cher) *n.*: point of time

irritable (EAR it uh bul) *adj.*: cranky; upset and impatient

prowling (PROW ling) *v.*: to move about in a slow, secret way, intended to escape observation

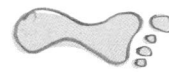

Recalling

1. Who usually slept in the attic bed? Where was this person at the time of the story?

2. Why was cousin Briggs Beall afraid to go to sleep at night? How did Thurber calm his fears?

3. Why did Thurber's mother wake up on the night of the incident?

4. Family members began shouting at each other. Write about two instances in which family members shouted at each other and their words were misinterpreted.

Interpreting

5. Write a list of all the events that occurred on the night of the incident from the time that Thurber's cot collapsed until Thurber's father caught a cold.

6. In the first paragraph of this story, Thurber introduces this incident as "the high-water mark of my youth in Columbus, Ohio." What does he mean by this comment?

Concluding

7. Do you think Thurber's family was typical? Explain your answer.

Examining Nonfiction

Humor comes in several forms. Thurber's humor is warm and friendly. He makes us laugh because he talks kindly and gently about exaggerated everyday events and everyday fears. We are all sometimes afraid of falling asleep forever or of burglars entering the house while we are sleeping. Yet Thurber takes these fears and exaggerates them to a point that we realize our fears are usually unfounded.

There is another type of humor that is harsh and belittling. This humor makes fun of people by degrading and mocking them for their everyday fears. This type of humor is called sarcasm. If Thurber had written a sarcastic story, he would have mocked Cousin Beall, his mother, and his father too. Do you think it is harder to write gentle humor or sarcastic humor? Support your opinion with examples from this story.

Thinking About Nonfiction

In the beginning of *The Night the Bed Fell*, Thurber claims that this story "makes a better recitation...than it does a piece of writing." In other words, Thurber prefers that this story be read aloud rather than silently. Do you agree? Think about this story and your reaction to it.

1. Do you think this story would have been funnier if the teacher had recited the story to you at an assembly?

2. Do you think the story was more humorous because you had a chance to read its words and think about its contents?

Creating and Writing

The Night the Bed Fell can be considered a story about one family's phobia concerning sleep and burglars. Yet ordinary people have many fears concerning their daily lives. Some people are afraid of heights, the dark, crowds, closed spaces, planes, trains, cars, etc.

Discuss with the class some of the phobias that exist today. Then try to write a short story about several people who share a certain fear. Use Thurber's story as a role model of a humorous story where a fear is exaggerated and, therefore, becomes humorous.

Into • *Barrio Boy*

Barrio Boy is the story of a young Mexican-American who enters a first-grade class for children from other countries. None of the children reads or writes English very well. By the end of the year, each child is well on the way to being an English-speaking American. Thanks to the serious, understanding principal and teacher, the children in the class are encouraged to value the language and customs of their parents as well as their new language and country.

Barrio Boy is the story of Ernesto Galarza, but it is also the story of thousands of children whose parents came from all over the world to start a new life in America. Within a few months, children who could not speak a word of English when they came were taught to read and write English. These children would go on to finish school successfully and make their contribution to America, the country that had opened its doors to them.

Focus

Biographies are usually written about famous people. Autobiographies, on the other hand, are written by people who—whether they are famous or not—feel that their life story will educate or inspire others. Although Ernesto Galarza is not a name most people would recognize, his story is of great importance. In it, we are shown a picture of an early 20th century public school. Far from being cold and unwelcoming, the school provided a special class designed to help new students from foreign lands. No country in the world offered such opportunity and promise to young people. For his part, Ernesto seized the chance to learn, and was soon promoted to a regular class. The American public schools played an important role in the lives of many other new Americans. Ernesto Galarza's story is an expression of thanks to America and to the public school system that was open to all.

About the Author

ERNESTO GALARZA was born in Mexico in 1905. After he and his family fled the Mexican Revolution, they settled in California. Some of the immigrant challenges he and his family experienced served as the basis for the story, *Barrio Boy*. Throughout his life Galarza concerned himself with the problems of the Mexican-American community. He was especially involved with educational affairs, and the rights of Mexican-American laborers. Galarza died in 1984.

Barrio Boy
Ernesto Galarza

My mother and I walked south on Fifth Street one morning to the corner of Q Street and turned right. Half of the block was occupied by the Lincoln School. It was a three story wooden building, with two wings that gave it the shape of a double-T connected by a central hall. It was a new building, painted yellow, with a shingled roof that was not like the red tile of the school in Mazatlán. I noticed other differences, none of them very reassuring.

We walked up the wide staircase hand in hand and through the door, which closed by itself. A mechanical contraption screwed to the top shut it behind us quietly.

Up to this point the adventure of enrolling me in the school had been carefully rehearsed. Mrs. Dodson had told us how to find it and we had circled it several times on our walks. Friends in the *barrio* explained that the director was called a principal, and that it was a lady not a man. They assured us that there was always a person at the school who could speak Spanish.

Exactly as we had been told, there was a sign on the door in both Spanish and English: "Principal." We crossed the hall and entered the office of Miss Nettie Hopley.

Miss Hopley was at a roll-top desk to one side, sitting in a swivel chair that moved on wheels. There was a sofa against the opposite wall, flanked by two windows and a door that opened on a small balcony. Chairs were set around a table and framed pictures hung on the walls of a man with long white hair and another with a sad face and a black beard.

The principal half turned in the swivel chair to look at us over the pinch glasses crossed on the ridge of her nose. To do this she had to duck her head slightly as if she were about to step through a low doorway.

What Miss Hopley said to us we did not know but we saw in her eyes a warm welcome and when she took off her glasses and straightened up she smiled wholeheartedly, like Mrs. Dodson. We were, of course, saying nothing, only catching the friendliness of her voice and the sparkle in her eyes while she said words we did not understand. She signaled us to the table. Almost tiptoeing across the office, I

Word Bank	**contraption** (kun TRAP shin) *n.*: device; gadget

maneuvered myself to keep my mother between me and the gringo lady. In a matter of seconds I had to decide whether she was a possible friend or a menace. We sat down.

Then Miss Hopley did a formidable thing. She stood up. Had she been standing when we entered she would have seemed tall. But rising from her chair she soared. And what she carried up and up with her was a superstructure,[1] firm shoulders, a straight sharp nose, full cheeks slightly molded by a curved line along the nostrils, thin lips that moved like steel springs, and a high forehead topped by hair gathered in a bun. Miss Hopley was not a giant in body but when she mobilized it to a standing position she seemed a match for giants. I decided I liked her.

She strode to a door in the far corner of the office, opened it and called a name. A boy of about ten years appeared in the doorway. He sat down at one end of the table. He was brown like us, a plump kid with shiny black hair combed straight back, neat, cool, and faintly obnoxious.

Miss Hopley joined us with a large book and some papers in her hand. She, too, sat down and the questions and answers began by way of our interpreter. My name was Ernesto. My mother's name was Henriqueta. My birth certificate was in San Blas. Here was my last report card from the Escuela Municipal Numero 3 para Varones of Mazatlán,[2] and so forth. Miss Hopley put things down in the book and my mother signed a card.

As long as the questions continued, Doña Henriqueta could stay and I was secure. Now that they were over, Miss Hopley saw her to the door, dismissed our interpreter and without further ado took me by the hand and strode down the hall to Miss Ryan's first grade.

Miss Ryan took me to a seat at the front of the room, into which I shrank—the better to survey her. She was, to skinny, somewhat runty me, of a withering height when she patrolled the class. And when I least expected it, there she was, crouching by my desk, her blond radiant face level with mine, her voice patiently maneuvering me over the awful idiocies of the English language.

During the next few weeks Miss Ryan overcame my fears of tall, energetic teachers as she bent over my desk to help me with a word in the pre-primer. Step by step, she loosened me and my classmates from the safe anchorage of the desk for recitations at the blackboard and consultations at her desk. Frequently she burst into happy announcements to the whole class. "Ito can read a sentence," and small Japanese Ito, squint-eyed and shy, slowly read aloud while the class listened in wonder: "Come. Skipper, come. Come and run." The Korean, Portuguese, Italian, and Polish first graders had similar moments of glory, no less shining than mine the day I conquered "butterfly," which I had been

_____

1. A *superstructure* (SOO pur STRUCK chur) is a large form.
2. *Escuela Municipal Numero 3 para Varones of Mazatlán* (ess KWAY luh moo NEE see PAAL NOO muh roe TRACE PAH ruh RONE ess mah saht LAHN) is Spanish for Municipal School Number 3 for the Boys of Mazatlán.

Word Bank	**maneuvered** (mun OOV erd) *v.*: to manage or move into or out of a position

formidable (FOR mid ih bul) *adj.*: threatening; causing fear, dread, and apprehension

anchorage (AYNG ker ij) *n.*: something that serves to hold a person or object firmly and securely

radiant (RAY dee int) *adj.*: shining; marked by an expression of love, confidence, or happiness

persistently pronouncing in standard Spanish as boo-ter-flee. "Children," Miss Ryan called for attention. "Ernesto has learned how to pronounce *butterfly*!" And I proved it with a perfect imitation of Miss Ryan. From that celebrated success, I was soon able to match Ito's progress as a sentence reader with "Come, butterfly, come fly with me."

Like Ito and several other first graders who did not know English, I received private lessons from Miss Ryan in the closet, a narrow hall off the classroom with a door at each end. Next to one of these doors Miss Ryan placed a large chair for herself and a small one for me. Keeping an eye on the class through the open door she read with me about sheep in the meadow and a frightened chicken going to see the king, coaching me out of my phonetic ruts in words like *pasture*, *bow-wow-wow*, *hay*, and *pretty*, which to my Mexican ear and eye had so many unnecessary sounds and letters. She made me watch her lips and then close my eyes as she repeated words I found hard to read. When we came to know each other better, I tried interrupting to tell Miss Ryan how we said it in Spanish. It didn't work. She only said "oh" and went on with *pasture*, *bow-wow-wow*, and *pretty*. It was as if in that closet we were both discovering together the secrets of the English language and grieving together over the tragedies of Bo-Peep. The main reason I was graduated with honors from the first grade was that I really admired Miss Ryan. Her radiant, no-nonsense character made us either afraid not to cooperate with her or admire her so we would not be afraid. I am not sure which. It was not only that we sensed she was with it, but also that she was with us.

Like the first grade, the rest of the Lincoln School was a sampling of the lower part of town where many races made their home. My pals in the second grade were Kazushi, whose parents spoke only Japanese; Matti, a skinny Italian boy; and Manuel, a fat Portuguese who would never get into a fight but wrestled you to the ground and just sat on you. Our assortment of nationalities included Koreans, Yugoslavs, Poles, Irish, and home-grown Americans.

At Lincoln, making us into Americans did not mean scrubbing away what made us originally foreign. The teachers called us as our parents did, or as close as they could pronounce our names in Spanish or Japanese. No one was ever scolded or punished for speaking in his native tongue on the playground. Matti told the class about his mother's down quilt, which she had made in Italy with the fine feathers of a thousand geese. Encarnación acted out how boys learned to fish in the Philippines. I astounded the third grade with the story of my travels on a stagecoach, which nobody else in the class had seen except in the museum at Sutter's Fort. After a visit to the Crocker Art Gallery and its collection of heroic paintings of the golden age of California, someone showed a silk scroll with a Chinese painting. Miss Hopley herself had a way of expressing wonder over these matters before a class, her eyes wide open until they popped slightly. It was easy for me to feel that becoming a proud American, as she said we should, did not mean feeling ashamed of being a Mexican.

Word Bank	**persistently** (per SIS tint lee) *adv.*: continuing without change; relentlessly; stubbornly

Recalling

1. Describe the principal's office.

2. Who was the interpreter for Ernesto and his mother?

3. What kind of information did Miss Ryan share with the class? How did it make Ernesto feel?

4. What was Ernesto's "celebrated success"?

5. What did Miss Ryan do during her private sessions with students in the hall?

Interpreting

6. Why did Ernesto decide the principal was a friend rather than a menace?

7. How did Miss Ryan make everyone feel comfortable in her classroom?

Concluding

8. Do you think that Miss Ryan's teaching methods helped the children adapt to an American school? Why or why not?

Examining Nonfiction

Autobiography is the story of the writer's own life. Because it would be impossible for him to include everything that ever happened to him, he must select those events that shaped him as a person.

1. Name two incidents that were important in young Ernesto's life.

2. Discuss two people who played an important role in Ernesto's schooling. Explain how they helped his development.

Thinking About Nonfiction

One of the reasons that it is so difficult to write a good autobiography is that it is difficult to relate a personal story in a totally accurate manner. Think back to an outing or event in your own family's history. Probably, if assigned to write this account, each member of your family would write a different version of the event. None of you is consciously distorting the facts, yet each of you believes their own version is the correct one.

Students in the same class may have very different interpretations of the same event. Imagine a snowball fight on a cold winter day. How would a reporter write a report of what happened during the fight? Whom would the reporter approach for information? Write a paragraph about how to find accurate information about what happened during the fight.

Creating and Writing

Remember the first day you entered school. Write how you felt, how your mother may have felt, how your other siblings may have felt, and how your new teacher may have felt. Then, try to combine the information into one essay. Describe as accurately as you can what happened on your first day of school, and how it affected the people involved.

Into • *Helen Keller*

From earliest childhood, Helen Keller could not see and could not hear. She could taste, smell, and feel objects. With these three senses she experienced the world more intensely than do most people with all five senses. Educated by her remarkable teacher, Anne Sullivan, she spoke several languages, graduated college with honors, lectured all over the world, and worked hard to improve the lives of blind people everywhere. Helen Keller's daily existence was so miraculous, that her life story has fascinated readers everywhere.

Focus

Helen Keller communicated with the world primarily through her sense of touch. She "read" by touching the Braille letters of books, she "listened" to music by feeling the vibrations of pianos, and she learned to talk by touching the throat of her teacher, Anne Sullivan. Yet, for her, the real world was what she saw in her mind. She was able to grasp ideas, beliefs, and philosophies. She understood concepts that would seem to require sight, such as color or dance. Pay particular attention to Helen's own words at the end of the piece. Are you truly seeing, hearing, tasting, smelling, and feeling this wonderful world?

About the Author

VAN WYCK BROOKS was born in New Jersey in 1886. A trip to Europe as a young man inspired him to become a writer. He later became a historian and biographer. Van Wyck Brooks was awarded many honors for his contributions including the Pulitzer Prize and eight honorary doctorates. Brooks died in 1963.

Helen Keller

Van Wyck Brooks

When I was in St. Augustine, Florida, in the winter of 1932, Helen Keller appeared at the Cathedral Lyceum, and I went to see and hear her there, drawn by curiosity, such as one feels for any world-famous person. For Helen Keller had been famous from the age of ten, when she had sat on Edward Everett Hale's knee and Queen Victoria asked Phillips Brooks about her. Mark Twain had said that the two most interesting characters of the nineteenth century were, quite simply, Napoleon and Helen Keller. Yet there she was in St. Augustine, still young, in 1932, and here she continues to be.

I remember one phrase she uttered then, referring to the subway in New York that "opened its jaws like a great beast." I was not aware then how familiar she was, literally, with the jaws of beasts, for she had once stroked a lion's mouth. The lion, it is true, was young and well fed in advance, but nevertheless she entered its cage boldly; for her "teacher," as she always called Anne Sullivan, the extraordinary woman who developed her mind, wished her to meet experience of every sort.

The daughter of a Confederate officer, Miss Keller was born on an Alabama farm and knew cows, mules, and horses from her earliest childhood; they had eaten apples from her hand and never harmed her; and her teacher, feeling that she should know wild animals as well, introduced her early to a circus zoo. She shook hands with a bear, she patted a leopard, she was lifted up to feel the ears of a giraffe. She encouraged elephants to wind their trunks about her neck, and big snakes wrapped their coils about her. Helen Keller, for this reason partly, grew up without fear, and she has remained both physically and morally fearless.

The world in which Helen Keller lives is built of touch sensations, devoid of physical color and devoid of sound,

> **Word Bank** **devoid** (dih VOYD) *adj.*: empty; not the usual or expected

and she has written much about the hand by which she lives and which takes the place of the hearing and sight of others. She has "ten eyes for sculpture," Professor Gaetano Salvemini[1] said when, in 1950, she visited Florence and he arranged for her to see Michelangelo's Medici tombs and the sculpture of Donatello in the Bargello.[2] Salvemini had movable scaffolds[3] set up so that she could pass her hands over the Medici heads. The sculptor Jo Davidson, who was present, said he had never seen these sculptures as when he watched her hands wandering over the forms.

Exploring the faces of her friends and people whom she has just met, she reads them as if she were clairvoyant,[4] and she can distinguish the Yankee twang and the Southern drawl she has never heard by touching the throats of the speakers. She says that hands are quite as easy to recognize as faces and reveal the secrets of character more openly. In her land of darkness and silence she can feel with her own hands the beautiful, the strong, the weak, the comic. She can tell from hands whether people have large natures or whether they have only "dormouse valor."[5]

Because two of her senses were cut off, nature augmented her three remaining senses, not the sense of touch alone but the sense of taste and the sense of smell. She tells in her *Journal* how in London, passing through a gate, she knew at once by the smell of burning leaves, with the smell of the grass, that she was in Green Park, and she says she can always distinguish Fifth Avenue from humbler New York streets by the odors issuing from the doors as she walks past. She knows the cosmetics that women are using and the kind of coffee they are roasting within and whether they use candles and burn soft coal or wood. "What lovely white lilacs!" she will exclaim, knowing they are white by touch or smell, for in texture and perfume white lilacs differ from purple.

Helen Keller, who cannot hear voices, feels vibrations. When an orchestra plays, she follows the music waves along the floor. Detecting on her desk upstairs the vibration of the pantry bell below, she answers with a shuffle of the feet, "Coming down!" "Listening" with her feet, she says, in a hotel dining room, she knows the moods and characters of people who walk past her, whether they are firm or indecisive, active or lazy, timid, weary, angry, or sad.

All this gave rise in early years to legends of a "wonder girl" that always annoyed Helen Keller—for she is the embodiment[6] of humor and simple good sense. Anne Sullivan took pains to keep her from being a prodigy,[7] but it was impossible to conceal the fact that she had a remarkable mind, and a still more remarkable will. Speaking of this, Emma Goldman said she proved that the human will had "an almost illimitable power."

Nothing could have been more tonic than Helen Keller's bringing-up, under the guidance of Anne Sullivan, on the farm in Alabama. They read and studied out of doors on the riverbank, in the woods, in the fields, in the shade, as

---

1. *Gaetano Salvemini* (GAY uh TAH no sahl VAY mee nee)
2. *Bargello* (bahr JAHL loe) is the name of a palace that is used as a museum now.
3. *Scaffolds* (SKAH foldz) are wooden platforms.
4. *Clairvoyant* (clair VOY unt) means naturally being able to see objects not present.
5. *Dormouse* (DOOR mouse) *valor* is the courage of the doormouse, a small rodent.
6. *Embodiment* (em BAHD ee mint) means the perfect example.
7. A *prodigy* (PRAHD ih jee) is a highly talented child.

Word Bank	**augmented** (awg MEN tid) *v.*: expanded; enlarged
	vibrations (vy BRAY shins) *n.*: shaking to and fro movements; a quivering or trembling motion
	detecting (dee TECKT ing) *v.*: discovering the true character of or the facts

feeling mountains and valleys and following the course of rivers. At the age of eighteen, if she had not mastered, she had learned much of geometry, algebra, physics, botany, zoology, and philosophy. She wrote good letters in French; later she spoke German. She was reading Latin too when she went to college. Unable to hear lectures or take notes, she graduated with honors from Radcliffe, where she wrote her autobiography in the class of Charles Copeland, the famous "Copey" who said she showed she could write better, in some of her work, than any other man or woman he had had as a pupil.

Few of the required books were printed for the blind, and she had to have whole books spelled into her hand. Always examining, observing, reflecting, surrounded by darkness and silence, she wrote that she found music and brightness within. Through all her thoughts flashed what she supposed was color. With her native traits of pluck[8] and courage, energy, tenacity, she was tough-minded and independent. She grew up fond of sports, riding a horse and a bicycle tandem, playing cards and chess, and all but completely self-reliant.

In *Midstream*, she wrote that she had read her Braille Bible so often that in many places the dots had been rubbed off. "The Bible," she has said, "is the only book that reaches up to the times in which we live. It speaks knowingly of the sun, the skies, the sea, and the beauty of distant stars…There are no differences in men. Differences are only as the variation in shadows cast by the sun."

Helen remembered, of a wild tulip tree. The fragrance of the mimosa blossoms, the pine needles, and grapes were blended with all her early lessons. She learned about the sun and rain, and how birds build their nests, about squirrels, frogs, wild flowers, rabbits, and insects; and, as it came back to her, everything that sang or bloomed, buzzed or hummed was part of her education.

It was Anne Sullivan who had invented the methods of connecting mind with mind that made all this possible, of course—and that seemed to be "superhuman," as Einstein remarked. What can one say of an intellect as handicapped as hers that carried her so far in so many directions? She early learned geography from maps that her teacher made out of river clay or sand,

---

8. Here, *pluck* means determination.

Word Bank	**reflecting** (rih FLECKT ing) *v.*: thinking about calmly or quietly

tenacity (tih NASS ih tee) *n.*: perseverance; persistence in seeking something valued or desired

Helen Keller has become a world citizen who stands for the real America that public men so often misrepresent. On her tours to help the blind in all the six continents, she has read in every country the signs of the times. She has understood Japan and Greece and especially perhaps the Bible lands, where she has lectured at universities from Cairo to Jerusalem and where new schools for the blind have risen as she passed. Reaching out to meet the minds of all sorts and conditions of men, she comprehends their needs and aspirations,[9] so that she is a true spokesman of our multiracial country that is already a vestibule[10] of the coming "one world."

Now it happens that, living myself in Connecticut not far from Helen Keller, I have taken a few notes about her in recent years, jotting down chance remarks of hers and other memoranda, comments that from time to time she had suggested. I offer some of these, unconnected as they are.

July 1945: Helen has been out picking blueberries today. She has only to touch them to know when they are ripe.

The paths and garden at her house are all so perfectly kept that I exclaimed over them. Helen does it. In summer she is up at five every morning, edging the driveway and the paths, weeding the flower beds. (She distinguishes by touch between the flowers and the weeds.)

Dinner with Helen and Salvemini at Professor Robert Pfeiffer's.[11] Our Florentine hostess, Mrs. Pfeiffer, played an Italian song. Helen stood with her left hand on the piano, waving her right hand, keeping time. In this way she knows by heart Beethoven's *Ninth Symphony* and recognizes many other compositions.

Someone asked her how she tells the difference between day and night. "Oh," she said, "in the day the air is lighter, odors are lighter, and there is more motion and more vibration in the atmosphere. At night the air is dense and one feels less motion in things."

September 1945: We rode downtown in a bus to Grand Central Station. Helen likes to feel the crowd around her. Suddenly she said, "There is a painter in the bus." I looked around and, sure enough, there was a house painter at the other end of the bus, twenty feet away.

October 1949: Helen comes to dinner. One of our friends asked Helen how she had come to understand abstractions.[12] She said she had found that good apples were sweet and that there were also bad apples that were bitter. Then she learned to think of the sweetness and bitterness apart from the apples, as ideas in themselves.

The fact is that Helen has a philosophic[13] mind. She relates in *My Religion* how, when she was twelve or so, she said to her teacher, "I have been in Athens." She meant, of course, in imagination, for she had been reading about Greece, but observe what followed in her thinking. She instantly perceived[14] that the "realness" of her mind was independent of conditions of place and body, that she had vividly seen and felt a place thousands of miles away precisely because she had a mind. How else could one explain this being "in Athens"? From that moment, she continued, "deafness and blindness were of no real account. They were to be relegated to the outer circle of my life."

December 1951: Usually Helen's typing is like an expert stenographer's, but the other day there were a few dim lines in one of her letters and she added this postscript: "Polly [Polly Thomson, Anne Sullivan's successor] says the writing of this machine doesn't please her critical eye. My apologies. H.K."

---

9. *Aspirations* (AS pur RAY shunz) are ambitions.
10. A *vestibule* (VESS tih byoo ul) is a hallway.
11. *Pfeiffer's* (FY ferz)
12. *Abstractions* (ab STRACK shunz) are non-concrete ideas.
13. *Philosophic* (FIL uh SAHF ik) means deeply probing.
14. *Perceived* (per SEEVD) means understood.

Polly likes to tease her, and she is sometimes severe with her. If Helen makes a mistake in typing, Polly makes her copy the page again. I must add, what all their friends know, that Polly is in her way as extraordinary a person as Helen. Without her vitality and her diplomatic sense, what could Helen do in her journeys about the world? And what inexhaustible buoyancy[15] both of them have! I have seen them together on a midnight train, when everyone else was asleep, smiling and chatting like birds on a branch in the morning.

June 1953: Helen is seventy-three years old today. This week she returned from a two-months' absence in South America. What variety there is in her mind! She is interested in everything. She recalled to me the dancing of La Argentina,[13] though how she conceived of this so well I cannot imagine. And what happy phrases come to her mind! Some children spelled words into her hand, and she said their small fingers were like "the wild flowers of conversation."

About Helen Keller, it seems to me, William James uttered the last word when he wrote, "The sum of it is that you are a *blessing*"—a verdict that has been ratified in hundreds of hospitals throughout the world where she has all but raised the dead. Someday the story will be told of the miracles she has performed, or what could have passed for miracles in less case-hardened ages, when the blind have opened inward eyes and really seen life for the first time after Helen Keller has walked and talked with them.

---

15. *Inexhaustible buoyancy* (ih nig ZAWST ih bul BOY un SEE) is untiring spirit.

Word Bank	**ratified** (RAD ih fyd) *v*.: approved; upheld
	vitality (vy TAA lih tee) *n*.: full of energy, strength, and vigor

A Word of Advice

From *Three Days to See*
by Helen Keller

I who am blind can give one hint to those who see—one admonition to those who would make full use of the gift of sight: Use your eyes as if tomorrow you would be stricken blind. And the same method can be applied to the other senses. Hear the music of voices, the song of a bird, the mighty strains of an orchestra, as if you would be stricken deaf tomorrow. Touch each object you want to touch as if tomorrow your tactile sense would fail. Smell the perfume of flowers, taste with relish each morsel, as if tomorrow you could never smell and taste again. Make the most of every sense; glory in all the facets of pleasure and beauty which the world reveals to you through the several means of contact which nature provides. But of all the senses, sight must be the most delightful.

Recalling

1. Why was Helen interested in and comfortable with animals?

2. How did Helen distinguish between the different accents of people speaking to her?

3. What were some of the teaching methods that Anne Sullivan used to teach Helen how to appreciate life around her?

4. What did Helen learn from feeling "vibrations"?

5. What hobbies did Helen have when she was growing up?

Interpreting

6. How did Helen use her sense of taste and smell to compensate for her missing senses?

7. Anne Sullivan was the perfect teacher for Helen Keller because Anne tried constantly to make Helen feel self-assured, self-confident, and independent. Give some examples of skills that Anne taught Helen that contributed to this.

8. How did Helen teach herself to understand abstract ideas?

Concluding

9. Mark Twain is quoted as saying that Helen Keller was one of the two most interesting characters of the 19th century. Write a paragraph agreeing or disagreeing with Mark Twain's assessment of Helen Keller. Support your opinion with evidence from the selection.

Examining Nonfiction

In *Helen Keller*, you are introduced to several different ways of presenting biographies. This selection begins with a collection of thoughts on Helen Keller. It changes into a sample of diary entries and observations of specific events. It concludes with A Word of Advice from *Three Days to See*, by Helen Keller. This short excerpt shows that Helen Keller was a powerful, talented writer who was able to speak honestly and sensitively about her disabilities.

This selection, therefore, shows three ways of acquiring information: recollections, diary entries, and direct quotes.

1. Do you feel one method of portraying Helen is more authentic than another method?

2. Which method would you use if you had to write a biography of a well-known personality? Why?

Thinking About Nonfiction

Van Wyck Brooks was a neighbor and friend of Helen Keller who had some contact with her. Brooks spent much time doing research before he wrote this biography. On the other hand, Anne Sullivan was Helen Keller's teacher and constant companion for many years.

1. Who do you think could write a more authentic biography of Helen Keller, Brooks or Sullivan?

2. Do you think the biographer has to know their subject very well, or do you think a biographer could do extensive research to make up for lack of personal knowledge of the subject about whom they are writing?

Creating and Writing

Select a prominent personality whom you know and admire. Think about incidents that occurred in this person's life. Think about positive interactions your friends and acquaintances have had with this person. How would you go about writing an authentic biography of this person, a biography that makes the reader think admirably about the life of this personality? How would you write a biography that portrays your character's unique characteristics and talents? Attempt to write this biography.

Into ● *Roberto Clemente: A Bittersweet Memoir*

Inside every athlete beats the heart of a real, feeling human being. We can learn about an athlete from charts, books, and computers; we can find out how far a ball was kicked, how fast a race was run, how high someone jumped. But to really know the person inside the athlete, we must go to the athlete's teachers and friends, and their letters and conversations. In this biographical sketch of the great baseball player, Roberto Clemente, we are taken back in time to the world of a shy little Puerto Rican boy with a big heart. We talk to his beloved teacher, to the scout who discovered him, and to one of his team members. When the story is finished, we feel we have encountered a strong, complex personality whose performance on the baseball field was thrilling, and whose devotion to those he cared for was unforgettable.

Focus

A good biography gives the reader the feeling that they have personally become friendly with the subject of the work. The biographer does this by carefully choosing those incidents in the person's life that most reflect the unique and outstanding characteristics of the subject. In this case, the researcher probably had to sift through many volumes of original documents until he found the incidents and the interviews that he wished to share with the readers of the biography of this outstanding person and baseball player.

About the Author

JERRY IZENBERG was born in 1930 in Newark, New Jersey. He became a sportswriter in 1950. A famous columnist, his works have been syndicated throughout the country. Through the course of his career, Izenberg interviewed many sports figures. His interviews with friends and acquaintances of Roberto Clemente became the basis for the biographical essay you are about to read.

ROBERTO CLEMENTE:

A Bittersweet Memoir

Jerry Izenberg

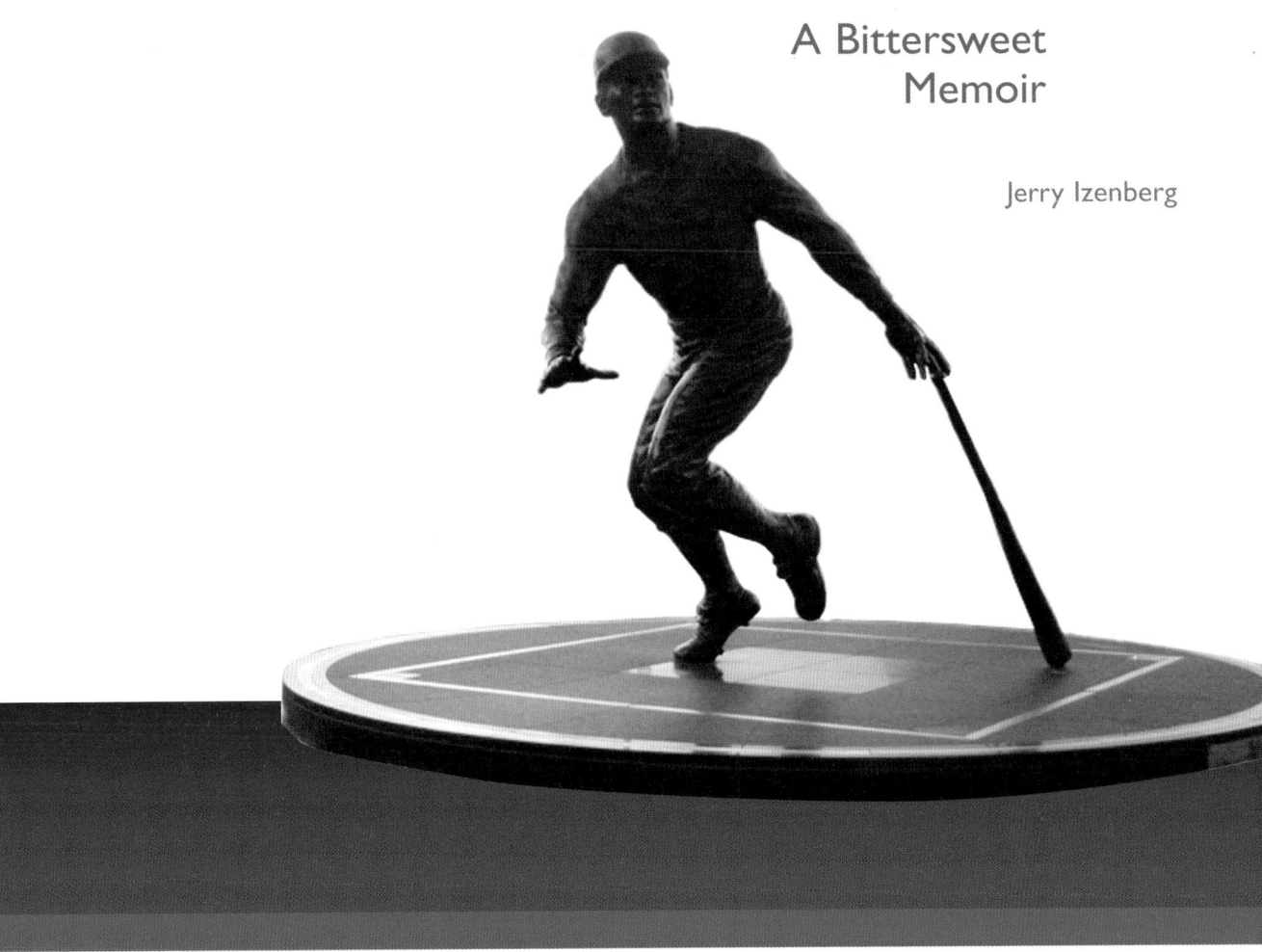

The record book will tell you that Roberto Clemente collected 3,000 hits during his major-league career. It will say that he came to bat 9,454 times, that he drove in 1,305 runs, and played 2,433 games over an eighteen-year span.

But it won't tell you about Carolina,[1] Puerto Rico, and the old square, and the narrow, twisting streets, and the roots that produced him. It won't tell you about the Julio Coronado[2] School and a remarkable woman named María Isabella Casares,[3] whom he called "Teacher" until the day he died and who helped to shape his life in times of despair and depression. It won't tell you about a man named Pedro Zarrilla,[4] who found him on a country softball team and put him in the uniform of the Santurce[5] club and who nursed him from a promising young athlete to a major-league superstar.

---

1. *Carolina* (kah roe LEE nuh)
2. *Julio Coronado* (HOO lee oh koe roe NAH thoe)
3. *María Isabella Casares* (mah REE uh eez ah BAY lah kah SAH raze)
4. *Pedro Zarrilla* (PAID roe say REE yah)
5. *Santurce* (sahn TOOR say)

And most of all, those cold numbers won't begin to delineate the man Roberto Clemente was. To even begin to understand what this magnificent athlete was all about, you have to work backward. The search begins at the site of its ending.

The car moves easily through the predawn streets of San Juan. It turns down a bumpy secondary road and moves past small shantytowns. Then there is another turn, onto hard-packed dirt and sand, and although the light has not yet quite begun to break, you can sense the nearness of the ocean. You can hear its waves, pounding harshly against the jagged rocks. You can smell its saltiness. The car noses to a stop, and the driver says, "From here you must walk." The place is called Punta Maldonado.[6]

"This is the nearest place," the driver tells me. "This is where they came by the thousands on that New Year's eve and New Year's day. Out there," he says, gesturing with his right hand, "out there, perhaps a mile and a half from where we stand. That's where we think the plane went down."

The final hours of Roberto Clemente were like this. Just a month or so

before, he had agreed to take a junior-league baseball team to Nicaragua and manage it in an all-star game in Managua.[7] He had met people and made friends there. He was not a man who made friends casually. He had always said that the people you wanted to give your friendship to were the people to whom you had to be willing to give something—no matter what the price.

Just two weeks after he returned from that trip, Managua, Nicaragua exploded into flames. The earth trembled, and people died. It was the worst earthquake anywhere in the hemisphere in a long time.

Back in Puerto Rico, a personality named Luis Vigereaux[8] heard the news and was moved to try to help the

---

6. *Punta Maldonado* (POON tah mahl doe NAH thoe)
7. *Managua* (mah NAH gwah) is the capital city of Nicaragua.
8. *Luis Vigereaux* (loo EES vee gay ROE)

Word Bank	delineate (dih LIN ee ayt) *v*.: to describe with accuracy or in detail

gesturing (JEST yur ing) *v*.: motioning with the body or the limbs to express an idea, a feeling, or an attitude

victims. He needed someone to whom the people would listen, someone who could say what had to be said and get the work done that had to be done and help the people who had to be helped.

"I knew," Luis Vigereaux said, "that Roberto was such a person, perhaps the only such person who would be willing to help."

And so the mercy project, which would eventually claim Roberto's life, began. He appeared publicly. But he needed a staging area. The city agreed to give him Sixto Escobar[9] Stadium.

"Bring what you can," he told the people. "Bring medicine…bring clothes…bring food…bring shoes…bring yourself to help us load. We need so much. Whatever you bring, we will use."

And the people of San Juan came. They walked through the heat, and they drove old cars and battered little trucks, and the mound of supplies grew and grew. Within two days, the first mercy planes left for Nicaragua.

Meanwhile, a ship had been chartered and loaded. And as it prepared to steam away, unhappy stories began to drift back from Nicaragua. Not all the supplies that had been flown in, it was rumored, were getting through. Puerto Ricans, who had flown the planes, had no passports, and Nicaragua was in a state of panic.

"We have people there who must be protected. Black-market types must not be allowed to get their hands on these supplies," Clemente told Luis Vigereaux. "Someone must make sure —particularly before the ship gets there. I'm going on the next plane."

The plane they had rented was an old DC-7. It was scheduled to take off at 4 P.M. on December 31, 1972. Long before takeoff time, it was apparent that the plane needed more work. It had even taxied onto the runway and then turned back. The trouble, a mechanic

who was at the airstrip that day conjectured, "had to do with both port engines.[10] We worked on them most of the afternoon."

The departure time was delayed an hour, and then two, and then three. At 9 P.M., even as the first stirrings of the annual New Year's eve celebration were beginning in downtown San Juan, the DC-7 taxied onto the runway, received clearance, rumbled down the narrow concrete strip, and pulled away from the earth. It headed out over the Atlantic and banked toward Nicaragua, and its tiny lights disappeared on the horizon.

Just ninety seconds later, the tower at San Juan International Airport received this message from the DC-7 pilot, "We are coming back around."

Just that.

Nothing more.

And then there was a great silence.

"It was almost midnight," recalls Rudy Hernández,[11] a former teammate of Roberto's. "We were having this party in my restaurant. Somebody turned on the radio, and the announcer was saying that Roberto's plane was feared missing. And then, because my place is on the beach, we saw these giant floodlights crisscrossing the waves, and we heard the sound of the helicopters and the little search planes."

Drawn by a common sadness, the people of San Juan began to make their way toward the beach, toward Punta Maldonado. A cold rain had begun to fall. It washed their faces and blended with the tears.

---

9. *Sixto Escobar* (SEECE toe ess koe BAHR)
10. *Port engines* are engines on the left side of the airplane.
11. *Hernandez* (ahr NAHN dess)

Word Bank	**battered** (BAT terd) *adj.*: worn or damaged by hard usage or by blows
	conjectured (kun JEK cherd) *v.*: guessed

They came by the thousands, and they watched for three days. Towering waves boiled up and made the search virtually impossible. The U.S. Navy sent a team of expert divers into the area, but the battering of the waves defeated them too. Midway through the week, the pilot's body was found in the swift-moving currents to the north. On Saturday, bits of the cockpit were sighted.

And then—nothing else.

Rudy Hernández[12] said, "I have never seen a time or a sadness like that. The streets were empty, the radios silent, except for the constant bulletins about Roberto. Traffic? Forget it. All of us cried. All of us who knew him, and even those who didn't, wept that week. There will never be another like Roberto."

Who was he...I mean really?

He was born in Carolina, Puerto Rico. Today the town has about 125,000 people, but when Roberto was born there in 1934, it was roughly one-sixth its current size.

María Isabella Casares is a school teacher. She has taught the children of Carolina for thirty years. Most of her teaching has been done in tenth-grade history classes. Carolina is her home, and its children are her children. And among all of those whom she calls her own (who are all the children she taught), Roberto Clemente was something even more special to her.

"His father was an overseer on a sugar plantation. He did not make much money," she explained in an empty classroom at Julio Coronado School. "But then, there are no rich children here. There have never been. Roberto was typical of them. I had known him when he was a small boy because my father had run a grocery store in Carolina and Roberto's parents used to shop there."

There is this thing that you have to know about María Isabella Casares before we hear more from her. What you have to know is that she is the model of what a teacher should be. Between her and her students even now, as back when Roberto attended her school, there is this common bond of mutual respect. Earlier in the day, I had watched her teach a class in the history of the Abolition Movement[12] in Puerto Rico. I don't speak much Spanish, but even to me it was clear that this is how a class should be, this is the kind of person who should teach, and these are the kinds of students such a teacher will produce.

With this as a background, what she has to say about Roberto Clemente carries much more impact.

"Each year," she said, "I let my students choose the seats they want to sit in. I remember the first time I saw Roberto. He was a very shy boy, and he went straight to the back of the room and chose the very last seat. Most of the time he would sit with his eyes down. He was an average student. But there was something very special about him. We would talk after class for hours. He wanted to be an engineer, you know, and perhaps he could have been. But then he began to play softball, and one day he came to me and said, 'Teacher, I have a problem.'

"He told me that Pedro Zarrilla, who was one of our most prominent baseball people, had seen him play and that Pedro wanted him to sign a professional contract with the Santurce Crabbers. He asked me what he should do.

---

12. *The Abolition Movement* (AA buh lih shun MOOV mint) was a movement to outlaw slavery.

Word Bank	**virtually** (VER choo uh lee) *adv.*: almost entirely; nearly; for all practical purposes

prominent (PRAHM in int) *adj.*: widely and popularly known; standing out

"I have thought about that conversation many times. I believe Roberto could have been almost anything, but G-d gave him a gift that few have, and he chose to use that gift. I remember that on that day I told him, 'This is your chance, Roberto. We are poor people in this town. This is your chance to do something. But if in your heart you prefer not to try, then, Roberto, that will be your problem—and your decision.' "

There was and there always remained a closeness between this boy-soon-to-be-a-man and his favorite teacher.

"Once, a few years ago, I was sick with a very bad back. Roberto, not knowing this, had driven over from Río Piedras,[13] where his house was, to see me," Mrs. Casares recalled.

"Where is the teacher?" Roberto asked Mrs. Casares's stepdaughter that afternoon.

"Teacher is sick, Roberto. She is in bed."

"Teacher," Roberto said, pounding on the bedroom door, "get up and put on your clothes. We are going to the doctor whether you want to or not."

"I got dressed," Mrs. Casares told me, "and he picked me up like a baby and carried me in his arms to the car. He came every day for fifteen days, and most days he had to carry me. But I went to the doctor and he treated me. Afterward, I said to the doctor that I wanted to pay the bill.

" 'Mrs. Casares,' he told me, 'please don't start with that Clemente or he will kill me. He has paid all your bills, and don't you dare tell him I have told you.'

"Well, Roberto was like that. We had been so close."

On the night Roberto Clemente's plane disappeared, Mrs. Casares was at home, and a delivery boy from the pharmacy stopped by and told her to turn on the radio and sit down. "I think something has happened to someone who is very close to you, Teacher, and I want to be here in case you need help."

María Isabella Casares heard the news. She is a brave woman, and months later, standing in front of the empty crypt in the cemetery at Carolina where Roberto Clemente was to have been buried, she said, "He was like a son to me. This is why I want to tell you about him. This is why you must make people—particularly our people, our Puerto Rican children—understand what he was. He was like my son, and he is all our sons in a way. We must make sure that the children never forget how beautiful a man he was."

The next person to touch Roberto Clemente was Pedro Zarrilla, who owned the Santurce club. He was the man who discovered Clemente on the country softball team, and he was the man who signed him for a four-hundred-dollar bonus.

"He was a skinny kid," Pedro Zarrilla recalls, "but even then he had those large, powerful hands, which we all noticed right away. He joined us, and he was nervous. But I watched him, and I said to myself, 'This kid can throw, and this kid can run, and this kid can hit. We will be patient with him.' The season had been through several games before I finally sent him in to play."

Luis Olmo remembers that game. Luis Olmo had been a major-league outfielder with the Brooklyn Dodgers. He had been a splendid ballplayer. Today he is in the insurance business in San Juan. He sat in his office and recalled very well that first moment when Roberto Clemente stepped up to bat.

"I was managing the other team. They had a man on base, and this skinny kid comes out. Well, we had never seen him, so we didn't really

---

13. *Río Piedras* (REE oh pee AY drahs)

know how to pitch to him. I decided to throw him a few bad balls and see if he'd bite.

"He hit the first pitch. It was an outside fast ball and he never should have been able to reach it. But he hit it down the line for a double. He was the best bad-ball hitter I have ever seen, and if you ask major-league pitchers who are pitching today, they will tell you the same thing. After a while, it got so that I just told my pitchers to throw the ball down the middle because he was going to hit it no matter where they put it, and at least if he decided not to swing, we'd have a strike on him.

"I played in the big leagues. I know what I am saying. He was the greatest we ever had…maybe one of the greatest anyone ever had. Why did he have to die?"

Once Pedro Zarrilla turned him loose, there was no stopping Roberto Clemente. As Clemente's confidence grew, he began to get better and better. He was the one the crowds came to see out at Sixto Escobar Stadium.

"You know, when Clemente was in the line-up," Pedro Zarrilla says, "there was always this undercurrent of excitement in the ball park. You knew that if he was coming to bat, he would do something spectacular. You knew that if he was on first base, he was going to try to get to second base. You knew that if he was playing right field and there was a man on third base, then that man on third base already knew what a lot of men on third base in the majors were going to find out—you don't try to get home against Roberto Clemente's arm."

Soon the major-league scouts began to make their moves, and in 1955 Roberto Clemente came to the Pittsburgh Pirates. He was the finest prospect the club had had in a long, long time. But the Pirates of those days were spectacular losers, and even

Roberto Clemente couldn't turn them around overnight.

"I will never forget how fast he became a superstar in this town," says Bob Friend, who became a great Pirate pitcher. "Later he would have troubles because he was either hurt or thought he was hurt, and some people would say that he was loafing. But I know he gave it his best shot, and he helped make us winners."

The first winning year was 1960, when the Pirates won the pennant and went on to beat the Yankees in the seventh game of the World Series. Whitey Ford, who pitched against him twice in that Series, recalls that Roberto actually made himself look bad on an outside pitch to encourage Whitey to come back with it. "I did," Ford recalls, "and he unloaded. Another thing I remember is the way he ran out a routine ground ball in the last game, and when we were a little slow covering, he beat it out. It was something most people forget, but it made the Pirates' victory possible."

The season was over. Roberto Clemente had hit safely in every World Series game. He had batted over .300. He had been a superstar. But when they announced the Most Valuable Player Award voting, Roberto had finished a distant third.

"I really don't think he resented the fact that he didn't win it," Bob Friend says. "What hurt—and in this he was right—was how few votes he got. He felt that he simply wasn't being accepted. He brooded about that a lot. I think his attitude became one of 'well, I'm going to show them from now on so that they will never forget.'

Word Bank	**undercurrent** (UN der KER int) *n.*: a force which is not readily visible

resented (ree ZEN tid) *v.*: felt annoyed with

"And you know, he sure did."

Roberto Clemente went home and married. He felt less alone. Now he could go on and prove what it was he had to prove. And he was determined to prove it.

His moment finally came. It took eleven years for the Pirates to win a World Series berth again, and when they did in 1971, it was Roberto Clemente who led the way. I will never forget him as he was during that 1971 Series with the Orioles, a Series that the Pirates figured to lose and in which they, in fact, dropped the first two games down in Baltimore.

When they got back to Pittsburgh for the middle slice of the tournament, Roberto Clemente went to work and led his team. He was a superstar during the five games that followed. He was the big man in the Series. He was the MVP.[14] He was everything he had ever dreamed of being on a ball field.

Most important of all, the entire country saw him do it, and never again—even though nobody knew it would end so tragically soon—was anyone ever to doubt his ability.

The following year, Clemente ended the season by collecting his three thousandth hit. Only ten other men had ever done that in the entire history of baseball.

"When I think of Roberto now," says Willie Stargell, his closest friend on the Pirates, "I think of the kind of man he was. There was nothing phony about him. He had his own ideas about how life should be lived, and if you didn't see it that way, then he let you know in so many ways, without words, that it was best you each go your separate ways.

"He was a man who chose his friends carefully. His was a friendship worth having. I didn't think many people took the time and the trouble to try to understand him, and I'll admit it wasn't easy. But he was worth it.

"The way he died, you know, I mean on that plane carrying supplies to Nicaraguans who'd been dying in that earthquake, well, I wasn't surprised he'd go out and do something like that. I wasn't surprised he'd go. I just never thought what happened could happen to him.

"But I know this. He lived a full life. And if he knew at that moment what the L-rd had decided, well, I really believe he would have said, 'I'm ready.' "

He was thirty-eight years old when he died. He touched the heart of Puerto Rico in a way that few people ever could. He touched a lot of other hearts too. He touched hearts that beat inside people of all colors of skin.

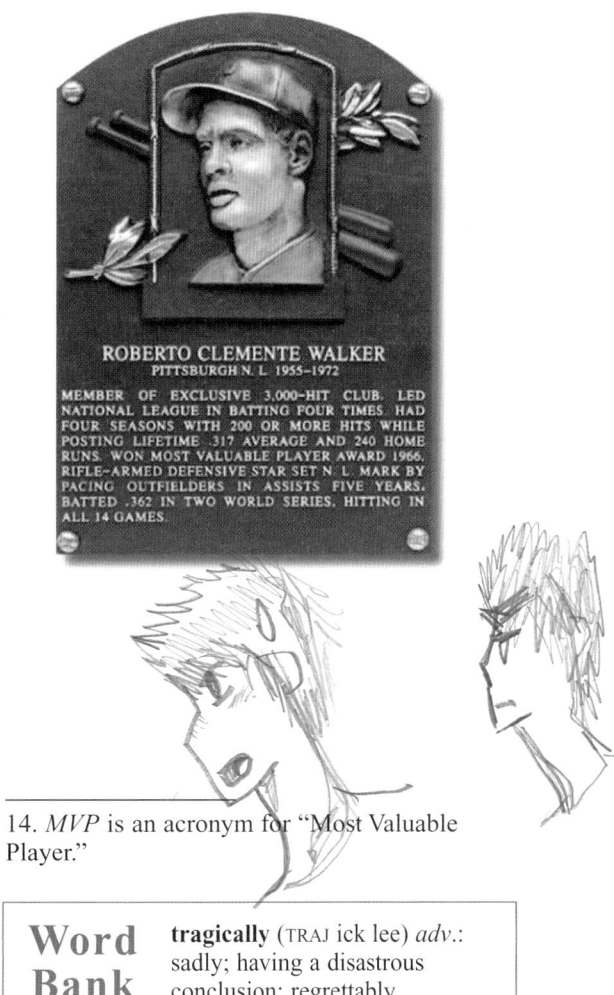

ROBERTO CLEMENTE WALKER
PITTSBURGH N. L. 1955–1972

MEMBER OF EXCLUSIVE 3,000-HIT CLUB. LED NATIONAL LEAGUE IN BATTING FOUR TIMES. HAD FOUR SEASONS WITH 200 OR MORE HITS WHILE POSTING LIFETIME .317 AVERAGE AND 240 HOME RUNS. WON MOST VALUABLE PLAYER AWARD 1966. RIFLE-ARMED DEFENSIVE STAR SET N. L. MARK BY PACING OUTFIELDERS IN ASSISTS FIVE YEARS. BATTED .362 IN TWO WORLD SERIES. HITTING IN ALL 14 GAMES.

14. *MVP* is an acronym for "Most Valuable Player."

Recalling

1. Why did the author go to a place called Punta Maldonado?

2. Why did Luis Vigereaux ask Clemente to visit Nicaragua?

3. How did Clemente help Mrs. Casares when she was sick in bed with a bad back?

4. What American baseball team did Clemente join?

5. Why was Clemente considered a baseball superstar?

6. How old was Clemente when he died?

Interpreting

7. What did Mrs. Casares mean when she said that Clemente was "...like my son, and he is all our sons in a way"?

8. Why did Clemente's teammates think he was special? Provide one or two examples to justify your response.

Concluding

9. The author has titled this selection, *Roberto Clemente: A Bittersweet Memoir*. Define the word "bittersweet," and explain how it refers to Clemente's life.

10. Why did Clemente feel disappointed when he did not win the Most Valuable Player Award in 1960? What did he decide to do about this? What did Clemente's reaction tell you about his personality?

Examining Nonfiction

Jerry Izenberg chose to provide us with a personal glimpse of Clemente's life by including extensive interviews with Roberto's teacher Maria Casares, and with Pedro Zarrilla, the owner of the first team for which Roberto played professionally.

1. Make a list of Clemente's character traits found in the incidents that Mrs. Casares and Mr. Zarrilla shared with Izenberg.

2. Do you think the author has created an authentic portrait of Clemente's personality and what distinguished him from other athletes?

Thinking About Nonfiction

The purpose of biography is to give the reader a realistic portrait of the subject of the work. The biographer wants the reader to identify with the subject and care about this person's life. Many people have heard of Helen Keller and Roberto Clemente. Therefore, their biographers had to find a way of telling us something new, touching, and interesting that could add to our previous knowledge of them.

In *Roberto Clemente: A Bittersweet Memoir*, the author begins his story with a visit to the site of Clemente's plane crash. Reference to this tragedy will create a sense of loss for this unselfish individual. The author then presents a series of personal stories about Clemente, ending with a summary of his sports accomplishments and interactions with his team buddies.

This story starts by telling the reader about Clemente's tragic death, and then moves backwards in time to his childhood. Would the author have done better to simply tell the story of Roberto Clemente's life in the proper order? Support your answer.

Creating and Writing

Roberto Clemente could have just played baseball and broken sports records; he could have settled easily into a rich lifestyle and forgotten his humble past. Instead, Clemente chose to honor it. He stayed in touch with fellow Puerto Ricans. He volunteered to carry supplies to Nicaragua after its devastating earthquake. It was this kindness that may have inspired Jerry Izenberg to title this selection, *Roberto Clemente: A Bittersweet Memoir*. Even though Roberto's life was short, it was filled with numerous acts of kindness and charity.

Can you think of someone from the past whose kindness was so overwhelming that people still remember it today? Can you think of incidents that illustrate the positive effects of that kindness? Write a short essay describing this thoughtful person. Include recollections of the incidents that illustrate their humanitarianism.

Into • *Florence Nightingale*

Florence Nightingale was one of the extraordinary people produced by 18th-century England. Educated, determined, and independent, she embodied the spirit of Victorian England. The problem was, she was a woman in a world where it was the men who were expected to accomplish great things. Had she done what was expected of her as a Victorian woman, she would have spent most of her life socializing with other members of British high society, and contributed to some charitable organizations. Instead, she used her intelligence, courage, wealth, and position to improve the lot of soldiers everywhere.

Before Florence Nightingale arrived on the scene, the injured British soldier was doomed to incompetent medical care, neglect, and an early death from infection and disease. Florence Nightingale used every ounce of her strength to change this situation. By the time she was done, conditions in British hospitals had moved from being primitive and cruel to modern and efficient.

Focus

Biography and historical essay may, at first glance, appear to be one and the same. However, there is a difference between them. **Biography** focuses on one person's life. The historical events included in the biography are part of the hero's life story. **Historical essay** focuses on one period of history. Because it is people who make history, much of historical essay is biographical, yet the essay's goal is to describe the time period, not the life of one individual.

Florence Nightingale is more a biography than it is a historical essay. Florence Nightingale is clearly the heroine of the story, and one can see that the historical background given is necessary to fully appreciate her achievements. Yet, the story is about more than just Florence herself. It is about the Crimean War and Victorian England. It is about a turning point in history for treatment of soldiers on the battlefield. It is about the modernization of medical treatment worldwide.

About the Authors

HENRY THOMAS and **DANA LEE THOMAS** were biographers of famous people. *Florence Nightingale* is an excerpt from a book, *Living Biographies of Famous Women*. In this essay, the authors tell of the great accomplishments of the renowned nurse, Florence Nightingale. Henry and Dana Lee Thomas published this inspiring biographical sketch in 1942.

I

"Forward, the Light Brigade!
Charge for the guns," he said:
Into the valley of Death
    Rode the six hundred.

Theirs not to reason why,
Theirs but to do and die:
Into the valley of Death
    Rode the six hundred.

When can their glory fade?
O the wild charge they made!
    All the world wondered.

Honor the charge they made!
Honor the Light Brigade,
    Noble six hundred!

Florence Nightingale

Henry Thomas and Dana Lee Thomas

Illustration of the hospital ward in Scutari

This is part of Tennyson's romantic picture of the battle of Balaklava,[1] in the Crimean War. But here is Florence Nightingale's realistic picture of the scene that *followed* the battle:

> At the hospital (in Scutari)[2] there are no clean shirts. The men have only rags saturated with blood. The hospital has been transformed from a barrack, and underneath its imposing mass are sewers loaded with filth, through which the wind blows fetid air up the pipes into the wards where the sick men are lying. Wounds and sickness, overcrowding and want of proper ventilation contribute to the foulness of the atmosphere. The wards are infested with rats, mice, and vermin. Flooring is defective; furniture and even the commonest utensils for cleanliness, decency, and comfort are lacking. The vermin might, if they had but unity of purpose, carry off the four miles of bedding on their backs and march with them into the War Office in London.

Tennyson speaks of the heroism of the men in the field. Florence Nightingale speaks of the stupidity of the men in the War Office. "The iron beds from England have arrived at Scutari, but the legs for the beds were put into another ship and sent on to Balaklava. The sick and the wounded at Scutari lie on mattresses on the stone floors." In another letter: "The officials in London have sent us plenty of rations, but they have forgotten to send us kettles to cook them in." And when finally the kettles arrived: "The meat was ordered to be cut into uniform pieces of the same size. Sometimes a patient got a lump entirely gristle, the next might be entirely fat or entirely bone; the fortunes of war."

The trouble with the (noncombatant) officials, said Miss Nightingale, was that they regarded the soldiers as military machines. "Suppose you break them and

---

1. *Balaklava* (BAHL uh KLAH vuh) is a port village in southern Russia. It was the site of the Crimean War in 1854 in which England, Turkey, France, and Sardinia fought Russia.
2. *Scutari* (SKOO tah ree) is a city located in Turkey.

Word Bank	**uniform** (YOO nih form) *adj.*: having the same form; alike

throw them into the dump heap; what then? We've got plenty of others to take their place."

Even the soldiers had come to look upon themselves as mere machines unworthy of the consideration of their superiors. "In going round the hospital with me," writes Miss Nightingale, "the Duke of Cambridge recognized a sergeant of the guard who had had at least one third of his body shot away, and said (the Duke) to him with a great oath, calling him by his right name and surname, 'Aren't you dead yet?' The man said to me afterward, with tears in his eyes: 'So feelin' of 'Is Royal 'Ighness, wasn't it, m'm? Bless' is' eart, 'e wondered why I ain't dead yet.' "

Into this cauldron of incompetence and pitilessness and suffering stepped Florence Nightingale with her heroic band of thirty-eight nurses, and created order out of chaos. Within a few months after her arrival at Scutari, the death rate in the hospital had been reduced from forty percent to less than three percent.

II

When Florence first announced to her parents that she wanted to become a nurse, they looked at her with open-mouthed astonishment. What? The daughter of one of the richest families in England to enter into one of the lowest of professions? Why, nursing was not even a profession in those days. "Most of the nursing"—we are quoting a contemporary physician—"is done by women thieves who, when brought into the police court, are given the option of going to prison or to hospital service. They are often found in sleep under the beds of their patients whose possessions they have stolen."

When, therefore, she announced her decision to her parents, "it was as if I had wanted to be a kitchen maid." It was not for *such* a career that they had raised their daughter. Mr. William Shore Nightingale, the master of Embley Park in Hampshire, had meant Florence to be a lady, like her elegant mother. Why, this girl was the prettiest and the most accomplished of all the Nightingale children. They had given her an education fit for a princess—higher mathematics, music, art, science, literature, Italian, German, and French —and she spoke these languages as fluently as she spoke English. She spoke the ancient languages, too. "A capital young lady," once remarked the geographer, Sir Henry de la Beche, to the archaeologist, Warrenton Smythe, "a capital young lady, indeed, if only she hadn't floored me with her Latin and Greek."

Florence Nightingale was a brilliant young lady, and as charming as she was brilliant. She had traveled all over Europe, and had gone up the Nile. She could converse with all sorts of people on all sorts of subjects. She had even attended the receptions of the Queen.[3] What in the world did she want?

"I want to get away from the boredom of it all." She had an independent way about her. And a temper. And a biting tongue in her mouth. "Piling up miscellaneous instruction," she said, "is the most disgusting of all pursuits." And almost as disgusting was the piling up of miscellaneous acquaintances among the smart set: watching Lord Melbourne[4]

---

3. *The Queen* refers to Queen Victoria, Queen of England from 1837 to 1901.
4. *Lord Melbourne* (LORD MELL burn) was a famous statesman.

snore after dinner in the royal presence; applauding Prince Albert[5] for his "imaginary" skill at billiards; "dowagering out"[6] with papa to "pay her respects" to people for whom she hadn't the slightest respect; complimenting Lady So-and-So on her "oh, so becoming" diamond brooch—which, in reality, became her like a "raspberry tart on a pumpkin."

Florence Nightingale wanted to get away from all this painted and powdered artificiality. She wanted to come to grips with life, to know real people in their real moments, their moments of suffering. Her father frequently made her read aloud to him from a Victorian book of good manners entitled *Passages in the Life of a Daughter and Home.* She preferred to read by herself, and a book of a quite different tenor, the *Annual Report of the Fliedner Institute.* This institute was a German training school for nurses.

Flo Nightingale had been born with a passion to nurse the wounded and the sick. Even as a child she had frequently left her games to mend her dolls and to bandage the wounds of the cottagers' animal pets in Embley. At the age of six, she tells us, she was already conscious of a "call" to a mission of mercy. As she grew older, she became more and more conscious of the star that she was bidden to follow. One afternoon —she was about eighteen at the time—Florence was walking with a friend on the lawn in front of the drawing room at Embley. "Do you know what I always think when I look at that row of windows?" she said. "I think how I should turn it into a hospital and just how I should place the beds." For a time, during her twenties, she thought of marrying and settling down. But she put out of her mind the thought of a married life. This sort of thing was not for her. In 1850 she wrote in her diary: "I am thirty now, no more childish things, no more vain things."

She was ready now to enter upon her mission.

"Father, Mother, I am going to be a nurse."

"Why, you're insane!"

"Maybe I am. All I can say is, thank G-d for my insanity."

III

Florence Nightingale had stolen many an hour from her social activities to study anatomy and to visit the county hospital. Once, on a trip to Germany, she spent two weeks at the Fliedner Nursing School. At first Herr Fliedner was afraid of her "frail aristocratic hands." But he didn't know her sturdy democratic heart. "You won't want to scrub that corridor floor," he said. "Just try me," she replied. And when he tried her, he knew that she was made for nursing.

Before long she proved to the English skeptics, too, that she was made for nursing. Appointed manager of the Harley Street Sanitarium—an "Establishment for Gentlewomen during Illness"—she showed that she could not only scrub floors but bind wounds and, what was even more important, revive hopes. And, figuratively speaking, slap faces. How she did love to slap the faces of the bigots! "Clarkey, dear," she writes to one of her friends, "my committee refused me to take in Catholic patients, whereupon I wished them good morning, unless I

---

5. *Prince Albert* was Queen Victoria's husband.
6. *"Dowagering out"* (DOU uh JUR ing OUT) is a made-up expression to describe visits to dowagers, who were dignified, older women.

| **Word Bank** | **sturdy** (STER dee) *adj.*: firmly built and strong; hardy |
| | **skeptics** (SKEHP ticks) *n.*: doubters |

bigots (BIG its) *n.*: people who treat other people or groups of people with prejudice and intolerance

might take in Catholics as well as Jews. So now it is settled and in print that we are to take in all denominations whatever, provided *I* make myself responsible for their visitors and bring them downstairs again in a noose and out into the street. Amen. From bigotry and all deceits, good L-rd deliver us!"

It was a herculean job that she undertook as the first female manager of a hospital—supervising the untrained and ill-disciplined nurses; spraining her back as she lifted a patient to the operating table; catching a hot stove-pipe in her arms to keep it from falling upon a sick child; holding down a blind woman who was threatened with insanity when an operation to restore her vision had failed; and defending herself against the petty jealousies and the continual bickerings of her male—and therefore her "superior"—colleagues.

Yet, with all her inexperience, she stood the ordeal and came out triumphant.

Reports were reaching England about the terrible conditions in the Crimean hospitals. "The old pensioners sent out to nurse the sick and wounded are not of the slightest use; the soldiers have to attend upon each other." "No sufficient preparations have been made for the care of the wounded—no bandages, no dressers, no nurses." The public began to clamor for a remedy to this evil state of affairs. And finally the clamor became crystallized into a single name— Florence Nightingale. "Why will not Florence Nightingale give herself to this work?" wrote Cardinal Manning[7] to the London *Times*.

And Florence Nightingale heard the cry, and answered it. She sent a letter to Sir Sidney Herbert, an intimate friend of hers who was then serving as the British Secretary of War. "A small private expedition of nurses has been organized for Scutari, and I have been asked to command it. We shall feed and lodge ourselves there, and are to be no expense

whatever to the country." And then, realizing the stodgy skepticism of Victorian officialdom, she added a postscript: "Would you or someone else reassure the War Office about my qualifications? Please tell them that this is not a lady but a real hospital nurse."

Reluctantly the War Office consented to let the lady play the nurse. The whole thing would be a failure—no doubt of it! But let the madcap have her way.

And so, on October 21, 1854, Florence Nightingale set sail for the Crimea. The excitement of the trip, the tossing of the boat (there was a hurricane in the Mediterranean), and the management of the thirty-eight none-too-obedient nurses whom she had taken along with her—all these proved too much for her strength. She was ill when she arrived in Scutari. The soldiers carried her stretcher in relays, fighting for the honor, from the pier to the chaplain's house.

But she rapidly recovered from her illness. Who had time to be sick when there were so many wounded to be cared for? And so many mistakes to be corrected? And so much stubbornness to be overcome? The officials in charge of the hospital insisted that "everything is just as it ought to be." And they wanted no woman "to interfere with the efficiency of our organization."

Their "efficiency" had resulted in a welter of misery and disorganization and filth. It was the fault of no one man, but of an entire stumbling system which tried to advance toward the future with

---

7. *Cardinal Manning* refers to Henry E. Manning (1809-1892), a Roman Catholic priest and writer.

Word Bank	**ordeal** (oar dee UHL) *n.*: a severe trial or experience
	consented (kun SEN tid) *v.*: gave approval; agreed
	efficiency (eh FISH ihn see) *n.*: effectiveness; productivity

eyes turned toward the past. Of the Scutari hospital, as of Dante's Inferno, it was said: "All hope abandon, ye who enter here."

But there was one who entered and who did not abandon hope. Florence Nightingale created sanity out of confusion through the simple process of cutting red tape. Shortly after her arrival, a consignment of 27,000 shirts was landed at Scutari and only waited to be unpacked. But the official "purveyor" refused to allow the unpacking "without the permission of the Board." For three weeks the sick and the wounded "lay shivering," while Miss Nightingale kept vainly begging to have them properly clothed. Finally the Board got around to the matter "in the regular routine of business" and issued the necessary permission. On the very next occasion when a consignment of shirts arrived at the hospital, Miss Nightingale took matters into her own hands. She ordered the nurses to open the bundles and to distribute the shirts, while the "purveyor" stood by wringing his hands and muttering that the world was going to "the women and the dogs."

But the women, under the leadership of Florence Nightingale, had their way. They scrubbed the floors and the walls of the hospital, they reorganized the wards and the kitchens and the laundries, they rearranged the distribution of the food so that nobody was obliged to go hungry, and they added to the menu a number of strengthening "appetizers," such as soups and wines and jellies—"preposterous luxuries!" growled Dr. Hall, the officer in charge. And they were able to do all this because they spent none of the government's money upon their "innovations," but depended upon Florence Nightingale's own funds, supplemented by generous contributions from a number of forward-looking men and women. "What a needless waste of money upon useless

rubbish!" wailed Lord Stratford de Redcliffe, the British ambassador to Turkey. "I do wish they would spend this money upon a *worthy* object."

When one of the wounded soldiers heard of this, he said, "This 'ospital is worthy and Miss Nightingale is our angel." The grateful patients at Scutari came to regard her as "the lady with the lamp." Her mere presence restored to life many a man whom the surgeons had given up as beyond hope. The soldiers idolized her. They followed her shadow as she passed through the wards. These battle-scarred men, who knew the meaning of fatigue, were amazed at the indefatigable energy of this angel of mercy. There were days when she would spend eight hours on her knees, dressing wounds and smoothing blankets over aching limbs. Sometimes she would assist the relays of surgeons at their operations for twenty hours at a stretch. How she found time for all her work was a mystery. For, in addition to her nursing, she attended to all the administrative and to many of the menial duties of the hospital. "I am really cook, housekeeper and scavenger, washerwoman, general dealer, storekeeper." And writer of letters extraordinary. Hundreds and hundreds of them. Letters with a *sting* to them, to awaken her sleeping countrymen out of their complacent dreams. "When I write civilly, I have a civil answer—*and nothing is done*. When I write furiously, I have a rude answer—*and something is done*."

Throughout her stay at Scutari, there was a continual struggle between an iron will and a granite wall of opposition. And the granite gave way. Amazed at her treatment of the soldiers as if they were

Word Bank	**innovations** (IN oh VAY shunz) *n.*: new ideas, methods, or devices
	fatigue (fih TEEG) *n.*: weariness or exhaustion from labor, exertion, or stress

human beings, the conservative officials kept grumbling, "You'll only spoil the brutes." And Miss Nightingale replied, "That's precisely what I want to do. I want to spoil them as brutes and transform them into men."

IV

She returned home an invalid for life. But her work, far from being over, was only just begun. Scutari was not the only hospital. The entire world was a sick room that needed nursing.

But again that intolerable opposition of the complacent and the blind. People praised her, and came in throngs to catch a glimpse of her, and did nothing to help her in her work. The government had offered her a man-of-war to bring her home to England. But she had refused it, preferring to slip into her country quietly and unannounced. "I don't want adulation. I want understanding."

And understanding was the last thing she was able to get. She tried to open a training school for nurses—a place where it would be possible "for a woman to be a person." And she was anxious to bring about a drastic reform in all the military hospitals and barracks of England. She interviewed every important personage in the government; she even secured an audience and "good wishes for success" from Queen Victoria. But always, when the road seemed open, some obstinate official would get in the way.

One of the most obstinate of them all was Lord Panmure, Sir Sidney Herbert's successor as Secretary of War. Lord Panmure—because of his immovable stubbornness Miss Nightingale called him "the Bison"— had nothing personally against her. He merely disliked what he called "her busybodiness." The Crimean War was over, the country was at peace, and he,

Lord Panmure, might be pleasantly engaged in his grouse shooting but for Miss Nightingale's silly notions about schools for nurses and military hospitals and sanitary reforms. What troublesome piffle! He would put a stop to all this—not by refusing his help, but by offering it and then giving as little of it as was humanly possible.

And so he began his campaign of benevolent negligence. And behind him stood a whole battalion of reactionaries[8] —dear, devoted friends of Miss Nightingale's, every one of them. "You are so tired and ill. Why don't you rest for a while, and then we can discuss the whole matter?"

She replied to the Bison and his "lords of the out-of-date" in one of her trenchant[9] letters: "I am lying without my head, without my claws, and you all peck at me." And then, to convince the *public* when she had failed to convince the *peers*,[10] she wrote a long and provocative book on the subject—*Notes on Nursing*—and personally attended to its publicity until it was translated into several languages and reached into hundreds of thousands of homes.

The public listened and came to her assistance with petitions and contributions. And finally even the Bison allowed himself reluctantly to be led by her steady hand. The training school for nurses was opened, the military hospital was built, and the sanitary reforms were instituted.

But the Bison, even in his captivity, tried to make one last show of his masculine prerogative. What would a

---

8. *Reactionaries* (ree ACK shun AIR eez) are people against change.
9. *Trenchant* (TREN chunt) means sharp and perceptive.
10. Here, *peers* refers to noblemen.

Word Bank	prerogative (prih RAHG ih tiv) *n.*: an exclusive or special right, power, or privilege; option

woman know about the building of hospitals? It was he, Lord Panmure, who would order the plans for the building. The plans were duly drawn up and the construction was already under way before Miss Nightingale had an opportunity to visit the project. And then to her consternation she saw that the new hospital was designed to reproduce all the worst faults of the outdated hospitals of the past. She urged the Bison to stop the work, but without avail. *He* knew what was best. "Look at the spot I have selected, and the front view!"

There was but one thing to do—make an appeal to Lord Palmerston, the Prime Minister, and point out to him, with appropriate charts, the evils of the old and the advantages of the new. And so, armed with her documents and her wrath, she visited the Prime Minister, spent several hours in his office, and left him convinced that she was in the right. "It seems to me," he wrote to Lord Panmure, "that (in the new hospital) all consideration of what would best tend to the comfort and recovery of the patients has been sacrificed to the vanity of the architect, whose sole object has been to make a building which should cut a dash when looked at from the Southampton River. Pray, therefore, stop all further progress in the work until the matter can be duly considered."

The work was stopped; and after the matter had been duly considered, the hospital was rebuilt in accordance with the plans of Florence Nightingale.

V

For the most part now she was unable to be on her feet. But she went on with her work. An extraordinary invalid, she lay in the upper room of a little house she had bought on South Street, received the visits of statesmen and generals and artists and poets and peers, and manipulated with her capable pale hands the strings of a hundred reforms. On very rare occasions she went out for a drive in the park. And then the eager crowds pressed around her carriage. The people adored her, for she had opened the windows of their old stuffy world to let in the air of a new physical strength and faith. One of the most interesting of the manifold activities of her old age was the writing of a three volume interpretation of the old truths in the light of modern needs. *Femina sum.*[11] "I am a woman, and therefore I am interested in everything that appertains to the children of the human family." She was eighty-two now, but not ready as yet to lay down her work. When her nurse tucked her in at night, she got out of bed to tuck in her nurse. And throughout the day, she was thinking and planning and dictating letters for the building of better hospitals, and a better world.

And now she was ninety, and no longer able to work. "The black camel that kneels at every house" was slowly approaching her door. One by one her mortal faculties left her. First it was her hands that died, and then her eyes, and then her mind. Fitful, fragmentary visions of the past kept flying over the broken screen of her memory. One night she woke with a start. "Am I the one who stood on that Crimean height?"

Yet before the end, one final flash of light. "Do you know where you are?" a friend asked her one day.

"Yes," she replied. "I am watching at the altar of murdered men." Then, with that old-time determination in her voice, "And as long as I live, I shall be fighting their cause!"

11. *Femina sum* (fay MEE nuh SOOM) means "I am a woman" in Latin.

Recalling

1. Give two examples of the inefficiency of the War Office.

2. How many nurses did Florence bring with her to Scutari?

3. Did Florence come from a rich or poor background?

4. What was Florence's position, and where did she work before she was sent to Scutari?

5. Why was Florence able to make "innovations" at the hospital in Scutari?

6. Florence fought long and hard to open a training school for nurses. What problem did she encounter with the actual construction of the building?

Interpreting

7. Why was a dying soldier glad that the Duke of Cambridge recognized him?

8. Why didn't Florence's parents want her to become a nurse?

9. How did Florence prove to the English skeptics that she was made for nursing?

Concluding

10. Florence treated the soldiers as human beings capable of recovering. Give an example of actions Florence took that supports this statement.

11. Did Florence ever convince Lord Panmure to support her work? What issue did they fight over? How was it finally resolved?

Examining Nonfiction

This story focuses more on Florence Nightingale's struggle to improve hospital conditions than on her life. Yet the authors have chosen to present a summary of Florence's early years which informs the reader of the privileged life that Florence gave up in order to work for her cause. Would you have preferred to learn more about Florence's childhood, or was the information the authors gave you sufficient? Did you value Florence's actions more because you knew of her background?

Thinking About Nonfiction

Is history driven more by events or people? In other words, would Florence Nightingale have been able to improve hospital conditions and start a nurse training program even if she had not been involved in the Crimean War? Would Florence have been as driven to reform the hospital system if she had not witnessed the horrors of the Crimean War? On her deathbed, Florence said, "As long as I live, I shall be fighting their cause!"

Was it the Crimean War that inspired Florence and motivated people to support her? Or would Florence have brought changes to the nursing profession even if she had lived during peaceful times in England? State your opinion, and support it with facts from this selection.

Creating and Writing

Florence Nightingale was an avid letter writer and speaker. She used all her strength to fight for better hospital conditions. People admired and honored her, but she wrote, "I don't want adulation, I want understanding."

Florence Nightingale felt that adulation was unproductive because the people who honored her most assumed she could accomplish impossible tasks alone. She felt that understanding led to action because the people who understood her valued, supported, and worked for her causes.

Imagine that your class took on a project involving a cause like feeding the poor, teaching people to read, or collecting money for an institution. Your class decides to ask Florence Nightingale for advice concerning the best way to publicize your cause. She responds with a letter. What does the letter say?

Into • Morning—"The Bird Perched for Flight"

Few of us take the time to notice how easily and comfortably we are transported from place to place. We step into an elevator on one floor, and step out of it on another floor, without giving our brief trip a moment's thought. Rarely do we appreciate how gracefully our cars, buses, trains, and ships move. Sometimes it takes a writer, an artist, or a poet to make us notice the wonder of modern transportation. Most wondrous of all is flight. And, most wondrous of all flying things is the rocket ship, speeding through space. Should you ever be fortunate enough to be present at the launching of a rocket, stop for a moment, and think of this story. Suddenly, you will feel you are witnessing an event of extraordinary beauty.

Focus

Poetic language is usually associated with the beauty of the natural world or the expression of emotions. Anne Lindbergh uses poetic language to describe the launching of a rocket. Throughout the story, the author combines images of the natural world with images of the rocket ship, almost as though the rocket were part of the scenery. However, as the story progresses in time from night to morning to day, Lindbergh associates the rocket with different parts of nature. In the predawn sky, the rocket and its launching tower are standing next to a palm tree, all three standing black against a shadowy sky. In the morning, the rocket is launched and, in the foreground flocks of ducks, herons, and birds flutter in alarm. What natural images are linked with the rocket later in the story? Do you think a rocket ship is as awesome as trees, birds, clouds, and stars?

About the Author

American author **ANNE MORROW LINDBERGH** was born in 1906 and died in 2001. The daughter of an American diplomat, Lindbergh grew up in Englewood, New Jersey. She was married to the famous aviator Charles Lindbergh. In the 1930s the kidnapping and murder of her infant son gained international press coverage. After this tragedy, she and her husband moved to Europe. Anne Morrow Lindbergh was an essayist known for sensitively portraying the characters she wrote about. An aviator like her husband, her travels influenced many of her works.

Morning—
"The Bird Perched for Flight"

Anne Morrow Lindbergh

We wake to the alarm at four-thirty and leave our motel at five-fifteen. The three astronauts must be already climbing into their seats at the top of their "thirty-six-story" rocket, poised for flight. The pilgrimage of sightseers has started to the Cape.[1] Already the buses have left and lines of cars are on the roads. It is dark, a little chilly, with a sky full of stars. As we approach the Cape we see again the rocket and its launching tower from far off over the lagoon. It is still illumined with searchlights, but last night's vision has vanished. It is no longer tender or biological but simply a machine, the newest and most perfected creation of a scientific age—hard, weighty metal.

We watch the launching with some of the astronauts and their families, from a site near the Vehicle Assembly Building. Our cars are parked on a slight rise of ground. People get out, walk about restlessly, set up cameras and adjust their binoculars. The launch pad is about three miles away, near the beach. We look across Florida marsh grass and palmettos. A cabbage palm stands up black against a shadowy sky, just left of the rocket and its launching tower. As dawn flushes the horizon, an egret[2] rises and lazily glides across the flats between us and the pad. It is a still morning. Ducks call from nearby inlets. Vapor trails of a high-flying plane turn pink in an almost cloudless sky. Stars pale in the blue.

With the morning light, Apollo 8 and its launching tower become clearer, harder, and more defined. One can see the details of installation. The dark sections on the smooth sides of the rocket, marking its stages, cut up the single fluid line. Vapor steams furiously off its side. No longer stark and simple, this morning the rocket is complicated, mechanical, earth-bound. Too weighty for flight, one feels.

People stop talking, stand in front of their cars, and raise binoculars to their

---

1. *The Cape* refers to Cape Canaveral, formerly Cape Kennedy, a peninsula on the east central coast of Florida where many American space launches take place.
2. An *egret* (EE grit) is a wading bird with long legs and a long neck.

Word Bank	
perched (PERCHT) *v.*: to settle or rest on a usually high place	
launching (LAWN ching) *n.*: to send forth with force; to release	
vapor (VAY per) *adj.*: steam	
furiously (FYOOR ee us lee) *adv.*: a stormy or turbulent appearance	

eyes. We peer nervously at the launch site and then at our wrist watches. Radio voices blare unnaturally loud from car windows. "Now only thirty minutes to launch time…fifteen minutes…six minutes…thirty seconds to go…twenty…T minus…fifteen…fourteen…thirteen…twelve…eleven…ten…nine… Ignition!"

A jet of steam shoots from the pad below the rocket. "Ahhhh!" The crowd gasps, almost in unison. Now great flames spurt, leap, belch out across the horizon. Clouds of smoke billow up on either side of the rocket, completely hiding its base. From the midst of this holocaust,[3] the rocket begins to rise—slowly, as in a dream, so slowly it seems to hang suspended on the cloud of fire and smoke. It's impossible—it can't rise. Yes, it rises, but heavily, as if the giant weight is pulled by an invisible hand out of the atmosphere, like the lead on a plumb line[4] from the depths of the sea. Slowly it rises and—because of our distance—silently, as in a dream.

Suddenly the noise breaks, jumps across our three separating miles—a shattering roar of explosions, a trip hammer over one's head, under one's feet, through one's body. The earth shakes; cars rattle; vibrations beat in the chest. A roll of thunder, prolonged, prolonged, prolonged.

I drop the binoculars and put my hands to my ears, holding my head to keep it steady. My throat tightens—am I going to cry?—my eyes are fixed on the rocket, mesmerized[5] by its slow ascent.

The foreground is now full of birds; a great flock of ducks, herons, small birds, rise pell-mell from the marshes at the noise. Fluttering in alarm and confusion, they scatter in all directions as if it were the end of the world. In the seconds I take to look at them, the rocket has left the tower.

It is up and away, a comet boring through the sky, no longer the vulnerable

---

3. *Holocaust* (HAHL uh kahst) means destruction.
4. A *lead* weight hangs on the end of a plumb line. A *plumb line* determines if an object is straight on a wall or its depth in water.
5. *Mesmerized* (MEZ muh RYZD) means hypnotized.

Word Bank   **vulnerable** (VUL nur uh bul) *adj.*: capable of being physically or emotionally wounded

untried child, no longer the earth-bound machine, or the weight at the end of a line, but sheer terrifying force, blasting upward on its own titanic[6] power.

It has gone miles into the sky. It is blurred by a cloud. No, it has made its own cloud—a huge vapor trail, which hides it. Out of the cloud something falls, cartwheeling down, smoking. "The first-stage cutoff,"[7] someone says. Where is the rocket itself?

There, above the cloud now, reappears the rocket, only a very bright star, diminishing every second. Soon out of sight, off to lunar space.

One looks earthward again. It is curiously still and empty. A cloud of brown smoke hangs motionless on the horizon. Its long shadow reaches us across the grass. The launch pad is empty. The abandoned launching tower is being sprayed with jets of water to cool it down. It steams in the bright morning air. Still dazed, people stumble into cars and start the slow, jammed trek back to town. The monotone of radio voices continues. One clings to this last thread of contact with something incredibly beautiful that has vanished.

"Where are they—where are they now?" In eleven minutes we get word. They are in earth orbit. They "look good"

in the laconic[8] space talk that comes down from over a hundred miles above earth. And one realizes again that it is the men above all that matter, the individuals who man the machine, give it heart, sight, speech, intelligence, and directions; and the men on earth who are backing them up, monitoring their every move, even to their heartbeats. This is not sheer power, it is power under control of man.

We drive slowly back to town. Above us the white vapor trail of the rocket is being scattered by wind into feathery shapes of heron's wings—the only mark in the sky of the morning's launching.

---

6. *Titanic* (ty TAAN ik) means huge and powerful.
7. *The first-stage cutoff* refers to the first of several rockets that are cut off a few minutes after the launch and fall back to earth.
8. *Laconic* (luh KAHN ik) means employing few words.

Word Bank

diminishing (dih MIN ish ing) *adj.*: decreasing; becoming gradually less

vanished (VAN isht) *v.*: passed quickly from sight; disappeared

monitoring (MAHN ih ter ing) *v.*: watching; keeping track of; checking

scattered (SKAT erd) *v.*: to separate and go in various directions

Recalling

1. Where and when did the launching of Apollo 8 occur?

2. What happened after the final countdown and the yell, "Ignition!"?

3. What kinds of sounds and vibrations accompanied the launching of Apollo 8?

Interpreting

4. Why was the Apollo launching scheduled for such an early morning hour?

5. Why were the spectators watching three miles away from the actual site?

6. Why were the spectators "dazed" after viewing the launching?

Concluding

7. This selection gives the time and place of the Apollo 8 launching but not the names of the astronauts. Do you think it should have provided their names as a part of a historical record of this event? Why or why not?

Examining Nonfiction

Anne Morrow Lindbergh takes what could have been reported in an unemotional way and draws us into the event through her sensitive and expressive writing. Can you think of two examples of events where reporting is intended to emotionally draw in the listeners or readers? The methods may include the way a tone of voice, spoken words, written words, or even music are used.

Thinking About Nonfiction

Anne Morrow Lindbergh discusses the liftoff of Apollo 8 in almost poetic terms. The title, *Morning—"The Bird Perched for Flight,"* is a reflection of Anne's use of poetic devices. You will recall that a **metaphor** is a figure of speech that compares two different types of things. The author uses an extended metaphor comparing Apollo 8 to the ducks, herons, and small birds that abound in the Florida marshlands. Find at least two examples of Lindbergh's use of this metaphor.

Creating and Writing

The mood of this selection is one of triumph. As Lindbergh writes, "This is not sheer power; it is power under control of man." She views the space program as a victory of technology and talent.

When the steam engine was invented, people felt the same way. Write a paragraph describing how the first steam engine looked as it rolled out of the railway station into the countryside and how you, the observer, felt about this "miracle of modern science."

Blueprint FOR READING

Into • *Rattlesnake Hunt*

Fear. It does different things to different people. Some people freeze. Some people run. Some people scream. Some people faint. And some don't know the meaning of the word.

In the following story, a writer is invited to join a scientist as he collects rattlesnakes in the Everglades for a scientific study. The scientist is calm, collected, and fearless. He understands the habits of rattlesnakes and feels safe in their presence. The writer is—well, she is like most people! What would your reaction be if you leaned down to pick a violet and found a rattlesnake staring you in the eye?

Focus

This true story is interesting both for its factual information and for its human interest. Similar, in this respect, to *Morning—"The Bird Perched for Flight," Rattlesnake Hunt* combines science with feeling. Learning about the habits of rattlers is eye-opening to most readers. The author helps us to view snakes as we would view other creatures, with curiosity rather than repulsion. The theme of the story, though, is not snakes; it is a thought-provoking lesson in how to overcome fear through learning about whatever it is that is frightening you.

About the Author

MARJORIE KINNAN RAWLINGS was born in 1896 in Washington, D.C. In 1928 Rawlings moved to a farm in backwoods Florida. This setting became a great inspiration for her novels, including her famous work *The Yearling*. Many of Rawlings' works reflect the conflict that exists between man and the environment. Rawlings received many honors and awards for her work including the Pulitzer Prize and the Newbery Medal of Honor. Marjorie K. Rawlings died in 1953 in Florida.

Rattlesnake Hunt

Marjorie Kinnan Rawlings

Ross Allen, a young Florida herpetologist,[1] invited me to join him on a hunt in the upper Everglades[2]— for rattlesnakes. Ross and I drove to Arcadia in his coupé[3] on a warm journey day.

I said, "How will you bring back the rattlesnakes?"

"In the back of my car."

My courage was not adequate to inquire whether they were thrown in loose and might be expected to appear between our feet. Actually, a large portable box of heavy close-meshed wire made a safe cage. Ross wanted me to write an article about his work and on our way to the unhappy hunting grounds I took notes on a mass of data that he had accumulated in years of herpetological research. The scientific and dispassionate detachment of the material and the man made a desirable approach to rattlesnake territory. As I had discovered with the insects and varmints,[4] it is difficult to be afraid of anything about which enough is known, and Ross' facts were fresh from the laboratory.

The hunting ground was Big Prairie, south of Arcadia and west of the northern tip of Lake Okeechobee. Big Prairie is a desolate cattle country, half marsh, half pasture, with islands of palm trees and cypress and oaks. At that time of year the cattlemen and Indians were burning the country, on

---

1. A *herpetologist* (HER puh TAHL uh jist) is an expert on reptiles and amphibians.
2. The *Everglades* (EV ur GLAYDZ) are the large swamplands of southern Florida, about 100 miles long and 50-75 miles wide.
3. A *coupé* (koo PAY) is a small, two-door car.
4. *Varmints* (VAHR mints) are troublesome animals.

Word Bank	**portable** (POR tih bul) *adj.*: capable of being carried or moved about

accumulated (uh KYOOM yoo layt id) *v.*: gathered or piled up little by little; amassed

desolate (DEZ uh lit) *adj.*: empty; having no inhabitants or visitors

the theory that the young fresh wire grass that springs up from the roots after a fire is the best cattle forage. Ross planned to hunt his rattlers in the forefront of the fires. They lived in winter, he said, in gopher holes, coming out in the midday warmth to forage, and would move ahead of the flames and be easily taken. We joined forces with a big man named Will, his snake-hunting companion of the territory, and set out in early morning, after a long rough drive over deep-rutted roads into the open wilds.

I hope never in my life to be so frightened as I was in those first few hours. I kept on Ross' footsteps, I moved when he moved, sometimes jolting into him when I thought he might leave me behind. He does not use the forked stick of conventional snake hunting, but a steel prong, shaped like an L, at the end of a long stout stick. He hunted casually, calling my attention to the varying vegetation, to hawks overhead, to a pair of the rare whooping cranes that flapped over us. In mid-morning he stopped short, dropped his stick, and brought up a five-foot rattlesnake draped limply over the steel L. It seemed to me that I should drop in my tracks.

"They're not active at this season," he said quietly. "A snake takes on the temperature of its surroundings. They can't stand too much heat for that reason, and when the weather is cool, as now, they're sluggish."

The sun was bright overhead, the sky a translucent blue, and it seemed to me that it was warm enough for any snake to do as it willed. The sweat poured down my back. Ross dropped the rattler in a crocus sack[5] and Will carried it. By noon, he had caught four. I felt faint and ill. We stopped by a pond and went swimming. The region was flat, the horizon limitless, and as I came out of the cool blue water I expected to find myself surrounded by a ring of rattlers. There were only Ross and Will, opening the lunch basket. I could not eat. Will went back and drove his truck closer,

---

5. A *crocus sack* (KRO kuss SAK) is a burlap bag.

Word Bank	**forage** (FOR idj) *v.:* search for provisions or food

limply (LIMP lee) *adv.:* lacking in strength, vigor, or firmness

translucent (tranz LOO sint) *adj.:* allowing light to pass through

for Ross expected the hunting to be better in the afternoon. The hunting was much better. When we went back to the truck to deposit two more rattlers in the wire cage, there was a rattlesnake lying under the truck.

Ross said, "Whenever I leave my car or truck with snakes already in it, other rattlers always appear. I don't know whether this is because they scent or sense the presence of other snakes, or whether in this arid area they come to the car for shade in the heat of the day."

The problem was scientific, but I had no interest.

That night Ross and Will and I camped out in the vast spaces of the Everglades prairies. We got water from an abandoned well and cooked supper under buttonwood bushes by a flowing stream. The camp fire blazed cheerfully under the stars and a new moon lifted in the sky. Will told tall tales of the cattlemen and the Indians and we were at peace.

Ross said, "We couldn't have a better night for catching water snakes."

After the rattlers, water snakes seemed innocuous enough. We worked along the edge of

the stream and here Ross did not use his L-shaped steel. He reached under rocks and along the edge of the water and brought out harmless reptiles with his hands. I had said nothing to him of my fears, but he understood them. He brought a small dark snake from under a willow root.

"Wouldn't you like to hold it?" he asked. "People think snakes are cold and clammy, but they aren't. Take it in your hands. You'll see that it is warm."

Again, because I was ashamed, I took the snake in my hands. It was not cold, it was not clammy, and it lay trustingly in my hands, a thing that lived and breathed and had mortality[6] like the rest of us. I felt an upsurgence of spirit.

The next day was magnificent. The air was crystal, the sky was aquamarine, and the far horizon of palms and oaks lay against the sky. I felt a new boldness and followed Ross bravely. He was making the rounds of the gopher holes. The rattlers came out in the mid-morning warmth and

---

6. Here, *mortality* means having life.

Word Bank   **arid** (AIR id) *adj.*: excessively dry

were never far away. He could tell by their trails whether one had come out or was still in the hole. Sometimes the two men dug the snake out. At times it was down so long and winding a tunnel that the digging was hopeless. Then they blocked the entrance and went on to other holes. In an hour or so they made the original rounds, unblocking the holes. The rattler in every case came out hurriedly, as though anything were preferable to being shut in. All the time Ross talked to me, telling me the scientific facts he had discovered about the habits of the rattlers.

"They pay no attention to a man standing perfectly still," he said, and proved it by letting Will unblock a hole while he stood at the entrance as the snake came out. It was exciting to watch the snake crawl slowly beside and past the man's legs. When it was at a safe distance he walked within its range of vision, which he had proved to be no higher than a man's knee, and the snake whirled and drew back in an attitude[7] of fighting defense. The rattler strikes only for paralyzing and killing its food, and for defense.

"It is a slow and heavy snake," Ross said. "It lies in wait on a small game trail and strikes the rat or rabbit passing by. It waits a few minutes, then follows along the trail, coming to the small animal, now dead or dying. It noses it from all sides, making sure that it is its own kill, and that it is dead and ready for swallowing."

A rattler will lie quietly without revealing itself if a man passes by and it thinks it is not seen. It slips away without fighting if given the chance. Only Ross' sharp eyes sometimes picked out the gray and yellow diamond pattern, camouflaged among the grasses. In the cool of the morning, chilled by the January air, the snakes showed no fight. They could be looped up limply over the steel L and dropped in a sack or up into the wire cage on the back of Will's truck. As the sun mounted in the sky and warmed the moist Everglades earth, the snakes were warmed too, and Ross warned that it was time to go more cautiously. Yet having learned that it was we who were the aggressors; that immobility meant complete safety; that the

---

7. An *attitude* (AT uh TOOD) is a position.

Word Bank
camouflaged (KAM ih flahjd) *v.*: concealed by means of disguise
cautiously (KAW shis lee) *adv.*: behaving carefully because of fear of danger
immobility (IM oh BILL ih tee) *n.*: the state of being motionless

snakes, for all their lightning flash in striking, were inaccurate in their aim, with limited vision; having watched again and again the liquid grace of movement, the beauty of pattern, suddenly I understood that I was drinking in freely the magnificent sweep of the horizon, with no fear of what might be at the moment under my feet. I went off hunting by myself, and though I found no snakes, I should have known what to do.

The sun was dropping low in the west. Masses of white cloud hung above the flat marshy plain and seemed to be tangled in the tops of distant palms and cypresses. The sky turned orange, then saffron.[8] I walked leisurely back toward the truck. In the distance I could see Ross and Will making their way in too. The season was more advanced than at the Creek, two hundred miles to the north, and I noticed that spring flowers were blooming among the lumpy hummocks.[9] I leaned over to pick a white violet. There was a rattlesnake under the violet.

If this had happened the week before, if it had happened the day before, I think I should have lain down and died on top of the rattlesnake, with no need of being struck and poisoned. The snake did not coil, but lifted its head and whirred its rattles lightly. I stepped back slowly and put the violet in a buttonhole. I reached forward and laid the steel L across the snake's neck, just back of the blunt head. I called to Ross:

"I've got one."

He strolled toward me.

"Well, pick it up," he said.

I released it and slipped the L under the middle of the thick body.

"Go put it in the box."

He went ahead of me and lifted the top of the wire cage. I made the truck with the rattler, but when I reached up the six feet to drop it in the cage, it slipped off the stick and dropped on Ross' feet. It made no effort to strike.

"Pick it up again," he said. "If you'll pin it down lightly and reach just back of its head with your hand, as you've seen me do, you can drop it in more easily."

I pinned it and leaned over.

"I'm awfully sorry," I said, "but you're pushing me a little too fast."

He grinned. I lifted it on the stick and again as I had it at head height, it slipped off, down Ross' boots and on top of his feet. He stood as still as a stump. I dropped the snake on his feet for the third time. It seemed to me that the most patient of rattlers might in time resent being hauled up and down, and for all the man's quiet certainty that in standing motionless there was no danger, would strike at whatever was nearest, and that would be Ross.

I said, "I'm just not man enough to keep this up any longer," and he laughed and reached down with his smooth quickness and lifted the snake back of the head and dropped it in the cage. It slid in among its mates and settled in a corner. The hunt was over and we drove back over the uneven trail to Will's village and left him and went on to Arcadia and home. Our catch for the two days was thirty-two rattlers.

I said to Ross, "I believe that tomorrow I could have picked up that snake."

Back at the Creek, I felt a new lightness. I had done battle with a great fear, and the victory was mine.

---

8. *Saffron* (SAAF rahn) is an orange-yellow color.
9. *Hummocks* (HUM ucks) are ridges of land where plants grow.

Recalling

1. Describe the type of country where the rattlesnake hunt occurred.

2. What type of tool did Ross use to gather the rattlesnakes?

3. Why were the snakes inactive at the time the story took place?

4. How does a rattlesnake attack its prey?

5. Do rattlers attack humans? If so, when?

Interpreting

6. What information helped Rawlings conquer her fear of rattlesnakes?

7. How did the author react to her first actual encounter with a rattler?

8. Why did Rawlings feel "a new lightness" when she and Ross returned to the Creek?

Concluding

9. Quote three sentences from this selection that convince the reader of the author's fear of snakes.

10. List two of Marjorie Kinnan Rawlings' personal characteristics that enabled her to overcome her fear.

Examining Nonfiction

In this selection, the author did not actually hook a rattlesnake herself. Therefore, there really was no physical proof that she had overcome her intense dislike of rattlers and conquered her fear. Yet her statement, "I believe that tomorrow I could have picked up that snake," is a statement of triumph over fear.

1. Do you think the scientific information that Rawlings received from Ross along with her one-time experience in the marshlands was enough to help her overcome her fear of snakes?

2. Do you think she will ever return? Or do you think that the author only undertook this adventure to cure her fear? Now that her fear is under control, do you think she will return to hunt rattlesnakes again?

Thinking About Nonfiction

Nonfiction adventure stories differ from regular fiction in that the outcome and resolution of plot do not occur at the end of the story, but take place during the journey itself, when the individual struggles to overcome the challenges they face.

1. Was the challenge in this selection the hunt for rattlesnakes or the attempt to overcome the author's fear?

2. Is Rawlings' personal challenge the reason this story is exciting?

3. Do the rattlers ever seem frightening to you?

4. What do you think is the main conflict of this story?

Creating and Writing

Some scientists believe that fears can be conquered by facing one's fear and gradually becoming exposed to the frightful object. This is how Marjorie Kinnan Rawlings conquered her fear of rattlesnakes.

Think of a fear that you or someone you know may have. Do you think it could be conquered by knowledge and gradual exposure? Write a paragraph referring to a specific fear and stating your opinion about how to overcome it.

Into • *Beneath the Crags of Malpelo Island*

In *Rattlesnake Hunt*, we learned of a woman who overcame her fear of rattlesnakes by learning about their habits and accompanying a scientist who was an expert snake handler. In the following story, we will see that all the expertise in the world is sometimes useless when dealing with an unforeseeable danger. Deep down in the sea, enclosed in the hulk of a sunken ship, haunted by the memory of the seven divers who have gone down and never returned, Harry finds himself facing an eight-armed monster. No air, no weapon—no hope? This is a story you will not easily forget, even if you wish you could!

Focus

Once again, we have a nonfiction story that is as exciting as anything fictional. Notice that the author does not write a dry, factual report of what happened. The story's style is identical to the style used for fiction; in fact, the reader is tempted to check the introduction to make sure that the story is really true. After you have read the story, go back and look for phrases that are not strictly "nonfiction." The author has injected opinion and emotion into his tale; this is one thing that distinguishes a nonfiction story from a scientific study.

About the Author

American essayist **HARRY EARL RIESEBERG** was born in 1892. Rieseberg published over four thousand articles in various newspapers and periodicals throughout the world. Even though Rieseberg was such a prolific writer, he did not consider himself an author. He felt that his expertise was in underwater exploration. He was an authority on recovering sunken boats and valuable artifacts from beneath the sea. Rieseberg was awarded "Mr. Treasure Hunter of 1964." His experiences with salvaging wrecks and treasure were the basis for his written work. His vast experiences have fascinated the American public for many years. He died in 1970.

Beneath the Crags[1] of Malpelo[2] Island

Harry Earl Rieseberg

With a smother of foam and bubbles the green water closed over me. When I was not too far down, I signaled the crew above to stop. Since they were new at this business, I wanted to see whether they would answer satisfactorily. When they promptly did so, I adjusted the air pressure in my diving dress and resumed my slow descent.

As I went I thought of the treasure supposedly lying in the wreck below. I thought, too, of the dangers lurking there and of the seven divers who had gone down to the wreck and never returned. Had I known the terror that awaited me, I might have stopped my descent then and there and gone back to the surface and safety.

The whole strange adventure had begun two weeks before in the little seaport town of Buenaventura,[3] Colombia. I had just returned from six months of salvage work[4] on several so-called treasure wrecks in the Gulf[5] waters. I had decided to return to the States for a long-needed rest.

But that was before I met Charlie Boyer in the office of the dock superintendent. Once a diver himself, he was quite interested in my recent experiences. When I mentioned that there were few unrecovered treasure wrecks left on the sea floor along the West Coast, he looked at me sharply and then stared ahead in silence.

I asked him, "What's the strangest thing you've ever heard of in these waters, Boyer?"

---

1. *Crags* (KRAAGZ) are steep, rugged rocks or cliffs.
2. *Malpelo Island* (mahl PAY loe EYE lind) is an island in the Pacific Ocean, off the western coast of South America.
3. *Buenaventura* (BWAY nah vayn TOO rah)
4. *Salvage* (SAL vij) *work* is finding and bringing back sunken cargo.
5. *Gulf* refers to Gulf Tortugas, off the west coast of Colombia.

Word Bank	**descent** (dih SENT) *n.*: the act of proceeding from a higher place to a lower one

For a brief moment he did not reply, then he said, "I think the salvage job off Malpelo Island, to the west of here, is the strangest, Lieutenant. But it's a long, long story."

I settled myself down comfortably to listen.

Many years ago, Boyer said, an unidentified Spanish schooner had hit the rocks off the end of Malpelo Island during a violent storm. The vessel had gone down immediately, with only one man surviving. Rescued from the deserted island, the man revealed that the sunken schooner had carried in its hold a vast sum in gold and silver bars, together with some other valuable cargo. That was all that was ever learned about the ship and its treasure; a few days later the survivor died from exposure.

Seven attempts had been made to recover the mysterious treasure cargo. In each case the diver never came up. All the air and life lines were snapped, and there was no sign of what had caused the series of tragedies.

The story chilled me. But there was a challenge in it.

"Boyer," I said, "if you're willing to take a chance with me on making the eighth attempt, I'll do the diving."

With a broad grin he jumped to his feet. "You mean that, Lieutenant? You aren't superstitious?"

My answer was a flat no.

The next two weeks were busy ones. We secured the best equipment we could in Buenaventura and hired a double crew of husky Colombians. It wasn't long before we were anchored off Malpelo Island and I was going down to the wreck of the ill-fated Spanish schooner.

As I caught the faint outline of the hulk beneath me, I fingered my shark knife nervously. About a hundred feet down, I landed on a rocky ledge that jutted out from the main rock ridge. Among these sharp crags I had to be mighty careful with my lines.

Word Bank	**jutted** (JUT id) *v.*: extended out, up, or forward

A hard rub on one of their jagged edges might put me in a bad spot. I was glad of one thing: there were no signs whatever of sharks as yet. In fact, not a large fish of any kind appeared among the long streamers of queer stuff that hung in the water around the old hulk.

In a few minutes I had landed on the slime-coated deck of the sunken schooner. The white superstructure[6] shone clean and fresh, as though it had recently been painted. In the faint light that penetrated from above, the wreck looked weird and sinister. It lay there, white and ghostly, with the high black walls of rock around it—much like a gigantic coffin lowered into a watery tomb.

The after-hatch[7] was open, its cover partly off; just forward appeared the companionway.[8] Making certain that neither of my lines was fouled,[9] I loosened my shark knife and strode forward. Climbing down the sand-covered steps to the heavy door of the chamber below, I moved ever more cautiously.

Then I saw it—and stood there, almost paralyzed, for a moment. Beside the half-open door appeared a large round object. *It was a copper diving helmet!*

Quickly I dug it out of the debris and sand. Stooping, I peered closer. In the light of my torch[10] I could see inside that helmet. I gazed down upon a skull—the white jaws wide apart in a set and uncanny grin!

Here was the first of the seven divers who had perished.

As I straightened up, the soft purr of the incoming air stopped abruptly. Then air started to whistle past my ears as it began to leave my suit. I

---

6. The *superstructure* (SOO pur STRUK chur) is the top of a ship above the deck.
7. The *after-hatch* is the entrance to the lower part of the ship.
8. The *companionway* (kum PAN yun WAY) are stairs leading to the area below the ship's deck.
9. *Fouled* (FOW ild) means entangled.
10. *Torch* is a British term for flashlight.

Word Bank

perished (PAIR isht) *v.*: ceased to exist; died

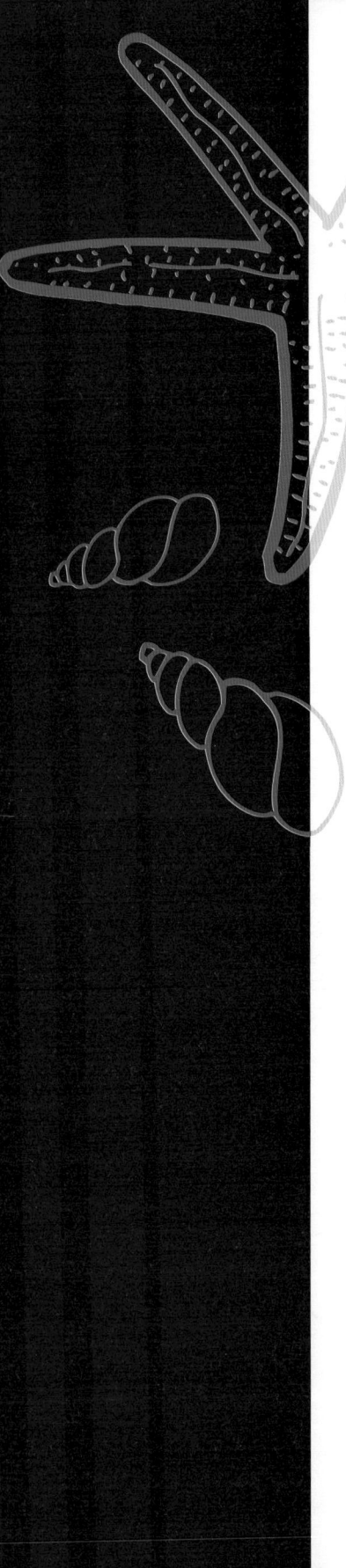

suddenly realized that my air hose was cut. I knew that the great pressure of water at that depth would empty my suit in a few seconds and I should be badly crushed.

Shutting off the intake valve, I felt enough air within my suit to last about five minutes. But for normal decompression[11] I needed more time than that to go up. Now I was in a tough spot. There seemed slight chance for my survival.

Stumbling up the companionway steps, I jerked out my shark knife. But on the deck nothing was in sight, nothing but those ghostly white planks and sharp black limestone rocks.

Now my suit was deflating fast. I pulled my signal cord quickly, and soon I was being slowly hauled upward. Of course I knew the terrible danger of being hauled up from deep water too fast. Often it causes caisson[12] disease, or the "bends." In fact, it can put a man out for good. At the halfway stage, I signaled for a stop. For a minute or two I hung at that level to lessen the shock.

When, at my signal, the crew started hauling up again, my eyes seemed to be bursting from their sockets. My body felt as if it had been gripped by some giant's hand that was crushing the remaining life from it.

They pulled me on deck, and the crew boys got my headpiece unscrewed just in time. I lay there helpless, almost unconscious. After undergoing decompression in our makeshift chamber,[13] I rested for two whole days.

On the third day the sea was calm and the day

---

11. *Normal decompression* (dee kum PRESH un) means the gradual return to normal atmospheric pressure.
12. *Caisson* (KAY sun) *disease* is chest tightness, joint pains, and violent muscle spasms which are caused by nitrogen bubbles that form in the body when deep sea divers return too rapidly to the surface.
13. The *chamber* is an area in which the air pressure can be adjusted so that a diver can gradually return to normal atmospheric pressure.

Word Bank	
abruptly (uh BRUPT lee) *adv.*: change without preparation or warning; unexpectedly suddenly
jerked (JURKT) *v.*: pushed, pulled, or twisted
deflating (dee FLAY ting) *v.*: releasing air or gas from

clear. We had rigged up a new air hose; the old one had been cut almost in two. What cut it I didn't know—perhaps some sharp edge on the old hulk or a pointed rock outcrop. Again I climbed over the side of the little salvage craft and sank slowly down past the wall of gloomy rocks.

I circled the entire deck, carefully watching my lines. Everything appeared the same as before—the water seemed as lifeless as ever. I climbed down the companionway toward the chamber below. The grim helmet with its grinning white skull lay where I had left it. This time, without hesitating, I began to dig away the sand that blocked the doorway. Soon I had the opening cleared. I peered in, then cautiously entered.

Inside was a space about fifteen feet wide. It was partly filled with crates and boxes of different sizes. One of the boxes had the top pried off. Excited, I quickly scraped away the thick sand and flashed my torch on the uncovered contents. It revealed several metal bars. Yes, here was the treasure. How much I had no idea, but if it was to be raised, I should have to arrange for steel slings to be dropped down to me. Then, counting the boxes and crates, I prepared to ascend.

Turning to retrace my steps, I noticed that the boxes were piled higher at the opposite end of the chamber, away from the doorway. To the right of these was a huge object heavily wrapped in a large tarpaulin. Striding clumsily across the room, I tore away the length of covering.

There before me was a great bronze statue. It had large eyes, probably made of precious stones. They were of different shades and seemed to be looking at me sorrowfully. At the base of the statue were a number of small bones, whitened and half buried in the sand. Among them two skulls grinned at me eerily. Close by lay a lead-soled boot, with remnants of a diver's suit still clinging to it.

I stood there trembling in the dark, eerie tomb. Then in the light of my torch something snakelike floated into my view. My scalp tightened, and I

> **Word Bank** **tarpaulin** (TAR pihl in) *n.*: a piece of waterproof material used for protecting exposed objects or areas

thought another diver was scheduled to "go out." Then, to my relief, I saw that it was only a long piece of rotted tarpaulin. By now my nerves were pretty raw, and I couldn't help thinking of the seven divers who had come down here—to stay.

In the midst of these thoughts I had a weird, uncanny feeling that somebody or something was watching me. So strong was this strange sense of a presence in the lonely, silent tomb that I turned and threw my torchlight about the chamber. It moved over the boxes and crates, played on the wall, and returned finally to the statue. As it shone past the bronze figure, I became faint with terror. For there, from behind the dim outlines of the boxes and crates, a huge shape was rising before my eyes. My heart pounded wildly, for the thing bulked across the doorway—and barring my exit—was a quivering, warty body rocking from side to side. The huge monster was fully fifteen feet across, with a ball of body at least four to five feet in width. The creature's long, slimy arms, or tentacles, were lined with many great saucer-like cups. And its ghoulish eyes watched my every movement.

Now I knew the fate of the seven lost divers, and I realized that I, too, was trapped in this watery grave. For there was only one way out of the chamber, and that was blocked by the swaying, writhing giant octopus!

Its long tentacles swayed and quivered continuously, almost rhythmically. They caressed the water, wrapping themselves about the crates and boxes. Then the creature crawled slowly along the floor in the sand toward me. I gazed at it in horror and edged backward out of its grasping reach. In spite of its great bulk and spreading arms it moved quickly.

As I watched, I could see the color of the huge, bloated body change from brown to dirty yellow, then to tan, and then to gray and white. And all the while those terrible eyes watched me.

I thought of the statue behind me. As I backed

Word Bank

writhing (RY thing) *v.*: twisted into coils

slowly and cautiously toward it, the octopus seemed to realize what my intent was, for it lunged with one of its tentacles directly at me. The powerful arm stirred the sand into a great cloud, the movement was so swift. Then, suddenly a wild plan occurred to me. It was a slim chance, but a man facing death will clutch at almost any straw.

Backing as far as I could into the corner of the chamber, I drew my shark knife from its sheath and waited. The fourteen-inch blade didn't seem to be an adequate weapon against such a monster, but I was used to the knife. With a half chance, I could let the terrible creature know that he had been in a fight.

Now it was enraged, changing from one color to another very quickly, its tentacles reaching always closer. I stood waiting. Desperately, the huge beast sought to clasp its suction-cupped arms about me. Hooking the torch to my belt, I waited just beyond reach. Suddenly an arm shot directly at me.

With a quick side swipe, I sliced through it, almost without knowing that my knife had made contact with flesh. Then another tentacle was severed from the sickening, wart-covered body. As still another arm was thrust at me, I sliced downward at it, lopping it off. Now I saw closely the monster's devilish eyes watching me fixedly with blank, goggling hatred.

A stream of blue-black fluid poured forth from the creature's ink sac,[14] spreading slowly upward and clouding the water all around me. Now I began to wonder whether my plan would succeed. I was desperate, cornered like a rat in a hole.

Another writhing tentacle shot forward. I managed to turn it aside with my knife, but failed to cut it off. But in the next instant, a back-handed blow from the tentacle smashed against my helmet. It hurled me backward against the wooden wall with a force that left me dazed, almost unconscious. Slowly I managed to stagger to my feet. I wasn't a second too soon, for the creature clamped onto my helmet and shook me violently. With a yell that

14. The *ink sac* (INK SAK) is an inky fluid released by octopi or squid to cloud the water and hide itself from attackers.

sounded hideous in my own ears, I drove my knife upward at the quivering arm wrapped about my helmet. The blade sliced deep through the boneless arm, its grip relaxing as the sinuous tentacle parted into two.

Now the octopus became wild with rage. Another huge arm groped for me. It flashed out as if to grip my helmet again, but dropped quickly and seized my left leg instead, throwing me off my feet. Again I slashed at it. And, with fiendish cunning, the creature changed its hold to my left arm, pulling me a little nearer to the doorway. I drove my knife upward once more, but luck was against me. The keen blade glanced wildly, and a second later it was wrenched from my hand!

Now I was completely helpless. In desperation I tried to brace myself, but there was nothing to brace against. I could not signal to the salvage ship above for help, because the huge monster's tentacles, those which remained, were staked across my lines. Inch by inch, the huge arm dragged me across the sand-covered floor of that watery tomb. As I came nearer, I could see the terrible eyes watching me through the clouded water. *The eighth victim that would never return to the surface.*

Suddenly a faint light shone on something that lay on the sand at my feet. *The shark knife!* I saw one last, crazy chance. I must take it or be torn to pieces by the nightmare that clutched me. Quickly I grabbed the steel knife. The tentacle on my left arm tightened, gave a quick jerk. Now I was within arm's reach of the terrible creature's body. I had to act quickly. Again I felt the grip tighten. Swiftly I raised the knife and drove the long blade full into the fearful monster's body at what I was certain was a vital spot…

At the very same moment something tore at my belt, and I felt a savage jerk as a stream of air bubbles shot out from the front of my diving suit. It was punctured.

Word Bank	**punctured** (PUNK churd) *v.*: pierced with a pointed instrument or object

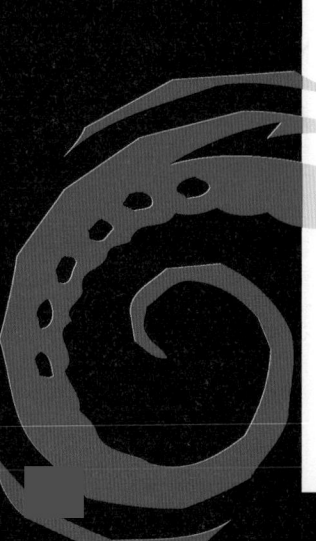

Then the very air seemed to tear apart. There was a blinding flash and a dull roar as I felt myself being whirled through space. Then came darkness.

Later I opened my eyes with a start, a sort of nervous twitch. Surely I must be dreaming, I thought, and closed my eyes for a few seconds. I opened them again and lay blinking, not knowing whether I was in this world or the next. My head cleared gradually and I caught the soft hiss of an air valve and saw that I was in a decompression lock. There were pressure gauges on the wall and a lone figure stood before them, adjusting the valves. Gingerly I rubbed the lump the size of an egg over my right ear and moved in the narrow bunk. The man at the valves turned to look at me. It was Boyer.

He eyed me a moment in silence, then quietly said, "Well, Lieutenant," with a look of concern on his face, "You did come back."

I was stiff and sore and numb—symptoms that tell a diver that he has been under the water too long. But I was fortunate to be alive at all! I wondered how I had managed to get back on the sloop, and Boyer explained:

"When we didn't hear from you for so long, I ordered two of the native divers to go down to see what was the matter. They found you with lines fouled and three tentacles of an octopus about you on the underdeck of the wreck. The creature was dead. They closed the air-pressure valves in your torn suit, cut away the lines and tentacles, and got you clear just in time. The suit was leaking fast, but they were able to get you on board before all the air was gone."

"Thank G-d, thank G-d!" I said.

For a moment or two we were silent, thinking of the narrow escape from a terrible death. I stood up, feeling quite groggy, but a lot better than I had expected. On deck I turned to Boyer and remarked, "Boyer, there are two things in this wide world I never want to meet again."

He smiled broadly. "What are they, Lieutenant?" he asked.

"Giant octopi and more octopi!" I answered with a grin.

Recalling

1. What made Harry decide to dive off the shores of Malpelo Island? Whom did he take with him?

2. Describe the type of suit that Harry was wearing. Why did Harry need to be so careful with the lines and valves?

3. Why couldn't the crew haul Harry up quickly?

4. What did Harry do with his shark knife?

Interpreting

5. How do you think the other seven divers perished?

6. Describe the octopus that threatened Harry's life.

7. How did Harry survive the attack of the octopus?

8. Who came to Harry's assistance and helped him return to the ship?

Concluding

9. What enabled Harry to respond humorously about the fact that he almost died underwater?

10. Do you think Harry ever went diving again after his close call with death? Explain.

Examining Nonfiction

In this selection, Harry Rieseberg had to make several life and death decisions concerning his survival at sea. He had to deal with a ferocious, unstable enemy that was huge and unpredictable. The author somehow survived this experience.

Imagine several weeks later, when Harry was fully recovered, he wrote a few paragraphs of advice to all those who would be diving for lost treasure. He suggested taking a few extra precautions based on his most recent experience. What do you think Harry wrote? Write one or two paragraphs of advice; you may inject some humor into your paragraphs.

Thinking About Nonfiction

Harry Rieseberg may have retold the story of his underwater adventures many times. Later, the crew members may have related this story to their friends. When Harry told the story, he was using the first-person point of view since Harry was the subject of the story. The crew members who told Harry's story used third-person point of view since they were telling a story about something that happened to someone else.

1. What point of view do you think is most effective when recounting a true story?

2. Do you think a story told in a third-person point of view could be as exciting as a story told in a first-person point of view?

Creating and Writing

Harry Earl Rieseberg undertook a huge, expensive, exotic adventure in the Pacific Ocean. We undertake smaller adventures when we go on family trips not knowing whom we will meet or which places we will visit. It is an adventure coming to school each day not knowing exactly what our teachers expect us to learn, what is being served for lunch, how we will score on tests, or how our classmates will treat us. Try to think of an adventure that you have had or heard about.

1. What did the people involved in this experience learn from the challenge?

2. What did you learn from the challenge? Share your thoughts with your class.

drama

Drama is literature written in verse or prose that is intended to portray life or tell a story through action and dialogue. Drama is an ancient literary form. Its source is rooted in oral tradition—the spoken stories handed down from generation to generation. Plays are written for groups of people who will be viewing or listening at the same time. When you read a play, you must imagine how it would appear or how it would sound. A successful drama seems so realistic that audiences feel they are witnessing actual events.

Several literary elements are especially important in drama. Setting arouses the interest of the audience and prepares them for the mood and atmosphere of the play. Costumes, lighting, makeup, and sound effects add to the excitement of the setting. The script must flow naturally by introducing and developing believable characters (*Grandpa and the Statue*). The conflict must be well developed and must build steadily until it reaches a climax and resolution (*Penicillin and Company*).

Dramatists are like puppeteers, pulling many strings, trying to find the best way to stage a performance that will entertain the audience and convey a message.

Into • *Penicillin and Company*

The play, *Penicillin and Company*, was originally written to be performed on the radio. Radio plays were a very popular form of entertainment in the United States from the 1930s to the 1950s. Since these plays were meant to be heard, and not seen, dialogue, the conversation between the characters, was very important. The lines of dialogue were used to advance the plot, describe the characters, and create the conflict in the play. Stage directions in the script told the actors how to speak their lines and told producers which sound effects to use. Good imagination on the part of the listener was the only other ingredient needed for a successful radio play.

Focus

As you read *Penicillin and Company*, imagine that you are listening to it on the radio. How would the characters' voices sound? Notice that the bracketed stage and music directions signal changes in the location or the time of the action. As you read the play, you will discover that a picture of the characters and setting is growing in your mind. Many people find that listening to radio plays helps develop their imagination.

About the Author

THELMA FELD wrote many radio plays in the 1950s. Although presented to a listening audience, Feld's creative, effective dialogue enabled them to "see" the performance. In the play *Penicillin and Company*, Thelma Feld wrote a radio play which educates the public about a major scientific discovery. Her avid interest in science comes across in the account of Dr. Arthur Fleming's discovery of penicillin in 1928. This event was a turning point in medical history.

Penicillin and Company

THELMA FELD

NARRATOR. Because of the men and events we're about to describe, millions of lives have been and will be saved. *Penicillin and Company* is the story of a miraculous accident—and of how it gave us the gift of life!…We begin our story in a small laboratory at St. Mary's Hospital in London. It's September of 1928. The day is hot and sticky. Dr. Alexander Fleming works at his table. He lifts the cover glass off one of the rows of plates and slides the plate under his microscope—when the door opens.

MRS. MULLENS (*the cleaning woman*). Oh, you still 'ere, Doctor?

FLEMING. Come in, come in, Mrs. Mullens.

MRS. MULLENS. Well, all right, seein' as 'ow I got to get my work done, though some people I know don't care 'ow late they work.

FLEMING. Now, Mrs. Mullens, a little more scrubbing and a little less talking, and this lab might be a fit place to work in.

MRS. MULLENS. Well, I like that!

FLEMING. No offense meant, Mrs. Mullens. It's hot, and I'm tired.

MRS. MULLENS. And 'ow am I to clean this place, with these nasty little dishes and bottles and 'eaven knows what all? I can 'ardly move about, it's so crowded.

FLEMING. Aye, it's a poor excuse for a laboratory, I'll grant you. (*Sighs*) But we must both do the best we can. Let's get on with our work.

MRS. MULLENS. It's that 'ot and stuffy, a body could choke to death. [*She starts to open window*]

FLEMING. No, no, we can't have that window open!

MRS. MULLENS. And why not, sir?

FLEMING. Something might come in—a foreign substance—

MRS. MULLENS. There's no foreigners around here, Doctor!

FLEMING. You see, these plates are sterile. On each one, I'm cultivating a family of microbes. With the window open, they might become contaminated—

MRS. MULLENS. Ah, come on, Doctor—a bit of fresh air won't do no 'arm!

FLEMING (*sighs*). All right. Leave the window open. This lab's impossible anyway. When I think of some of the labs I've seen—all gleaming and polished and ultrasterile.[1]

MRS. MULLENS. A smart man like you deserves the best, Doctor. That's what I was sayin' to my husband only this morning. "'erbert," I said, "a smart man like the—"

FLEMING. Yes, yes, Mrs. Mullens. And now, if you don't mind—

MRS. MULLENS. "A smart man like Doctor Fleming," I said, "'e deserves the best. Whatever 'e's lookin' for in 'is nasty old germs—I 'ope 'e finds it!"

[*Musical bridge*]

NARRATOR. What was Dr. Fleming looking for in his microbe cultures that hot September day? Certainly not for a discovery that would change the history of medical science. As a matter of fact, some days before he'd received a letter from a book publisher, asking him to write a chapter in a new textbook on bacteriology.[2] Dr. Fleming was well-known as an expert bacteriologist, a logical man to contribute to a textbook. And so, on this hot September day, he was studying a row of microbe cultures. Would one of his specimens reveal some new secret about the invisible killers?

FLEMING. (*as though to himself*) Now let's see—here's a new one. Wonder how it's coming along. I'll just lift the cover glass and see…Now then—it looks all right. Nothing unusual. But wait a minute…Oh, no—something's got into this one! Looks like a bit of mold growing right on top of the microbes. Well, this slide's ruined. Might as well get rid of it.

MRS. MULLENS. Is anything wrong, Doctor?

---

1. Here, *ultrasterile* means very clean and free of germs.
2. *Bacteriology* (BAK teer ee AH luj ee) is the branch of science that deals with bacteria (germs).

Word Bank	microbes (MY krohbz) *n.*: very small disease-causing bacteria or organisms

FLEMING. Oh. You still here, Mrs. Mullens?

MRS. MULLENS. I like that! 'oo d'ye think's been scrubbing that nasty sink?

FLEMING. Yes, yes, of course.

MRS. MULLENS. What's wrong, Doctor?

FLEMING. The usual. Just another specimen down the drain.

MRS. MULLENS. Now isn't that a shame! You don't suppose something flew in that window like you said, Doctor!

FLEMING. Not into *this* culture. It's two weeks old and I never uncovered it till just now.

MRS. MULLENS. Well, as long as it's not my fault—

FLEMING. No, wait a minute. I *did* uncover it for a moment last Monday.

MRS. MULLENS. And that's when something flew in?

FLEMING. Who knows? If this lab were really sterile, maybe I could keep my specimens clean. As it is.... (*sighs*)

MRS. MULLENS. You goin' to chuck it away?

FLEMING. I suppose so…No, wait. Might as well have a look at it.

MRS. MULLENS. I'll go finish that sink.

Nasty-looking mess, I don't mind saying—

FLEMING. Now, I'll just slip this under the microscope and have a look. All right, let's see what we have here. Yes—it *is* a piece of mold growing right on top of the germs. Just ordinary mold, I'd say—like a bit of stuff on bread or cheese; a spore might have flown into the lab from that confounded window… Say—this *is* curious. Where there isn't any mold, the germs are growing fast, like the little monsters they are—but around the mold itself, there *aren't* any bacteria! None at all! It's incredible! I've never seen a mold do that before! Around the mold there's a *clear zone*, where the germs have been dissolved! The little monsters have disappeared!

[*Musical bridge*]

NARRATOR. Something about the mold was killing the deadly microbes. What was it? Dr. Fleming had to find out. For weeks he studied the mold—grew it and transplanted it and studied it again. One fact was clear:

Word Bank

specimen (SPESS ih milin) *n.*: a portion of material for use in testing, examination, or study; a sample

spore (SPOR) *n.*: a simple one-celled organism produced by plants, fungi, and other microorganisms

FLEMING. This substance kills the microbes of pneumonia, diphtheria, and meningitis. Its power is astounding!

NARRATOR. But many questions had to be answered. One big question was raised by one of Dr. Fleming's colleagues:

RIDLEY. Let me ask you this, Alex. If this substance, the stuff you call penicillin, if this penicillin is strong enough to kill these microbes—is it safe to use on human tissues?

FLEMING. I don't know. All I know is, it's murder on the microbes here in the lab.

RIDLEY. But anything that strong will kill animals or human beings. It will wreck their tissues!

FLEMING. Yes, there's always that possibility. We'll have to find out.

NARRATOR. Step number one in finding out: Dr. Fleming tested his penicillin on white blood cells.

FLEMING. So far, so good. The white blood cells are unharmed!

NARRATOR. Step number two: Dr. Fleming injected the penicillin into a rabbit.

FLEMING. Excellent! The rabbit scarcely batted an eye!

NARRATOR. Step number three: Dr. Fleming went to the hospital ward.

He poured penicillin into the raw wound of a patient.

FLEMING. There is no irritant effect! We have a new chemical that means death to microbes—and is harmless to human tissues!

[*Musical bridge*]

NARRATOR. Time and again Dr. Fleming proved that penicillin was harmless to the human body—but would it cure an infection? He couldn't be sure. He said to his colleague, Dr. Ridley:

FLEMING. It takes *weeks* to get even a tiny dose. Weeks just to make a lab test!

RIDLEY. Well, can't we store up enough of the penicillin to give it a real test? Save it bit by bit?

FLEMING. Impossible! By the time we've collected enough to cure anything, the stuff's no good.

RIDLEY. If only we could isolate the chemical in pure form!

FLEMING. Yes, *if only*! Here we have a powerful microbe killer, and we don't even know exactly what it is!

RIDLEY. But we're on the right trail, Alex.

FLEMING. About all we've done is *name* the stuff.

RIDLEY. You've done much more.

FLEMING. Some day, a chemist may come along and find out exactly what penicillin is and manufacture it. In the meantime, penicillin is a dead pigeon!

[*Musical bridge*]

NARRATOR. Thus came to an end the first chapter in the story of penicillin. The next chapter began at Oxford University on the eve of World War II.[3] A doctor named Howard Florey was looking through some old reports on germ killers…and one day, he told his colleague, Dr. Chain:

FLOREY. This is very curious! Eight years ago this man found a splendid substance. I wonder why he didn't do any more with it.

CHAIN. Maybe it was too tricky to handle. One of those impossible chemicals.

FLOREY. No—not impossible. Very difficult, perhaps—but not impossible.

CHAIN. The problem seemed to be in *storing* the stuff. Fleming could never collect enough to give it a real test.

FLOREY. You know, Chain—I've been wondering.

CHAIN. Yes?

FLOREY. If we could get penicillin as a dry powder—and *keep* it dry—it wouldn't go bad. We could store it for weeks, months, even years!

CHAIN. Well, why don't we give it a try?

FLOREY. Come on—let's get started!

[*Musical bridge*]

NARRATOR. Dr. Florey and Dr. Chain began where Dr. Fleming had stopped. In the Oxford laboratories, the penicillin hunters kept grimly on with their work. Now there was a desperate reason to succeed.

VOICE (*filter*). At dawn today, Hitler invaded Poland. Great Britain is at war!

NARRATOR. Britain at war needed guns and planes and tanks. She also needed drugs—microbe killers to fight the plagues and wound infections which accompany war. Now penicillin was a life-or-death affair. And then one day:

FLOREY. Dr. Chain, I think we're ready for a real test!

CHAIN. It will work, Dr. Florey. I'm sure of it.

FLOREY. It did with mice. The results were clear-cut.

---

3. *World War II* was a war that took place between 1939 and 1945. In September of 1939, England entered World War II. The United States did not enter the war until December 1941.

CHAIN. All right, Doctor—let's go to the hospital. We're going to make the real test!

[*Musical bridge*]

FLETCHER (*attending doctor at the hospital*). Dr. Florey—we've got your man.

FLOREY. Who's the patient?

FLETCHER. A policeman, forty-three years old. Been in the hospital for four months.

FLOREY. What's the diagnosis?

FLETCHER. A strep infection. Started on his face and spread to the lungs and blood.

FLOREY. And he's not responding to treatment?

FLETCHER. His case is hopeless. If penicillin doesn't work, he'll be dead in twenty-four hours!

[*Musical bridge*]

FLOREY. Nurse—how's he doing?

NURSE. He's still alive after twelve hours, Doctor. That's all we can say!

FLOREY. Keep up the injections every three hours!

[*Musical bridge*]

FLOREY. How's the patient, Nurse?

NURSE. Doctor, I can hardly believe it. He's getting better!

FLOREY. Let's see the chart… hmmm…temperature down, pain

disappearing, blood count improving. This is most encouraging! Keep up the injections, Nurse.

[*Musical bridge*]

FLOREY. Well, Nurse? How is he?

NURSE. In another week he'll be out of bed!

FLOREY. Good, good.

NURSE. Would you like to see for yourself? Come on.

[*Sound of door opening*]

NURSE. I've brought you a visitor. Here's Dr. Florey!

LONDON BOBBY. I say, Doctor—this bloomin' stuff took me right back from the grave. Fooled them all, I did. I'm real grateful to you, Doctor!

[*Musical bridge*]

FLOREY (*tired*). Well, Nurse, that'll be all the injections for today.

NURSE. Dr. Florey, shall I start them tomorrow at eight—as usual?

FLOREY. No. No injections tomorrow.

NURSE. Dr. Florey—are you sure?

FLOREY (*gruffly*). No injections tomorrow, or the next day—or ever!

NURSE. But Doctor—the patient is still sick. He needs more penicillin! You know that!

Word Bank	**strep** (STREP) *n.*: an abbreviation of streptococcus, a disease-causing bacteria

FLOREY (*pause*). We've run out of penicillin.

NURSE (*gasps*). But he's been doing so well! Can't you make some more?

FLOREY. It would take weeks—and the patient will be dead by then.

[*Music: up...and fade under*]

NARRATOR. With deep sorrow Dr. Florey wrote in his report:

FLOREY. The attempt to treat this case proved that penicillin could be given over a period of five days. The dose of penicillin was too small; additional doses were not available in time. We must go on with our search for large quantities of penicillin!

NARRATOR. First Dr. Fleming—then Dr. Florey. Both had blazed the trail, but the real problem had yet to be solved: mass production of penicillin.

FLOREY. We simply can't make enough of the stuff. With Hitler bombing us every day, our factories going all-out making war material—

CHAIN. What are we to do, Dr. Florey?

FLOREY. Pack up your things. We're going to America!

[*Musical bridge*]

NARRATOR. Five months before Pearl Harbor, Dr. Florey arrived in the United States.

FLOREY. Gentlemen, we must have help on penicillin. We can't do it alone.

AMERICAN VOICE. Will it help you win the war?

FLOREY. Yes! yes!

AMERICAN VOICE. Then what are we waiting for? Let's go!

NARRATOR. All our nation's resources went to work on the problem. Chemical laboratories, hospitals, research foundations—all worked around the clock to solve the penicillin problem...mass production of this life-giving chemical. At last, one day, Dr. Florey was told:

AMERICAN VOICE. Dr. Florey, we're making a trillion units a month—more than a thousand pounds. The battle of penicillin production has been won!

[*Musical bridge*]

NARRATOR. Thanks to penicillin, thousands of lives were saved on the battlefields and at home. Today, penicillin is only one of many wonder-drugs, weapons in man's constant war against disease. Already these medical weapons have eased the suffering and pain of millions—and added years to our lives!

THE END

Recalling

1. When and where does Dr. Fleming do his work?

2. Does he find any problems in his laboratory?

3. What does Dr. Fleming discover growing on the specimen?

4. What does this make him realize?

5. What does Dr. Fleming name the substance, and what does he test it on?

6. Why couldn't the substance be used to cure an infection?

7. Who were the next two doctors to experiment with penicillin?

8. What idea did Dr. Florey have? Why was it so urgent for Dr. Florey and his colleague to succeed?

9. What were the results the first time the two doctors treated a patient with penicillin? What difficulty did they have? What did they decide to do?

Interpreting

10. Early in the play, Dr. Fleming says, "Aye, it's a poor excuse for a laboratory, I'll grant you. But we must both do the best we can. Let's get on with our work." What do you learn about Dr. Fleming's personality from this quote?

11. "Pack up your things. We're going to America!" What does this quote tell you about Dr. Florey's character?

12. Why do you think the play was called *Penicillin and Company*?

Concluding

13. How do you think most scientists develop ideas and experiments? Are they original or based on the work and research of past scientists and present colleagues?

Examining Drama

Dialogue is the conversation between characters. While reading the dialogue in a play, focus on what is said that moves the plot forward or that gives you background information. In *Penicillin and Company*, dialogue is an important key to understanding the characters and their personalities.

Reread the dialogue between Dr. Fleming and Mrs. Mullens and between Dr. Fletcher and Dr. Florey. What does the dialogue tell you about these characters and their relationships with each other?

Thinking About Drama

The listener of a radio play discovers the true nature and personality of each character through dialogue. How the lines are spoken by the actors also gives the listener clues to the characters' nature. For example, when Dr. Fleming notices something different on a specimen he says with interest, "Looks like a bit of mold growing right on top of the microbes." The expression in his voice reflects his surprise, and fear that something may have gone wrong with the experiment. This signals to the audience that Dr. Fleming is a committed scientist who is eager to make an important and useful discovery.

What can you infer about Dr. Fleming's feelings from the following lines?

1. "Say—this *is* curious. Where there isn't any mold, the germs are growing fast, like the little monsters they are—but around the mold itself, there *aren't* any bacteria! None at all! It's incredible!"

2. "Yes, *if only*! Here we have a powerful microbe killer, and we don't even know exactly what it is!"

Creating and Writing

Imagine that you are a doctor working in a science laboratory at the same time as Dr. Fleming. Instead of being supportive of his experiments and discoveries, you do not believe in the power of penicillin. Write dialogue that might occur between you and Dr. Fleming, including clear directions to the actors about how to speak their lines. Make sure to model it after the dialogue in the play.

Into • *Grandpa and the Statue*

What does America mean to you? The Statue of Liberty is a symbol of the freedom that is America's promise to all of her citizens. Every new immigrant that enters the country through New York Harbor passes the huge statue of Lady Liberty holding her torch, inviting the poor, the homeless, and the persecuted to find safety and hope in America.

Today, we take the Statue of Liberty's existence for granted. When it was first erected, however, there were those who questioned its worth. As in all free societies, everyone had an opinion about it. Grandpa cannot see why a statue should be put up at all. A good hotel for a weary traveler would be much more useful, he says. As the drama unfolds, Grandpa and the audience develop a deeper appreciation for what the statue means to Americans and to freedom-loving people the world over.

Focus

This play contains a **flashback**. That means that one of the characters remembers something from their past, and a scene of that past is then played on stage. The flashback in *Grandpa and the Statue* is very important to the play, because the development of the main character, Grandpa, takes place during the flashback. As you read the play, trace the changes in young Monaghan and Grandpa. The play begins and ends in a veterans' hospital. Why do you suppose the playwright set his story there?

About the Author

American playwright **ARTHUR MILLER** was born in 1915 in New York City. Miller is considered one of America's most important playwrights. Miller wrote many plays which address society's problems, such as *Death of a Salesman*, which received a Pulitzer Prize. Early in his career, Arthur Miller wrote radio plays such as the one you are about to read. The themes of immigration, family, and patriotism are common in many of his works. He died in 2005 in Connecticut.

GRANDPA
AND THE
STATUE

ARTHUR MILLER

CHARACTERS

ANNOUNCER	GRANDFATHER MONAGHAN	JACK	GIRL
AUGUST	CHILD MONAGHAN	MIKE	YOUNG MAN
YOUNG MONAGHAN	GEORGE	JOE	MEGAPHONE VOICE
SHEEAN	CHARLEY	ALF	VETERAN

[*Music: Theme*]

ANNOUNCER. The scene is the fourth floor of a giant army hospital overlooking New York Harbor. A young man sitting in a wheel chair is looking out a window: just looking. After a while another young man in another wheel chair rolls over to him and both look.

[*Music out*]

AUGUST. You want to play some checkers with me, Monaghan?

MONAGHAN. Not right now.

AUGUST. Okay. [*Slight pause*] You don't want to go feeling blue, Monaghan.

MONAGHAN. I'm not blue.

AUGUST. All you do most days is sit here looking out this window.

MONAGHAN. What do you want me to do, jump rope?

AUGUST. No, but what do you get out of it?

MONAGHAN. It's a beautiful view. Some companies make millions of dollars just printing that view on postcards.

AUGUST. Yeh, but nobody keeps looking at a postcard six, seven hours a day.

MONAGHAN. I come from around here, it reminds me of things. My young days.

AUGUST. That's right, you're Brooklyn, aren't you?

MONAGHAN. My house is only about a mile away.

AUGUST. That so. Tell me, are you looking at just the water all the time? I'm curious. I don't get a kick out of this view.

MONAGHAN. There's the Statue of Liberty out there. Don't you see it?

AUGUST. Oh, that's it. Yeh, that's nice to look at.

MONAGHAN. I like it. Reminds me of a lot of laughs.

AUGUST. Laughs? The Statue of Liberty?

MONAGHAN. Yeh, my grandfather. He got all twisted up with the Statue of Liberty.

AUGUST. [*Laughs a little*] That so? What happened?

MONAGHAN. Well. My grandfather was the stingiest man in Brooklyn. "Mercyless" Monaghan, they used to call him. He even used to save umbrella handles.

AUGUST. What for?

MONAGHAN. Just couldn't stand seeing anything go to waste. After a big windstorm there'd be a lot of broken umbrellas laying around in the streets.

AUGUST. Yeh?

MONAGHAN. He'd go around picking them up. In our house the closets were always full of umbrella handles. My grandma used to say that he would go across the Brooklyn Bridge on the trolley just because he could come back on the same nickel. See, if you stayed on the trolley they'd let you come back for the same nickel.

AUGUST. What'd he do, just go over and come back?

MONAGHAN. Yeh, it made him feel good. Savin' money. Two and a half cents.

AUGUST. So how'd he get twisted up with the Statue of Liberty?

MONAGHAN. Well, way back in 1887 around there they were living on Butler Street. Butler Street, Brooklyn, practically runs right down to the river. One day he's sitting on the front porch, reading a paper he borrowed from the neighbors, when along comes this man Jack Sheean who lived up the block.

[*Music: Sneak into above speech, then bridge, then out*]

SHEEAN. [*Slight brogue*] A good afternoon to you, Monaghan.

MONAGHAN. How're you, Sheean, how're ya?

SHEEAN. Fair, fair. And how's Mrs. Monaghan these days?

MONAGHAN. Warm. Same as everybody else in summer.

SHEEAN. I've come to talk to you about the fund, Monaghan.

MONAGHAN. What fund is that?

SHEEAN. The Statue of Liberty Fund.

MONAGHAN. Oh, that.

SHEEAN. It's time we come to grips with the subject, Monaghan.

MONAGHAN. I'm not interested, Sheean.

SHEEAN. Now hold up on that a minute. Let me tell you the facts. This here Frenchman has gone and built a fine statue of Liberty. It costs the L-rd knows how many millions to build. All they're askin' us to do is contribute enough to put up a base for the statue to stand on.

MONAGHAN. I'm not…!

SHEEAN. Before you answer me. People all over the whole United States are puttin' in for it. Butler Street is doin' the same. We'd like to hand up a flag on the corner saying—"Butler Street, Brooklyn is one hundred percent behind the Statue of Liberty." And Butler Street *is* a hundred percent subscribed except for you. Now will you give us a dime, Monaghan? One dime and we can put up the flag. Now what do you say to that?

MONAGHAN. I'm not throwin' me good money away for somethin' I don't even know exists.

SHEEAN. Now what do you mean by that?

MONAGHAN. Have you seen this statue?

SHEEAN. No, but it's in a warehouse. And as soon as we get the money to build the pedestal they'll take it and put it up on that island in the river, and all the boats comin' in from the

old country will see it there and it'll raise the hearts of the poor immigrants to see such a fine sight on their first look at this country.

MONAGHAN. And how do I know it's in this here warehouse at all?

SHEEAN. You read your paper, don't you? It's been in all the papers for the past year.

MONAGHAN. Ha, the papers? Last year I read in the paper that they were about to pave Butler Street and take out all the holes. Turn around and look at Butler Street, Mr. Sheean.

SHEEAN. All right. I'll do this: I'll take you to the warehouse and show you the statue. Will you give me a dime then?

MONAGHAN. Well…I'm not sayin' I would, and I'm not sayin' I wouldn't. But I'd be more *likely* if I saw the thing large as life, I would.

SHEEAN. [*Peeved*] All right, then. Come along.

[*Music up and down and out*]

[*Footsteps, in a warehouse…echo… they come to halt*]

Now then. Do you see the Statue of Liberty or don't you see it?

MONAGHAN. I see it all right, but it's all broke!

SHEEAN. *Broke*! They brought it from France on a boat. They had to take it apart, didn't they?

MONAGHAN. You got a secondhand statue, that's what you got, and I'm not payin' for new when they've shipped us something that's all smashed to pieces.

SHEEAN. Now just a minute, just a minute. Visualize what I'm about to tell you, Monaghan, get the picture of it. When this statue is put together it's going to stand ten stories high. Could they get a thing ten stories high into a four-story building such as this is? Use your good sense, now, Monaghan.

MONAGHAN. What's that over there?

SHEEAN. Where?

MONAGHAN. That tablet there in her hand. What's it say? July Eye Vee [IV] MDCCLXXVI…what…what's all that?

SHEEAN. That means July 4, 1776. It's in Roman numbers. Very high class.

MONAGHAN. What's the good of it? If they're going to put a sign on her they ought to put it: Welcome All. That's it. Welcome All.

SHEEAN. They decided July 4, 1776, and July 4, 1776, it's going to be!

MONAGHAN. All right, then let them get their dime from somebody else!

SHEEAN. Monaghan!

MONAGHAN. No, sir! I'll tell you something. I didn't think there was a statue but there is. She's all broke, it's true, but she's here and maybe they can get her together. But even if they do, will you tell me what sort of a welcome to immigrants it'll be, to have a gigantic thing like that in the middle of the river and in her hand is July Eye Vee MCDVC… whatever it is?

SHEEAN. That's the date the country was made!

Monaghan. Forget about the date! A man comin' in from the sea wants a place to stay, not a date. When I come from the old country I git off at the dock and there's a feller says to me, "Would you care for a room for the night?" "I would that," I sez, and he sez, "All right then, follow me." He takes me to a rooming house. I no sooner sign me name on the register—which I was able to do even at that time—when I look around and the feller is gone clear away and took my valise in the bargain. A statue anyway can't move off so fast, but if she's going to welcome let her say welcome, not this MCDC…

Sheean. All right, then, Monaghan. But all I can say is, you've laid a disgrace on the name of Butler Street. I'll put the dime in for ya.

Monaghan. Don't connect me with it! It's a swindle, is all it is. In the first place, it's broke; in the second place, if they do put it up it'll come down with the first high wind that strikes it.

Sheean. The engineers say it'll last forever.

Monaghan. And I say it'll topple into the river in a high wind! Look at the inside of her. She's all hollow!

Sheean. I've heard everything now, Monaghan. Just about everything. Good-bye.

Monaghan. What do you mean, good-bye? How am I to get back to Butler Street from here?

Sheean. You've got legs to walk.

Monaghan. I'll remind you that I came on the trolley.

Sheean. And I'll remind you that I paid your fare and I'm not repeating the kindness.

Monaghan. Sheean? You've stranded me!

[*Music up and down*]

Young Monaghan. That was grandpa. That's why I have to laugh every time I look at the statue now.

August. Did he ever put the dime in?

Young Monaghan. Well—in a way. What happened was this: his daughters got married and finally my mom…put *me* out on Butler Street. I got to be pretty attached to grandpa. He'd even give me an umbrella handle and make a sword out of it for me. Naturally, I wasn't very old before he began working on me about the statue.

[*High wind*]

Child Monaghan. [*Softly, as though grandpa is in bed*] Grampa?

Monaghan. [*Awakened*] Heh? What are you doin' up?

Child Monaghan. Ssssh! Listen!

[*Wind rising up and fading. Rising higher and fading*]

Monaghan. [*Gleefully*] Aaaaaah! Yes, yes. This'll do it, boy. This'll do it! First thing in the morning we'll go down to the docks and I'll bet you me life that Mr. Sheean's statue is

Word Bank

peeved (PEEVD) *adj.*: annoyed

register (REJ ih stur) *n.*: a written record containing regular entries of items, details, events, or names

swindle (SWIN dul) *n.*: an act of deceit; a trick

smashed down and layin' on the bottom of the bay. Go to sleep now, we'll have a look first thing.

[*Music up and down*]

[*Footsteps*]

CHILD MONAGHAN. If it fell down, all the people will get their dimes back, won't they, grampa? Slow down, I can't walk so fast.

MONAGHAN. Not only will they get their dimes back, but Mr. Sheean and the whole crew that engineered the collection are going to rot in jail. Now mark my words. Here, now, we'll take a short cut around this shed…

[*Footsteps continue a moment, then gradually…disappointedly they come to a halt*]

CHILD MONAGHAN. She's…she's still standing, grampa.

MONAGHAN. She is that. [*Uncomprehending*] I don't understand it. That was a terrible wind last night. Terrible.

CHILD MONAGHAN. Maybe she's weaker though. Heh?

MONAGHAN. Why…sure, that must be it. I'll wager she's hangin' by a thread. [*Realizing*] Of course! That's why they put her out there in the water so when she falls down she won't be flattening out a lot of poor innocent people. Hey—feel that?

CHILD MONAGHAN. The wind! It's starting to blow again!

MONAGHAN. Sure, and look at the sky blackening over!

[*Wind rising*]

Feel it comin' up! Take your last look at the statue, boy. If I don't mistake me eyes she's takin' a small list to Jersey already!

[*Music up and down*]

YOUNG MONAGHAN. It was getting embarrassing for me on the block. I kept promising the other kids that when the next wind came the statue would come down. We even had a game. Four or five kids would stand in a semicircle around one kid who was the statue. The statue kid had to stand on his heels and look right in our eyes. Then we'd all take a deep breath and blow in his face. He'd fall down like a stick of wood. They all believed me and grampa… …until one day. We were standing around throwing rocks at an old milk can…

[*Banging of rocks against milk can*]

GEORGE. [*Kid*] What're you doin'?

CHILD MONAGHAN. What do we look like we're doin'?

GEORGE. I'm going someplace tomorrow.

CHARLEY. [*Kid*] I know. Watch out, I'm throwin'.

[*Can being hit*]

GEORGE. I mean after…

JACK. Where?

GEORGE. My old man's going to take me out on the Statue of Liberty boat.

[*Banging against can abruptly stops*]

CHILD MONAGHAN. You're not going out on the statue, though, are you?

GEORGE. Sure, that's where we're going.

CHILD MONAGHAN. But you're liable to get killed. Supposing there's a high wind tomorrow?

GEORGE. My old man says that statue couldn't fall down if all the wind in the world and John L. Sullivan[1] hit it at the same time.

CHILD MONAGHAN. Is that so?

GEORGE. Yeh, that's so. My old man says that the only reason your grandfather's saying that it's going to fall down is that he's ashamed he didn't put a dime in for the pedestal.

CHILD MONAGHAN. Is that so?

GEORGE. Yeh, that's so.

CHILD MONAGHAN. Well, you tell your old man that if he gets killed tomorrow not to come around to my grandfather and say he didn't warn him!

JACK. Hey, George, would your father take me along?

GEORGE. I'll ask him, maybe he—

CHILD MONAGHAN. What, are you crazy, Jack?

MIKE. Ask him if he'd take me too, will ya, George?

CHILD MONAGHAN. Mike, what's the matter with you?

JOE. Me too, George, I'll ask my mother for money.

CHILD MONAGHAN. Joe! Didn't you hear what my grampa said?

JOE. Well…I don't really believe that any more.

CHILD MONAGHAN. You don't be…

MIKE. Me neither.

JACK. I don't really think your grampa knows what he's talkin' about.

CHILD MONAGHAN. He don't, heh? [*Ready to weep*] Okay…Okay. [*Bursting out*] I just hope that wind blows tomorrow, boy! I just hope that wind blows!

[*Music up and down*]

[*Creaking of a rocking chair*]

MONAGHAN. Huh?

CHILD MONAGHAN. Can you stop rocking for a minute?

[*Rocking stops*]

Can you put down your paper?

[*Rustle of paper*]

I—I read the weather report for tomorrow.

MONAGHAN. The weather report…

CHILD MONAGHAN. Yeh. It says fair and cool.

MONAGHAN. What of it?

CHILD MONAGHAN. I was wondering. Supposing you and me we went on a boat tomorrow. You know, I see the water every day when I go down to the docks to play, but I never sat on it. I mean in a boat.

---

1. *John L. Sullivan* was a well-known American boxer in the late-19th century.

Word Bank

engineered (EN jin eared) *v.*: planned; designed or produced

pedestal (PED ih stuhl) *n.*: the base of an upright structure

MONAGHAN. Oh. Well, we might take the ferry on the Jersey side. We might do that.

CHILD MONAGHAN. Yeh, but there's nothing to see in Jersey.

MONAGHAN. You can't go to Europe tomorrow.

CHILD MONAGHAN. No, but couldn't we go toward the ocean? Just… *toward* it?

MONAGHAN. Toward it. What—what is it on your mind, boy? What is it now?

CHILD MONAGHAN. Well…I…

MONAGHAN. Oh, you want to take the Staten Island ferry. Sure, that's in the direction of the sea.

CHILD MONAGHAN. No, grampa, not the Staten Island ferry.

MONAGHAN. You don't mean— [*Breaks off*] Boy!

CHILD MONAGHAN. All the kids are going tomorrow with Georgie's old man.

MONAGHAN. You don't believe me any more.

CHILD MONAGHAN. I do, grampa, but…

MONAGHAN. You don't. If you did you'd stay clear of the Statue of Liberty for love of your life!

CHILD MONAGHAN. But, grampa, when is it going to fall down? All I do is wait and wait.

MONAGHAN. [*With some uncertainty*] You've got to have faith.

CHILD MONAGHAN. But every kid in my class went to see it and now the ones that didn't are going tomorrow.

And they all keep talking about it and all I do…Well, I can't keep telling them it's a swindle. I—I wish we could see it, grampa. It don't cost so much to go.

MONAGHAN. As long as you put it that way I'll have to admit I'm a bit curious meself as to how it's managed to stand upright so long. Tell you what I'll do. Barrin' wind, we'll chance it tomorrow.

CHILD MONAGHAN. Oh, gramp!

MONAGHAN. But! If anyone should ask you where we went you'll say—Staten Island. Are y'on?

CHILD MONAGHAN. Okay, sure. Staten Island.

MONAGHAN. [*Secretively*] We'll take the early boat, then. Mum's the word, now. For if old man Sheean hears that I went out there I'll have no peace from the thief the rest of m'life.

[*Music up and down*]

[*Boat whistles*]

CHILD MONAGHAN. Gee, it's nice ridin' on a boat, ain't it, grampa?

MONAGHAN. Never said there was anything wrong with the boat. Boat's all right. You're sure now that Georgie's father is takin' the kids in the afternoon.

CHILD MONAGHAN. Yeh, that's when they're going. Gee, look at those two sea gulls. Wee!—look at them swoop! They caught a fish!

MONAGHAN. What I can't understand is what all these people see in that statue that they'll keep a boat like this full makin' the trip, year in year

out. To hear the newspapers talk, if the statue was gone we'd be at war with the nation that stole her the followin' mornin' early. All it is is a big high pile of French copper.

CHILD MONAGHAN. The teachers say it shows us that we got liberty.

MONAGHAN. Bah! If you've got liberty you don't need a statue to tell you you got it; and if you haven't got liberty no statue's going to do you any good tellin' you you got it. It was a criminal waste of the people's money. [*Quietly*] And just to prove it to you I'll ask this feller sitting right over there what he sees in it. You'll see what a madness the whole thing was. Say, mister?

ALF. Hey?

MONAGHAN. I beg your pardon. I'm a little strange here, and curious. Could you tell me why you're going to the Statue of Liberty?

ALF. Me? Well, I tell ya. I always wanted to take an ocean voyage. This is a pretty big boat—bigger than the ferries—so on Sunday, sometimes, I take the trip. It's better than nothing.

MONAGHAN. Thank you. [*To the kid*] So much for the great meaning of the statue, me boy. We'll talk to this lady standing at the rail. I just want you to understand why I didn't give Sheean me dime. Madame, would you be good enough to…Oh pardon me. [*To kid*] Better pass her by, she don't look so good. We'll ask that girl there. Young lady, if you'll pardon the curiosity of an old man…could you

tell me in a few good words what it is about that statue that brings you out here?

GIRL. What statue?

MONAGHAN. Why, the Statue of Liberty up ahead. We're coming up to it.

GIRL. Statue of Liberty! Is this the Statue of Liberty boat?

MONAGHAN. Well, what'd you think it was?

GIRL. Oh, my! I'm supposed to be on the Staten Island ferry! Where's the ticket man? [*Going away*] Ticket man! Where's the ticket man?

CHILD MONAGHAN. Gee whiz, nobody seems to want to see the statue.

MONAGHAN. Just to prove it, let's see this fellow sitting on this bench here. Young man, say…

YOUNG MAN. I can tell you in one word. For four days I haven't had a minute's peace. My kids are screaming, my wife is yelling, upstairs they play the piano all day long. The only place I can find that's quiet is a statue. That statue is my silent friend. Every Sunday I beat it out to the island and sit next to her and she don't talk.

CHILD MONAGHAN. I guess you were right, grampa. Nobody seems to think it means anything.

MONAGHAN. Not only doesn't mean anything, but if they'd used the money to build an honest roomin' house on that island, the immigrants would have a place to spend the night, their valises wouldn't get robbed, and they—

MEGAPHONE VOICE. *Please keep your seats while the boat is docking. Statue of Liberty—all out in five minutes.*

CHILD MONAGHAN. Look down there, gramp! There's a peanut stand! Could I have some?

MONAGHAN. I feel the wind comin' up. I don't think we dare take the time.

[*Music up and down*]

CHILD MONAGHAN. Sssssseuuuuww! Look how far you can see! Look at that ship way out in the ocean!

MONAGHAN. It is, it's quite a view. Don't let go of me hand now.

CHILD MONAGHAN. I betcha we could almost see California.

MONAGHAN. It's probably that grove of trees way out over there. They do say it's beyond Jersey.

CHILD MONAGHAN. Feels funny. We're standing right inside her head. Is that what you meant…July IV, MCD…?

MONAGHAN. That's it. That tablet in her hand. Now shouldn't they have put Welcome All on it instead of that foreign language? Say! Do you feel her rockin'?

CHILD MONAGHAN. Yeah, she's moving a little bit. Listen, the wind!

[*Whistling of wind*]

MONAGHAN. We better get down, come on! This way!

CHILD MONAGHAN. No, the stairs are this way! Come on!

[*Running in echo. Then quick stop*]

MONAGHAN. No, I told you they're the other way! Come!

VETERAN. [*Calm, quiet voice*] Don't get excited, pop. She'll stand.

MONAGHAN. She's swayin' awful.

VETERAN. That's all right. I been up here thirty, forty times. She gives with the wind, flexible. Enjoy the view, go on.

MONAGHAN. Did you say you've been up here forty times?

VETERAN. About that many.

MONAGHAN. What do you find here that's so interesting?

VETERAN. It calms my nerves.

MONAGHAN. Ah. It seems to me it would make you more nervous than you were.

VETERAN. No, not me. It kinda means something to me.

MONAGHAN. Might I ask what?

VETERAN. Well…I was in the Philippine War[2]…back in '98. Left my brother back there.

MONAGHAN. Oh, yes. Sorry I am to hear it. Young man, I suppose, eh?

VETERAN. Yeh. We were both young. This is his birthday today.

MONAGHAN. Oh, I understand.

VETERAN. Yeh, this statue is about the only stone he's got. In my mind I feel it is anyway. This statue kinda

---

2. *The Philippine War*, more frequently called the Spanish-American War, was a brief conflict between Spain and the United States in 1898.

looks like what we believe. You know what I mean?

Monaghan. Looks like what we believe…I…I never thought of it that way. I…I see what you mean. It does look that way. [*Angrily*] See now, boy? If Sheean had put it that way I'd a give him me dime. [*Hurt*] Now, why do you suppose he didn't tell me that? Come down now. I'm sorry, sir, we've got to get out of here.

[*Music up and down*]

[*Footsteps under*]

Hurry now, I want to get out of here. I feel terrible. I do, boy. That Sheean, that fool. Why didn't he tell me that? You'd think…

Child Monaghan. What does this say?

[*Footsteps halt*]

Monaghan. Why, it's just a tablet, I suppose. I'll try it with me spectacles, just a minute. Why, it's a poem, I believe…"Give me your tired, your poor, your huddled masses yearning to breathe free, the wretched refuse of your teeming shore. Send these, the homeless, tempest-tost to me, I lift…my lamp beside…the golden door!" Oh, dear. [*Ready to weep*] It had Welcome All on it all the time. Why didn't Sheean tell me? I'd a given a quarter! Boy…go over there and here's a nickel and buy yourself a bag of them peanuts.

Child Monaghan. [*Astonished*] Gramp!

Monaghan. Go on now, I want to study this a minute. And be sure the man gives you full count.

Child Monaghan. I'll be right back.

[*Footsteps running away*]

Monaghan. [*To himself*] "Give me your tired, your poor, your huddled masses…"[3]

[*Music swells from a sneak to full, then under to background*]

Young Monaghan. [*Soldier*] I ran over and got my peanuts and stood there cracking them open, looking around. And I happened to glance over to grampa. He had his nose right up to that bronze tablet, reading it. And then he reached into his pocket and kinda spied around over his eyeglasses to see if anybody was looking, and then he took out a coin and stuck it in a crack of cement over the tablet.

[*Coin falling onto concrete*]

It fell out and before he could pick it up I got a look at it. It was a half a buck. He picked it up and pressed it into the crack so it stuck. And then he came over to me and we went home.

[*Music: Change to stronger, more forceful theme*]

That's why, when I look at her now through this window, I remember that time and that poem, and she really seems to say, Whoever you are, wherever you come from, Welcome All. Welcome Home.

[*Music: Flare up to finish*]

---

3. *"Give me your tired…"* is a quote from the poem American poet Emma Lazarus wrote about the Statue of Liberty. It is engraved on the statue's pedestal.

Recalling

1. What is Young Monaghan looking at when the play begins?

2. What does it remind him of?

3. What was Grandfather Monaghan's nickname?

4. What did Sheean want Grandfather Monaghan to do?

5. Why didn't Grandfather Monaghan want to contribute?

6. Where did Sheean decide to take him?

7. What didn't Grandfather Monaghan like about the sign on the statue?

8. What did Grandfather Monaghan think would happen to the statue?

9. Where did Child Monaghan want his grandfather to take him? Did his grandfather want to go too? Explain.

10. What happened when they actually went inside? What did the Veteran tell them?

11. What did Grandfather Monaghan discover on the tablet?

Interpreting

12. What did Young Monaghan mean when he said that his grandfather "got all twisted up with the Statue of Liberty"?

13. Why do you think it was so important for the Irish immigrants of Butler Street to join forces with mainstream America on this project?

14. How do you think Child Monaghan felt after being told by all the boys that they were going to see the statue?

15. Grandfather Monaghan said, "You've got to have faith," when his grandson asked him when the statue was going to collapse. What does this answer to his grandson's question tell you about Grandfather Monaghan's character?

16. What did the veteran mean by "This statue kinda looks like what we believe"?

17. When do you begin to see the effect that the statue finally had on Grandfather?

18. Do you think that the memories that Young Monaghan has of his grandfather's connection with the statue have affected his attitude towards it? Explain.

Concluding

19. Name some monuments, statues, or landmarks that have special significance for Americans. Have you seen any of them? Why do they affect so many Americans?

Examining Drama

In *Grandpa and the Statue*, the character most fully developed and who changes, is Grandfather Monaghan. Through Grandfather's change in attitude and behavior, the theme of putting a higher goal before immediate self-interest is played out for the audience.

1. In the beginning of the play, Young Monaghan tells the audience his grandfather was the "stingiest man in Brooklyn." Find the dialogue further into the play that reveals this side of Grandfather's personality.

2. Grandfather Monaghan does not change on his own. He is motivated by minor characters. One such minor character is the Veteran, whom Grandfather meets at the Statue of Liberty. What does the Veteran say to Grandfather, that makes him rethink his views of the Statue of Liberty?

3. What is the connection between Young Monaghan's being a patient in an army hospital and the theme of the play?

Thinking About Drama

Arthur Miller wrote *Grandpa and the Statue* so that his audience could think about the themes of national pride, immigration, and the capacity of people for change. These themes are evident throughout the play, and the audience sees them mainly through the dialogue of Miller's characters.

1. Write down a line from the play that emphasizes the theme of national pride.

2. Write down a line from the play that emphasizes the important role of immigrants in the United States.

3. Write down a quote from the play that shows a person's changing his way of thinking and behaving.

Creating and Writing

Imagine yourself in the position of Grandfather Monaghan. You were asked to contribute to a cause and you refuse because you think it is worthless. After arguing, you realize its value.

Write a dialogue between yourself and the person who asks for the contribution. Then, write a paragraph describing your feelings both after the argument and then later when you conclude the fund is worthwhile after all. Include answers to the following questions:

1. How did you come to terms with your having been wrong?

2. What did it take for you to put away your pride and admit that you were wrong?

the novel

The Voyages of Dr. Dolittle

A novel is a full-length narrative written in prose. It contains all the elements of fiction that are present in a short story: plot, character, setting, and theme. A novel may contain some of the elements of poetry as well as actual poems. Dialogue and speeches performed in plays may also be included. The length of a novel allows for the luxury of employing all the literary forms that are showcased in this textbook.

Novels afford the reader the opportunity to become well-acquainted with many characters and the diverse lives they lead. A novel's length allows for the development of complex characters, secondary characters, and even interesting, well-developed minor characters become part of the action. The novel may contain more than one plot and setting. The atmosphere can shift from pleasant to dangerous and then back to pleasant. The theme of a novel can be revealed in different ways: through action, dialogue, or conflict.

Just as short stories are like brief afternoon trips to different locales, novels are like lengthy stays with new friends in different settings.

Into • *The Voyages of Dr. Dolittle*
Part One—Chapters 1-6

Talking birds, unheard-of animals, voyages around the world—these are just a few of the things that make *The Voyages of Dr. Dolittle* one of the most popular children's books in the English language. The story is told by a narrator, Tommy Stubbins, who is a young boy at the time the story takes place. Tommy lives in a small English town by the sea. His parents cannot afford to send him to school, so he has all day to wander through the town, meeting its various characters, and dreaming of becoming a sailor. By the time we encounter Dr. Dolittle, we have been treated to lively descriptions of the town, its odd assortment of laborers, and the doctor's house and pets.

Focus

The story draws you in right from the start by having Tommy Stubbins serve as narrator. It is easy for the reader to identify with young Tommy as he shares his observations, thoughts, and dreams with us. Tommy's power of description is wonderful. He describes the people and places with just enough detail to make them seem real. He is a good mimic, recording their accents and movements so well, we can almost see them. He uses the dialogue of one character to tell us about another. Altogether, Tommy is a master storyteller.

About the Author

HUGH LOFTING was born in 1886. Of Irish descent, Lofting was born in England but spent most of his life in the United States. Lofting created one of literature's most beloved characters, Dr. Dolittle, during World War I. He actually invented this character in letters to his children. *The Story of Dr. Dolittle* was published in 1920. The novel you are about to read, *The Voyages of Dr. Dolittle*, was a sequel to that book. It was published in 1923 and received the Newbery Medal. Hugh Lofting wrote a total of eleven Dr. Dolittle books. Lofting died in 1947.

PROLOGUE

All that I have written so far about Doctor Dolittle I heard long after it happened from those who had known him—indeed a great deal of it took place before I was born. But I now come to set down that part of the great man's life which I myself saw and took part in.

Many years ago the Doctor gave me permission to do this. But we were both of us so busy then voyaging around the world, having adventures and filling notebooks full of natural history that I never seemed to get time to sit down and write of our doings.

Now of course, when I am quite an old man, my memory isn't so good anymore. But whenever I am in doubt and have to hesitate and think, I always ask Polynesia, the parrot.

That wonderful bird (she is now nearly two hundred and fifty years old) sits on the top of my desk, usually humming sailor songs to herself, while I write this book. And, as everyone who ever met her knows, Polynesia's memory is the most marvelous memory in the world. If there is any happening I am not quite sure of, she is always able to put me right, to tell me exactly how it took place, who was there and everything about it. In fact sometimes I almost think I ought to say that this book was written by Polynesia instead of me.

Very well then, I will begin. And first of all I must tell you something about myself and how I came to meet the Doctor.

PART I

1

THE COBBLER'S SON

My name was Tommy Stubbins, son of Jacob Stubbins, the cobbler of Puddleby-on-the-Marsh; and I was nine and a half years old. At that time Puddleby was only quite a small town. A river ran through the middle of it; and over this river there was a very old stone bridge, called Kingsbridge, which led you from the marketplace on one side to the yard on the other.

Sailing-ships came up this river from the sea and anchored near the bridge. I used to go down and watch the sailors unloading the ships upon the river-wall. The sailors sang strange songs as they pulled upon the ropes; and I learned these songs by heart. And I would sit on the river-wall with my feet dangling over the water and sing with the men, pretending to myself that I too was a sailor.

For I longed always to sail away with those brave ships when they turned their backs on Puddleby and went creeping down the river again, across the wide lonely marshes to the sea. I longed to go with them out into the world to seek my fortune in foreign lands—Africa, India, China and Peru! When they got round the bend in the river and the water was hidden from view, you could still see their huge brown sails towering over the roofs of the town, moving onward slowly—like some gentle giants that walked among the houses without noise. What strange things would they have seen, I wondered, when next they

Word Bank	cobbler (KAHB lur) *n.*: repairer or maker of shoes

came back to anchor at Kingsbridge! And, dreaming of the lands I had never seen, I'd sit on there, watching till they were out of sight.

Three great friends I had in Puddleby in those days. One was Joe, the mussel-man, who lived in a tiny hut by the edge of the water under the bridge. This old man was simply marvelous at making things. I never saw a man so clever with his hands. He used to mend my toy ships for me which I sailed upon the river; he built windmills out of packing-cases and barrel-staves; and he could make the most wonderful kites from old umbrellas.

Joe would sometimes take me in his mussel-boat, and when the tide was running out we would paddle down the river as far as the edge of the sea to get mussels and lobsters to sell. And out there on the cold lonely marshes we would see wild geese flying, and curlews and redshanks and many other kinds of seabirds that live among the samphire and the long grass of the great salt fen. And as we crept up the river in the evening, when the tide had turned, we would see the lights on Kingsbridge twinkle in the dusk, reminding us of teatime and warm fires.

Another friend I had was Matthew Mugg, the cat's-meat-man. He was a funny old person with a bad squint. He looked rather awful but he was really quite nice to talk to. He knew everybody in Puddleby; and he knew all the dogs and all the cats. In those times being a cat's-meat-man was a regular business. And you could see one nearly any day going through the streets with a wooden tray full of pieces of meat stuck on skewers crying, "Meat! M-E-A-T!" People paid him to give this meat to their cats and dogs instead of feeding them on dog biscuits or the scraps from the table.

I enjoyed going round with old Matthew and seeing the cats and dogs come running to the garden-gates whenever they heard his call. Sometimes he let me give the meat to the animals myself; and I thought this was great fun. He knew a lot about dogs and he would tell me the names of the different kinds as we went through the town. He had several dogs of his own; one, a whippet, was a very fast runner, and Matthew used to win prizes with her at the Saturday coursing races; another, a terrier, was a fine ratter. The cat's-meat-man used to make a business of rat-catching for the millers and farmers as well as his other trade of selling cat's-meat.

My third great friend was Luke the Hermit.[1] But of him I will tell you more later on.

I did not go to school; because my father was not rich enough to send me. But I was extremely fond of animals. So I used to spend my time collecting birds' eggs and butterflies, fishing in the river, rambling through the countryside after blackberries and mushrooms and helping the mussel-man mend his nets.

Yes, it was a very pleasant life I lived in those days long ago—though of course I did not think so then. I was nine and a half years old; and, like all boys, I wanted to grow up—not knowing how well off I was with

---

1. A *hermit* (HER mit) is a person who lives apart from society.

no cares and nothing to worry me. Always I longed for the time when I should be allowed to leave my father's house, to take passage in one of those brave ships, to sail down the river through the misty marshes to the sea—out into the world to seek my fortune.

2

I Hear of the Great Naturalist

One early morning in the Springtime, when I was wandering among the hills at the back of the town, I happened to come upon a hawk with a squirrel in its claws. It was standing on a rock and the squirrel was fighting very hard for its life. The hawk was so frightened when I came upon it suddenly like this, that it dropped the poor creature and flew away. I picked the squirrel up and found that two of its legs were badly hurt. So I carried it in my arms back to the town.

When I came to the bridge I went into the mussel-man's hut and asked him if he could do anything for it. Joe put on his spectacles and examined it carefully. Then he shook his head.

"Yon crittur's got a broken leg," he said—"and another badly cut an' all. I can mend you your boats, Tom, but I haven't the tools nor the learning to make a broken squirrel seaworthy. This is a job for a surgeon—and for a right smart one an' all. There be only one man I know who could save yon crittur's life. And that's John Dolittle."

"Who is John Dolittle?" I asked. "Is he a vet?"

"No," said the mussel-man. "He's no vet. Doctor Dolittle is a nacheralist."

"What's a nacheralist?"

"A nacheralist," said Joe, putting away his glasses and starting to fill his pipe, "is a man who knows all about animals and butterflies and plants and rocks an' all. John Dolittle is a very great nacheralist. I'm surprised you never heard of him—and you daft over animals. He knows a whole lot about shellfish—that I know from my own knowledge. He's a quiet man and don't talk much; but there's folks who do say he's the greatest nacheralist in the world."

"Where does he live?" I asked.

"Over on the Oxenthorpe Road, t'other side the town. Don't know just which house it is, but 'most anyone 'cross there could tell you, I reckon. Go and see him. He's a great man."

So I thanked the mussel-man, took up my squirrel again and started off towards the Oxenthorpe Road.

The first thing I heard as I came into the marketplace was someone calling "Meat! M-E-A-T!"

Word Bank   surgeon (SUR jun) *n.*: a medical specialist who performs surgery

"There's Matthew Mugg," I said to myself. "He'll know where this Doctor lives. Matthew knows everyone."

So I hurried across the marketplace and caught him up.

"Matthew," I said, "do you know Doctor Dolittle?"

"Do I know John Dolittle!" said he. "Well, I should think I do! I know him as well as I know my own wife—better, I sometimes think. He's a great man—a very great man."

"Can you show me where he lives?" I asked. "I want to take this squirrel to him. It has a broken leg."

"Certainly," said the cat's-meat-man. "I'll be going right by his house directly. Come along and I'll show you."

So off we went together.

"Oh, I've known John Dolittle for years and years," said Matthew as we made our way out of the marketplace. "But I'm pretty sure he ain't home just now. He's away on a voyage. But he's liable to be back any day. I'll show you his house and then you'll know where to find him."

All the way down the Oxenthorpe Road Matthew hardly stopped talking about his great friend, Doctor John Dolittle—"M.D." He talked so much that he forgot all about calling out "Meat!" until we both suddenly noticed that we had a whole procession of dogs following us patiently.

"Where did the Doctor go to on this voyage?" I asked as Matthew handed round the meat to them.

"I couldn't tell you," he answered. "Nobody never knows where he goes, nor when he's going, nor when he's coming back. He lives all alone except for his pets. He's made some great voyages and some wonderful discoveries. Last time he came back he told me he'd found a tribe of Red Indians in the Pacific Ocean—lived on two islands, they did. Yes, he's a wonderful man is the Doctor. And as for animals, well, there ain't no one knows as much about 'em as what he does."

"How did he get to know so much about animals?" I asked.

The cat's-meat-man stopped and leant down to whisper in my ear.

"He talks their language," he said in a hoarse, mysterious voice.

"The animal's language?" I cried.

"Why certainly," said Matthew. "All animals have some kind of a language. Some sorts talk more than others; some only speak in sign-language, like deaf-and-dumb. But the Doctor, he understands them all—birds as well as animals. We keep it a secret though, him and me, because folks only laugh at you when you speak of it. Why, he can even write animal-language. He reads aloud to his pets. He's wrote history-books in monkey-talk, poetry in canary language and comic songs for magpies to sing. It's a fact. He's now busy learning the language of the shellfish. But he says it's hard work—and he has caught some terrible colds, holding his head underwater so much. He's a great man."

"He certainly must be," I said. "I do wish he were home so I could meet him."

"Well, there's his house, look," said the cat's-meat-man—"that little one at the bend in the road there—the one high up—like it was sitting on the wall above the street."

We were now come beyond the edge of the town. And the house that Matthew pointed out was quite a small one standing by itself. There seemed to be a big garden around it; and this garden was much higher than the road, so you had to go up a flight of steps in the wall before you reached the front gate at the top. I could see that there were many fine fruit trees in the garden, for their branches hung down over the wall in places. But the wall was so high I could not see anything else.

When we reached the house Matthew went up the steps to the front gate and I followed him. I thought he was going to go into the garden; but the gate was locked. A dog came running down from the house; and he took several pieces of meat which the cat's-meat-man pushed through the bars of the gate, and some paper bags full of corn and bran. I noticed that this dog did not stop to eat the meat, as any ordinary dog would have done, but he took all the things back to the house and disappeared. He had a curious wide collar round his neck which looked as though it were made of brass or something. Then we came away.

"The Doctor isn't back yet," said Matthew, "or the gate wouldn't be locked."

"What were all those things in paper-bags you gave the dog?" I asked.

"Oh, those were provisions," said Matthew— "things for the animals to eat. The Doctor's house is simply full of pets. I give the things to the dog, while the Doctor's away, and the dog gives them to the other animals."

"And what was that curious collar he was wearing round his neck?"

"That's a solid gold dog-collar," said Matthew. "It was given to him when he was with the Doctor on one of his voyages long ago. He saved a man's life."

"How long has the Doctor had him?" I asked.

"Oh, a long time. Jip's getting pretty old now. That's why the Doctor doesn't take him on his voyages anymore. He leaves him behind to take care of the house. Every Monday and Thursday I bring the food to the gate here and give it to him through the bars. He never lets anyone come inside the garden while the Doctor's away—not even me, though he knows me well. But you'll always be able to tell if the Doctor's back or not—because if he is, the gate will surely be open."

So I went off home to my father's house and put my squirrel to bed in an old wooden box full of straw. And there I nursed him myself and took care of him as best I could till the time should come when the Doctor would return. And every day I went to the little house with the big garden on the edge of town and tried the gate to see if it were locked. Sometimes the dog, Jip, would come down to the gate to meet me. But though he always wagged his tail and seemed glad to see me, he never let me come inside the garden.

3

THE DOCTOR'S HOME

One Monday afternoon towards the end of April my father asked me to take some shoes which he had mended to a house on the other side of the town. They were for a Colonel Bellowes who was very particular.

I found the house and rang the bell at the front door. The Colonel opened it, stuck out a very red face and said, "Go round to the tradesmen's entrance—go to the back door." Then he slammed the door shut.

I felt inclined to throw the shoes into the middle of his flower-bed. But I thought my father might be angry, so I didn't. I went round to the back door, and there the Colonel's wife met me and took the shoes from me. She looked a timid little woman and had her hands all over flour as though she were making bread. She seemed to be terribly afraid of her husband whom I could still hear stumping round the house somewhere, grunting indignantly because I had come to the front door. Then she asked me in a whisper if I would have a bun and a glass of milk. And I said, "Yes, please."

After I had eaten the bun and milk, I thanked the Colonel's wife and came away. Then I thought that before I went home I would go and see if the Doctor had come back yet. I had been to his house once already that morning. But I thought I'd just like to go and take another look. My squirrel wasn't getting any better and I was beginning to be worried about him.

So I turned into the Oxenthorpe Road and started off towards the Doctor's house. On the way I noticed that the sky was clouding over and that it looked as though it might rain.

I reached the gate and found it still locked. I felt very discouraged. I had been coming here every day for a week now. The dog, Jip, came to the gate and wagged his tail as usual, and then sat down and watched me closely to see that I didn't get in.

I began to fear that my squirrel would die before the Doctor came back. I turned away sadly, went down the steps onto the road and turned towards home again.

I wondered if it were suppertime yet. Of course I had no watch of my own, but I noticed a gentleman coming towards me down the road; and when he got nearer I saw it was the Colonel out for a walk. He was all wrapped up in smart overcoats and mufflers and bright-colored gloves. It was not a very cold day but he had so many clothes on he looked like a pillow inside a roll of blankets. I asked him if he would please tell me the time.

He stopped, grunted and glared down at me—his red face growing redder still; and when he spoke it sounded like the cork coming out of a ginger-beer bottle.

"Do you imagine for one moment," he spluttered, "that I am going to get myself all unbuttoned just to tell a little boy like you *the time*!" And he went stumping down the street, grunting harder than ever.

I stood still a moment looking after him and wondering how old I would have to be, to have him go to the trouble of getting his watch out. And then, all of a sudden, the rain came down in torrents.

I have never seen it rain so hard. It got dark, almost like night. The wind began to blow; the thunder rolled; the lightning flashed; and in a moment the gutters of the road were flowing like a river. There was no place handy to take shelter, so I put my head down against the driving wind and started to run towards home.

I hadn't gone very far when my head bumped into something soft and I sat down suddenly on the pavement. I looked up to see whom I had run into. And there in front of me, sitting on the wet pavement like myself, was a little round man with a very kind face. He wore a shabby high hat and in his hand he had a small black bag.

"I'm very sorry," I said. "I had my head down and I didn't see you coming."

To my great surprise, instead of getting angry at being knocked down, the little man began to laugh.

"You know this reminds me," he said, "of a time once when I was in India. I ran full tilt into a woman in a thunderstorm. But she was carrying a pitcher of molasses on her head and I had treacle² in my hair for weeks afterwards—the flies followed me everywhere. I didn't hurt you, did I?"

"No," I said. "I'm all right."

"It was just as much my fault as it was yours, you know," said the little man. "I had my head down too—but look here, we mustn't sit talking like this. You must be soaked. I know I am. How far have you got to go?"

"My home is on the other side of the town," I said, as we picked ourselves up.

"My goodness, but that *was* a wet pavement!" said he. "And I declare it's coming down worse than ever. Come along to my house and get dried. A storm like this can't last."

He took hold of my hand and we started running back down the road together. As we ran I began to wonder who this funny little man could be, and where he lived. I was a perfect stranger to him, and yet he was taking me to his own home to get dried. Such a change, after the old red-faced Colonel who had refused even to tell me the time! Presently we stopped.

"Here we are," he said.

I looked up to see where we were and found myself back at the foot of the steps leading to the little house with the big garden! My new friend was already running up the steps and opening the gate with some keys he took from his pocket.

---

2. *Treacle* (TREE kul) is another name for molasses.

"Surely," I thought, "this cannot be the great Doctor Dolittle himself!"

I suppose after hearing so much about him I had expected someone very tall and strong and marvelous. It was hard to believe that this funny little man with the kind smiling face could be really he. Yet here he was, sure enough, running up the steps and opening the very gate which I had been watching for so many days!

The dog, Jip, came rushing out and started jumping up on him and barking with happiness. The rain was splashing down heavier than ever.

"Are you Doctor Dolittle?" I shouted as we sped up the short garden-path to the house.

"Yes, I'm Doctor Dolittle," said he, opening the front door with the same bunch of keys. "Get in! Don't bother about wiping your feet. Never mind the mud. Take it in with you. Get in out of the rain!"

I popped in, he and Jip following. Then he slammed the door behind us.

The storm had made it dark enough outside; but inside the house, with the door closed, it was as black as night. Then began the most extraordinary noise that I have ever heard. It sounded like all sorts and kinds of animals and birds calling and squeaking and screeching at the same time. I could hear things trundling down the stairs and hurrying along passages. Somewhere in the dark a duck was quacking, a cock was crowing, a dove was cooing, an owl was hooting, a lamb was bleating and Jip was barking. I felt birds' wings fluttering and fanning near my face. Things kept bumping into my legs and nearly upsetting me. The whole front hall seemed to be filling up with animals. The noise, together with roaring of the rain, was tremendous; and I was beginning to grow a little bit scared when I felt the Doctor take hold of my arm and shout into my ear.

"Don't be alarmed. Don't be frightened. These are just some of my pets. I've been away three months and they are glad to see me home again. Stand still where you are till I strike a light. My Gracious, what a storm!—Just listen to that thunder!"

So there I stood in the pitch-black dark, while all kinds of animals which I couldn't see chattered and

---

Word Bank **chattered** (CHAT urd) *v.*: uttered rapidly repeated, unclear sounds

jostled around me. It was a curious and a funny feeling. I had often wondered, when I had looked in from the front gate, what Doctor Dolittle would be like and what the funny little house would have inside it. But I never imagined it would be anything like this. Yet somehow after I had felt the Doctor's hand upon my arm I was not frightened, only confused. It all seemed like some queer dream; and I was beginning to wonder if I was really awake, when I heard the Doctor speaking again: "My blessed matches are all wet. They won't strike. Have you got any?"

"No, I'm afraid I haven't," I called back.

"Never mind," said he. "Perhaps Dab-Dab can raise us a light somewhere."

Then the Doctor made some funny clicking noises with his tongue and I heard someone trundle up the stairs again and start moving about in the rooms above.

Then we waited quite a while without anything happening.

"Will the light be long in coming?" I asked. "Some animal is sitting on my foot and my toes are going to sleep."

"No, only a minute," said the Doctor. "She'll be back in a minute."

And just then I saw the first glimmerings of a light around the landing above. At once all the animals kept quiet.

"I thought you lived alone," I said to the Doctor.

"So I do," said he. "It is Dab-Dab who is bringing the light."

I looked up the stairs trying to make out who was coming. I could not see around the landing but I heard the most curious footsteps on the upper flight. It sounded like someone hopping down from one step to the other, as though he were using only one leg.

As the light came lower, it grew brighter and began to throw strange jumping shadows on the walls.

"Ah—at last!" said the Doctor. "Good old Dab-Dab!"

And then I thought I *really* must be dreaming. For there, craning her neck round the bend of the landing, hopping down the stairs on one leg, came a spotless white duck. And in her right foot she carried a lighted candle!

4

THE WIFF-WAFF

When at last I could look around me I found that the hall was indeed simply full of animals. It seemed to me that almost every kind of creature from the countryside must be there: a pigeon, a white rat, an owl, a badger, a jackdaw—there was even a small pig, just in from the rainy garden, carefully wiping his feet on the mat while the light from the candle glistened on his wet pink back.

The Doctor took the candlestick from the duck and turned to me.

"Look here," he said: "you must get those wet clothes off—by the way, what is your name?"

"Tommy Stubbins," I said.

"Oh, are you the son of Jacob Stubbins, the shoemaker?"

"Yes," I said.

"Excellent bootmaker, your father," said the Doctor. "You see these?" and he held up his right foot to show me the enormous boots he was wearing. "Your father made me these boots four years ago, and I've been wearing them ever since—perfectly wonderful boots—Well now, look here, Stubbins. You've got to change those wet things—and quick. Wait a moment till I get some more candles lit, and then we'll go upstairs and find some dry clothes. You'll have to wear an old suit of mine till we can get yours dry again by the kitchen-fire."

So presently when more candles had been lighted round different parts of the house, we went upstairs; and when we had come into a bedroom the Doctor opened a big wardrobe and took out two suits of old clothes. These we put on. Then we carried our wet ones down to the kitchen and started a fire in the big chimney. The coat of the Doctor's which I was wearing was so large for me that I kept treading on my own coattails while I was helping to fetch the wood up from the cellar. But very soon we had a huge big fire blazing up the chimney and we hung our wet clothes around on chairs.

"Now let's cook some supper," said the Doctor.—"You'll stay and have supper with me, Stubbins, of course?"

Already I was beginning to be very fond of this funny little man who called me "Stubbins," instead of "Tommy" or "little lad" (I did so hate to be called "little lad"!). This man seemed to begin right away treating me as though I were a grown-up friend of his. And when he asked me to stop and have supper with him I felt terribly proud and happy. But I suddenly remembered that I had not told my mother that I would be out late. So very sadly I answered, "Thank you very much. I would like to stay, but I am afraid that my mother will begin to worry and wonder where I am if I don't get back."

"Oh, but my dear Stubbins," said the Doctor, throwing another log of wood on the fire, "your clothes aren't dry yet. You'll have to wait for them, won't you? By the time they are ready to put on we will have supper cooked and eaten—Did you see where I put my bag?"

"I think it is still in the hall," I said. "I'll go and see."

I found the bag near the front door. It was made of black leather and looked very, very old. One of its latches was broken and it was tied up round the middle with a piece of string.

"Thank you," said the Doctor when I brought it to him.

"Was that bag all the luggage you had for your voyage?" I asked.

"Yes," said the Doctor, as he undid the piece of string. "I don't believe in a lot of baggage. It's such a nuisance. Life's too short to fuss with it. And it isn't really necessary, you know—Where *did* I put those sausages?"

The Doctor was feeling about inside the bag. First he brought out a loaf of new bread. Next came a glass jar with a curious metal top to it. He held this up to the light very carefully before he set it down upon the table; and I could see that there was some strange little water-creature swimming about inside. At last the Doctor brought out a pound of sausages.

"Now," he said, "all we want is a frying-pan."

We went into the scullery[3] and there we found some pots and pans hanging against the wall. The Doctor took down the frying-pan. It was quite rusty on the inside.

"Dear me, just look at that!" said he. "That's the worst of being away so long. The animals are very good and keep the house wonderfully clean as far as they can. Dab-Dab is a perfect marvel as a housekeeper. But some things of course they can't manage. Never mind, we'll soon clean it up. You'll find some silver-sand down there, under the sink, Stubbins. Just hand it up to me, will you?"

In a few moments we had the pan all shiny and bright and the sausages were put over the kitchen-fire and a beautiful frying smell went all through the house.

While the Doctor was busy at the cooking I went and took another look at the funny little creature swimming about in the glass jar.

"What is this animal?" I asked.

"Oh that," said the Doctor, turning round—"that's a Wiff-Waff. Its full name is *hippocampus pippitopitus*. But the natives just call it a Wiff-Waff—on account of the way it waves its tail, swimming, I imagine. That's what I went on this last voyage for, to get that. You see I'm very busy just now trying to learn the language of the shellfish. They *have* languages, of that I feel sure. I can talk a little shark language and porpoise dialect myself. But what I particularly want to learn now is shellfish."

"Why?" I asked.

"Well, you see, some of the shellfish are the oldest kind of animals in the world that we know of. We find their shells in the rocks—turned to stone—thousands of years old. So I feel quite sure that if I could only get to talk their language, I should be able to learn a whole lot about what the world was like ages and ages and ages ago. You see?"

"But couldn't some of the other animals tell you as well?"

"I don't think so," said the Doctor, prodding the sausages with a fork. "To be sure, the monkeys I knew in Africa some time ago were very helpful in telling me about bygone days; but they only went back a thousand years or so. No, I am certain that the oldest history in the world is to be had from the shellfish—and from them only. You see most of the other animals that were alive in those very ancient times have now become extinct."

"Have you learned any shellfish language yet?" I asked.

"No. I've only just begun. I wanted this particular kind of a pipe-fish because he is half a shellfish and half an ordinary fish. I went all the way to the Eastern Mediterranean after him. But I'm very much afraid he isn't going to be a great deal of help to me. To tell you the truth, I'm

---

3. The *scullery* (SKULL ur ee) is the kitchen.

rather disappointed in his appearance. He doesn't *look* very intelligent, does he?"

"No, he doesn't," I agreed.

"Ah," said the Doctor. "The sausages are done to a turn. Come along—hold your plate near and let me give you some."

Then we sat down at the kitchen-table and started a hearty meal.

It was a wonderful kitchen, that. I had many meals there afterwards and I found it a better place to eat in than the grandest dining-room in the world. It was so cozy and homelike and warm. It was so handy for the food too. You took it right off the fire, hot, and put it on the table and ate it. And you could watch your toast toasting at the fender and see it didn't burn while you drank your soup. And if you had forgotten to put the salt on the table, you didn't have to get up and go into another room to fetch it; you just reached round and took the big wooden box off the dresser behind you. Then the fireplace—the biggest fireplace you ever saw—was like a room in itself. You could get right inside it even when the logs were burning and sit on the wide seats either side and roast chestnuts after the meal was over—or listen to the kettle singing, or tell stories, or look at picture-books by the light of the fire. It was a marvelous kitchen. It was like the Doctor, comfortable, sensible, friendly and solid.

While we were gobbling away, the door suddenly opened and in marched the duck, Dab-Dab, and the dog, Jip, dragging sheets and pillowcases behind them over the clean tiled floor. The Doctor, seeing how surprised I was, explained: "They're just going to air the bedding for me in front of the fire. Dab-Dab is a perfect treasure of a housekeeper; she never forgets anything. I had a sister once who used to keep house for me (poor, dear Sarah! I wonder how she's getting on—I haven't seen her in many years). But she wasn't nearly as good as Dab-Dab. Have another sausage?"

The Doctor turned and said a few words to the dog and duck in some strange talk and signs. They seemed to understand him perfectly.

"Can you talk in squirrel language?" I asked.

"Oh yes. That's quite an easy language," said the Doctor. "You could learn that yourself without a great deal of trouble. But why do you ask?"

"Because I have a sick squirrel at home," I said. "I took it away from a hawk. But two of its legs are badly hurt and I wanted very much to have you see it, if you would. Shall I bring it tomorrow?"

"Well, if its leg is badly broken I think I had better see it tonight. It may be too late to do much; but I'll come home with you and take a look at it."

So presently we felt the clothes by the fire and mine were found to be quite dry. I took them upstairs to the bedroom and changed, and when I came down the Doctor was all ready waiting for me with his little black bag full of medicines and bandages.

"Come along," he said. "The rain has stopped now."

Outside it had grown bright again and the evening sky was all red with the setting sun; and thrushes were singing in the garden as we opened the gate to go down onto the road.

5

POLYNESIA

"I think your house is the most interesting house I was ever in," I said as we set off in the direction of the town. "May I come and see you again tomorrow?"

"Certainly," said the Doctor. "Come any day you like. Tomorrow I'll show you the garden and my private zoo."

"Oh, have you a zoo?" I asked.

"Yes," said he. "The larger animals are too big for the house, so I keep them in a zoo in the garden. It is not a very big collection but it is interesting in its way."

"It must be splendid," I said, "to be able to talk all the languages of the different animals. Do you think I could ever learn to do it?"

"Oh surely," said the Doctor—"with practice. You have to be very patient, you know. You really ought to have Polynesia to start you. It was she who gave me my first lessons."

"Who is Polynesia?" I asked.

"Polynesia was a West African parrot I had. She isn't with me anymore now," said the Doctor sadly.

"Why—is she dead?"

"Oh no," said the Doctor. "She is still living, I hope. But when we reached Africa she seemed so glad to get back to her own country. She wept for joy. And when the time came for me to come back here I had not the heart to take her away from that sunny land—although, it is true, she did offer to come. I left her in Africa—Ah well! I have missed her terribly. She wept again when we left. But I think I did the right thing. She was one of the best friends I ever had. It was she who first gave me the idea of learning the animal languages and becoming an animal doctor. I often wonder if she remained happy in Africa, and whether I shall ever see her funny, old, solemn face again—Good old Polynesia!— A most extraordinary bird—Well, well!"

Just at that moment we heard the noise of someone running behind us; and turning round we saw Jip the dog rushing down the road after us, as fast as his legs could bring him. He seemed very excited about something, and as soon as he came up to us, he started barking and whining to the Doctor in a peculiar way. Then the Doctor too seemed to get all worked up and began talking and making queer signs to the dog. At length he turned to me, his face shining with happiness.

"Polynesia has come back!" he cried. "Imagine it. Jip says she has just arrived at the house. My! And it's five years since I saw her—Excuse me a minute."

He turned as if to go back home. But the parrot, Polynesia, was already flying towards us. The Doctor clapped his hands like a child getting a new toy; while the swarm of sparrows in the roadway fluttered, gossiping, up onto the fences, highly scandalized to see a gray and scarlet parrot skimming down an English lane.

On she came, straight onto the Doctor's shoulder, where she immediately began talking a steady stream in a language I could not understand. She seemed to have a terrible lot to say. And very soon the Doctor had forgotten all about me and my squirrel and Jip and everything else; till at length the bird clearly asked him something about me.

"Oh excuse me, Stubbins!" said the Doctor. "I was so interested listening to my old friend here. We must get on and see this squirrel of yours—Polynesia, this is Thomas Stubbins."

The parrot, on the Doctor's shoulder, nodded gravely towards me and then, to my great surprise, said quite plainly in English, "How do you do? I remember the night you were born. It was a terribly cold winter. You were a very ugly baby."

"Stubbins is anxious to learn animal language," said the Doctor. "I was just telling him about you and the lessons you gave me when Jip ran up and told us you had arrived."

"Well," said the parrot, turning to me, "I may have started the Doctor learning but I never could have done even that, if he hadn't first taught me to understand what I was saying when I spoke English. You see, many parrots can talk like a person, but very few of them understand what they are saying. They just say it because—well, because they fancy it is smart or, because they know they will get crackers given them."

By this time we had turned and were going towards my home with Jip running in front and Polynesia still perched on the Doctor's shoulder. The bird chattered incessantly, mostly about Africa; but now she spoke in English, out of politeness to me.

"How is Prince Bumpo getting on?" asked the Doctor.

"Oh, I'm glad you asked me," said Polynesia. "I almost forgot to tell you. What do you think?—*Bumpo is in England*!"

"In England!—You don't say!" cried the Doctor. "What on earth is he doing here?"

"His father, the king, sent him here to a place called—er—Bullford, I think it was—to study lessons."

"Bullford!—Bullford!" muttered the Doctor. "I never heard of that place—Oh, you mean Oxford."

"Yes, that's the place—Oxford," said Polynesia. "I knew it had cattle in it somewhere. Oxford—that's the place he's gone to."

"Well, well," murmured the Doctor. "Fancy Bumpo studying at Oxford—Well, well!"

Word Bank

gravely (GRAYV lee) *adv.*: with serious bearing or manner

anxious (ANK shuss) *adj.*: *here*, eager; *generally*, extremely worried and uneasy

incessantly (in SESS int lee) *adv.*: in an unceasing manner; without intermission; continually

"There were great doings in Jolliginki when he left. He was scared to death to come. He was the first man from that country to go abroad. He thought he was going to be eaten by white cannibals or something. You know what those natives are—ignorant! Well!—But his father made him come. He said that all the black kings were sending their sons to Oxford now. It was the fashion and he would have to go. Bumpo wanted to bring his wife with him. But the king wouldn't let him do that either. Poor Bumpo went off in tears—and everybody in the palace was crying too. You never heard such a hullabaloo."

"And how is Chee-Chee getting on?—Chee-Chee," added the Doctor in explanation to me, "was a pet monkey I had years ago. I left him too in Africa when I came away."

"Well," said Polynesia frowning,—"Chee-Chee is not entirely happy. I saw a good deal of him the last few years. He got dreadfully homesick for you and the house and the garden. It's funny, but I was just the same way myself. You remember how crazy I was to get back to the dear old land? And Africa *is* a wonderful country—I don't care what anybody says. Well, I thought I was going to have a perfectly grand time. But somehow—I don't know—after a few weeks it seemed to get tiresome. I just couldn't seem to settle down. Well, to make a long story short, one night I made up my mind that I'd come back here and find you. So I hunted up old Chee-Chee and told him about it. He said he didn't blame me a bit—felt exactly the same way himself. Africa was so deadly quiet after the life we had led with you. He missed the stories you used to tell us out of your animal books—and the chats we used to have sitting round the kitchen-fire on winter nights. The animals out there were very nice to us and all that. But somehow the dear kind creatures seemed a bit stupid. Chee-Chee said he had noticed it too. But I suppose it wasn't they who had changed; it was we who were different. When I left, poor old Chee-Chee broke down and cried. He said he felt as though his only friend were leaving him—though, as you know, he has simply millions of relatives there. He said it didn't seem fair that I should have wings to fly over here anytime I liked, and him with no way to follow me. But mark my words, I wouldn't be a bit surprised if he found a way to come—someday. He's a smart lad, is Chee-Chee."

At this point we arrived at my home. My father's shop was closed and the shutters were up; but my mother was standing at the door looking down the street.

"Good evening, Mrs. Stubbins," said the Doctor. "It is my fault your son is so late. I made him stay to supper while his clothes were drying. He was soaked to the skin; and so was I. We ran into one another in the storm and I insisted on his coming into my house for shelter."

"I was beginning to get worried about him," said my mother. "I am thankful to you, Sir, for looking after him so well and bringing him home."

Word Bank	**tiresome** (TY ehr sum) *adj.*: possessing a quality that tires, bores, or annoys

"Don't mention it—don't mention it," said the Doctor. "We have had a very interesting chat."

"Who might it be that I have the honor of addressing?" asked my mother staring at the gray parrot perched on the Doctor's shoulder.

"Oh, I'm John Dolittle. I dare say your husband will remember me. He made me some very excellent boots about four years ago. They really are splendid," added the Doctor, gazing down at his feet with great satisfaction.

"The Doctor has come to cure my squirrel, Mother," said I. "He knows all about animals."

"Oh, no," said the Doctor, "not all, Stubbins, not all about them by any means."

"It is very kind of you to come so far to look after his pet," said my mother. "Tom is always bringing home strange creatures from the woods and the fields."

"Is he?" said the Doctor. "Perhaps he will grow up to be a naturalist someday. Who knows?"

"Won't you come in?" asked my mother. "The place is a little untidy because I haven't finished the spring cleaning yet. But there's a nice fire burning in the parlor."

"Thank you!" said the Doctor. "What a charming home you have!"

And after wiping his enormous boots very, very carefully on the mat, the great man passed into the house.

6

THE WOUNDED SQUIRREL

Inside we found my father busy practicing on the flute beside the fire. This he always did, every evening, after his work was over.

The Doctor immediately began talking to him about flutes and piccolos and bassoons; and presently my father said, "Perhaps you perform upon the flute yourself, Sir. Won't you play us a tune?"

"Well," said the Doctor, "it is a long time since I touched the instrument. But I would like to try. May I?"

Then the Doctor took the flute from my father and played and played and played. It was wonderful. My mother and father sat as still as statues, staring up at the ceiling as if time had stood still; and even I, who didn't bother much about music except on the mouth-organ —even I felt all sad and cold and creepy and wished I had been a better boy.

"Oh I think that was just beautiful!" sighed my mother when at length the Doctor stopped.

"You are a great musician, Sir," said my father, "a very great musician. Won't you please play us something else?"

"Why certainly," said the Doctor—"Oh, but look here, I've forgotten all about the squirrel."

"I'll show him to you," I said. "He is upstairs in my room."

So I led the Doctor to my bedroom at the top of the house and showed him the squirrel in the packing-case filled with straw.

The animal, who had always seemed very much afraid of me—though I had tried hard to make him feel at home, sat up at once when the Doctor came into the room and started to chatter. The Doctor chattered back in the same way and the squirrel when he lifted up to have his leg examined, appeared to be rather pleased than frightened.

I held a candle while the Doctor tied the leg up in what he called "splints," which he made out of matchsticks with his penknife.

"I think you will find that his leg will get better now in a very short time," said the Doctor closing up his bag. "Don't let him run about for at least two weeks yet, but keep him in the open air and cover him up with dry leaves if the nights get cool. He tells me he is rather lonely here, all by himself, and is wondering how his wife and children are getting on. I have assured him you are a man to be trusted; and I will send a squirrel who lives in my garden to find out how his family are and to bring him news of them. He must be kept cheerful at all costs. Squirrels are naturally a very cheerful, active race. It is very hard for them to lie still doing nothing. But you needn't worry about him. He will be all right."

Then we went back again to the parlor and my mother and father kept him playing the flute till after ten o'clock.

Although my parents both liked the Doctor tremendously from the first moment that they saw him, and were very proud to have him come and play to us (for we were really terribly poor) they did not realize then what a truly great man he was one day to become. Of course now, when almost everybody in the whole world has heard about Doctor Dolittle and his books, if you were to go to that little house in Puddleby where my father had his cobbler's shop you would see, set in the wall over the old-fashioned door, a stone with writing on it which says: "JOHN DOLITTLE, THE FAMOUS NATURALIST, PLAYED THE FLUTE IN THIS HOUSE IN THE YEAR 1839."

I often look back upon that night long, long ago. And if I close my eyes and think hard I can see that parlor just as it was then: a funny little man in coattails, with a round kind face, playing away on the flute in front of the fire; my mother on one side of him and my father on the other, holding their breath and listening with their eyes shut; myself, with Jip, squatting on the carpet at his feet, staring into the coals; and Polynesia perched on the mantlepiece beside his shabby high hat, gravely swinging her head from side to side in time to the music. I see it all, just as though it were before me now.

And then I remember how, after we had seen the Doctor out at the front door, we all came back into the parlor and talked about him till it was still later; and even after I did go to bed (I had never stayed up so late in my life before) I dreamed about him and a band of strange clever animals that played flutes and fiddles and drums the whole night through.

Studying THE SELECTION

Recalling

1. How old was Polynesia, and what was so special about her?

2. Why did Tommy envy the sailors?

3. What did Tommy do instead of attending school?

4. Who fed the animals when Dr. Dolittle was away?

5. How did Dr. Dolittle care for Tommy's injured squirrel?

Interpreting

6. Describe Joe and Matthew Mugg.

7. What did Joe mean when he said that Dr. Dolittle was a naturalist?

8. Why did Dr. Dolittle want to learn the language of the shellfish? Why was this hard work for Dr. Dolittle?

Concluding

9. Give an example of the rough way Colonel Bellowes treats Tommy.

10. Give two examples of Dr. Dolittle's kind attitude towards Tommy.

11. What can you learn about Dr. Dolittle from the way he interacted with Polynesia?

Examining the Novel

A very definite picture of Dr. Dolittle has been presented in these first chapters. Make a list of Dr. Dolittle's positive character traits. Then, make a list of his physical characteristics.

Thinking About the Novel

There will be many settings in this novel. The book begins in Puddleby-on-the-Marsh, a small town on a river. Tommy introduces us to his friends, Joe, Matthew Mugg, and Luke the Hermit, even before he introduces us to Dr. Dolittle. We get a sense of the closeness of a small town where sailors drop by, but otherwise life is somewhat boring.

1. Why do you think the author began the novel with this setting instead of immediately taking us on a voyage with Dr. Dolittle?

2. Why do you think the author introduced us to several minor characters before introducing us to Dr. Dolittle?

Creating and Writing

The author has fun with names. The name of the town is Puddleby-on-the-Marsh. Colonel Bellowes shouts. Why do you think the doctor is named Dr. Dolittle? The first chapters of a book usually give the reader some idea of the way the author writes. The way in which the author plays with names will probably be repeated in future chapters of the book. As you read this novel, look for the meaning behind the names of most of the characters.

Think of stories you may have written for class. Did you have trouble finding names for your characters? Consider the following names: Jack Bookish, Jack Gooddeed, Jack Paper, Jack Multiply, Jack Comma, Jack Scream, Jack Domuch. If you were a writer who was writing an amusing story, what kinds of people would these be? Choose one of these names, or make up your own name, and write a paragraph about what might happen to one of these people if he found a wounded squirrel in his backyard.

Blueprint FOR READING

Into • *The Voyages of Dr. Dolittle*
Part One—Chapters 7-15

As the story moves along, the reader discovers that one of its themes is the importance of treating all beings, great and small, with respect. One of the things that makes the story so appealing to readers of all ages, is the way in which most of the characters relate to one another. Even the villains are not overly disrespectful! The respectful behavior of all the main characters allows the action to flow smoothly; the author focuses on moving the plot forward, rather than on conflict between characters.

Focus

While Dr. Dolittle hardly has a bad word for anyone, the animals have sharp tongues. Polynesia's lines contain some biting humor, and her understanding of the darker side of people's and animals' natures seems at times better than Dr. Dolittle's understanding of them. Notice that each of the main characters (including animals) has a distinct personality. As you read, notice how consistent the behavior of each animal is. Hugh Lofting knew clearly what personality he wished each animal to have.

7

SHELLFISH TALK

The next morning, although I had gone to bed so late the night before, I was up frightfully early. The first sparrows were just beginning to chirp sleepily on the slates outside my attic window when I jumped out of bed and scrambled into my clothes.

I could hardly wait to get back to the little house with the big garden—to see the Doctor and his private zoo. For the first time in my life I forgot all about breakfast; and creeping down the stairs on tiptoe, so as not to wake my mother and father, I opened the front door and popped out into the empty, silent street.

When I got to the Doctor's gate I suddenly thought that perhaps it was too early to call on anyone; and I began to wonder if the Doctor would be up yet. I looked into the garden. No one seemed to be about. So I opened the gate quietly and went inside.

As I turned to the left to go down a path between some hedges, I heard a voice quite close to me say, "Good morning. How early you are!"

I turned around, and there, sitting on the top of a privet hedge, was the gray parrot, Polynesia.

"Good morning," I said. "I suppose I am rather early. Is the Doctor still in bed?"

"Oh no," said Polynesia. "He has been up an hour and a half. You'll find him in the house somewhere. The front door is open. Just push it and go in. He is sure to be in the kitchen cooking breakfast—or working in his study. Walk right in. I am waiting to see the sun rise. But upon my world I believe it's forgotten to rise. It is an awful climate, this. Now if we were in Africa the world would be blazing with sunlight at this hour of the morning. Just see that mist rolling over those cabbages. It is enough to give you rheumatism to look at it. Beastly climate—Beastly! Really I don't know why anything but frogs ever stay in England—Well, don't let me keep you. Run along and see the Doctor."

"Thank you," I said. "I'll go and look for him."

When I opened the front door I could smell bacon frying, so I made my way to the kitchen. There I discovered a large kettle boiling away over the hearth. It seemed to me that the bacon was getting all dried up with the heat. So I pulled the dish a little further away from the fire and went on through the house looking for the Doctor.

I found him at last in the Study. I did not know then that it was called the Study. It was certainly a very interesting room, with telescopes and microscopes and all sorts of other strange things which I did not understand about but wished I did. Hanging on the walls were pictures of animals and fishes and strange plants and collections of birds' eggs and seashells in glass cases.

The Doctor was standing at the main table in his dressing-gown. At first I thought he was washing his face. He had a square glass box before him full of water. He was holding one ear under the water while he covered the other with his left hand. As I came in he stood up.

"Good morning, Stubbins," said he. "Going to be a nice day, don't you think? I've just been listening to the Wiff-Waff. But he is very disappointing—very."

"Why?" I said. "Didn't you find that he has any language at all?"

"Oh yes," said the Doctor, "he has a language. But it is such a poor language—only a few words, like 'yes' and 'no'—'hot' and 'cold.' That's all he can say. It's very disappointing. You see he really belongs to two different families of fishes. I thought he was going to be tremendously helpful—Well, well!"

"I suppose," said I, "that means he hasn't very much sense—if his language is only two or three words?"

"Yes, I suppose it does. Possibly it is the kind of life he leads. You see, they are very rare now, these Wiff-Waffs—very rare and very solitary. They swim around the deepest parts of the ocean entirely by themselves—always alone. So I presume they really don't need to talk much."

"Perhaps some kind of a bigger shellfish would talk more," I said. "After all, he is very small, isn't he?"

"Yes," said the Doctor, "that's true. Oh I have no doubt that there are shellfish who are good talkers—not the least doubt. But the big shellfish—the biggest of them, are so hard to catch. They are only to be found in the deep parts of the sea; and as they don't swim very much, but just crawl along the floor of the ocean most of the time, they are very seldom taken in nets. I do wish I could find some way of going down to the bottom of the sea. I could learn a lot if I could only do that. But we are forgetting all about breakfast—Have you had breakfast yet, Stubbins?"

I told the Doctor that I had forgotten all about it and he at once led the way into the kitchen.

"Yes," he said, as he poured the hot water from the kettle into the tea-pot, "if a man could only manage to get right down to the bottom of the sea, and live there a while, he would discover some wonderful things—things that people have never dreamed of."

"But men do go down, don't they?" I asked—"divers and people like that?"

"Oh yes, to be sure," said the Doctor. "Divers go down. I've been down myself in a diving-suit, for that matter. But my!—they only go where the sea is shallow. Divers can't go down where it is really deep. What I would like to do is to go down to the great depths—where it is miles deep—Well, well, I dare say I shall manage it someday. Let me give you another cup of tea."

Word Bank	**solitary** (SAHL ih TAIR ee) *adj.*: being, living, or going alone or without companions

8

ARE YOU A GOOD NOTICER?

Just at that moment Polynesia came into the room and said something to the Doctor in bird language. Of course I did not understand what it was. But the Doctor at once put down his knife and fork and left the room.

"You know it is an awful shame," said the parrot as soon as the Doctor had closed the door. "Directly he comes back home, all the animals over the whole countryside get to hear of it and every sick cat and mangy rabbit for miles around comes to see him and ask his advice. Now there's a big fat hare outside at the back door with a squawking baby. Can she see the Doctor, please!—Thinks it's going to have convulsions. Stupid little thing's been eating Deadly Nightshade[4] again, I suppose. The animals are *so* inconsiderate at times—especially the mothers. They come round and call the Doctor away from his meals and wake him out of his bed at all hours of the night. I don't know how he stands it—really I don't. Why, the poor man never gets any peace at all! I've told him time and again to have special hours for the animals to come. But he is so frightfully kind and considerate. He never refuses to see them if there is anything really wrong with them. He says the urgent cases must be seen at once."

"Why don't some of the animals go and see the other doctors?" I asked.

"Oh Good Gracious!" exclaimed the parrot, tossing her head scornfully. "Why, there aren't any other animal-doctors—not real doctors. Oh of course there *are* those vet persons, to be sure. But, bless you, they're no good. You see, they can't understand the animals' language; so how can you expect them to be any use? Imagine yourself, or your father, going to see a doctor who could not understand a word you say—nor even tell you in your own language what you must do to get well!

---

4. *Deadly Nightshade* is a poisonous plant.

Poof!—those vets! They're that stupid, you've no idea!—Put the Doctor's bacon down by the fire, will you?—to keep hot till he comes back."

"Do you think I would ever be able to learn the language of the animals?" I asked, laying the plate upon the hearth.

"Well, it all depends," said Polynesia. "Are you clever at lessons?" "I don't know," I answered, feeling rather ashamed. "You see, I've never been to school. My father is too poor to send me."

"Well," said the parrot, "I don't suppose you have really missed much—to judge from what *I* have seen of schoolboys. But listen: are you a good noticer?—Do you notice things well? I mean, for instance, supposing you saw two cock-starlings on an apple-tree, and you only took one good look at them—would you be able to tell one from the other if you saw them again the next day?"

"I don't know," I said. "I've never tried."

"Well that," said Polynesia, brushing some crumbs off the corner of the table with her left foot—"that is what you call powers of observation—noticing the small things about birds and animals: the way they walk and move their heads and flip their wings; the way they sniff the air and twitch their whiskers and wiggle their tails. You have to notice all those little things if you want to learn animal language. For you see, lots of the animals hardly talk at all with their tongues; they use their breath or their tails or their feet instead. That is because many of them, in the olden days when lions and tigers were more plentiful, were afraid to make a noise for fear the savage creatures heard them. Birds, of course, didn't care; for they always had wings to fly away with. But that is the first thing to remember: being a good noticer is terribly important in learning animal language."

"It sounds pretty hard," I said.

"You'll have to be very patient," said Polynesia. "It takes a long time to say even a few words properly. But if you come here often I'll give you a few lessons myself. And once you get started you'll be surprised how fast you get on. It would indeed be a good thing if you could learn. Because then you could do some of the work for the Doctor—I mean the easier work, like bandaging and giving pills. Yes, yes, that's a good idea of mine. 'Twould be a great thing if the poor man could get some help—and some rest. It is a scandal the way he works. I see no reason why you shouldn't be able to help him a great deal—That is, if you are really interested in animals."

"Oh, I'd love that!" I cried. "Do you think the Doctor would let me?"

"Certainly," said Polynesia—"as soon as you have learned something about doctoring. I'll speak of it to him myself—Sh! I hear him coming. Quick—bring his bacon back onto the table."

9

THE GARDEN OF DREAMS

When breakfast was over the Doctor took me out to show me the garden. Well, if the house had been interesting, the garden was a hundred times more so. Of all the gardens I have ever seen that was the most delightful, the most fascinating. At first you did not realize how big it was. You never seemed to come to the end of it. When at last you were quite sure that you had seen it all, you would peer over a hedge, or turn a corner, or look up some steps, and there was a whole new part you never expected to find.

It had everything—everything a garden can have, or ever has had. There were wide, wide lawns with carved stone seats, green with moss. Over the lawns hung weeping-willows, and their feathery bough-tips brushed the velvet grass when they swung with the wind. The old flagged paths had high, clipped, yew hedges either side of them, so that they looked like the narrow streets of some old town; and through the hedges, doorways had been made; and over the doorways were shapes like vases and peacocks and half-moons all trimmed out of the living trees. There was a lovely marble fishpond with golden carp and blue water-lilies in it and big green frogs. A high brick wall alongside the kitchen garden was all covered with pink and yellow peaches ripening in the sun. There was a wonderful great oak, hollow in the trunk, big enough for four men to hide inside. Many summerhouses there were, too—some of wood and some of stone; and one of them was full of books to read. In a corner, among some rocks and ferns, was an outdoor fireplace, where the Doctor used to fry liver and bacon when he had a notion to take his meals in the open air. There was a couch as well on which he used to sleep, it seems, in warm summer nights when the nightingales were singing at their best; it had wheels on it so it could be moved about under any tree they sang in. But the thing that fascinated me most of all was a tiny little tree-house, high up in the top branches of a great elm, with a long rope ladder leading to it. The Doctor told me he used it for looking at the moon and the stars through a telescope.

It was the kind of garden where you could wander and explore for days and days—always coming upon something new, always glad to find the old spots over again. That first time that I saw the Doctor's garden I was so charmed by it that I felt I would like to live in it—always and always—and never go outside of it again. For it had everything within its walls to give happiness, to make living pleasant—to keep the heart at peace. It was the Garden of Dreams.

One peculiar thing I noticed immediately I came into it; and that was what a lot of birds there were about. Every tree seemed to have two or three nests in it. And heaps of other wild creatures appeared to be making themselves at home there, too. Stoats and tortoises and dormice seemed to be quite common, and not in the least shy. Toads of different colors and sizes hopped about the lawn as though it belonged to them. Green lizards (which were very rare in Puddleby) sat up on the stones in the sunlight and blinked at us. Even snakes were to be seen.

"You need not be afraid of them," said the Doctor, noticing that I started somewhat when a large black snake wiggled across the path right in front of us. "These fellows are not poisonous. They do a great deal of good in keeping down many kinds of garden-pests. I play the flute to them sometimes in the evening. They love it. Stand right up on their tails and carry on to no end. Funny thing, their taste for music."

"Why do all these animals come and live here?" I asked. "I never saw a garden with so many creatures in it."

"Well, I suppose it's because they get the kind of food they like; and nobody worries or disturbs them. And then, of course, they know me. And if they or their children get sick I presume they find it handy to be living in a doctor's garden—Look! You see that sparrow on the sundial, swearing at the blackbird down below? Well, he has been coming here every summer for years. He comes from London. The country sparrows round about here are always laughing at him. They say he chirps with such a Cockney accent. He is a most amusing bird—very brave but very cheeky. He loves nothing better than an argument, but he always ends it by getting rude. He is a real city bird. In London he lives around St. Paul's Cathedral. 'Cheapside,' we call him."

"Are all these birds from the country round here?" I asked.

"Most of them," said the Doctor. "But a few rare ones visit me every year who ordinarily never come near England at all. For instance, that handsome little fellow hovering over the snapdragon there, he's a Ruby-throated Hummingbird. Comes from America. Strictly speaking, he has no business in this climate at all. It is too cool. I make him sleep in the kitchen at night. Then every August, about the last week of the month, I have a Purple Bird-of-Paradise come all the way from Brazil to see me. She is a very great swell. Hasn't arrived yet of course. And there are a few others, foreign birds from the tropics mostly, who drop in on me in the course of the summer months. But come, I must show you the zoo."

10

THE PRIVATE ZOO

I did not think there could be anything left in that garden which we had not seen. But the Doctor took me by the arm and started off down a little narrow path and after many windings and twistings and turnings we found ourselves before a small door in a high stone wall. The Doctor pushed it open.

Inside was still another garden. I had expected to find cages with animals inside them. But there were none to be seen. Instead there were little stone houses here and there all over the garden; and each house had a window and a door. As we walked in, many of these doors opened and animals came running out to us evidently expecting food.

"Haven't the doors any locks on them?" I asked the Doctor.

"Oh yes," he said, "every door has a lock. But in my zoo the doors open from the inside, not from the out. The locks are only there so the animals can go and shut themselves *in* anytime they want to get away from the annoyance of other animals or from people who might come here. Every animal in this zoo stays here because he likes it, not because he is made to."

"They all look very happy and clean," I said. "Would you mind telling me the names of some of them?"

"Certainly. Well now: that funny-looking thing with plates on his back, nosing under the brick over there, is a South American armadillo. The little chap talking to him is a Canadian woodchuck. They both live in those holes you see at the foot of the wall. The two little beasts doing antics in the pond are a pair of Russian minks—and that reminds me: I must go and get them some herrings from the town before noon—it is early-closing today. That animal just stepping out of his house is an antelope, one of the smaller South African kinds. Now let us move to the other side of those bushes there and I will show you some more."

"Are those deer over there?" I asked.

"*Deer*!" said the Doctor. "Where do you mean?"

"Over there," I said, pointing—"nibbling the grass border of the bed. There are two of them."

"Oh, that," said the Doctor with a smile. "That isn't two animals: that's one animal with two heads—the only two-headed animal in the world. It's called the 'pushmi-pullyu.' I brought him from Africa. He's very tame—acts as a kind of night-watchman for my zoo. He only sleeps with one head at a time, you see—very handy—the other head stays awake all night."

"Have you any lions or tigers?" I asked as we moved on.

"No," said the Doctor. "It wouldn't be possible to keep them here— and I wouldn't keep them even if I could. If I had my way, Stubbins, there wouldn't be a single lion or tiger in captivity anywhere in the world. They never take to it. They're never happy. They never settle down. They are always thinking of the big countries they have left behind. You can see it in their eyes, dreaming—dreaming always of the great open spaces where they were born; dreaming of the deep, dark jungles where their mothers first taught them how to scent and track the deer. And what are they given in exchange for all this?" asked the Doctor, stopping in his walk and growing all red and angry—"What are

| **Word Bank** | annoyance (uh NOY intz) *n.*: a source of irritation |
| | antics (AN tiks) *n.*: attention-drawing, often wildly playful or funny acts or actions |

they given in exchange for the glory of an African sunrise, for the twilight breeze whispering through the palms, for the green shade of the matted, tangled vines, for the cool, big-starred nights of the desert, for the patter of the waterfall after a hard day's hunt? What, I ask you, are they given in exchange for *these*? Why, a bare cage with iron bars; an ugly piece of dead meat thrust in to them once a day; and a crowd of fools to come and stare at them with open mouths!—No, Stubbins. Lions and tigers, the Big Hunters, should never, never be seen in zoos."

The Doctor seemed to have grown terribly serious—almost sad. But suddenly his manner changed again and he took me by the arm with his same old cheerful smile.

"But we haven't seen the butterfly-houses yet—nor the aquariums. Come along. I am very proud of my butterfly-houses."

Off we went again and came presently into a hedged enclosure. Here I saw several big huts made of fine wire netting, like cages. Inside the netting all sorts of beautiful flowers were growing in the sun, with butterflies skimming over them. The Doctor pointed to the end of one of the huts where little boxes with holes in them stood in a row.

"Those are the hatching-boxes," said he. "There I put the different kinds of caterpillars. And as soon as they turn into butterflies and moths they come out into these flower-gardens to feed."

"Do butterflies have a language?" I asked.

"Oh I fancy they have," said the Doctor—"and the beetles too. But so far I haven't succeeded in learning much about insect languages. I have been too busy lately trying to master the shellfish talk. I mean to take it up though."

At that moment Polynesia joined us and said, "Doctor, there are two guinea-pigs at the back door. They say they have run away from the boy who kept them because they didn't get the right stuff to eat. They want to know if you will take them in."

"All right," said the Doctor. "Show them the way to the zoo. Give them the house on the left, near the gate—the one the black fox had. Tell them what the rules are and give them a square meal—Now, Stubbins, we will go on to the aquariums. And first of all I must show you my big, glass, seawater tank where I keep my shellfish."

11

My Schoolmaster, Polynesia

Well, there were not many days after that, you may be sure, when I did not come to see my new friend. Indeed I was at his house practically all day and every day. So that one evening my mother asked me jokingly why I did not take my bed over there and live at the Doctor's house altogether.

After a while I think I got to be quite useful to the Doctor, feeding his pets for him; helping to make new houses and fences for the zoo; assisting with the sick animals that came; doing all manner of odd jobs about the place. So that although I enjoyed it all very much (it was indeed like living in a new world) I really think the Doctor would have missed me if I had not come so often.

And all this time Polynesia came with me wherever I went, teaching me bird language and showing me how to understand the talking signs of the animals. At first I thought I would never be able to learn at all—it seemed so difficult. But the old parrot was wonderfully patient with me—though I could see that occasionally she had hard work to keep her temper.

Soon I began to pick up the strange chatter of the birds and to understand the funny talking antics of the dogs. I used to practice listening to the mice behind the wainscot after I went to bed, and watching the cats on the roofs and pigeons in the market-square of Puddleby.

And the days passed very quickly—as they always do when life is pleasant; and the days turned into weeks, and weeks into months; and soon the roses in the Doctor's garden were losing their petals and yellow leaves lay upon the wide green lawn. For the summer was nearly gone.

One day Polynesia and I were talking in the library. This was a fine long room with a grand mantlepiece and the walls were covered from the ceiling to the floor with shelves full of books: books of stories, books on gardening, books about medicine, books of travel; these I loved—and especially the Doctor's great atlas with all its maps of the different countries of the world.

This afternoon Polynesia was showing me the books about animals which John Dolittle had written himself.

"My!" I said, "what a lot of books the Doctor has—all the way around the room! Goodness! I wish I could read! It must be tremendously interesting. Can you read, Polynesia?"

"Only a little," said she. "Be careful how you turn those pages—don't tear them. No, I really don't get time enough for reading—much. That letter there is a *k* and this is a *b*."

"What does this word under the picture mean?" I asked.

"Let me see," she said, and started spelling it out. "B-A-B-O-O-N— that's *Monkey*. Reading isn't nearly as hard as it looks, once you know the letters."

"Polynesia," I said, "I want to ask you something very important."

"What is it, my boy?" said she, smoothing down the feathers of her right wing. Polynesia often spoke to me in a very patronizing way. But I did not mind it from her. After all, she was nearly two hundred years old; and I was only ten.

"Listen," I said, "my mother doesn't think it is right that I come here for so many meals. And I was going to ask you: supposing I did a whole lot more work for the Doctor—why couldn't I come and live here altogether? You see, instead of being paid like a regular gardener or workman, I would get my bed and meals in exchange for the work I did. What do you think?"

"You mean you want to be a proper assistant to the Doctor, is that it?"

"Yes. I suppose that's what you call it," I answered. "You know you said yourself that you thought I could be very useful to him."

"Well"—she thought a moment—"I really don't see why not. But is this what you want to be when you grow up, a naturalist?"

"Yes," I said, "I have made up my mind. I would sooner be a naturalist than anything else in the world."

"Humph!—Let's go and speak to the Doctor about it," said Polynesia. "He's in the next room—in the study. Open the door very gently—he may be working and not want to be disturbed."

I opened the door quietly and peeped in. The first thing I saw was an enormous black retriever dog[5] sitting in the middle of the hearth-rug with his ears cocked up, listening to the Doctor who was reading aloud to him from a letter.

"What *is* the Doctor doing?" I asked Polynesia in a whisper.

"Oh, the dog has had a letter from his friend and he has brought it to the Doctor to read for him. That's all. Her name is Minnie Dooley and she lives on the other side of the town. She and her brother have gone away to the seaside for the Summer; and the old retriever is heart-broken. So they write letters to him—in English of course. And as the old dog doesn't understand them, he brings them here, and the Doctor turns them into dog language for him. I think Minnie must have written that she is coming back—to judge from the dog's excitement. Just look at him carrying on!"

Indeed the retriever seemed to be suddenly overcome with joy. As the Doctor finished the letter the old dog started barking at the top of his voice, wagging his tail wildly and jumping about the study. He took the letter in his mouth and ran out of the room snorting hard and mumbling to himself.

"He's going down to meet the coach," whispered Polynesia. "That dog's devotion to those children is more than I can understand. You should see Minnie! She's the most conceited little minx that ever walked. She squints too."

12

MY GREAT IDEA

Presently the Doctor looked up and saw us at the door. "Oh—come in, Stubbins," said he, "did you wish to speak to me? Come in and take a chair."

"Doctor," I said, "I want to be a naturalist—like you—when I grow up."

"Oh you do, do you?" murmured the Doctor. "Humph!—Well!—Dear me!—You don't say!—Well, well! Have you er—have you spoken to your mother and father about it?"

"No, not yet," I said. "I want you to speak to them for me. You would do it better. I want to be your helper—your assistant, if you'll have me.

---

5. A *retriever* (rih TREE vur) *dog* is an active, medium-sized dog.

Last night my mother was saying that she didn't consider it right for me to come here so often for meals. And I've been thinking about it a good deal since. Couldn't we make some arrangement—couldn't I work for my meals and sleep here?"

"But my dear Stubbins," said the Doctor, laughing, "you are quite welcome to come here for three meals a day all year round. I'm only too glad to have you. Besides, you do do a lot of work, as it is. I've often felt that I ought to pay you for what you do—But what arrangements was it that you thought of?"

"Well, I thought," said I, "that perhaps you would come and see my mother and father and tell them that if they let me live here with you and work hard, that you will teach me to read and write. You see my mother is awfully anxious to have me learn reading and writing. And besides, I couldn't be a proper naturalist without, could I?"

"Oh, I don't know so much about that," said the Doctor. "It is nice, I admit, to be able to read and write. But naturalists are not all alike, you know. For example: this young fellow that people are talking about so much now—he's a Cambridge graduate—reads and writes very well. And then Cuvier—he used to be a tutor. But listen, the greatest naturalist of them all doesn't even know how to write his own name nor to read the *A B C*."

"Who is he?" I asked.

"He is a mysterious person," said the Doctor—"a very mysterious person. His name is Long Arrow, the son of Golden Arrow. He is a Red Indian."

"Have you ever seen him?" I asked.

"No," said the Doctor, "I've never seen him. No white man has ever met him. I fancy that University graduate doesn't even know that he exists. He lives almost entirely with the animals and with the different tribes of Indians—usually somewhere among the mountains of Peru. Never stays long in one place. Goes from tribe to tribe, like a sort of Indian wanderer."

"How do you know so much about him?" I asked—"if you've never even seen him?"

"The Purple Bird-of-Paradise," said the Doctor—"she told me all about him. She says he is a perfectly marvelous naturalist. I got her to take a message to him for me last time she was here. I am expecting her back any day now. I can hardly wait to see what answer she has brought from him. It is already almost the last week of August. I do hope nothing has happened to her on the way."

"But why do the animals and birds come to you when they are sick?" I said—"Why don't they go to see him, if he is so very wonderful?"

"It seems that my methods are more up to date," said the Doctor. "But from what the Purple Bird-of-Paradise tells me, Long Arrow's knowledge of natural history must be positively tremendous. His specialty is botany—plants and all that sort of thing. But he knows a lot about birds and animals too. He's very good on bees and beetles—But now tell me, Stubbins, are you quite sure that you really want to be a naturalist?"

"Yes," said I, "my mind is made up."

"Well you know, it isn't a very good profession for making money. Not at all, it isn't. Most of the good naturalists don't make any money whatever. All they do is *spend* money, buying butterfly-nets and cases for birds' eggs and things. It is only now, after I have been a naturalist for many years, that I am beginning to make a little money from the books I write."

"I don't care about money," I said. "I want to be a naturalist. Won't you please come and have dinner with my mother and father next Thursday—I told them I was going to ask you—and then you can talk to them about it. You see, there's another thing: if I'm living with you, and sort of belong to your house and business, I shall be able to come with you next time you go on a voyage."

"Oh, I see," said he, smiling. "So you want to come on a voyage with me, do you?—Ah hah!"

"I want to go on all your voyages with you. It would be much easier for you if you had someone to carry the butterfly-nets and notebooks. Wouldn't it now?"

For a long time the Doctor sat thinking, drumming on the desk with his fingers, while I waited, terribly impatiently, to see what he was going to say.

At last he shrugged his shoulders and stood up.

"Well, Stubbins," said he, "I'll come and talk it over with you and your parents next Thursday. And—well, we'll see. We'll see. Give your mother and father my compliments and thank them for their invitation, will you?"

Then I tore home like the wind to tell my mother that the Doctor had promised to come.

13

A Traveler Arrives

The next day I was sitting on the wall of the Doctor's garden after tea, talking to Dab-Dab. I had now learned so much from Polynesia that I could talk to most birds and some animals without a great deal of difficulty. I found Dab-Dab a very nice, old, motherly bird—though not nearly so clever and interesting as Polynesia. She had been housekeeper for the Doctor many years now.

Well, as I was saying, the old duck and I were sitting on the flat top of the garden-wall that evening, looking down into the Oxenthorpe Road below. We were watching some sheep being driven to market in

---

| **Word Bank** | **voyages** (VOY ij iz) *n.*: act or instances of traveling; journeys by water |
| | **impatiently** (im PAYSH int lee) *adv.*: restlessly; in a manner that is without patience |

Puddleby; and Dab-Dab had just been telling me about the Doctor's adventures in Africa. For she had gone on a voyage with him to that country long ago.

Suddenly I heard a curious distant noise down the road, towards the town. It sounded like a lot of people cheering. I stood up on the wall to see if I could make out what was coming. Presently there appeared round a bend a great crowd of schoolchildren following a very ragged, curious-looking woman.

"What in the world can it be?" cried Dab-Dab.

The children were all laughing and shouting. And certainly the woman they were following was most extraordinary. She had very long arms and the most stooping shoulders I have ever seen. She wore a straw hat on the side of her head with poppies on it; and her skirt was so long for her it dragged on the ground like a ball-gown's train. I could not see anything of her face because of the wide hat pulled over her eyes. But as she got nearer to us and the laughing of the children grew louder, I noticed that her hands were very dark in color, and hairy, like a witch's.

Then all of a sudden Dab-Dab at my side startled me by crying out in a loud voice, "Why, it's Chee-Chee!—Chee-Chee has come back at last! How dare those children tease him! I'll give the little imps something to laugh at!"

And she flew right off the wall down into the road and made straight for the children, squawking away in a most terrifying fashion and pecking at their feet and legs. The children made off down the street back to the town as hard as they could run.

The strange-looking figure in the straw hat stood gazing after them a moment and then came wearily up to the gate. It didn't bother to undo the latch but just climbed right over the gate as though it were something in the way. And then I noticed that it took hold of the bars with its feet, so that it really had four hands to climb with. But it was only when I at last got a glimpse of the face under the hat that I could be really sure it was a monkey.

Chee-Chee—for it was he—frowned at me suspiciously from the top of the gate, as though he thought I was going to laugh at him like the other boys and girls. Then he dropped into the garden on the inside and immediately started taking off his clothes. He tore the straw hat in two and threw it down into the road. Then he took off his bodice[6] and skirt, jumped on them savagely and began kicking them round the front garden.

Presently I heard a screech from the house, and out flew Polynesia, followed by the Doctor and Jip.

"Chee-Chee!—Chee-Chee!" shouted the parrot. "You've come at last! I always told the Doctor you'd find a way. How ever did you do it?"

They gathered round him shaking him by his four hands, laughing and asking him a million questions at once. Then they all started back for the house.

"Run up to my bedroom, Stubbins," said the Doctor, turning to me. "You'll find a bag of peanuts in the small left-hand drawer of the bureau. I have always kept them there in case he might come back unexpectedly someday. And wait a minute—see if Dab-Dab has any bananas in the pantry. Chee-Chee hasn't had a banana, he tells me, in two months."

When I came down again to the kitchen I found everybody listening attentively to the monkey who was telling the story of his journey from Africa.

14

Chee-Chee's Voyage

It seems that after Polynesia had left, Chee-Chee had grown more homesick than ever for the Doctor and the little house in Puddleby. At last he had made up his mind that by hook or crook he would follow her. And one day, going down to the seashore, he saw a lot of people, black and white, getting onto a ship that was coming to England. He tried to get on too. But they turned him back and drove him away. And presently he noticed a whole big family of funny people passing onto the ship. And one of the children in this family reminded Chee-Chee of a cousin of his with whom he had once been close. So he said to himself, "That girl looks just as much like a monkey as I look like a girl. If I could only get some clothes to wear I might easily slip onto the ship amongst these families, and people would take me for a girl. Good idea!"

So he went off to a town that was quite close, and hopping in through an open window he found a skirt and bodice lying on a chair. They belonged to a fashionable black lady who was taking a bath. Chee-Chee put them on. Next he went back to the seashore, mingled with the crowd there and at last sneaked safely onto the big ship. Then he thought he had better hide, for fear people might look at him too closely. And he stayed hidden all the time the ship was sailing to England—only coming out at night, when everybody was asleep, to find food.

When he reached England and tried to get off the ship, the sailors saw at last that he was only a monkey dressed up in girl's clothes; and they wanted to keep him for a pet. But he managed to give them the slip; and once he was on shore, he dived into the crowd and got away. But he was

---

6. A *bodice* (BAHD iss) is a blouse.

still a long distance from Puddleby and had come right across the whole breadth of England.

He had a terrible time of it. Whenever he passed through a town all the children ran after him in a crowd, laughing; and often silly people caught hold of him and tried to stop him, so that he had to run up lampposts and climb to chimney-pots to escape from them. At night he used to sleep in ditches or barns or anywhere he could hide; and he lived on the berries he picked from the hedges and the cobnuts that grew in the copses. At length, after many adventures and narrow squeaks, he saw the tower of Puddleby Church and he knew that at last he was near his old home.

When Chee-Chee had finished his story he ate six bananas without stopping and drank a whole bowlful of milk.

"My!" he said, "why wasn't I born with wings, like Polynesia, so I could fly here? You've no idea how I grew to hate that hat and skirt. I've never been so uncomfortable in my life. All the way from Bristol here, if the wretched hat wasn't falling off my head or catching in the trees, those beastly skirts were tripping me up and getting wound round everything. Goodness, I was glad to see old Puddleby this morning when I climbed over the hill by Bellaby's farm!"

"Your bed on top of the plate-rack in the scullery is all ready for you," said the Doctor. "We never had it disturbed in case you might come back."

"Yes," said Dab-Dab, "and you can have the old smoking-jacket of the Doctor's which you used to use as a blanket, in case it is cold in the night."

"Thanks," said Chee-Chee. "It's good to be back in the old house again. Everything's just the same as when I left—except the clean roller-towel on the back of the door there—that's new—Well, I think I'll go to bed now. I need sleep."

Then we all went out of the kitchen into the scullery and watched Chee-Chee climb the plate-rack like a sailor going up a mast. On the top, he curled himself up, pulled the old smoking-jacket over him, and in a minute he was snoring peacefully.

"Good old Chee-Chee!" whispered the Doctor. "I'm glad he's back."

"Yes—good old Chee-Chee!" echoed Dab-Dab and Polynesia.

Then we all tiptoed out of the scullery and closed the door very gently behind us.

15

I Become a Doctor's Assistant

When Thursday evening came there was great excitement at our house. My mother had asked me what were the Doctor's favorite dishes, and I had told her: spare ribs, sliced beetroot, fried bread, shrimps and treacle-tart. Tonight she had them all on the table waiting for him; and she was now fussing round the house to see if everything was tidy and in readiness for his coming.

At last we heard a knock upon the door, and of course it was I who got there first to let him in.

The Doctor had brought his own flute with him this time. And after supper was over (which he enjoyed very much) the table was cleared away and the washing-up left in the kitchen-sink till the next day. Then the Doctor and my father started playing duets.

They got so interested in this that I began to be afraid that they would never come to talking over my business. But at last the Doctor said, "Your son tells me that he is anxious to become a naturalist."

And then began a long talk which lasted far into the night. At first both my mother and father were rather against the idea—as they had been from the beginning. They said it was only a boyish whim and that I would get tired of it very soon. But after the matter had been talked over from every side, the Doctor turned to my father and said, "Well now, supposing, Mr. Stubbins, that your son came to me for two years— that is, until he is twelve years old. During those two years he will have time to see if he is going to grow tired of it or not. Also during that time, I will promise to teach him reading and writing and perhaps a little arithmetic as well. What do you say to that?"

"I don't know," said my father, shaking his head. "You are very kind and it is a handsome offer you make, Doctor. But I feel that Tommy ought to be learning some trade by which he can earn his living later on."

Then my mother spoke up. Although she was nearly in tears at the prospect of my leaving her house while I was still so young, she pointed out to my father that this was a grand chance for me to get learning.

"Now Jacob," she said, "you know that many lads in town have been to the Grammar School till they were fourteen or fifteen years old. Tommy can easily spare these two years for his education; and if he learns no more than to read and write, the time will not be lost. Though goodness knows," she added, getting out her handkerchief to cry, "the house will seem terribly empty when he's gone."

"I will take care that he comes to see you, Mrs. Stubbins," said the Doctor—"every day, if you like. After all, he will not be very far away."

Well, at length my father gave in; and it was agreed that I was to live with the Doctor and work for him for two years in exchange for learning to read and write and for my board and lodging.

"Of course," added the Doctor, "while I have money I will keep Tommy in clothes as well. But money is a very irregular thing with me; sometimes I have some, and then sometimes I haven't."

"You are very good, Doctor," said my mother, drying her tears. "It seems to me that Tommy is a very fortunate boy."

And then, thoughtless, selfish little imp that I was, I leaned over and whispered in the Doctor's ear, "Please don't forget to say something about the voyages."

"Oh, by the way," said John Dolittle, "of course occasionally my work requires me to travel. You will have no objection, I take it, to your son's coming with me?"

My poor mother looked up sharply, more unhappy and anxious than ever at this new turn; while I stood behind the Doctor's chair, my heart thumping with excitement, waiting for my father's answer.

"No," he said slowly after a while. "If we agree to the other arrangement I don't see that we've the right to make any objection to that."

Well, there surely was never a happier boy in the world than I was at that moment. My head was in the clouds. I trod on air. I could scarcely keep from dancing round the parlor. At last the dream of my life was to come true! At last I was to be given a chance to seek my fortune, to have adventures! For I knew perfectly well that it was now almost time for the Doctor to start upon another voyage. Polynesia had told me that he hardly ever stayed at home for more than six months at a stretch. Therefore he would be surely going again within a fortnight.[7] And I—I, Tommy Stubbins, would go with him! Just to think of it!—to cross the Sea, to walk on foreign shores, to roam the World!

---

7. A *fortnight* (FORT NYT) is two weeks.

Recalling

1. Why did Dr. Dolittle want to go to the bottom of the sea?

2. Where was the Garden of Dreams? Why did Tommy say it was the most delightful and fascinating garden he had ever seen?

3. Why did so many animals choose to live in Dr. Dolittle's zoo? What was unique about this zoo?

4. Name four animals in the zoo.

5. Write a paragraph describing how Chee-Chee returned to Dr. Dolittle's home.

Interpreting

6. Why would a good "noticer" be able to learn the languages of animals?

7. Why did Dr. Dolittle refuse to keep lions and tigers in his zoo? What does this tell you about Dr. Dolittle's feelings about animals?

Concluding

8. Why did Tommy want to become a naturalist? What did Tommy also want to do with and for Dr. Dolittle?

Examining the Novel

Wiff-Waff, the small shellfish, had a very limited vocabulary. He speaks only a few words because he is a solitary fish that lives deep in the ocean and does not come in contact with many other shellfish. When Dr. Dolittle discovers this fact, he does not pester Wiff-Waff for more information—he accepts Wiff-Waff's limitations. How is this action in keeping with the theme of this book?

Thinking About the Novel

Tommy's parents reluctantly agree to let Tommy work and live with Dr. Dolittle. Were they right in allowing Tommy to become an assistant to the Doctor? What might have happened to Tommy if he had not joined Dr. Dolittle? Write a paragraph stating your views.

Creating and Writing

The pushmi-pullyu is an interesting animal created in the imagination of the novel's author. If a thief were to break into Dr. Dolittle's zoo, what would the pushmi-pullyu do? What special feature of the pushmi-pullyu made him such a good "watchman" for the zoo?

Into • *The Voyages of Dr. Dolittle*
Part Two—Chapters 1-8

Part Two of the book brings us closer to Dr. Dolittle's long-awaited journey. But first, Dr. Dolittle and Tommy must visit a courthouse to save a man from hanging. The prosecuting attorney is dishonest, and the witness is, himself, a criminal. The most honest participant in the trial is a dog! The courthouse scene is **satire**, which means that the author is using humor and exaggeration to mock and criticize the English system of justice.

Focus

The courthouse scene does not really move the plot along. Rather, it seems to serve as a way for the author to make a point about British courts. This scene is enjoyable to read because the idea of a dignified English judge listening to the barking and growling of a dog and a man as they testified in court is very funny! You will notice other places in the story where the author seems more interested in making a point about some issue, than about moving the plot along. Watch the animals' dialogue. You will find many of Hugh Lofting's opinions scattered among the animals' lines.

PART II

1

THE CREW OF THE CURLEW

From that time on of course my position in the town was very different. I was no longer a poor cobbler's son. I carried my nose in the air as I went down the High Street with Jip in his gold collar at my side; and snobbish little boys who had despised me before because I was not rich enough to go to school now pointed me out to their friends and whispered, "You see him? He's a doctor's assistant—and only ten years old!"

But their eyes would have opened still wider with wonder if they had but known that I and the dog that was with me could talk to one another.

Two days after the Doctor had been to our house to dinner he told me very sadly that he was afraid that he would have to give up trying to learn the language of the shellfish—at all events for the present.

"I'm very discouraged, Stubbins, very. I've tried the mussels and the clams, the oysters and the whelks, cockles and scallops; seven different kinds of crabs and all the lobster family. I think I'll leave it for the present and go at it again later on."

"What will you turn to now?" I asked.

"Well, I rather thought of going on a voyage, Stubbins. It's quite a time now since I've been away. And there is a great deal of work waiting for me abroad."

"When shall we start?" I asked.

"Well, first I shall have to wait till the Purple Bird-of-Paradise gets here. I must see if she has any message for me from Long Arrow. She's late. She should have been here ten days ago. I hope to goodness she's all right."

"Well, hadn't we better be seeing about getting a boat?" I said. "She is sure to be here in a day or so; and there will be lots of things to do to get ready in the meantime, won't there?"

"Yes, indeed," said the Doctor. "Suppose we go down and see your friend Joe, the mussel-man. He will know about boats."

"I'd like to come too," said Jip.

"All right, come along," said the Doctor, and off we went.

Joe said yes, he had a boat—one he had just bought—but it needed three people to sail her. We told him we would like to see it anyway.

So the mussel-man took us off a little way down the river and showed us the neatest, prettiest, little vessel that ever was built. She was called

---

Word Bank   despised (diss PYZD) *v.*: looked down on; hated

the *Curlew*. Joe said he would sell her to us cheap. But the trouble was that the boat needed three people, while we were only two.

"Of course I shall be taking Chee-Chee," said the Doctor. "But although he is very quick and clever, he is not as strong as a man. We really ought to have another person to sail a boat as big as that."

"I know of a good sailor, Doctor," said Joe—"a first-class seaman who would be glad of the job."

"No, thank you, Joe," said Doctor Dolittle. "I don't want any seamen. I couldn't afford to hire them. And then they hamper me so, seamen do, when I'm at sea. They're always wanting to do things the proper way; and I like to do them *my* way—Now let me see: who could we take with us?"

"There's Matthew Mugg, the cat's-meat-man," I said.

"No, he wouldn't do. Matthew's a very nice fellow, but he talks too much—mostly about his rheumatism.[1] You have to be frightfully particular whom you take with you on long voyages."

"How about Luke the Hermit?" I asked.

"That's a good idea—splendid—if he'll come. Let's go and ask him right away."

2

LUKE THE HERMIT

The Hermit was an old friend of ours, as I have already told you. He was a very peculiar person. Far out on the marshes he lived in a little bit of a shack—all alone except for his brindle bulldog. No one knew where he came from—not even his name. Just "Luke the Hermit" folks called him. He never came into the town; never seemed to want to see or talk to people. His dog, Bob, drove them away if they came near his hut. When you asked anyone in Puddleby who he was or why he lived out in that lonely place by himself, the only answer you got was, "Oh, Luke the Hermit? Well, there's some mystery about him. Nobody knows what it is. But there's a mystery. Don't go near him. He'll set the dog on you."

Nevertheless there were two people who often went out to that little shack on the fens:[2] the Doctor and myself. And Bob, the bulldog, never barked when he heard us coming. For we liked Luke; and Luke liked us.

This afternoon, crossing the marshes we faced a cold wind blowing from the East. As we approached the hut Jip put up his ears and said, "That's funny!"

"What's funny?" asked the Doctor.

---

1. *Rheumatism* (ROOM uh TIZ um) is a medical condition characterized by inflammation of the joints.
2. *Fen* is wet, low land.

Word Bank   hamper (HAM pur) *v.*: interfere with; restrict the movement of

"That Bob hasn't come out to meet us. He should have heard us long ago—or smelt us. What's that queer noise?"

"Sounds to me like a gate creaking," said the Doctor. "Maybe it's Luke's door, only we can't see the door from here; it's on the far side of the shack."

"I hope Bob isn't sick," said Jip; and he let out a bark to see if that would call him. But the only answer he got was the wailing of the wind across the wide, salt fen.

We hurried forward, all three of us thinking hard.

When we reached the front of the shack we found the door open, swinging and creaking dismally in the wind. We looked inside. There was no one there.

"Isn't Luke at home then?" said I. "Perhaps he's out for a walk."

"He is *always* at home," said the Doctor frowning in a peculiar sort of way. "And even if he were out for a walk he wouldn't leave his door banging in the wind behind him. There is something queer about this— What are you doing in there, Jip?"

"Nothing much—nothing worth speaking of," said Jip examining the floor of the hut extremely carefully.

"Come here, Jip," said the Doctor in a stern voice. "You are hiding something from me. You see signs and you know something—or you guess it. What has happened? Tell me. Where is the Hermit?"

"I don't know," said Jip looking very guilty and uncomfortable. "I don't know where he is."

"Well, you know something. I can tell it from the look in your eye. What is it?"

But Jip didn't answer.

For ten minutes the Doctor kept questioning him. But not a word would the dog say.

"Well," said the Doctor at last, "it is no use our standing around here in the cold. The Hermit's gone. That's all. We might as well go home to luncheon."

As we buttoned up our coats and started back across the marsh, Jip ran ahead pretending he was looking for water-rats.

"He knows something all right," whispered the Doctor. "And I think he knows what has happened too. It's funny, his not wanting to tell me. He has never done that before—not in eleven years. He has always told me everything—Strange—very strange!"

"Do you mean you think he knows all about the Hermit, the big mystery about him which folks hint at and all that?"

"I shouldn't wonder if he did," the Doctor answered slowly. "I noticed something in his expression the moment we found that door open and the hut empty. And the way he sniffed the floor too—it told him something, that floor did. He saw signs we couldn't see—I wonder

Word Bank	**dismally** (DIZ muh lee) *adv*.: threateningly; miserably
	stern (STURN) *adj*.: strict; forbidding

why he won't tell me. I'll try him again. Here, Jip! Jip!—Where is the dog? I thought he went on in front."

"So did I," I said. "He was there a moment ago. I saw him as large as life. Jip—Jip—Jip—Jip!"

But he was gone. We called and called. We even walked back to the hut. But Jip had disappeared.

"Oh well," I said, "most likely he has just run home ahead of us. He often does that, you know. We'll find him there when we get back to the house."

But the Doctor just closed his coat-collar tighter against the wind and strode on muttering, "Odd—very odd!"

3

Jip and the Secret

When we reached the house the first question the Doctor asked of Dab-Dab in the hall was, "Is Jip home yet?"

"No," said Dab-Dab, "I haven't seen him."

"Let me know the moment he comes in, will you, please?" said the Doctor, hanging up his hat.

"Certainly I will," said Dab-Dab. "Don't be long over washing your hands; the lunch is on the table."

Just as we were sitting down to luncheon in the kitchen we heard a great racket at the front door. I ran and opened it. In bounded Jip.

"Doctor!" he cried, "come into the library quick. I've got something to tell you—No, Dab-Dab, the luncheon must wait. Please hurry, Doctor. There's not a moment to be lost. Don't let any of the animals come—just you and Tommy."

"Now," he said, when we were inside the library and the door was closed, "turn the key in the lock and make sure there's no one listening under the windows."

"It's all right," said the Doctor. "Nobody can hear you here. Now what is it?"

"Well, Doctor," said Jip (he was badly out of breath from running), "I know all about the Hermit—I have known for years. But I couldn't tell you."

"Why?" asked the Doctor.

"Because I'd promised not to tell anyone. It was Bob, his dog, that told me. And I swore to him that I would keep the secret."

"Well, and are you going to tell me now?"

"Yes," said Jip, "we've got to save him. I followed Bob's scent just now when I left you out there on the marshes. And I found him. And I said to him, 'Is it all right,' I said, 'for me to tell the Doctor now? Maybe he can do something.' And Bob says to me, 'Yes,' says he, 'it's all right because—' "

"Oh, for Heaven's sake, go on, go on!" cried the Doctor. "Tell us what the mystery is—not what you said to Bob and what Bob said to you. What has happened? Where *is* the Hermit?"

"He's in Puddleby Jail," said Jip. "He's in prison."

"In prison!"

"Yes."

"What for?—What's he done?"

Jip went over to the door and smelt at the bottom of it to see if anyone were listening outside. Then he came back to the Doctor on tiptoe and whispered, "*He killed a man!*"

"L-rd preserve us!" cried the Doctor, sitting down heavily in a chair and mopping his forehead with a handkerchief. "When did he do it?"

"Fifteen years ago—in a Mexican gold-mine. That's why he has been a hermit ever since. He shaved off his beard and kept away from people out there on the marshes so he wouldn't be recognized. But last week, it seems these newfangled policemen came to Town; and they heard there was a strange man who kept to himself all alone in a shack on the fen. And they got suspicious. For a long time people had been hunting all over the world for the man that did that killing in the Mexican gold-mine fifteen years ago. So these policemen went out to the shack, and they recognized Luke by a mole[3] on his arm. And they took him to prison."

"Well, well!" murmured the Doctor. "Who would have thought it?— Luke, the philosopher!—Killed a man!—I can hardly believe it."

"It's true enough unfortunately," said Jip. "Luke did it. But it wasn't his fault. Bob says so. And he was there and saw it all. He was scarcely more than a puppy at the time. Bob says Luke couldn't help it. He *had* to do it."

"Where is Bob now?" asked the Doctor.

"Down at the prison. I wanted him to come with me here to see you; but he won't leave the prison while Luke is there. He just sits outside the door of the prison-cell and won't move. He doesn't even eat the food they give him. Won't you please come down there, Doctor, and see if there is anything you can do? The trial is to be this afternoon at two o'clock. What time is it now?"

"It's ten minutes past one."

"Bob says he thinks they are going to kill Luke for a punishment if they can prove that he did it—or certainly keep him in prison for the rest of his life. Won't you please come? Perhaps if you spoke to the judge and told him what a good man Luke really is they'd let him off."

"Of course I'll come," said the Doctor getting up and moving to go. "But I'm very much afraid that I shan't be of any real help." He turned

---

3. A *mole* is a mark.

Word Bank	**philosopher** (fil AHSS uh fer) *n.*: one who studies ideas and seeks wisdom

at the door and hesitated thoughtfully.

"And yet—I wonder—"

Then he opened the door and passed out with Jip and me close at
his heels.

4

BOB

Dab-Dab was terribly upset when she found we were going away
again without luncheon; and she made us take some cold meat-pies
in our pockets to eat on the way.

When we got to Puddleby Courthouse (it was next door to the
prison), we found a great crowd gathered around the building.

This was the week of the Assizes—a business which happened every
three months, when many pickpockets and other bad characters were
tried by a very grand judge who came all the way from London. And
anybody in Puddleby who had nothing special to do used to come to the
Courthouse to hear the trials.

But today it was different. The crowd was not made up of just a few
idle people. It was enormous. The news had run through the countryside
that Luke the Hermit was to be tried for killing a man and that the great
mystery which had hung over him so long was to be cleared up at last.
The butcher and the baker had closed their shops and taken a holiday. All
the farmers from round-about, and all the townsfolk, were there with
their Sunday clothes on, trying to get seats in the Courthouse or gossiping outside in low whispers. The High Street was so crowded you could
hardly move along it. I had never seen the quiet old town in such a state
of excitement before. For Puddleby had not had such an Assizes since
1799, when Ferdinand Phipps, the Rector's oldest son, had robbed the
bank.

If I hadn't had the Doctor with me I am sure I would never have been
able to make my way through the mob packed around the Courthouse
door. But I just followed behind him, hanging on to his coattails; and at
last we got safely into the jail.

"I want to see Luke," said the Doctor to a very grand person in a blue
coat with brass buttons standing at the door.

"Ask at the Superintendent's office," said the man. "Third door on the
left down the corridor."

"Who is that person you spoke to, Doctor?" I asked as we went along
the passage.

"He is a policeman."

"And what are policemen?"

"Policemen? They are to keep people in order. They've just been
invented—by Sir Robert Peel. That's why they are also called 'peelers'
sometimes. It is a wonderful age we live in. They're always thinking of
something new—This will be the Superintendent's office, I suppose."

From there another policeman was sent with us to show us the way.

Outside the door of Luke's cell we found Bob, the bulldog, who wagged his tail sadly when he saw us. The man who was guiding us took a large bunch of keys from his pocket and opened the door.

I had never been inside a real prison-cell before; and I felt quite a thrill when the policeman went out and locked the door after him, leaving us shut in the dimly-lighted, little, stone room. Before he went, he said that as soon as we had done talking with our friend we should knock upon the door and he would come and let us out.

At first I could hardly see anything, it was so dim inside. But after a little I made out a low bed against the wall, under a small barred window. On the bed, staring down at the floor between his feet, sat the Hermit, his head resting in his hands.

"Well, Luke," said the Doctor in a kindly voice, "they don't give you much light in here, do they?"

Very slowly the Hermit looked up from the floor.

"Hulloa, John Dolittle. What brings you here?"

"I've come to see you. I would have been here sooner, only I didn't hear about all this till a few minutes ago. I went to your hut to ask you if you would join me on a voyage; and when I found it empty I had no idea where you could be. I am dreadfully sorry to hear about your bad luck. I've come to see if there is anything I can do."

Luke shook his head.

"No, I don't imagine there is anything can be done. They've caught me at last. That's the end of it, I suppose."

He got up stiffly and started walking up and down the little room.

"In a way I'm glad it's over," said he. "I never got any peace, always thinking they were after me—afraid to speak to anyone. They were bound to get me in the end—Yes, I'm glad it's over."

Then the Doctor talked to Luke for more than half an hour, trying to cheer him up; while I sat around wondering what I ought to say and wishing I could do something.

At last the Doctor said he wanted to see Bob; and we knocked upon the door and were let out by the policeman.

"Bob," said the Doctor to the big bulldog in the passage, "come out with me into the porch. I want to ask you something."

"How is he, Doctor?" asked Bob as we walked down the corridor into the Courthouse porch.

"Oh, Luke's all right. Very miserable of course, but he's all right. Now tell me, Bob: you saw this business happen, didn't you? You were there when the man was killed, eh?"

"I was, Doctor," said Bob, "and I tell you—"

"All right," the Doctor interrupted, "that's all I want to know for the present. There isn't time to tell me more now. The trial is just going to begin. There are the judge and the lawyers coming up the steps. Now listen, Bob: I want you to stay with me when I go into the courtroom. And whatever I tell you to do, do it. Do you understand? Don't make any scenes. Don't bite anybody, no matter what they may say about Luke. Just behave perfectly quietly and answer any question I may ask you—truthfully. Do you understand?"

"Very well. But do you think you will be able to get him off, Doctor?" asked Bob. "He's a good man, Doctor. He really is. There never was a better."

"We'll see, we'll see, Bob. It's a new thing I'm going to try. I'm not sure the judge will allow it. But—well, we'll see. It's time to go into the courtroom now. Don't forget what I told you. Remember: for Heaven's sake don't start biting anyone or you'll get us all put out and spoil everything."

5

MENDOZA

Inside the courtroom everything was very solemn and wonderful. It was a high, big room. Raised above the floor, against the wall was the Judge's desk; and here the judge was already sitting—an old, handsome man in a marvelous big wig of gray hair and a gown of black. Below him was another wide, long desk at which lawyers in white wigs sat. The whole thing reminded me of a school.

"Those twelve men at the side," whispered the Doctor—"those in pews like a choir, they are what is called the jury. It is they who decide whether Luke is guilty—whether he did it or not."

"And look!" I said, "there's Luke himself in a sort of pulpit-thing with policemen each side of him. And there's another pulpit, the same kind, the other side of the room, see—only that one's empty."

"That one is called the witness-box," said the Doctor. "Now I'm going down to speak to one of those men in white wigs; and I want you to wait here and keep these two seats for us. Bob will stay with you. Keep an eye on him—better hold on to his collar. I shan't be more than a minute or so."

Word Bank solemn (SAHL um) *adj.*: serious; characterized by dignity

---

With that the Doctor disappeared into the crowd which filled the main part of the room.

Then I saw the judge take up a funny little wooden hammer and knock on his desk with it. This, it seemed, was to make people keep quiet, for immediately everyone stopped buzzing and talking and began to listen very respectfully. Then another man in a black gown stood up and began reading from a paper in his hand.

He mumbled away exactly as though he were saying his prayers and didn't want anyone to understand what language they were in. But I managed to catch a few words:

"*Biz—biz—biz—biz—biz*—otherwise known as Luke the Hermit, of —*biz—biz—biz—biz*—for killing his partner with—*biz—biz—biz*—otherwise known as Bluebeard Bill on the night of the—*biz—biz—biz*—in the *biz—biz—biz*—of Mexico. Therefore Her Majesty's—*biz—biz—biz*—"

At this moment I felt someone take hold of my arm from the back, and turning round I found the Doctor had returned with one of the men in white wigs.

"Stubbins, this is Mr. Percy Jenkyns," said the Doctor. "He is Luke's lawyer. It is his business to get Luke off—if he can."

Mr. Jenkyns seemed to be an extremely young man with a round smooth face like a boy. He shook hands with me and then immediately turned and went on talking with the Doctor.

"Oh, I think it is a perfectly precious idea," he was saying. "Of *course* the dog must be admitted as a witness; he was the only one who saw the thing take place. I'm awfully glad you came. I wouldn't have missed this for anything. My hat! Won't it make the old court sit up? They're always frightfully dull, these Assizes. But this will stir things. A bulldog witness for the defense! I do hope there are plenty of reporters present—Yes, there's one making a sketch of the prisoner. I shall become known after this—And won't Conkey be pleased? My hat!"

He put his hand over his mouth to smother a laugh and his eyes fairly sparkled with mischief.

"Who is Conkey?" I asked the Doctor.

"Sh! He is speaking of the judge up there, the Honorable Eustace Beauchamp Conckley."

"Now," said Mr. Jenkyns, bringing out a notebook, "tell me a little more about yourself, Doctor. You took your degree as Doctor of Medicine at Durham, I think you said. And the name of your last book was?"

I could not hear anymore for they talked in whispers; and I fell to looking round the court again.

Of course I could not understand everything that was going on, though it was all very interesting. People kept getting up in the place the Doctor called the witness-box, and the lawyers at the long table asked

---

Word Bank sketch (SKECH) *n*.: a rough drawing

them questions about "the night of the 29th." Then the people would get down again and somebody else would get up and be questioned.

One of the lawyers (who, the Doctor told me afterwards, was called the Prosecutor)[4] seemed to be doing his best to get the Hermit into trouble by asking questions which made it look as though he had always been a very bad man. He was a nasty lawyer, this Prosecutor, with a long nose.

Most of the time I could hardly keep my eyes off poor Luke, who sat there between his two policemen, staring at the floor as though he weren't interested. The only time I saw him take any notice at all was when a small dark man with wicked, little, watery eyes got up into the witness-box. I heard Bob snarl under my chair as this person came into the courtroom and Lukes's eyes just blazed with anger and contempt.

This man said his name was Mendoza and that he was the one who had guided the Mexican police to the mine after Bluebeard Bill had been killed. And at every word he said I could hear Bob down below me muttering between his teeth, "It's a lie! It's a lie! I'll chew his face. It's a lie!"

And both the Doctor and I had hard work keeping the dog under the seat.

Then I noticed that our Mr. Jenkyns had disappeared from the Doctor's side. But presently I saw him stand up at the long table to speak to the judge.

"Your Honor," said he, "I wish to introduce a new witness for the defense, Doctor John Dolittle, the naturalist. Will you please step into the witness-stand, Doctor?"

There was a buzz of excitement as the Doctor made his way across the crowded room; and I noticed the nasty lawyer with the long nose lean down and whisper something to a friend, smiling in an ugly way which made me want to pinch him.

Then Mr. Jenkyns asked the Doctor a whole lot of questions about himself and made him answer in a loud voice so the whole court could hear. He finished up by saying, "And you are prepared to swear, Doctor Dolittle, that you understand the language of dogs and can make them understand you? Is that so?"

"Yes," said the Doctor, "that is so."

"And what, might I ask," put in the judge in a very quiet, dignified voice, "has all this to do with the killing of er—er—Bluebeard Bill?"

"This, Your Honor," said Mr. Jenkyns, talking in a very grand manner as though he were on a stage in a theater: "there is in this courtroom at the present moment a bulldog, who was the only living thing that saw the

---

4. A *prosecutor* (PRAH suh KYOOT ur) is a lawyer who conducts proceedings for the government.

Word Bank   eminent (EM in ent) *adj.*: outstanding; prominent

man killed. With the Court's permission I propose to put that dog in the witness-stand and have him questioned before you by the eminent scientist, Doctor John Dolittle."

6

THE JUDGE'S DOG

At first there was a dead silence in the Court. Then everybody began whispering or giggling at the same time, till the whole room sounded like a great hive of bees. Many people seemed to be shocked; most of them were amused; and a few were angry.

Presently up sprang the nasty lawyer with the long nose.

"I protest, Your Honor," he cried, waving his arms wildly to the judge. "I object. The dignity of this court is in peril. I protest."

"I am the one to take care of the dignity of this court," said the judge.

Then Mr. Jenkyns got up again. (If it hadn't been such a serious matter, it was almost like a Punch-and-Judy show: somebody was always popping down and somebody else popping up.)

"If there is any doubt on the score of our being able to do as we say, Your Honor will have no objection, I trust, to the Doctor's giving the Court a demonstration of his powers—of showing that he actually can understand the speech of animals?"

I thought I saw a twinkle of amusement come into the old judge's eyes as he sat considering a moment before he answered.

"No," he said at last, "I don't think so." Then he turned to the Doctor.

"Are you quite sure you can do this?" he asked.

"Quite, Your Honor," said the Doctor—"quite sure."

"Very well then," said the judge. "If you can satisfy us that you really are able to understand canine testimony, the dog shall be admitted as a witness. I do not see, in that case, how I could object to his being heard. But I warn you that if you are trying to make a laughingstock of this Court it will go hard with you."

"I protest, I protest!" yelled the long-nosed Prosecutor. "This is a scandal, an outrage to the Bar!"

"Sit down!" said the judge in a very stern voice.

"What animal does Your Honor wish me to talk with?" asked the Doctor.

"I would like you to talk to my own dog," said the judge. "He is outside in the cloakroom. I will have him brought in; and then we shall see what you can do."

Then someone went out and fetched the judge's dog, a lovely great Russian wolfhound with slender legs and shaggy coat. He was a proud and beautiful creature.

"Now, Doctor," said the judge, "did you ever see this dog before?—Remember you are in the witness-stand and under oath."

"No, Your Honor, I never saw him before."

"Very well then, will you please ask him to tell you what I had for supper last night? He was with me and watched me while I ate."

Then the Doctor and the dog started talking to one another in signs and sounds; and they kept at it for quite a long time. And the Doctor began to giggle and get so interested that he seemed to forget all about the Court and the judge and everything else.

"What a time he takes!" I heard a woman in front of me whispering. "He's only pretending. Of course he can't do it! Who ever heard of talking to a dog? He must think we're children."

"Haven't you finished yet?" the judge asked the Doctor. "It shouldn't take that long just to ask what I had for supper."

"Oh no, Your Honor," said the Doctor. "The dog told me that long ago. But then he went on to tell me what you did after supper."

"Never mind that," said the judge. "Tell me what answer he gave you to my question."

"He says you had a mutton-chop, two baked potatoes, a pickled walnut and a glass of ale."

The Honorable Eustace Beauchamp Conckley went white to the lips.

"Sounds like witchcraft," he muttered. "I never dreamed—"

"And after supper," the Doctor went on, "he says you went to see a prize-fight and then sat up playing cards for money till twelve o'clock and came home singing, 'We wont get—'"

"That will do," the judge interrupted, "I am satisfied you can do as you say. The prisoner's dog shall be admitted as a witness."

"I protest, I object!" screamed the Prosecutor. "Your Honor, this is—"

"Sit down!" roared the judge. "I say the dog shall be heard. That ends the matter. Put the witness on the stand."

And then for the first time in the solemn history of England a dog was put in the witness-stand of Her Majesty's Court of Assizes. And it was I, Tommy Stubbins (when the Doctor made a sign to me across the room), who proudly led Bob up the aisle, through the astonished crowd, past the frowning, spluttering, long-nosed Prosecutor, and made him comfortable on a high chair in the witness-box; from where the old bulldog sat scowling down over the rail upon the amazed and gaping jury.

7

THE END OF THE MYSTERY

The trial went swiftly forward after that. Mr. Jenkyns told the Doctor to ask Bob what he saw on the "night of the 29th"; and when Bob had told all he knew and the Doctor had turned it into English for the judge and the jury, this was what he had to say:

"On the night of the 29th of November, 1824, I was with my master, Luke Fitzjohn (otherwise known as Luke the Hermit) and his two partners, Manuel Mendoza and William Boggs (otherwise known as Bluebeard Bill) on their gold-mine in Mexico. For a long time these three men had been hunting for gold; and they had dug a deep hole in the ground. On the morning of the 29th gold was discovered, lots of it, at the bottom of this hole. And all three, my master and his two partners, were very happy about it because now they would be rich. But Manuel Mendoza asked Bluebeard Bill to go for a walk with him. These two men I had always suspected of being bad. So when I noticed that they left my master behind, I followed them secretly to see what they were up to. And in a deep cave in the mountains I heard them arrange together to kill Luke the Hermit so that they should get all the gold and he have none."

At this point the judge asked, "Where is the witness Mendoza? Constable, see that he does not leave the court."

But the wicked little man with the watery eyes had already sneaked out when no one was looking and he was never seen in Puddleby again.

"Then," Bob's statement went on, "I went to my master and tried very hard to make him understand that his partners were dangerous men. But it was no use. He did not understand dog language. So I did the next best thing: I never let him out of my sight but stayed with him every moment of the day and night.

"Now the hole that they had made was so deep that to get down and up it you had to go in a big bucket tied on the end of a rope; and the three men used to haul one another up and let one another down the mine in this way. That was how the gold was brought up too—in the bucket. Well, about seven o'clock in the evening my master was standing at the top of the mine, hauling up Bluebeard Bill who was in the bucket. Just as he had got Bill halfway up I saw Mendoza come out of the hut where we all lived. Mendoza thought that Bill was away buying groceries. But he wasn't: he was in the bucket. And when Mendoza saw Luke hauling and straining on the rope he thought he was pulling up a bucketful of gold. So he drew a pistol from his pocket and came sneaking up behind Luke to shoot him.

"I barked and barked to warn my master of the danger he was in; but he was so busy hauling up Bill (who was a heavy fat man) that he took no notice of me. I saw that if I didn't do something quick he would surely be shot. So I did a thing I've never done before: suddenly and savagely I bit my master in the leg from behind. Luke was so hurt and startled that he did just what I wanted him to do: he let go of the rope with both hands at once and turned round. And then, *Crash!* Down went Bill in his bucket to the bottom of the mine and he was killed.

"While my master was busy scolding me Mendoza put his pistol in his pocket, came up with a smile on his face and looked down the mine.

" 'Why, Good Gracious!' said he to Luke, 'You've killed Bluebeard Bill. I must go and tell the police'—hoping, you see, to get the whole mine to himself when Luke should be put in prison. Then he jumped on his horse and galloped away.'"

"And soon my master grew afraid; for he saw that if Mendoza only told enough lies to the police, it *would* look as though he had killed Bill on purpose. So while Mendoza was gone he and I stole away together secretly and came to England. Here he shaved off his beard and became a hermit. And ever since, for fifteen years, we've remained in hiding. This is all I have to say. And I swear it is the truth, every word."

When the Doctor finished reading Bob's long speech the excitement among the twelve men of the jury was positively terrific. One, a very old man with white hair, began to weep in a loud voice at the thought of poor Luke hiding on the fen for fifteen years for something he couldn't help. And all the others set to whispering and nodding their heads to one another.

In the middle of all this up got that horrible Prosecutor again, waving his arms more wildly than ever.

"Your Honor," he cried, "I must object to this evidence as biased. Of course the dog would not tell the truth against his own master. I object. I protest."

"Very well," said the judge, "you are at liberty to cross-examine. It is your duty as Prosecutor to prove his evidence untrue. There is the dog: question him, if you do not believe what he says."

I thought the long-nosed lawyer would have a fit. He looked first at the dog, then at the Doctor, then at the judge, then back at the dog scowling from the witness-box. He opened his mouth to say something; but no words came. He waved his arms some more. His face got redder and redder. At last, clutching his forehead, he sank weakly into his seat and had to be helped out of the courtroom by two friends. As he was half carried through the door he was still feebly murmuring, "I protest—I object—I protest!"

8

THREE CHEERS

Next the judge made a very long speech to the jury; and when it was over all the twelve jurymen got up and went out into the next room. And at that point the Doctor came back, leading Bob, to the seat beside me.

Word Bank **biased** (BY ust) *adj.*: prejudiced

"What have the jurymen gone out for?" I asked.

"They always do that at the end of a trial—to make up their minds whether the prisoner did it or not."

"Couldn't you and Bob go in with them and help them make up their minds the right way?" I asked.

"No, that's not allowed. They have to talk it over in secret. Sometimes it takes—My Gracious, look, they're coming back already! They didn't spend long over it."

Everybody kept quite still while the twelve men came tramping back into their places in the pews. Then one of them, the leader—a little man—stood up and turned to the judge. Everyone was holding his breath, especially the Doctor and myself, to see what he was going to say. You could have heard a pin drop while the whole courtroom, the whole of Puddleby in fact, waited with craning necks and straining ears to hear the weighty words.

"Your Honor," said the little man, "the jury returns a verdict of *Not Guilty*."

"What's that mean?" I asked, turning to the Doctor.

But I found Doctor John Dolittle, the famous naturalist, standing on top of a chair, dancing about on one leg like a schoolboy.

"It means he's free!" he cried, "Luke is free!"

"Then he'll be able to come on the voyage with us, won't he?"

But I could not hear his answer; for the whole courtroom seemed to be jumping up on chairs like the Doctor. The crowd had suddenly gone crazy. All the people were laughing and calling and waving to Luke to show him how glad they were that he was free. The noise was deafening.

Then it stopped. All was quiet again; and the people stood up respectfully while the judge left the Court. For the trial of Luke the Hermit, that famous trial which to this day they are still talking of in Puddleby, was over.

In the hush while the judge was leaving, a sudden shriek rang out, and there, in the doorway stood a woman, her arms outstretched to the Hermit.

"Luke!" she cried, "I've found you at last!"

"It's his wife," the woman in front of me whispered. "She ain't seen 'im in fifteen years, poor dear! What a lovely reunion. I'm glad I came. I wouldn't have missed this for anything!"

As soon as the judge had gone the noise broke out again; and now the folks gathered round Luke and his wife and shook them by the hand and congratulated them and laughed over them and cried over them.

"Come along, Stubbins," said the Doctor, taking me by the arm, "let's get out of this while we can."

"But aren't you going to speak to Luke?" I said—"to ask him if he'll come on the voyage?"

"It wouldn't be a bit of use," said the Doctor. "His wife's come for him. No man stands any chance of going on a voyage when his wife hasn't seen him in fifteen years. Come along. Let's get home to tea. We didn't have any lunch, remember. And we've earned something to eat.

We'll have one of these mixed meals, lunch and tea combined—with watercress and meat. Nice change. Come along."

Just as we were going to step out at a side door I heard the crowd shouting, "The Doctor! The Doctor! Where's the Doctor? The Hermit would have been hanged if it hadn't been for the Doctor. Speech! Speech!—The Doctor!"

And a man came running up to us and said, "The people are calling for you, Sir."

"I'm very sorry," said the Doctor, "but I'm in a hurry."

"The crowd won't be denied, Sir," said the man. "They want you to make a speech in the marketplace."

"Beg them to excuse me," said the Doctor—"with my compliments. I have an appointment at my house—a very important one which I may not break. Tell Luke to make a speech. Come along, Stubbins, this way."

"Oh L-rd!" he muttered as we got out into the open air and found another crowd waiting for him at the side door. "Let's go up that alley-way—to the left. Quick!—Run!"

We took to our heels, darted through a couple of side streets and just managed to get away from the crowd.

It was not till we had gained the Oxenthorpe Road that we dared to slow down to a walk and take our breath. And even when we reached the Doctor's gate and turned to look backwards towards the town, the faint murmur of many voices still reached us on the evening wind.

"They're still clamoring for you," I said. "Listen!"

The murmur suddenly swelled up into a low distant roar; and although it was a mile and a half away you could distinctly hear the words, "Three cheers for Luke the Hermit: Hooray!—Three cheers for his dog: Hooray!—Three cheers for his wife: Hooray!—Three cheers for the Doctor: Hooray! Hooray! HOO-R-A-Y!"

Recalling

1. What was the *Curlew*? What was the trouble with the *Curlew*?

2. What happened on the night of November 29th?

3. What did Manuel Mendoza try to do to Luke the Hermit on the night of November 29th? Why?

Interpreting

4. Why didn't Dr. Dolittle ask Luke to join them on their trip?

5. Why didn't Dr. Dolittle speak to the crowd after the trial?

Concluding

6. Was Dr. Dolittle right in not asking Luke to join them on their voyage? What did his explanation tell you about Dr. Dolittle's knowledge of human nature?

Examining the Novel

1. Why was the true story of Luke the Hermit told through the mouth of a dog?

2. Does this technique confirm once again the theme of this novel?

3. Does it make the courtroom scene humorous?

4. Would you have preferred if Dr. Dolittle had convinced the court of Luke's innocence in some other way?

Thinking About the Novel

Think about the reasons that Luke preferred to hide and become a hermit rather than confront the people who had accused him of murder. What type of person would run and hide rather than stay and face his accusers?

Creating and Writing

In Luke's case, a dog defended his owner. There are many stories of dogs who have saved people's lives. The quality that dogs possess is loyalty to the owners who feed them and tend to their needs. Can you think of a story in which a pet saved its owner, or can you make one up? Tell the story in one or two detailed paragraphs.

Into • *The Voyages of Dr. Dolittle*
Part Two—Chapters 9-12

In this section, the author adds an element of tension. As the time approaches for Dr. Dolittle to embark on a new adventure, not only Tommy, but also the reader, becomes more excited and eager to set sail. Mysterious people and places are introduced—people we want to meet and places we want to see. The theme of exploration—both geographical and intellectual—is highlighted in this section. As we imagine we are setting off in the *Curlew* we are filled with excitement and anticipation. This eagerness to discover new creatures, to learn new languages, to travel to foreign lands, is a feeling Hugh Lofting wants each of us to experience and to carry into our real lives.

Focus

Related to the theme of exploration is the theme of the value of knowledge. When Dr. Dolittle hears that Long Arrow is lost, he is not only disappointed to not meet him face to face, but he feels that Long Arrow's vast knowledge of the natural sciences is a great loss to the knowledge of the human race. This theme is touched on earlier in the story, when Tommy wishes he could read so that he could learn what was written in Dr. Dolittle's many books. Dr. Dolittle himself treasures any and all knowledge. He seeks to learn the language of the shellfish— not to help them in some way, but just for the sake of knowledge. As you continue to read the story, look for these two themes: exploration and the value of knowledge.

9

THE PURPLE BIRD-OF-PARADISE

Polynesia was waiting for us on the front porch. She looked full of some important news.

"Doctor," said she, "the Purple Bird-of-Paradise has arrived!"

"At last!" said the Doctor. "I had begun to fear some accident had befallen her. And how is Miranda?"

From the excited ways in which the Doctor fumbled his key into the lock I guessed that we were not going to get our tea right away, even now.

"Oh, she seemed all right when she arrived," said Polynesia—"tired from her long journey of course but otherwise all right. But what *do* you think? That mischief-making sparrow, Cheapside, insulted her as soon as she came into the garden. When I arrived on the scene she was in tears and was all for turning round and going straight back to Brazil tonight. I had the hardest work persuading her to wait till you came. She's in the study. I shut Cheapside in one of your bookcases and told him I'd tell you exactly what happened the moment you got home."

The Doctor frowned, then walked silently and quickly to the study.

Here we found the candles lit; for the daylight was nearly gone. Dab-Dab was standing on the floor mounting guard over one of the glass-fronted bookcases in which Cheapside had been imprisoned. The noisy little sparrow was still fluttering angrily behind the glass when we came in.

In the center of the big table, perched on the inkstand, stood the most beautiful bird I have ever seen. She had a deep violet-colored breast, scarlet wings and a long, long sweeping tail of gold. She was unimaginably beautiful but looked dreadfully tired. Already she had her head under her wing; and she swayed gently from side to side on top of the inkstand like a bird that has flown long and far.

"Sh!" said Dab-Dab. "Miranda is asleep. I've got this little imp Cheapside in here. Listen, Doctor: for Heaven's sake send that sparrow away before he does any more mischief. He's nothing but a vulgar little nuisance. We've had a perfectly awful time trying to get Miranda to stay. Shall I serve your tea in here, or will you come into the kitchen when you're ready?"

"We'll come into the kitchen, Dab-Dab," said the Doctor. "Let Cheapside out before you go, please."

Dab-Dab opened the bookcase door and Cheapside strutted out trying hard not to look guilty.

"Cheapside," said the Doctor sternly, "what did you say to Miranda when she arrived?"

"I didn't say nothing, Doc, straight I didn't. That is, nothing much. I was picking up crumbs off the gravel path when she comes swanking into the garden, turning up her nose in all directions, as though she owned the

---

Word Bank frowned (FROUND) *v.*: contracted the brow in displeasure; looked displeased

earth—just because she's got a lot of colored plumage. A London sparrow's as good as her any day. I don't hold by these gawdy bedizened foreigners nohow. Why don't they stay in their own country?"

"But what did you say to her that got her so offended?"

"All I said was, 'You don't belong in an English garden; you ought to be in a milliner's window.' That's all."

"You ought to be ashamed of yourself, Cheapside. Don't you realize that this bird has come thousands of miles to see me— only to be insulted by your impertinent tongue as soon as she reaches my garden? What do you mean by it?—If she had gone away again before I got back tonight I would never have forgiven you—Leave the room."

Sheepishly, but still trying to look as though he didn't care, Cheapside hopped out into the passage and Dab-Dab closed the door.

The Doctor went up to the beautiful bird on the inkstand and gently stroked its back. Instantly its head popped out from under its wing.

10

LONG ARROW THE SON OF GOLDEN ARROW

"Well, Miranda," said the Doctor. "I'm terribly sorry this has happened. But you mustn't mind Cheapside; he doesn't know any better. He's a city bird; and all his life he has had to squabble for a living. You must make allowances. He doesn't know any better."

Miranda stretched her gorgeous wings wearily. Now that I saw her awake and moving I noticed what a superior, well-bred manner she had. There were tears in her eyes and her beak was trembling.

"I wouldn't have minded so much," she said in a high silvery voice, "if I hadn't been so dreadfully worn out—That and something else," she added beneath her breath.

"Did you have a hard time getting here?" asked the Doctor.

"The worst passage I ever made," said Miranda. "The weather—Well there. What's the use? I'm here anyway."

Word Bank   impertinent (im PUR tih nint) *adj.*: rude

"Tell me," said the Doctor as though he had been impatiently waiting to say something for a long time: "what did Long Arrow say when you gave him my message?"

The Purple Bird-of-Paradise hung her head.

"That's the worst part of it," she said. "I might almost as well have not come at all. I wasn't able to deliver your message. I couldn't find him. *Long Arrow, the son of Golden Arrow, has disappeared!*"

"Disappeared!" cried the Doctor. "Why, what's become of him?"

"Nobody knows," Miranda answered. "He had often disappeared before, as I have told you—so that the Indians didn't know where he was. But it's a mighty hard thing to hide away from the birds. I had always been able to find some owl or martin who could tell me where he was—if I wanted to know. But not this time. That's why I'm nearly a fortnight late in coming to you: I kept hunting and hunting, asking every-where. I went over the whole length and breadth of South America. But there wasn't a living thing could tell me where he was."

There was a sad silence in the room after she had finished; the Doctor was frowning in a peculiar sort of way and Polynesia scratched her head.

"Did you ask the black parrots?" asked Polynesia. "They usually know everything."

"Certainly I did," said Miranda. "And I was so upset at not being able to find out anything, that I forgot all about observing the weather-signs before I started my flight here. I didn't even bother to break my journey at the Azores, but cut right across, making for the Straits of Gibraltar— as though it were June or July. And of course I ran into a perfectly fright-ful storm in mid-Atlantic. I really thought I'd never come through it. Luckily I found a piece of a wrecked vessel floating in the sea after the storm had partly died down; and I roosted on it and took some sleep. If I hadn't been able to take that rest I wouldn't be here to tell the tale."

"Poor Miranda! What a time you must have had!" said the Doctor. "But tell me, were you able to find out whereabouts Long Arrow was last seen?"

"Yes. A young albatross told me he had seen him on Spidermonkey Island."

"Spidermonkey Island? That's somewhere off the coast of Brazil, isn't it?"

"Yes, that's it. Of course I flew there right away and asked every bird on the island—and it is a big island, a hundred miles long. It seems that Long Arrow was visiting some peculiar Indians that live there; and that when last seen he was going up into the mountains looking for rare med-icine-plants. I got that from a tame hawk, a pet, which the Chief of the Indians keeps for hunting partridges with. I nearly got caught and put in a cage for my pains too. That's the worst of having beautiful feathers: it's as much as your life is worth to go near most humans—They say, 'oh how pretty!' and shoot an arrow or a bullet into you. You and Long Arrow were the only two men that I would ever trust myself near—out of all the people in the world."

"But was he never known to have returned from the mountains?"

"No. That was the last that was seen or heard of him. I questioned the seabirds around the shores to find out if he had left the island in a canoe. But they could tell me nothing."

"Do you think that some accident has happened to him?" asked the Doctor in a fearful voice.

"I'm afraid it must have," said Miranda shaking her head.

"Well," said John Dolittle slowly, "if I could never meet Long Arrow face to face it would be the greatest disappointment in my whole life. Not only that, but it would be a great loss to the knowledge of the human race. For, from what you have told me of him, he knew more natural science than all the rest of us put together; and if he has gone without anyone to write it down for him, so the world may be the better for it, it would be a terrible thing. But you don't really think that he is dead, do you?"

"What else can I think?" asked Miranda, bursting into tears, "when for six whole months he has not been seen by flesh, fish or fowl?"

11

BLIND TRAVEL

This news about Long Arrow made us all very sad. And I could see from the silent dreamy way the Doctor took his tea that he was dreadfully upset. Every once in a while he would stop eating altogether and sit staring at the spots on the kitchen tablecloth as though his thoughts were far away; till Dab-Dab, who was watching to see that he got a good meal, would cough or rattle the pots in the sink.

I did my best to cheer him up by reminding him of all he had done for Luke and his wife that afternoon. And when that didn't seem to work, I went on talking about our preparations for the voyage.

"But you see, Stubbins," said he as we rose from the table and Dab-Dab and Chee-Chee began to clear away, "I don't know where to go now. I feel sort of lost since Miranda brought me this news. On this voyage I had planned going to see Long Arrow. I had been looking forward to it for a whole year. I felt he might help me in learning the language of the shellfish—and perhaps in finding some way of getting to the bottom of the sea. But now?—He's gone! And all his great knowledge has gone with him."

Then he seemed to fall a-dreaming again.

"Just to think of it!" he murmured. "Long Arrow and I, two students—Although I'd never met him, I felt as though I knew him quite well. For, in his way—without any schooling—he has, all his life, been trying to do the very things which I have tried to do in mine—And now he's gone!—A whole world lay between us—And only a bird knew us both!"

We went back into the study, where Jip brought the Doctor his slippers and his pipe. And after the pipe was lit and the smoke began to fill the room the old man seemed to cheer up a little.

Word Bank rattle (RAT il) *v.*: to make or cause a rapid succession of short, sharp noises; clatter

"But you will go on some voyage, Doctor, won't you?" I asked—"even if you can't go to find Long Arrow."

He looked up sharply into my face; and I suppose he saw how anxious I was. Because he suddenly smiled his old, boyish smile and said, "Yes, Stubbins. Don't worry. We'll go. We mustn't stop working and learning, even if poor Long Arrow has disappeared—But where to go: that's the question. Where shall we go?"

There were so many places that I wanted to go that I couldn't make up my mind right away. And while I was still thinking, the Doctor sat up in his chair and said, "I tell you what we'll do, Stubbins: it's a game I used to play when I was young—before Sarah came to live with me. I used to call it Blind Travel. Whenever I wanted to go on a voyage, and I couldn't make up my mind where to go, I would take the atlas and open it with my eyes shut. Next, I'd wave a pencil, still without looking, and stick it down on whatever page had fallen open. Then I'd open my eyes and look. It's a very exciting game, is Blind Travel. Because you have to promise, before you begin, that you will go to the place the pencil touches, come what may. Shall we play it?"

"Oh, let's!" I almost yelled. "How thrilling! I hope it's China—or Borneo—or Baghdad."

And in a moment I had scrambled up the bookcase, dragged the big atlas from the top shelf and laid it on the table before the Doctor.

I knew every page in that atlas by heart. How many days and nights I had lingered over its old faded maps, following the blue rivers from the mountains to the sea; wondering what the little towns really looked like, and how wide were the sprawling lakes! I had had a lot of fun with that atlas, traveling, in my mind, all over the world. I can see it now: the first page had no map; it just told you that it was printed in Edinburgh in 1808, and a whole lot more about the book. The next page was the Solar System, showing the sun and planets, the stars and the moon. The third page was the chart of the North and South Poles. Then came the hemispheres, the oceans, the continents and the countries.

As the Doctor began sharpening his pencil a thought came to me.

"What if the pencil falls upon the North Pole," I asked, "will we have to go there?"

"No. The rules of the game say you don't have to go anyplace you've been to before. You are allowed another try. I've been to the North Pole," he ended quietly, "so we shan't have to go there."

I could hardly speak with astonishment.

"*You've been to the North Pole*!" I managed to gasp out at last. "But I thought it was still undiscovered. The map shows all the places explorers have reached to, *trying* to get there. Why isn't your name down if you

Word Bank	scrambled (SKRAM buld) *v.*: hurried; climbed up by moving quickly
	lingered (LING urd) *v.*: was slow in parting from
	gasp (GASP) *v.*: to catch one's breath with shock

discovered it?"

"I promised to keep it a secret. And you must promise me never to tell anyone. Yes, I discovered the North Pole in April, 1809. But shortly after I got there the polar bears came to me in a body and told me there was a great deal of coal there, buried beneath the snow. They knew, they said, that human beings would do anything, and go anywhere, to get coal. So would I please keep it a secret. Because once people began coming up there to start coal-mines, their beautiful snow-covered country would be spoiled—and there was nowhere else in the world cold enough for polar bears to be comfortable. So of course I had to promise them I would. Ah, well, it will be discovered again someday, by somebody else. But I want the polar bears to have their playground to themselves as long as possible. And I daresay it will be a good while yet—for it certainly is a fiendish place to get to—Well now, are we ready?—Good! Take the pencil and stand here close to the table. When the book falls open, wave the pencil round three times and jab it down. Ready?—All right. Shut your eyes."

It was a tense and fearful moment—but very thrilling. We both had our eyes shut tight. I heard the atlas fall open with a bang. I wondered what page it was: England or Asia. If it should be the map of Asia, so much would depend on where that pencil would land. I waved three times in a circle. I began to lower my hand. The pencil touched the page.

"All right," I called out, "it's done."

12

DESTINY AND DESTINATION

We both opened our eyes; then bumped our heads together with a crack in our eagerness to lean over and see where we were to go.

The atlas lay open at a map called, *Chart of the South Atlantic Ocean*. My pencil-point was resting right in the center of a tiny island. The name of it was printed so small that the Doctor had to get out his strong spectacles to read it. I was trembling with excitement.

"*Spidermonkey Island*," he read out slowly. Then he whistled softly beneath his breath. "Of all the extraordinary things! You've hit upon the very island where Long Arrow was last seen on earth—I wonder—Well, well! How very singular!"

"We'll go there, Doctor, won't we?" I asked.

"Of course we will. The rules of the game say we've got to."

"I'm so glad it wasn't Oxenthorpe or Bristol," I said. "It'll be a grand voyage, this. Look at all the sea we've got to cross. Will it take us long?"

"Oh, no," said the Doctor—"not very. With a good boat and a good wind we should make it easily in four weeks. But isn't it extraordinary? Of all the places in the world you picked out that one with your eyes shut. Spidermonkey Island after all! Well, there's one good thing about it: I shall be able to get some Jabizri beetles."

"What are Jabizri beetles?"

"They are a very rare kind of beetle with peculiar habits. I want to study them. There are only three countries in the world where they are to be found. Spidermonkey Island is one of them. But even there they are very scarce."

"What is this little question-mark after the name of the island for?" I asked, pointing to the map.

"That means that the island's position in the ocean is not known very exactly—that it is somewhere *about* there. Ships have probably seen it in that neighborhood, that is all, most likely. It is quite possible we shall be the first white men to land there. But I daresay we shall have some difficulty in finding it first."

How like a dream it all sounded! The two of us sitting there at the big study-table; the candles lit; the smoke curling towards the dim ceiling from the Doctor's pipe—the two of us sitting there, talking about finding an island in the ocean and being the first white men to land upon it!

"I'll bet it will be a great voyage," I said. "It looks like a lovely island on the map. Will there be natives there?"

"No. An unusual tribe of Indians lives on it, Miranda tells me."

At this point the poor Bird-of-Paradise stirred and woke up. In our excitement we had forgotten to speak low.

"We are going to Spidermonkey Island, Miranda," said the Doctor. "You know where it is, do you not?"

"I know where it was the last time I saw it," said the bird. "But whether it will be there still, I can't say."

"What do you mean?" asked the Doctor. "It is always in the same place surely?"

"Not by any means," said Miranda. "Why, didn't you know?—Spidermonkey Island is a *floating* island. It moves around all over the place—usually somewhere near southern South America. But of course I could surely find it for you if you want to go there."

At this fresh piece of news I could contain myself no longer. I was bursting to tell someone. I ran dancing and singing from the room to find Chee-Chee.

At the door I tripped over Dab-Dab, who was just coming in with her wings full of plates, and fell headlong on my nose.

"Has the boy gone crazy?" cried the duck. "Where do you think you're going, ninny?"

"To Spidermonkey Island!" I shouted, picking myself up and doing cartwheels down the hall—"Spidermonkey Island! Hooray!—And it's a *floating* island!"

"You're going to Bedlam, I should say," snorted the housekeeper. "Look what you've done to my best china!"

But I was far too happy to listen to her scolding; and I ran on, singing, into the kitchen to find Chee-Chee.

Recalling

1. What did Cheapside say to Miranda that insulted her? Why did he hurl this insult at Miranda?

2. Why did Dr. Dolittle want to meet Long Arrow?

3. Who last saw Long Arrow? Where was Long Arrow when he was seen?

4. How long has it been since Long Arrow was last seen?

5. What are Jabizri beetles?

Interpreting

6. Why was Miranda two weeks late?

7. What is Blind Travel?

8. Why didn't Dr. Dolittle tell anyone that he had discovered the North Pole?

Concluding

9. Why isn't the exact location of Spidermonkey Island known? How did Tommy behave when Miranda told him she could find the island? Why did he react in this way?

Examining the Novel

One of Dr. Dolittle's admirable character traits is his modesty. He doesn't think he is extraordinary for being able to speak with animals, or cure the problems the animals bring to him. Dr. Dolittle does not think he should be praised for helping Luke. Rather, Dr. Dolittle thinks of himself as a student who spends his life studying the wonders of nature. Why is Dr. Dolittle so upset when he hears that Long Arrow is missing? What did he seek to learn from Long Arrow?

Thinking About the Novel

Dr. Dolittle considers animals part of nature. The doctor has respect for all natural phenomena. How does Dr. Dolittle's decision to keep his North Pole trip a secret show his respect for nature? Do you agree with Dr. Dolittle's decision not to tell anybody about his trip to the North Pole? Write a paragraph explaining your view.

Creating and Writing

Miranda, the Purple Bird-of-Paradise, is beautiful. She represents the unique and gorgeous wildlife that exists in far-flung jungles and forests around the world. Hunters try to trap these birds for their feathers. Others try to trap these birds and put them in cages as pets. Dr. Dolittle believes that Miranda's beauty belongs in its natural habitat, the jungles of South America.

The rainforests are the world's jewelry boxes, filled with thousands of unique animals and plants. Some of these plants contain lifesaving properties; the plants are converted into medicine that fights many diseases.

The rainforests contain animals that have adapted well to their environment. In the forest, Miranda's feathers would be hidden in the tall trees where she flies. It is only outside the rainforest that Miranda's beautiful feathers make her an easy target for hunters.

What should be done about the beautiful birds of the rainforests and jungles? Should they be trapped and kept as pets or should they be protected? Is there a way to do both: trap some but allow others to fly freely? Can there be a compromise in this situation?

Write an essay about an animal or bird that exists in the jungles or rainforests. For example, your essay could be about parrots, elephants, lions, or tigers. What do you think should be done with these animals? How can we enjoy their beauty and also value the place from which they came?

Blueprint FOR READING

Into • *The Voyages of Dr. Dolittle*
Part Three—Chapters 1-5

In this section, we encounter several old and new minor characters. Joe the mussel-man, Matthew Mugg, Ben Butcher, Bumpo Kahbooboo, and Mr. and Mrs. Luke, all play a role in the story. Unlike the major characters, Dr. Dolittle and Tommy Stubbins, the minor characters are one-dimensional. That means that they are not fully described; the author focuses on one or two of their personality traits. The minor characters add interest and, often, humor to the story.

Focus

Part of the story's humor comes from the comical behavior of the minor characters. The "able seaman," for example, is very big, very strong, very coarse, and very rude! As you read, notice the other minor characters. They, too, have exaggerated appearances and behavior. Each one is, to some extent, a **caricature**, which means a funny, exaggerated example of a certain type of person.

PART 3

1

THE THIRD MAN

That same week we began our preparations for the voyage. Joe, the mussel-man, had the *Curlew* moved down the river and tied it up along the river-wall, so it would be more handy for loading. And for three whole days we carried provisions down to our beautiful new boat and stowed them away.

I was surprised to find how roomy and big she was inside. There were three little cabins, a saloon (or dining-room) and underneath all this, a big place called the hold where the food and extra sails and other things were kept.

I think Joe must have told everybody in the town about our coming voyage, because there was always a regular crowd watching us when we brought the things down to put aboard. And of course sooner or later old Matthew Mugg was bound to turn up.

"My Goodness, Tommy," said he, as he watched me carrying on some sacks of flour, "but that's a pretty boat! Where might the Doctor be going on this voyage?"

"We're going to Spidermonkey Island," I said proudly.

"And be you the only one the Doctor's taking along?"

"Well, he has spoken of wanting to take another man," I said; "but so far he hasn't made up his mind."

Matthew grunted; then squinted up at the graceful masts of the *Curlew*.

"You know, Tommy," said he, "if it wasn't for my rheumatism I've half a mind to come with the Doctor myself. There's something about a boat standing ready to sail that always did make me feel venturesome and travelish-like. What's that stuff in the cans you're taking on?"

"This is treacle," I said—"twenty pounds of treacle."

"My Goodness," he sighed, turning away sadly. "That makes me feel more like going with you than ever—But my rheumatism is that bad I can't hardly—"

I didn't hear anymore for Matthew had moved off, still mumbling, into the crowd that stood about the wharf. The clock in Puddleby Tower struck noon and I turned back, feeling very busy and important, to the task of loading.

Word Bank	**provisions** (pruh VIZH unz) *n.*: a stock of needed materials and supplies
	venturesome (VEN chur SUM) *adj.*: taking a bold, daring risk; adventurous

But it wasn't very long before someone else came along and interrupted my work. This was a huge, big, burly man with a red beard and tattoo-marks all over his arms. He wiped his mouth with the back of his hand, spat twice onto the river-wall and said, "Boy, where's the skipper?"

"The *skipper*!—Who do you mean?" I asked.

"The captain—Where's the captain of this craft?" he said, pointing to the *Curlew*.

"Oh, you mean the Doctor," said I. "Well, he isn't here at present."

At that moment the doctor arrived with his arms full of notebooks and butterfly-nets and glass cases and other natural things. The big man went up to him, respectfully touching his cap.

"Good morning, Captain," said he. "I heard you was in need of hands for a voyage. My name's Ben Butcher, able seaman."

"I am very glad to know you," said the Doctor. "But I'm afraid I shan't be able to take on any more crew."

"Why, but Captain," said the able seaman, "you surely ain't going to face deep-sea weather with nothing more than this bit of a lad to help you—and with a cutter that big!"

The Doctor assured him that he was; but the man didn't go away. He hung around and argued. He told us he had known of many ships being sunk through "undermanning." He got out what he called his *stiffikit*—a paper which said what a good sailor he was—and implored us, if we valued our lives, to take him.

But the Doctor was quite firm—polite but determined—and finally the man walked sorrowfully away, telling he never expected to see us alive again.

Callers of one sort and another kept us quite busy that morning. The Doctor had no sooner gone below to stow away his notebooks than another visitor appeared upon the gangplank. This was a most extraordinary-looking black man, dressed in a fashionable frock coat with an enormous bright red cravat. On his head was a straw hat with a gay band; and over this he held a large green umbrella. He was very smart in every respect except his feet. He wore no shoes or socks.

Word Bank	**implored** (im PLORD) *v.*: begged; asked for earnestly

"Pardon me," said he; bowing elegantly, "but is this the ship of the physician Dolittle?"

"Yes," I said, "did you wish to see him?"

"I did—if it will not be discommodious," he answered.

"Who shall I say it is?"

"I am Bumpo Kahbooboo, Crown Prince of Jolliginki."

I ran downstairs at once and told the Doctor.

"How fortunate!" cried John Dolittle. "My old friend Bumpo! Well, well!—He's studying at Oxford, you know. How good of him to come all this way to call on me!" And he tumbled up the ladder to greet his visitor.

The strange black man seemed to be overcome with joy when the Doctor appeared and shook him warmly by the hand.

"News reached me," he said, "that you were about to sail upon a voyage. I hastened to see you before your departure. I am sublimely ecstasied that I did not miss you."

"You very nearly did miss us," said the Doctor. "As it happened, we were delayed somewhat in getting the necessary number of men to sail our boat. If it hadn't been for that, we would have been gone three days ago."

"How many men does your ship's company yet require?" asked Bumpo.

"Only one," said the Doctor—"But it is so hard to find the right one."

"Methinks I detect something of the finger of Destination in this," said Bumpo. "How would I do?"

"Splendidly," said the Doctor. "But what about your studies? You can't very well just go off and leave your university career to take care of itself, you know."

"I need a holiday," said Bumpo. "Even had I not gone with you, I intend at the end of this term to take a three-months' absconsion—But besides, I shall not be neglecting my edification if I accompany you. Before I left Jolliginki my august father, the King, told me to be sure and travel plenty. You are a man of great studiosity. To see the world in your company is an opportunity not to be sneezed upon. No, no, indeed."

"How did you like the life at Oxford?" asked the Doctor.

"Oh, passably, passably," said Bumpo. "I liked it all except the algebra and the shoes. The algebra hurt my head and the shoes hurt my feet. I threw the shoes over a wall as soon as I got out of the college quadrilateral this morning; and the algebra I am happily forgetting very fast—I liked Cicero[1]—Yes, I think Cicero's fine—so simultaneous. By the way, they tell me his son is rowing for our college next year—charming fellow."

---

1. *Cicero* (SIS uh roe) was a Roman orator noted for his eloquence.

Word Bank	**simultaneous** (sy mul TAY nee us) *adj.*: occurring at the same time

The Doctor looked down at the black man's huge bare feet thoughtfully a moment.

"Well," he said slowly, "there is something in what you say, Bumpo, about getting an education from the world as well as from the college. And if you are really sure that you want to come, we shall be delighted to have you. Because, to tell you the truth, I think you are exactly the man we need."

2

GOOD-BYE!

Two days after that we had all in readiness for our departure.

On this voyage Jip begged so hard to be taken that the Doctor finally gave in and said he could come. Polynesia and Chee-Chee were the only other animals to go with us. Dab-Dab was left in charge of the house and the animal family we were to leave behind.

Of course, as is always the way, at the last moment we kept remembering things we had forgotten; and when we finally closed the house up and went down the steps to the road, we were all burdened with armfuls of odd packages.

Halfway to the river, the Doctor suddenly remembered that he had left the stockpot boiling on the kitchen-fire. However, we saw a black-bird flying by who nested in our garden, and the Doctor asked her to go back for us and tell Dab-Dab about it.

Down at the river-wall we found a great crowd waiting to see us off.

Standing right near the gangplank were my mother and father. I hoped that they would not make a scene, or burst into tears or anything like that. But as a matter of fact they behaved quite well. My mother said something about being sure not to get my feet wet; and my father just smiled a crooked sort of smile, patted me on the back and wished me luck. Good-byes are awfully uncomfortable things and I was glad when it was over and we passed onto the ship.

We were a little surprised not to see Matthew Mugg among the crowd. We had felt sure that he would be there; and the Doctor had intended to give him some extra instructions about the food for the animals we had left at the house.

At last, after much pulling and tugging, we got the anchor up and undid a lot of mooring-ropes. Then the *Curlew* began to move gently down the river with the outrunning tide, while the people on the wall cheered and waved their handkerchiefs.

We bumped into one or two other boats getting out into the stream; and at one sharp bend in the river we got stuck on a mudbank for a few minutes. But though the people on the shore seemed to get very excited at these things, the Doctor did not appear to be disturbed by them in the least.

"These little accidents will happen in the most carefully regulated voyages," he said as he leaned over the side and fished for his boots which had got stuck in the mud while we were pushing off. "Sailing is much easier when you get out into the open sea. There aren't so many silly things to bump into."

For me indeed it was a great and wonderful feeling, that getting out into the open sea, when at length we passed the little lighthouse at the mouth of the river and found ourselves free of the land. It was all so new and different: just the sky above you and sea below. This ship, which was to be our house and our street, our home and our garden, for so many days to come, seemed so tiny in all this wide water—so tiny and yet so snug, sufficient, safe.

I looked around me and took in a deep breath. The Doctor was at the wheel steering the boat which was now leaping and plunging gently through the waves. (I had expected to feel seasick at first but was delighted to find that I didn't.) Bumpo had been told off to go downstairs and prepare dinner for us. Chee-Chee was coiling up ropes in the stern and laying them in neat piles. My work was fastening down the things on the deck so that nothing could roll about if the weather should grow rough when we got further from the land. Jip was up in the peak of the boat with ears cocked and nose stuck out—like a statue, so still—his keen old eyes keeping a sharp lookout for floating wrecks, sandbars, and other dangers. Each one of us had some special job to do, part of the proper running of a ship. Even old Polynesia was taking the sea's temperature with the Doctor's bath-thermometer tied on the end of a string, to make sure there were no icebergs near us. As I listened to her muttering softly to herself because she couldn't read the pesky figures in the fading light, I realized that the voyage had begun in earnest and that very soon it would be night—my first night at sea!

3

OUR TROUBLES BEGIN

Just before suppertime Bumpo appeared from downstairs and went to the Doctor at the wheel.

"A stowaway in the hold, Sir," said he in a very businesslike seafaring voice. "I just discovered him, behind the flour-bags."

"Dear me!" said the Doctor. "What a nuisance! Stubbins, go down with Bumpo and bring the man up. I can't leave the wheel just now."

So Bumpo and I went down into the hold; and there, behind the flour-bags, plastered in flour from head to foot, we found a man. After we had swept most of the flour off him with a broom, we discovered that it was Matthew Mugg. We hauled him upstairs sneezing and took him before the Doctor.

"Why Matthew!" said John Dolittle. "What on earth are you doing here?"

Word Bank	**sufficient** (suh FISH int) *adj.*: enough to meet the needs of a situation

"The temptation was too much for me, Doctor," said the cat's-meat-man. "You know I've often asked you to take me on voyages with you and you never would. Well, this time, knowing that you needed an extra man, I thought if I stayed hid till the ship was well at sea you would find I came in handy-like and keep me. But I had to lie so doubled up, for hours, behind them flour-bags, that my rheumatism came on something awful. I just had to change my position; and of course just as I stretched out my legs along comes this here cook of yours and sees my feet sticking out—Don't this ship roll something awful! How long has this storm been going on? I reckon this damp sea air wouldn't be very good for my rheumatics."

"No, Matthew it really isn't. You ought not to have come. You are not in any way suited to this kind of a life. I'm sure you wouldn't enjoy a long voyage a bit. We'll stop in at Penzance and put you ashore. Bumpo, please go downstairs to my bunk; and listen: in the pocket of my dressing-gown you'll find some maps. Bring me the small one—with blue pencil marks at the top. I know Penzance is over here on our left somewhere. But I must find out what lighthouses there are before I change the ship's course and sail inshore."

"Very good, Sir," said Bumpo, turning round smartly and making for the stairway.

"Now Matthew," said the Doctor, "you can take the coach from Penzance to Bristol. And from there it is not very far to Puddleby, as you know. Don't forget to take the usual provisions to the house every Thursday, and be particularly careful to remember the extra supply of herrings for the baby minks."

While we were waiting for the maps Chee-Chee and I set about lighting the lamps: a green one on the right side of the ship, a red one on the left and a white one on the mast.

At last we heard someone trundling on the stairs again and the Doctor said, "Ah, here's Bumpo with the maps at last!"

But to our great astonishment it was not Bumpo alone that appeared but *three* people.

"Goodness! Who are these?" cried John Dolittle.

"Two more stowaways, Sir," said Bumpo stepping forward briskly. "I found them in your cabin hiding under the bunk. One woman and one man, Sir. Here are the maps."

"This is too much," said the Doctor feebly. "Who are they? I can't see their faces in this dim light. Strike a match, Bumpo."

You could never guess who it was. It was Luke and his wife. Mrs. Luke appeared to be very miserable and seasick.

They explained to the Doctor, that after they had settled down to live together in the little shack out on the fens, so many people came to visit them (having heard about the great trial) that life became impossible; and they had decided to escape from Puddleby in this manner—for they had no money to leave any other way—and try to find some new place to live where they and their story wouldn't be so well known. But as soon as the ship had begun to roll Mrs. Luke had got dreadfully unwell.

Poor Luke apologized many times for being such a nuisance and said that the whole thing had been his wife's idea.

The Doctor, after he had sent below for his medicine-bag and had given Mrs. Luke some *sal volatile*[2] and smelling salts, said he thought the best thing to do would be for him to lend them some money and put them ashore at Penzance with Matthew. He also wrote a letter for Luke to take with him to a friend the Doctor had in the town of Penzance who, it was hoped, would be able to find Luke work to do there.

As the Doctor opened his purse and took out some gold coins I heard Polynesia, who was sitting on my shoulder watching the whole affair, mutter under her breath, "There he goes—lending his last blessed penny-three pounds ten—all the money we had for the whole trip! Now we haven't the price of a postage-stamp aboard if we should lose an anchor or have to buy a pint of tar—Well, let's pray we don't run out of food—Why doesn't he give them the ship and walk home?"

Presently with the help of the map the course of the boat was changed and, to Mrs. Luke's great relief, we made for Penzance and dry land.

I was tremendously interested to see how a ship could be steered into a port at night with nothing but lighthouses and a compass to guide you. It seemed to me that the Doctor missed all the rocks and sandbars very cleverly.

We got into that funny little Cornish harbor about eleven o'clock that night. The Doctor took his stowaways onshore in our small rowboat which we kept on the deck of the *Curlew* and found them rooms at the hotel there. When he got back he told us that Mrs. Luke had gone straight to bed and was feeling much better.

It was now after midnight; so we decided to stay in the harbor and wait till morning before setting out again.

I was glad to get to bed, although I felt that staying up so tremendously late was great fun. As I climbed into the bunk over the Doctor's and pulled the blankets snugly round me, I found I could look out of the porthole at my elbow, and, without raising my head from the pillow, could see the lights of Penzance swinging gently up and down with the motion of the ship at anchor. It was like being rocked to sleep with a little show going on to amuse you. I was just deciding that I liked the life of the sea very much when I fell fast asleep.

---

2. *Sal volatile* (SAHL VO LAT uh LEE) is a strong-smelling solution of ammonium carbonate in alcohol or ammonia water.

4

Our Troubles Continue

The next morning when we were eating a very excellent breakfast of kidneys and liver, prepared by our good cook Bumpo, the Doctor said to me, "I was just wondering, Stubbins, whether I should stop at the Capa Blanca Islands or run right across for the coast of Brazil. Miranda said we could expect a spell of excellent weather now—for four and a half weeks at least."

"Well," I said, spooning out the sugar at the bottom of my cocoa-cup, "I should think it would be best to make straight across while we are sure of good weather. And besides the Purple Bird-of-Paradise is going to keep a lookout for us, isn't she? She'll be wondering what's happened to us if we don't get there in about a month."

"True, quite true, Stubbins. On the other hand, the Capa Blancas make a very convenient stopping place on our way across. If we should need supplies or repairs it would be very handy to put in there."

"How long will it take us from here to the Capa Blancas?" I asked.

"About six days," said the Doctor—"Well, we can decide later. For the next two days at any rate our direction would be the same practically in either case. If you have finished breakfast let's go and get under way."

Upstairs I found our vessel surrounded by white and gray seagulls who flashed and circled about in the sunny morning air, looking for food-scraps thrown out by the ships into the harbor.

By about half past seven we had the anchor up and the sails set to a nice steady breeze; and this time we got out into the open sea without bumping into a single thing. We met the Penzance fishing fleet coming in from the night's fishing, and very trim and neat they looked, in a line like soldiers, with their red-brown sails all leaning over the same way and the white water dancing before their bows.

For the next three or four days everything went smoothly and nothing unusual happened. During this time we all got settled down into our regular jobs; and in spare moments the Doctor showed each of us how to take our turns at the wheel, and the proper manner of keeping a ship on her right course, and what to do if the wind changed suddenly. We divided the twenty four hours of the day into three spells; and we took it in turns to sleep our eight hours and be awake sixteen. So the ship was well looked after, with two of us always on duty.

Besides that, Polynesia, who was an older sailor than any of us, and really knew a lot about running ships, seemed to be always awake—except when she took her couple of winks in the sun, standing on one leg beside the wheel. You may be sure that no one ever got a chance to stay abed more than his eight hours while Polynesia was around. She used to watch the ship's clock; and if you overslept a half-minute, she would come down to the cabin and peck you gently on the nose till you got up.

I very soon grew to be quite fond of our friend Bumpo, with his grand way of speaking and his enormous feet which someone was always stepping on or falling over. Although he was much older than I was and had been to college he never tried to lord it over me. He seemed to be forever smiling and kept all of us in good humor. It wasn't long before I began to see the Doctor's good sense in bringing him—in spite of the fact that he knew nothing whatever about sailing or travel.

On the morning of the fifth day out, just as I was taking the wheel over from the Doctor, Bumpo appeared and said, "The salt beef is nearly all gone, Sir."

"The salt beef!" cried the Doctor. "Why, we brought a hundred and twenty pounds with us. We couldn't have eaten that in five days. What can have become of it?"

"I don't know, Sir, I'm sure. Every time I go down to the stores I find another hunk missing. If it is rats that are eating it, then they are certainly colossal rodents."

Polynesia who was walking up and down a stay-rope taking her morning exercise, put in, "We must search the hold. If this is allowed to go on we will all be starving before a week is out. Come downstairs with me, Tommy, and we will look into this matter."

So we went downstairs into the store-room and Polynesia told us to keep quite still and listen. This we did. And presently we heard from a dark corner of the hold the distinct sound of someone snoring.

"Ah, I thought so," said Polynesia. "It's a man—and a big one. Climb in there, both of you, and haul him out. It sounds as though he were behind that barrel—Gosh! We seem to have brought half of Puddleby with us. Anyone would think we were a penny ferryboat. Such cheek! Haul him out."

So Bumpo and I lit a lantern and climbed over the stores. And there, behind the barrel, sure enough, we found an enormous bearded man fast asleep with a well-fed look on his face. We woke him up.

"Washamarrer?" he said sleepily.

It was Ben Butcher, the able seaman.

Polynesia spluttered like an angry firecracker.

"This is the last straw," said she. "The one man in the world we least wanted. Shiver my timbers, what cheek!"

"Would it not be advisable," suggested Bumpo, "while the varlet[3] is

---

3. A *varlet* (VAHR lit) is a knight's attendant.

<table>
<tr><td>**Word Bank**</td><td>colossal (kuh LAHS il) *adj.*: of very great size; gigantic</td></tr>
</table>

still sleepy, to strike him on the head with some heavy object and push him through a porthole into the sea?"

"No. We'd get into trouble," said Polynesia. "We're not in Jolliginki now, you know—worse luck!—Besides, there never was a porthole big enough to push that man through. Bring him upstairs to the Doctor." So we led the man to the wheel where he respectfully touched his cap to the Doctor.

"Another stowaway, Sir," said Bumpo smartly.

I thought the poor Doctor would have a fit.

"Good morning, Captain," said the man. "Ben Butcher, able seaman, at your service. I knew you'd need me, so I took the liberty of stowing away—much against my conscience. But I just couldn't bear to see you poor landsmen set out on this voyage without a single real seaman to help you. You'd never have got home alive if I hadn't come—Why look at your mainsail, Sir—all loose at the throat. First gust of wind come along, and away goes your canvas overboard—Well, it's all right now I'm here. We'll soon get things in shipshape."

"No, it isn't all right," said the Doctor, "it's all wrong. And I'm not at all glad to see you. I told you in Puddleby I didn't want you. You had no right to come."

"But Captain," said the able seaman, "you can't sail this ship without me. You don't understand navigation. Why, look at the compass now: you've let her swing a point and a half off her course. It's madness for you to try to do this trip alone—if you'll pardon my saying so, Sir. Why—why, you'll lose the ship!"

"Look here," said the Doctor, a sudden stern look coming into his eyes, "losing a ship is nothing to me. I've lost ships before and it doesn't bother me in the least. When I set out to go to a place, I get there. Do you understand? I may know nothing whatever about sailing and navigation, but I get there just the same. Now you may be the best seaman in the world, but on *this* ship you're just a plain ordinary nuisance—very plain and very ordinary. And I am now going to call[4] the nearest port and put you ashore."

"Yes, and think yourself lucky," Polynesia put in, "that you are not locked up for stowing away and eating all our salt beef."

"I don't know what the mischief we're going to do now," I heard her whisper to Bumpo. "We've no money to buy anymore; and that salt beef was the most important part of the stores."

"Would it not be good political economy," Bumpo whispered back, "if we salted the able seaman and ate him instead? I should judge that he would weigh more than a hundred and twenty pounds."

"How often must I tell you," snapped Polynesia, "those things are not done on the Doctor's ships—Still," she murmured after a moment's

---

4. Here, *call* means to make a brief stop or visit at a place.

thought, "it's an awfully bright idea. I don't suppose anybody saw him come onto the ship—Oh, but Heavens! We haven't got enough salt. Besides, he'd be sure to taste of tobacco."

5

POLYNESIA HAS A PLAN

Then the Doctor told me to take the wheel while he made a little calculation with his map and worked out what new course we should take.

"I shall have to run for the Capa Blancas after all," he told me when the seaman's back was turned. "Dreadful nuisance! But I'd sooner swim back to Puddleby than have to listen to that fellow's talk all the way to Brazil."

Indeed he was a terrible person, this Ben Butcher. You'd think that anyone after being told he wasn't wanted would have the decency to keep quiet. But not Ben Butcher. He kept going round the deck pointing out all the things we had wrong. According to him there wasn't a thing right on the whole ship. The anchor was hitched up wrong; the hatches weren't fastened down properly; the sails were put on back to front; all our knots were the wrong kind of knots.

At last the Doctor told him to stop talking and go downstairs. He refused—said he wasn't going to be sunk by landlubbers while he was still able to stay on deck.

This made us feel a little uneasy. He was such an enormous man there was no knowing what he might do if he got really obstreperous.

Bumpo and I were talking about this downstairs in the dining-saloon when Polynesia, Jip and Chee-Chee came and joined us. And, as usual, Polynesia had a plan.

"Listen," she said, "I am certain this Ben Butcher is a smuggler and a bad man. I am a very good judge of seamen, remember, and I don't like the cut of this man's jib. I—"

"Do you really think," I interrupted, "that it *is* safe for the Doctor to cross the Atlantic without any regular seamen on his ship?"

You see it had upset me quite a good deal to find that all the things wc had been doing were wrong; and I was beginning to wonder what might happen if we ran into a storm—particularly as Miranda had only said the weather would be good for a certain time; and we seemed to be having so many delays. But Polynesia merely tossed her head scornfully.

"Oh, dear me, my boy," said she, "you're always safe with John Dolittle. Remember that. Don't take any notice of that stupid old salt. Of course it is perfectly true the Doctor does do everything wrong. But with him it doesn't matter. Mark my words, if you travel with John Dolittle you always get there, as you heard him say. I've been with him lots of times and I know. Sometimes the ship is upside down when you get there, and sometimes it's right way up. But you get there just the same. And then of course there's another thing about the Doctor," she added thoughtfully: "he always has extraordinary good luck. He may have his troubles; but with him things seem to have a habit of turning out all right in the end. I remember once when we were going through the Straits of Magellan the wind was so strong—"

"But what are we going to do about Ben Butcher?" Jip put in. "You had some plan Polynesia, hadn't you?"

"Yes. What I'm afraid of is that he may hit the Doctor on the head when he's not looking and make himself captain of the *Curlew*. Bad sailors do that sometimes. Then they run the ship their own way and take it where they want. That's what you call a mutiny."

"Yes," said Jip, "and we ought to do something pretty quick. We can't reach the Capa Blancas before the day after tomorrow at best. I don't like to leave the Doctor alone with him for a minute. He smells like a very bad man to me."

"Well, I've got it all worked out," said Polynesia. "Listen: is there a key in that door?"

We looked outside the dining-room and found that there was.

"All right," said Polynesia. "Now, Bumpo lays the table for lunch and we all go and hide. Then at twelve o'clock Bumpo rings the dinner-bell down here. As soon as Ben hears it he'll come down expecting more salt beef. Bumpo must hide behind the door outside. The moment that Ben is seated at the dining-table Bumpo slams the door and locks it. Then we've got him. See?"

"How stratagenious!"[5] Bumpo chuckled. "I'll lay the table at once."

"Yes and take that Worcestershire sauce off the dresser with you when you go out," said Polynesia. "Don't leave any loose eatables around. That fellow has had enough to last any man for three days. Besides, he won't be so inclined to start a fight when we put him ashore at the Capa Blancas if we thin him down a bit before we let him out."

So we all went and hid ourselves in the passage where we could watch what happened. And presently Bumpo came to the foot of the stairs and rang the dinner-bell like mad. Then he hopped behind the dining-room door and we all kept still and listened.

Almost immediately, *thump, thump, thump*, down the stairs tramped Ben Butcher, the able seaman. He walked into the dining-saloon, sat himself down at the head of the table in the Doctor's place, tucked a napkin under his fat chin and heaved a sigh of expectation.

Then, *bang*! Bumpo slammed the door and locked it.

"That settles him for a while," said Polynesia coming out of her hiding-place. "Now let him teach navigation to the sideboard. Gosh, the cheek of the man! I've forgotten more about the sea than that lumbering lout will ever know. Let's go upstairs and tell the Doctor. Bumpo, you will have to serve the meals in the cabin for the next couple of days."

And bursting into a rollicking Norwegian sea-song, she climbed up to my shoulder and we went on deck.

---

5. *Stratagenious* (STRAT uh JEEN ee us) is a made-up combination of the words "strategic" and "genius," meaning brilliantly strategic.

Recalling

1. Who was Ben Butcher, and why did he want to go on Dr. Dolittle's ship?

2. Who did Dr. Dolittle invite to come along on the journey?

3. What was each participant's special task on board?

4. Who was the first stowaway? What was done with him?

5. Who else was hiding on the ship? What happened to them?

Interpreting

6. Why was Bumpo exactly the man that Dr. Dolittle was looking for?

7. What happened to the salt beef?

Concluding

8. How did Polynesia, with Bumpo's help, solve the problem of what to do with Ben Butcher?

9. If Polynesia were human, what type of a person would she be? Would you like to know her?

Examining the Novel

Dr. Dolittle has a varied crew on his ship. Each one of those invited by the Doctor had a special task to perform. Do you think there will be any tension between the members of this group? Why do you think Polynesia, Chee-Chee, Bumpo, Tommy, Jip, and the Doctor all get along so well?

Thinking About the Novel

How did Dr. Dolittle react to the stowaways? How did his reactions to Matthew Mugg and Luke the Hermit and his wife differ from his reaction to Ben Butcher? Why was Dr. Dolittle much angrier at Ben than he was at the others? Write a paragraph in which you approve or disapprove of Dr. Dolittle's reactions to the stowaways. Support your answer using details from the story.

Creating and Writing

Dr. Dolittle wanted to take Bumpo along because he had a sense of humor and a great deal of common sense. He was practical and good-natured. Write a paragraph describing a meal on board the *Curlew*. Be descriptive and humorous. Include examples of Bumpo's good nature.

Into • *The Voyages of Dr. Dolittle*
Part Three—Chapters 6-9

This section of the story highlights the important themes of adventure and respect for all living things. The adventure theme continues with our travelers' visit to the Capa Blanca Islands. The narrow, twisting streets and the warm and lively people make Capa Blanca an exciting place to visit. Tommy enjoys sleeping on beds placed in the street though he doubts his parents would enjoy the experience. Adventure is for the young, or at least the young at heart. This is what makes Dr. Dolittle so unusual. Although he is middle-aged and wise, he is as lighthearted and adventurous as a boy.

The second theme, respect for all living things, is expressed in Dr. Dolittle's opposition to bullfights. Dr. Dolittle's courage, creativity, and determination are all on display as he fights against the terrible practice of bullfighting.

A third theme of the novel is the unimportance of wealth and material things. Dr. Dolittle lives simply and is satisfied with little. He uses what money he has to help others and to satisfy his simple needs. Tommy follows the good doctor's example—to him, sleeping on a borrowed bed in the middle of the street is an adventure, not an inconvenience.

Focus

One of Dr. Dolittle's qualities is dislike of honor or arrogance. When Dr. Dolittle does something heroic, he likes to disappear before people honor him and thank him. After saving Luke, earlier in the story, and here, after the bullfight, Dr. Dolittle runs from the scene. He seems always to want to get on to the next task, and not get sidetracked by honor and flattery. He also dislikes arrogance in others. Can you find any examples in this or previous chapters of Dr. Dolittle's distaste for arrogant people?

6

THE BED-MAKER OF MONTEVERDE

We remained three days in the Capa Blanca Islands. There were two reasons why we stayed there so long when we were really in such a hurry to get away. One was the shortage in our provisions caused by the able seaman's enormous appetite. When we came to go over the stores and make a list, we found that he had eaten a whole lot of other things besides the beef. And having no money, we were sorely puzzled how to buy more. The Doctor went through his trunk to see if there was anything he could sell. But the only thing he could find was an old watch with the hands broken and the back dented in; and we decided this would not bring us in enough money to buy much more than a pound of tea. Bumpo suggested that he sing comic songs in the streets which he had learned in Jolliginki. But the Doctor said he did not think that the islanders would care for African music.

The other thing that kept us was the bullfight. In these islands, which belonged to Spain, they had bullfights every Sunday. It was on a Friday that we arrived there; and after we had got rid of the able seaman we took a walk through the town.

It was a very funny little town, quite different from any that I had ever seen. The streets were all twisty and winding and so narrow that a wagon could only just pass along them. The houses overhung at the top and came so close together that people in the attics could lean out of the windows and shake hands with their neighbors on the opposite side of the street. The Doctor told us the town was very, very old. It was called Monteverde.

As we had no money of course we did not go to a hotel or anything like that. But on the second evening when we were passing by a bed-maker's shop we noticed several beds, which the man had made, standing on the pavement outside. The Doctor started chatting in Spanish to the bed-maker who was sitting at his door whistling to a parrot in a cage. The Doctor and the bed-maker got very friendly talking about birds and things. And as it grew near to suppertime the man asked us to stop and sup with him.

This of course we were very glad to do. And after the meal was over (very nice dishes they were, mostly cooked in olive-oil—I particularly liked the fried bananas) we sat outside on the pavement again and went on talking far into the night.

At last when we got up to go back to our ship, this very nice shopkeeper wouldn't hear of our going away on any account. He said the streets down by the harbor were very badly lighted and there was no moon. We would surely get lost. He invited us to spend the night with him and go back to our ship in the morning.

Well, we finally agreed; and as our good friend had no spare bedrooms, the three of us, the Doctor, Bumpo and I, slept on the beds set out for sale on the pavement before the shop. The night was so hot we needed no coverings. It was great fun to fall asleep out of doors like this, watching the people walking to and fro and the gay life of the streets. It seemed to me that Spanish people never went to bed at all. Late as it was, all the little restaurants and cafés around us were wide open, with customers drinking coffee and chatting merrily at the small tables outside. The sound of a guitar strumming softly in the distance mingled with the clatter of chinaware and the babble of voices.

Somehow it made me think of my mother and father far away in Puddleby, with their regular habits, the evening practice on the flute and the rest—doing the same thing every day. I felt sort of sorry for them in a way, because they missed the fun of this traveling life, where we were doing something new all the time—even sleeping differently. But I suppose if they had been invited to go to bed on a pavement in front of a shop they wouldn't have cared for the idea at all. It is funny how some people are.

7

THE DOCTOR'S WAGER

Next morning we were awakened by a great racket. There was a procession coming down the street, a number of men in very gay clothes followed by a large crowd of ladies and cheering children. I asked the Doctor who they were.

"They are the bullfighters," he said. "There is to be a bullfight tomorrow."

"What is a bullfight?" I asked.

To my great surprise the Doctor got red in the face with anger. It reminded me of the time when he had spoken of the lions and tigers in his private zoo.

"A bullfight is a stupid, cruel, disgusting business," said he. "These Spanish people are most lovable and hospitable folk. How they can

| **Word Bank** | **racket** (RAK it) *n.*: confused, loud noise |
| | **procession** (pro SESH un) *n.*: a group of individuals moving along in an orderly way |

enjoy these wretched bullfights is a thing I could never understand."

Then the Doctor went on to explain to me how a bull was first made very angry by teasing and then allowed to run into a circus where men came out with red cloaks, waved them at him, and ran away. Next the bull was allowed to tire himself out by tossing and killing a lot of poor, old, broken-down horses who couldn't defend themselves. Then when the bull was thoroughly out of breath and wearied by this, a man came out with a sword and killed the bull.

"Every Sunday," said the Doctor, "in almost every big town in Spain there are six bulls killed like that and as many horses."

"But aren't the men ever killed by the bull?" I asked.

"Unfortunately very seldom," said he. "A bull is not nearly as dangerous as he looks, even when he's angry, if you are only quick on your feet and don't lose your head. These bullfighters are very clever and nimble. And the people think no end of them. A famous bullfighter (or matador,[6] as they call them) is a more important man in Spain than a king—Here comes another crowd of them round the corner, look. See the people throwing kisses to them. Ridiculous business!"

At that moment our friend the bed-maker came out to see the procession go past. And while he was wishing us good morning and inquiring how we had slept, a friend of his walked up and joined us. The bed-maker introduced this friend to us as Don Enrique Cardenas.

Don Enrique, when he heard where we were from, spoke to us in English. He appeared to be a well-educated, gentlemanly sort of person.

"And you go to see the bullfight tomorrow, yes?" he asked the Doctor pleasantly.

"Certainly not," said John Dolittle firmly. "I don't like bullfights—cruel, cowardly shows."

Don Enrique nearly exploded. I never saw a man get so excited. He told the Doctor that he didn't know what he was talking about. He said bullfighting was a noble sport and that the matadors were the bravest men in the world.

"Oh, rubbish!" said the Doctor. "You never give the poor bull a chance. It is only when he is all tired and dazed that your precious matadors dare to try to kill him."

I thought the Spaniard was going to strike the Doctor he got so angry. While he was still spluttering to find words, the bed-maker came between them and took the Doctor aside. He explained to John Dolittle in a whisper that this Don Enrique Cardenas was a very important person; that it

---

6. A *matador* (MAT uh DOR) is a bullfighter.

| **Word Bank** | **hospitable** (hahs PIT uh bul) *adj.*: giving a generous and friendly welcome |
| | **cowardly** (COW urd lee) *adv.*: in a weak manner; not bravely |

was he who supplied the bulls—a special, strong black kind—from his own farm for all the bullfights in the Capa Blancas. He was a very rich man, the bed-maker said, a most important personage. He mustn't be allowed to take offense on any account.

I watched the Doctor's face as the bed-maker finished, and I saw a flash of boyish mischief come into his eyes as though an idea had struck him. He turned to the angry Spaniard.

"Don Enrique," he said, "you tell me your bullfighters are very brave men and skillful. It seems I have offended you by saying that bullfighting is a poor sport. What is the name of the best matador you have for tomorrow's show?"

"Pepito de Malaga," said Don Enrique, "one of the greatest names, one of the bravest men, in all Spain."

"Very well," said the Doctor, "I have a proposal to make to you. I have never fought a bull in my life. Now supposing I were to go into the ring tomorrow with Pepito de Malaga and any other matadors you choose; and if I can do more tricks with a bull than they can, would you promise to do something for me?"

Don Enrique threw back his head and laughed.

"Man," he said, "you must be mad! You would be killed at once. One has to be trained for years to become a proper bullfighter."

"Supposing I were willing to take the risk of that—You are not afraid, I take it, to accept my offer?"

The Spaniard frowned.

"Afraid!" he cried, "Sir, if you can beat Pepito de Malaga in the bull-ring I'll promise you anything it is possible for me to grant."

"Very good," said the Doctor, "now I understand that you are quite a powerful man in these islands. If you wished to stop all bullfighting here after tomorrow, you could do it, couldn't you?"

"Yes," said Don Enrique proudly—"I could."

"Well that is what I ask of you—if I win my wager," said John Dolittle. "If I can do more with angry bulls than can Pepito de Malaga, you are to promise me that there shall never be another bullfight in the Capa Blancas so long as you are alive to stop it. Is it a bargain?"

The Spaniard held out his hand.

"It is a bargain," he said—"I promise. But I must warn you that you are merely throwing your life away, for you will certainly be killed. However, that is no more than you deserve for saying that bullfighting is an unworthy sport. I will meet you here tomorrow morning if you should wish to arrange any particulars. Good day, Sir."

As the Spaniard turned and walked into the shop with the bed-maker, Polynesia, who had been listening as usual, flew up onto my shoulder and whispered in my ear, "I have a plan. Get hold of Bumpo and come someplace where the Doctor can't hear us. I want to talk to you."

I nudged Bumpo's elbow and we crossed the street and pretended to look into a jeweler's window; while the Doctor sat down upon his bed to lace up his boots, the only part of his clothing he had taken off for the night.

"Listen," said Polynesia, "I've been breaking my head trying to think up some way we can get money to buy those stores with; and at last I've got it."

"The money?" said Bumpo.

"No, silly. The idea—to make the money with. Listen: the Doctor is simply bound to win this game tomorrow, sure as you're alive. Now all we have to do is to make a side bet with these Spaniards—they're great on gambling—and the trick's done."

"What's a side bet?" I asked.

"Oh I know what that is," said Bumpo proudly. "We used to have lots of them at Oxford when boat-racing was on. I go to Don Enrique and say, 'I bet you a hundred pounds the Doctor wins.' Then if he does win, Don Enrique pays me a hundred pounds; if he doesn't, I have to pay Don Enrique."

"That's the idea," said Polynesia. "Only don't say a hundred pounds: say two-thousand five-hundred pesetas. Now come and find old Don Ricky-ticky and try to look rich."

So we crossed the street again and slipped into the bed-maker's shop while the Doctor was still busy with his boots.

"Don Enrique," said Bumpo, "allow me to introduce myself. I am the Crown Prince of Jolliginki. Would you care to have a small bet with me on tomorrow's bullfight?"

Don Enrique bowed.

"Why certainly," he said. "I shall be delighted. But I must warn you that you are bound to lose. How much?"

"Oh a mere truffle," said Bumpo—"just for the fun of the thing, you know. What do you say to three-thousand pesetas?"

"I agree," said the Spaniard bowing once more. "I will meet you after the bullfight tomorrow."

"So that's all right," said Polynesia as we came out to join the Doctor. "I feel as though quite a load has been taken off my mind."

8

THE GREAT BULLFIGHT

The next day was a great day in Monteverde. All the streets were hung with flags; and everywhere gaily dressed crowds were to be seen flocking towards the bullring, as the big circus was called where the fights took place.

The news of the Doctor's challenge had gone round the town and, it seemed, had caused much amusement to the islanders. The very idea of a mere foreigner daring to match himself against the great Pepito de Malaga!—Serve him right if he got killed!

The Doctor had borrowed a bullfighter's suit from Don Enrique; and very gay and wonderful he looked in it, though Bumpo and I had hard work getting the waistcoat to close in front and even then the buttons kept bursting off it in all directions.

When we set out from the harbor to walk to the bullring, crowds of small boys ran after us making fun of the Doctor's fatness, calling out, "*Juan Hagapoco, el grueso matador!*" which is the Spanish for, "John Dolittle, the fat bullfighter."

As soon as we arrived the Doctor said he would like to take a look at the bulls before the fight began; and we were at once led to the bull pen where, behind a high railing, six enormous black bulls were tramping around wildly.

In a few hurried words and signs the Doctor told the bulls what he was going to do and gave them careful instructions for their part of the show. The poor creatures were tremendously glad when they heard that there was a chance of bullfighting being stopped; and they promised to do exactly as they were told.

Of course the man who took us in there didn't understand what we were doing. He merely thought the fat Englishman was crazy when he saw the Doctor making signs and talking in ox tongue.

From there the Doctor went to the matadors' dressing-rooms while Bumpo and I with Polynesia made our way into the bullring and took our seats in the great open-air theater.

It was a very gay sight. Thousands of ladies and gentlemen were there, all dressed in their smartest clothes; and everybody seemed very happy and cheerful.

Right at the beginning Don Enrique got up and explained to the people that the first item on the program was to be a match between the English Doctor and Pepito de Malaga. He told them what he had promised if the Doctor should win. But the people did not seem to think there was much chance of that. A roar of laughter went up at the very mention of such a thing.

When Pepito came into the ring everybody cheered, the ladies clapped and the men waved their hats.

Presently a large door on the other side of the ring was rolled back and in galloped one of the bulls; then the door was closed again. At once the matador became very much on the alert. He waved his red cloak and the bull rushed at him. Pepito stepped nimbly aside and the people cheered again.

This game was repeated several times. But I noticed that whenever Pepito got into a tight place and seemed to be in real danger from the bull, an assistant of his, who always hung around somewhere near, drew the bull's attention upon himself by waving another red cloak. Then the bull would chase the assistant and Pepito was left in safety. Most often, as soon as he had drawn the bull off, this assistant ran for the high fence and vaulted out of the ring to save himself. They evidently had it all arranged, these matadors; and it didn't seem to me that they were in any very great danger from the poor clumsy bull so long as they didn't slip and fall.

After about ten minutes of this kind of thing the small door into the matadors' dressing-room opened and the Doctor strolled into the ring. As soon as his fat figure, dressed in sky-blue velvet, appeared, the crowd rocked in their seats with laughter.

Juan Hagapoco, as they had called him, walked out into the center of the ring and bowed to the bull. Then he bowed to Pepito. While he was bowing to Pepito's assistant the bull started to rush at him from behind.

"Look out! Look out!—The bull! You will be killed!" yelled the crowd.

But the Doctor calmly finished his bow. Then turning round he folded his arms, fixed the onrushing bull with his eye and frowned a terrible frown.

Presently a curious thing happened: the bull's speed got slower and slower. It almost looked as though he were afraid of that frown. Soon he stopped altogether. The Doctor shook his finger at him. He began to tremble. At last, tucking his tail between his legs, the bull turned round and ran away.

The crowd gasped. The Doctor ran after him round and round the ring they went, both of them puffing and blowing like grampuses. Excited whispers began to break out among the people. This was something new in bullfighting, to have the bull running away from the man, instead of the man away from the bull. At last in the tenth lap, with a final burst of speed, Juan Hagapoco, the English matador, caught the poor bull by the tail.

Then leading the now timid creature into the middle of the ring, the Doctor made him do all manner of tricks; standing on the hind legs, standing on the front legs, dancing, hopping, rolling over. He finished up by making the bull kneel down; then he got onto his back and did handsprings and other acrobatics on the beast's horns.

Pepito and his assistant had their noses sadly out of joint. The crowd had forgotten them entirely. They were standing together by the fence not far from where I sat, muttering to one another and slowly growing green with jealousy.

Finally the Doctor turned towards Don Enrique's seat and bowing said in a loud voice, "This bull is no good anymore. He's terrified and out of breath. Take him away, please."

"Does the caballero[7] wish for a fresh bull?" asked Don Enrique.

_____
7. A *caballero* (KAB uh LAIR oh) is a horseman.

"No," said the Doctor, "I want five fresh bulls. And I would like them all in the ring at once, please."

At this a cry of horror burst from the people. They had been used to seeing matadors escaping from one bull at a time. But *five*!—That must mean certain death.

Pepito sprang forward and called to Don Enrique not to allow it, saying it was against all the rules of bullfighting. ("Ha!" Polynesia chuckled into my ear. "It's like the Doctor's navigation: he breaks all the rules; but he gets there. If they'll only let him, he'll give them the best show for their money they ever saw.") A great argument began. Half the people seemed to be on Pepito's side and half on the Doctor's side. At last the Doctor turned to Pepito and made another very grand bow which burst the last button off his waistcoat.

"Well, of course if the caballero is afraid—" he began with a bland smile.

"Afraid!" screamed Pepito. "I am afraid of nothing on earth. I am the greatest matador in Spain. With this right hand I have killed nine hundred and fifty-seven bulls."

"All right then," said the Doctor, "let us see if you can kill five more. Let the bulls in!" he shouted. "Pepito de Malaga is not afraid."

A dreadful silence hung over the great theater as the heavy door into the bull pen was rolled back. Then with a roar the five big bulls bounded into the ring.

"Look fierce," I heard the Doctor call to them in cattle language. "Don't scatter. Keep close. Get ready for a rush. Take Pepito, the one in purple, first. But for Heaven's sake don't kill him. Just chase him out of the ring—Now then, all together, go for him!"

The bulls put down their heads and all in line, like a squadron of cavalry, charged across the ring straight for poor Pepito.

For one moment the Spaniard tried his hardest to look brave. But the sight of the five pairs of horns coming at him at full gallop was too much. He turned white to the lips, ran for the fence, vaulted it and disappeared.

"Now the other one," the Doctor hissed. And in two seconds the gallant assistant was nowhere to be seen. Juan Hagapoco, the fat matador, was left alone in the ring with five rampaging bulls.

The rest of the show was really well worth seeing. First, all five bulls went raging round the ring, butting at the fence with their horns, pawing up the sand, hunting for something to kill. Then each one in turn would pretend to catch sight of the Doctor for the first time and giving a bellow of rage, would lower his wicked-looking horns and shoot like an arrow across the ring as though he meant to toss him to the sky.

It was really frightfully exciting. And even I, who knew it was all arranged beforehand, held my breath in terror for the Doctor's life when I saw how near they came to sticking him. But just at the last moment, when the horns' points were two inches from the sky-blue waistcoat, the Doctor would spring nimbly to one side and the great brutes would go thundering harmlessly by, missing him by no more than a hair.

Then all five of them went for him together, completely surrounding him, slashing at him with their horns and bellowing with fury. How he escaped alive I don't know. For several minutes his round figure could hardly be seen at all in that scrimmage of tossing heads, stamping hoofs and waving tails. It was, as Polynesia had foretold, the greatest bullfight ever seen.

One woman in the crowd got quite hysterical and screamed up to Don Enrique, "Stop the fight! Stop the fight! He is too brave a man to be killed. This is the most wonderful matador in the world. Let him live! Stop the fight!"

But presently the Doctor was seen to break loose from the mob of animals that surrounded him. Then catching each of them by the horns, one after another, he would give their heads a sudden twist and throw them down flat on the sand. The great fellows acted their parts extremely well. I have never seen trained animals in a circus do better. They lay there panting on the ground where the Doctor threw them as if they were exhausted and completely beaten.

Then with a final bow John Dolittle took a cigar from his pocket, lit it and strolled out of the ring.

9

WE DEPART IN A HURRY

As soon as the door closed behind the Doctor the most tremendous noise I have ever heard broke loose. Some of the men appeared to be angry (friends of Pepito's, I suppose); but most called and called to have the Doctor come back into the ring.

When at length he did so they seemed to go entirely mad over him. You never saw anything like it—a perfect shower of jewelry and roses.

But the Doctor just smiled up at them, bowed once more and backed out.

"Now, Bumpo," said Polynesia, "this is where you go down and gather up all those trinkets and we'll sell 'em. That's what the big matadors do; leave the jewelry on the ground and their assistants collect it for them. We might as well lay in a good supply of money while we've got the chance—you never know when you may need it when you're traveling with the Doctor. Never mind the roses—you can leave them—but don't leave any rings. And when you've finished go and get your three-thousand pesetas out of Don Ricky-ticky. Tommy and I will meet you outside and we'll pawn the gew-gaws at that shop opposite the bed-maker's. Run along—and not a word to the Doctor, remember."

Outside the bullring we found the crowd still in a great state of excitement. Violent arguments were going on everywhere. Bumpo joined us with his pockets bulging in all directions; and we made our way slowly through the dense crowd to that side of the building where the matadors' dressing-room was. The Doctor was waiting at the door for us.

"Good work, Doctor!" said Polynesia, flying onto his shoulder—
"Great work!—But listen: I smell danger. I think you had better get back
to the ship now as quick and as quietly as you can. Put your overcoat on
over that giddy suit. I don't like the looks of this crowd. More than half
of them are furious because you've won. Don Ricky-ticky must now stop
the bullfighting—and you know how they love it. What I'm afraid of is
that some of these matadors who are just mad with jealousy may start
some dirty work. I think this would be a good time for us to get away."

"I dare say you're right, Polynesia," said the Doctor—"You usually
are. The crowd does seem to be a bit restless. I'll slip down to the ship
alone—so I shan't be so noticeable; and I'll wait for you there. You come
by some different way. But don't be long about it. Hurry!"

As soon as the Doctor had departed Bumpo sought out Don Enrique
and said, "Honorable Sir, you owe me three-thousand pesetas."

Without a word, but looking cross-eyed with annoyance, Don
Enrique paid his bet.

We next set out to buy the provisions; and on the way we hired a cab
and took it along with us.

Not very far away we found a big grocer's shop which seemed to sell
everything to eat. We went in and bought up the finest lot of food you
ever saw in your life.

As a matter of fact, Polynesia had been right about the danger we
were in. The news of our victory must have spread like lightning through
the whole town. For as we came out of the shop and loaded the cab up
with our stores, we saw various little knots of angry men hunting round
the streets, waving sticks and shouting, "The Englishmen! Where are
those accursed Englishmen who stopped the bullfighting?—Hang them
to a lamppost!—Throw them in the sea! The Englishmen!—We want the
Englishmen!"

After that we didn't waste any time, you may be sure. Bumpo
grabbed the Spanish cabdriver and explained to him in signs that if he
didn't drive down to the harbor as fast as he knew how and keep his
mouth shut the whole way, he would choke the life out of him. Then we
jumped into the cab on top of the food, slammed the door, pulled down
the blinds and away we went.

"We won't get a chance to pawn the jewelry now," said Polynesia, as
we bumped over the cobbly streets. "But never mind—it may come in
handy later on. And anyway we've got two-thousand five-hundred pesetas left out of the bet. Don't give the cabby more than two pesetas fifty,
Bumpo. That's the right fare, I know."

Well, we reached the harbor all right and we were mighty glad to find
that the Doctor had sent Chee-Chee back with the rowboat to wait for us
at the landing-wall.

Unfortunately while we were in the middle of loading the supplies
from the cab into the boat, the angry mob arrived upon the wharf and
made a rush for us. Bumpo snatched up a big beam of wood that lay near

and swung it round and round his head, letting out dreadful African battle-yells the while. This kept the crowd off while Chee-Chee and I hustled the last of the stores into the boat and clambered in ourselves. Bumpo threw his beam of wood into the thick of the Spaniards and leapt in after us. Then we pushed off and rowed like mad for the *Curlew*.

The mob upon the wall howled with rage, shook their fists and hurled stones and all manner of things after us. Poor old Bumpo got hit on the head with a bottle. But as he had a very strong head it only raised a small bump while the bottle smashed into a thousand pieces.

When we reached the ship's side the Doctor had the anchor drawn up and the sails set and everything in readiness to get away. Looking back we saw boats coming out from the harbor-wall after us, filled with angry, shouting men. So we didn't bother to unload our rowboat but just tied it onto the ship's stern with a rope and jumped aboard.

It only took a moment more to swing the *Curlew* round in the wind; and soon we were speeding out of the harbor on our way to Brazil.

"Ha!" sighed Polynesia, as we all flopped down on the deck to take a rest and get our breath. "That wasn't a bad adventure—quite reminds me of my old seafaring days when I sailed with the smugglers—Golly, that was the life!—Never mind your head, Bumpo. It will be all right when the Doctor puts a little arnica[8] on it. Think what we got out of the scrape: a boatload of ship's stores, pockets full of jewelry and thousands of pesetas. Not bad, you know—not bad."

---

8. *Arnica* (AHR nih kuh) is dried flower heads used as a treatment for sprains or bruises.

Recalling

1. What were the two reasons that Dr. Dolittle stayed in Capa Blanca for three days?

2. Why did Dr. Dolittle, Tommy, and Bumpo sleep on beds outside the bed-maker's shop?

3. What was the bargain that Dr. Dolittle struck with Don Enrique Cardenas?

Interpreting

4. Why did Dr. Dolittle hate the sport of bullfighting?

5. How did Polynesia plan to earn money from the bullfight?

6. Why wasn't Pepito de Malaga injured in the bullring?

Concluding

7. What happened when Dr. Dolittle first went into the ring? Why did this happen?

8. How did the five bulls treat Dr. Dolittle in the ring? Why did they act this way?

9. Why were the townspeople angry at Dr. Dolittle? Do you think their anger was justified?

Examining the Novel

Dr. Dolittle effectively banned bullfighting from Monteverde.

1. What methods did he use to achieve his aim? Would he have been more effective using other methods of convincing the people that bullfighting was wrong?

2. Do you think the methods that Dr. Dolittle used were consistent with his philosophy and personality? Explain.

Thinking About the Novel

These chapters illustrate interesting aspects of Polynesia's character. Make a list of commands that Polynesia gave to Bumpo and Tommy. Then make a list of five words that might be used to describe Polynesia's character traits.

Creating and Writing

One of the reasons that Dr. Dolittle might have objected to bullfighting is that the bulls are kept caged just for the benefit of the spectators who watch the sport. The bulls are not allowed to roam freely. Dogs, cats, and assorted animals are also kept in people's homes and not allowed to roam freely. Write a paragraph stating your views about keeping animals as pets. It might help if you focus on answering these questions: Is it fair to the animals? Should only certain animals be allowed as pets? Should people be required to take classes and obtain a license of some sort before they can become pet owners?

Into • *The Voyages of Dr. Dolittle*
Part Four—Chapters 1-5

Remember that when *The Voyages of Dr. Dolittle* was written, modern visual media did not exist. The reader had to imagine how each setting looked, based on the description in the book. The better the writer, the clearer a picture the reader had. As you read this section, you will probably be so caught up in the action, that you won't give a moment's thought to the style in which it is written. When you are done, though, you will discover that you have such a strong picture in your mind of the storm, that you will feel almost as though you had watched the scene rather than read it. This does not happen by itself; it takes a very skillful author to make you see the action. See if you can identify some of the techniques the author uses to bring the story to life. Do you think you could use these techniques in your own writing?

Focus

One way in which the author gives life to his settings and action is through the use of similes. Similes compare two things using the word "like" or "as." A few examples are "sparkling like a jeweled palace in a fairy-story"(p. 557); "with their mouths open like half-witted flounders" (p. 561); "shreds of clouds swept like tattered witches" (p. 567); "I remember seeing the sails...go overboard like a penny balloon" (p. 568).

Notice also how clear a picture the author draws with adjectives: "quiet peaceful days" (p. 557); "a nasty persevering brute" (p. 560); "the blazing noonday sun," just to list a few. How many more examples of the good use of adjectives can you find in this section?

PART IV

1

SHELLFISH LANGUAGE AGAIN

Miranda, the Purple Bird-of-Paradise, had warned us rightly when she had foretold a good spell of weather. For three weeks the good ship *Curlew* plowed her way through smiling seas before a steady powerful wind.

I suppose most real sailors would have found this part of the voyage dull. But not I. As we got further South and further West the face of the sea seemed different every day. And all the little things of a voyage which an old hand would have hardly bothered to notice were matters of great interest for my eager eyes.

We did not pass many ships. When we did see one, the Doctor would get out his telescope and we would all take a look at it. Sometimes he would signal to it, asking for news, by hauling up little colored flags upon the mast; and the ship would signal back to us in the same way. The meaning of all the signals was printed in a book which the Doctor kept in the cabin. He told me it was the language of the sea and that all ships could understand it whether they be English, Dutch, or French.

Our greatest happening during those first weeks was passing an iceberg.[1] When the sun shone on it it burst into a hundred colors, sparkling like a jeweled palace in a fairy-story. Through the telescope we saw a mother polar bear with a cub sitting on it, watching us. The Doctor recognized her as one of the bears who had spoken to him when he was discovering the North Pole. So he sailed the ship up close and offered to take her and her baby onto the *Curlew* if she wished it. But she only shook her head, thanking him; she said it would be far too hot for the cub on the deck of our ship, with no ice to keep his feet cool. It had been indeed a very hot day; but the nearness of that great mountain of ice made us all turn up our coat-collars and shiver with the cold.

During those quiet peaceful days I improved my reading and writing a great deal with the Doctor's help. I got on so well that he let me keep the ship's log. This is a big book kept on every ship, a kind of diary, in which the number of miles run, the direction of your course and everything else that happens is written down.

The Doctor too, in what spare time he had, was nearly always writing— in his notebooks. I used to peep into these sometimes, now that I could read, but I found it hard work to make out the Doctor's handwriting. Many of these notebooks seemed to be about sea things. There were six

---

1. An *iceberg* is a large, floating mass of ice detached from a glacier.

thick ones filled full with notes and sketches of different seaweeds; and there were others on seabirds; others on sea worms; others on seashells. They were all someday to be rewritten, printed and bound like regular books.

One afternoon we saw, floating around us, great quantities of stuff that looked like dead grass. The Doctor told me this was gulfweed. A little further on it became so thick that it covered all the water as far as the eye could reach; it made the *Curlew* look as though she were moving across a meadow instead of sailing the Atlantic.

Crawling about upon this weed, many crabs were to be seen. And the sight of them reminded the Doctor of his dream of learning the language of the shellfish. He fished several of these crabs up with a net and put them in his listening-tank to see if he could understand them. Among the crabs he also caught a strange-looking, chubby, little fish which he told me was called a Silver Fidgit.

After he had listened to the crabs for a while with no success, he put the fidget into the tank and began to listen to that. I had to leave him at this moment to go and attend to some duties on the deck. But presently I heard him below shouting for me to come down again.

"Stubbins," he cried as soon as he saw me—"a most extraordinary thing—Quite unbelievable—I'm not sure whether I'm dreaming—Can't believe my own senses. I—I—I—"

"Why, Doctor," I said, "what is it?—What's the matter?"

"The fidgit," he whispered, pointing with a trembling finger to the listening-tank in which the little round fish was still swimming quietly, "he talks English! And—and—and *he whistles tunes*—English tunes!"

"Talks English!" I cried—"Whistles!—Why, it's impossible."

"It's a fact," said the Doctor, white in the face with excitement. "It's only a few words, scattered, with no particular sense to them—all mixed up with his own language which I can't make out yet. But they're English words, unless there's something very wrong with my hearing— And the tune he whistles, it's as plain as anything—always the same tune. Now you listen and tell me what you make of it. Tell me everything you hear. Don't miss a word."

I went to the glass tank upon the table while the Doctor grabbed a notebook and a pencil. Undoing my collar I stood upon the empty packing-case he had been using for a stand and put my right ear down under the water.

For some moments I detected nothing at all—except, with my dry ear, the heavy breathing of the Doctor as he waited, all stiff and anxious, for me to say something. At last from within the water sounding like a child singing miles and miles away, I heard an unbelievably thin, small voice.

"Ah!" I said.

Word Bank	**detected** (dee TEK tid) *v.*: discovered or determined the existence or presence of

"What is it?" asked the Doctor in a hoarse, trembly whisper. "What does he say?"

"I can't quite make it out," I said. "It's mostly in some strange fish language—Oh, but wait a minute!—Yes, now I get it—'No smoking'…'My, here's a queer one!' 'Popcorn and picture postcards here'…'This way out'…'Don't spit'—What funny things to say, Doctor!—Oh, but wait!—Now he's whistling the tune."

"What tune is it?" gasped the Doctor.

"John Peel."

"Ah hah," cried the Doctor, "that's what I made it out to be." And he wrote furiously in his notebook.

I went on listening.

"This is most extraordinary," the Doctor kept muttering to himself as his pencil went wiggling over the page—"Most extraordinary—but frightfully thrilling. I wonder where he—"

"Here's some more," I cried—"some more English…'*The big tank needs cleaning*'…That's all. Now he's talking fish-talk again."

"The big tank!" the Doctor murmured frowning in a puzzled kind of way. "I wonder where on earth he learned—"

Then he bounded up out of his chair.

"I have it," he yelled, "this fish has escaped from an aquarium. Why, of course! Look at the kind of things he has learned; 'Picture postcards'—They always sell them in aquariums; 'Don't spit'; 'No smoking'; 'This way out'—the things the attendants say. And then, 'My, here's a queer one!' That's the kind of thing that people exclaim when they look into the tanks. It all fits. There's no doubt about it, Stubbins: we have here a fish who has escaped from captivity. And it's quite possible—not certain, by any means, but quite possible—that I may now, through him, be able to establish communication with the shellfish. This is a great piece of luck."

2

THE FIDGET'S STORY

Well, now that he was started once more upon his old hobby of the shellfish languages, there was no stopping the Doctor. He worked right through the night.

A little after midnight I fell asleep in a chair; about two in the morning Bumpo fell asleep at the wheel; and for five hours the *Curlew* was allowed to drift where she liked. But still John Dolittle worked on, trying his hardest to understand the fidgit's language, struggling to make the fidgit understand him.

Word Bank   **captivity** (kap TIV ih tee) *n.*: confinement; imprisonment; the state of being held captive

When I woke up it was broad daylight again. The Doctor was still standing at the listening-tank, looking as tired as an owl and dreadfully wet. But on his face there was a proud and happy smile.

"Stubbins," he said as soon as he saw me stir, "I've done it. I've got the key to the fidgit's language. It's a frightfully difficult language—quite different from anything I ever heard. The only thing it reminds me of—slightly—is ancient Greek. It isn't shellfish; but it's a big step towards it. Now, the next thing, I want you to take a pencil and a fresh notebook and write down everything I say. The fidgit has promised to tell me the story of his life. I will translate it into English and you put it down in the book. Are you ready?"

Once more the Doctor lowered his ear beneath the level of the water; and as he began to speak, I started to write. And this is the story that the fidgit told us.

Thirteen Months in an Aquarium

"I was born in the Pacific Ocean, close to the coast of Chile. I was one of a family of two-thousand five-hundred and ten. Soon after our mother and father left us, we youngsters got scattered. The family was broken up—by a herd of whales who chased us. I and my sister, Clippa (she was my favorite sister), had a very narrow escape for our lives. As a rule, whales are not very hard to get away from if you are good at dodging—if you've only got a quick swerve. But this one that came after Clippa and myself was a very mean whale. Every time he lost us under a stone or something he'd come back and hunt and hunt till he routed us out into the open again. I never saw such a nasty, persevering brute.

"Well, we shook him at last—though not before he had worried us for hundreds of miles northward, up the west coast of South America. But luck was against us that day. While we were resting and trying to get our breath, another family of fidgits came rushing by, shouting, 'Come on! Swim for your lives! The dogfish are coming!'

"Now dogfish are particularly fond of fidgits. We are, you might say, their favorite food—and for that reason we always keep away from deep, muddy waters. What's more, dogfish are not easy to escape from; they are terribly fast and clever hunters. So up we had to jump and on again.

"After we had gone a few more hundred miles we looked back and saw that the dogfish were gaining on us. So we turned into a harbor. It happened to be one on the west coast of the United States. Here we guessed, and hoped, the dogfish would not be likely to follow us. As it happened, they didn't even see us turn in, but dashed on northward and we never saw them again. I hope they froze to death in the Arctic Seas.

"But, as I said, luck was against us that day. While I and my sister were cruising gently round the ships anchored in the harbor looking for orange-peels, a great delicacy with us—Swoop! Bang!—we were caught in a net.

"We struggled for all we were worth; but it was no use. The net was small-meshed and strongly made. Kicking and flipping we were hauled up the side of the ship and dumped down on the deck, high and dry in the blazing noonday sun.

"Here a couple of old men in whiskers and spectacles leaned over us, making strange sounds. Some codling had got caught in the net the same time as we were. These the old men threw back into the sea; but us they seemed to think very precious. They put us carefully into a large jar and after they had taken us on shore they went to a big house and changed us from the jar into glass boxes full of water. This house was on the edge of the harbor; and a small stream of seawater was made to flow through the glass tank so we could breathe properly. Of course we had never lived inside glass walls before; and at first we kept on trying to swim through them and got our noses awfully sore bumping the glass at full speed.

"Then followed weeks and weeks of weary idleness. They treated us well, so far as they knew how. The old fellows in spectacles came and looked at us proudly twice a day and saw that we had the proper food to eat, the right amount of light and that the water was not too hot or too cold. But oh, the dullness of that life! It seemed we were a kind of a show. At a certain hour every morning the big doors of the house were thrown open and everybody in the city who had nothing special to do came in and looked at us. There were other tanks filled with different kinds of fishes all round the walls of the big room. And the crowds would go from tank to tank, looking in at us through the glass—with their mouths open, like half-witted flounders. We got so sick of it that we used to open our mouths back at them; and this they seemed to think highly comical.

"One day my sister said to me, 'Think you, Brother, that these strange creatures who have captured us can talk?'

" 'Surely,' said I, 'have you not noticed that some talk with the lips only, some with the whole face, and yet others discourse with the hands? When they come quite close to the glass you can hear them. Listen!'

"At that moment a female, larger than the rest, pressed her nose up against the glass, pointed at me and said to her young behind her, 'Oh, look, here's a queer one!'

"And then we noticed that they nearly always said this when they looked in. And for a long time we thought that such was the whole extent of the language, this being a people of but few ideas. To help pass away the weary hours we learned it by heart, 'Oh, look, here's a queer one!' But we never got to know what it meant. Other phrases, however, we did get the meaning of; and we even learned to read a little in man-talk. Many big signs there were, set up upon the walls; and when we saw that the keepers stopped the people from spitting and smoking, pointed to these signs angrily and read them out loud, we knew then that these writings signified, *No Smoking* and *Don't Spit*.

"Then in the evenings, after the crowd had gone, the same aged male with one leg of wood, swept up the peanut-shells with a broom every

---

Word Bank   discourse (DISS korce) *v*.: converse; talk

night. And while he was so doing he always whistled the same tune to himself. This melody we rather liked; and we learned that too by heart—thinking it was part of the language.

"Thus a whole year went by in this dismal place. Some days new fishes were brought into the other tanks; and other days old fishes were taken out. At first we had hoped we would only be kept there for a while, and that after we had been looked at sufficiently we would be returned to freedom and the sea. But as month after month went by, and we were left undisturbed, our hearts grew heavy within our prison-walls of glass and we spoke to one another less and less.

"One day, when the crowd was thickest in the big room, a woman with a red face fainted from the heat. I watched through the glass and saw that the rest of the people got highly excited—though to me it did not seem to be a matter of very great importance. They threw cold water on her and carried her out into the open air.

"This made me think mightily; and presently a great idea burst upon me.

" 'Sister,' I said, turning to poor Clippa who was sulking at the bottom of our prison trying to hide behind a stone from the stupid gaze of the children who thronged about our tank, 'supposing that we pretended we were sick: do you think they would take us also from this stuffy house?'

" 'Brother,' said she wearily, 'that they might do. But most likely they would throw us on a rubbish-heap, where we would die in the hot sun.'

" 'But,' said I, 'why should they go abroad to seek a rubbish-heap, when the harbor is so close? While we were being brought here I saw men throwing their rubbish into the water. If they would only throw us also there, we could quickly reach the sea.'

" 'The Sea!' murmured poor Clippa with a faraway look in her eyes (she had fine eyes, had my sister, Clippa). 'How like a dream it sounds—the Sea! Oh brother, will we ever swim in it again, think you? Every night as I lie awake on the floor of this evil-smelling dungeon I hear its hearty voice ringing in my ears. How I have longed for it! Just to feel it once again, the nice, big, wholesome homeliness of it all! To jump, just to jump from the crest of an Atlantic wave, laughing in the trade wind's spin drift, down into the blue-green swirling trough! To chase the shrimps on a summer evening, when the sky is red and the light's all pink within the foam! To lie on the top, in the doldrums' noonday calm, and warm your tummy in the tropic sun! To wander hand in hand once more through the giant seaweed forests of the Indian Ocean, seeking the delicious eggs of the pop-pop! To play hide-and-seek among the castles of the coral towns with their pearl and jasper windows spangling the floor of the Spanish Main! To picnic in the anemone-meadows, dim blue and lilac-gray, that lie in the lowlands beyond the South Sea Garden! To throw somersaults on the springy sponge-beds of the Mexican Gulf! To

| **Word Bank** | **dismal** (DIZ mul) *adj.*: gloomy or depressing; particularly bad |
| | **sulking** (SUL king) *v.*: being moodily silent |

poke about among the dead ships and see what wonders and adventures lie inside!—And then, on winter nights when the Northeaster whips the water into froth, to swoop down and down to get away from the cold, down to where the water's warm and dark, down and still down, till we spy the twinkle of the fire-eels far below where our friends and cousins sit chatting round the Council Grotto—chatting, Brother, over the news and gossip of *the Sea*!…Oh—'

And then she broke down completely, sniffling.

" 'Stop it!' I said. 'You make me homesick. Look here; let's pretend we're sick—or better still, let's pretend we're dead; and see what happens. If they throw us on a rubbish-heap and we fry in the sun, we'll not be much worse off than we are here in this smelly prison. What do you say? Will you risk it?'

" 'I will,' she said—'and gladly.'

"So next morning two fidgits were found by the keeper floating on the top of the water in their tank, stiff and dead. We gave a mighty good imitation of dead fish—although I say it myself. The keeper ran and got the old gentleman with spectacles and whiskers. They threw up their hands in horror when they saw us. Lifting us carefully out of the water they laid us on wet cloths. That was the hardest part of all. If you're a fish and get taken out of the water you have to keep opening and shutting your mouth to breathe at all—and even that you can't keep up for long. And all this time we had to stay stiff as sticks and breathe silently through half-closed lips.

"Well, the old fellows poked us and felt us and pinched us till I thought they'd never be done. Then, when their backs were turned a moment, a wretched cat got up on the table and nearly ate us. Luckily the old men turned round in time and shooed her away. You may be sure though that we took a couple of good gulps of air while they weren't looking; and that was the only thing that saved us from choking. I wanted to whisper to Clippa to be brave and stick it out. But I couldn't even do that; because, as you know, most kinds of fish-talk cannot be heard—not even a shout—unless you're under water.

"Then, just as we were about to give it up and let on that we were alive, one of the old men shook his head sadly, lifted us up and carried us out of the building.

" 'Now for it!' I thought to myself. 'We'll soon know our fate: liberty or the garbage-can.'

"Outside, to our unspeakable horror, he made straight for a large ash-barrel which stood against the wall on the other side of a yard. Most happily for us, however, while he was crossing this yard a very dirty man with a wagon and horses drove up and took the ash-barrel away. I suppose it was his property.

Word Bank wretched (RECH id) *adj.*: appearing mean or miserable; suffering

"Then the old man looked around for some other place to throw us. He seemed about to cast us upon the ground. But he evidently thought that this would make the yard untidy and he desisted. The suspense was terrible. He moved outside the yard-gate and my heart sank once more as I saw that he now intended to throw us in the gutter of the roadway. But (fortune was indeed with us that day), a large man in blue clothes and silver buttons stopped him in the nick of time. Evidently, from the way the large man lectured and waved a short thick stick, it was against the rules of the town to throw dead fish in the streets.

"At last, to our unutterable joy, the old man turned and moved off with us towards the harbor. He walked so slowly, muttering to himself all the way and watching the man in blue out of the corner of his eye, that I wanted to bite his finger to make him hurry up. Both Clippa and I were actually at our last gasp.

"Finally he reached the seawall and giving us one last sad look he dropped us into the waters of the harbor.

"Never had we realized anything like the thrill of that moment, as we felt the salt wetness close over our heads. With one flick of our tails we came to life again. The old man was so surprised that he fell right into the water, almost on top of us. From this he was rescued by a sailor with a boat-hook; and the last we saw of him, the man in blue was dragging him away by the coat-collar, lecturing him again. Apparently it was also against the rules of the town to throw dead fish into the harbor.

"But we?—What time or thought had we for his troubles? *We were free*! In lightning leaps, in curving spurts, in crazy zigzags—whooping, shrieking with delight, we sped for home and the open sea!

"That is all of my story and I will now, as I promised last night, try to answer any questions you may ask about the sea, on condition that I am set at liberty as soon as you have done."

The Doctor: "Is there any part of the sea deeper than that known as Nero Deep—I mean the one near the Island of Guam?"

The Fidgit: "Why, certainly. There's one much deeper than that near the mouth of the Amazon River. But it's small and hard to find. We call it 'The Deep Hole.' And there's another in the Antarctic Sea."

The Doctor: "Can you talk any shellfish language yourself?"

The Fidgit: "No, not a word. We regular fishes don't have anything to do with the shellfish. We consider them a low class."

The Doctor: "But when you're near them, can you hear the sound they make talking—I mean without necessarily understanding what they say?"

The Fidgit: "Only with the very largest ones. Shellfish have such weak small voices it is almost impossible for any but their own kind to hear them. But with the bigger ones it is different. They make a sad, booming noise, rather like an iron pipe being knocked with a stone—only not nearly so loud of course."

The Doctor: "I am most anxious to get down to the bottom of the sea—to study many things. But we land animals, as you no doubt know, are unable to breathe under water. Have you any ideas that might help me?"

The Fidgit: "I think that for both your difficulties the best thing for you to do would be to try and get hold of the Great Glass Sea Snail."

The Doctor: "Er—who, or what, is the Great Glass Sea Snail?"

The Fidgit: "He is an enormous saltwater snail, one of winkly family, but as large as a big house. He talks quite loudly—when he speaks, but this is not often. He can go to any part of the ocean, at all depths because he doesn't have to be afraid of any creature in the sea. His shell is made of transparent mother-o'-pearl so that you can see through it; but it's thick and strong. When he is out of his shell, and he carries it empty on his back, there is room in it for a wagon and a pair of horses. He has been seen carrying his food in it when traveling."

The Doctor: "I feel that that is just the creature I have been looking for. He could take me and my assistant inside his shell and we could explore the deepest depths in safety. Do you think you could get him for me?"

The Fidgit: "Alas! No. I would willingly if I could; but he is hardly ever seen by ordinary fish. He lives at the bottom of the Deep Hole, and seldom comes out—And into the Deep Hole, the lower waters of which are muddy, fishes such as we are afraid to go."

The Doctor: "Dear me! That's a terrible disappointment. Are there many of this kind of snail in the sea?"

The Fidgit: "Oh no. He is the only one in existence, since his second wife died long, long ago. He is the last of the Giant Shellfish. He belongs to past ages. They say he is very old."

The Doctor: "Good Gracious, what wonderful things he could tell me! I do wish I could meet him."

The Fidgit: "Were there any more questions you wished to ask me? This water in your tank is getting quite warm and sickly. I'd like to be put back into the sea as soon as you can spare me."

The Doctor: "Just one more thing; when Christopher Columbus crossed the Atlantic in 1492, he threw overboard two copies of his diary sealed in barrels. One of them was never found. It must have sunk. I would like to get it for my library. Do you happen to know where it is?"

The Fidgit: "Yes, I do. That too is in the Deep Hole. When the barrel sank the currents drifted it northwards down what we call the Orinoco Slope, till it finally disappeared into the Deep Hole. If it was any other part of the sea I'd try and get it for you; but not there."

The Doctor: "Well, that is all, I think. I hate to put you back into the sea, because I know that as soon as I do, I'll think of a hundred other questions I wanted to ask you. But I must keep my promise. Would you care for anything before you go?—it seems a cold day—some cracker-crumbs or something?"

The Fidgit: "No, I won't stop. All I want just at present is fresh seawater."

The Doctor: "I cannot thank you enough for all the information you have given me. You have been very helpful and patient."

The Fidgit: "Pray do not mention it. It has been a real pleasure to be of assistance to the great John Dolittle. You are, as of course you know, already quite famous among the better class of fishes. Good-bye!— and good luck to you, to your ship and to all your plans!"

The Doctor carried the listening-tank to a porthole, opened it and emptied the tank into the sea.

"Good-bye!" he murmured as a faint splash reached us from without.

I dropped my pencil on the table and leaned back with a sigh. My fingers were so stiff with writers' cramp that I felt as though I should never be able to open my hand again. But I, at least, had had a night's sleep. As for the poor Doctor, he was so weary that he had hardly put the tank back upon the table and dropped into a chair, when his eyes closed and he began to snore.

In the passage outside Polynesia scratched angrily at the door. I rose and let her in.

"A nice state of affairs!" she stormed. "What sort of a ship is this? There's that black man upstairs asleep under the wheel; the Doctor asleep down here; and you making pothooks in a copybook with a pencil! Expect the ship to steer herself to Brazil? We're just drifting around the sea like an empty bottle—and a week behind time as it is. What's happened to you all?"

She was so angry that her voice rose to a scream. But it would have taken more than that to wake the Doctor.

I put the notebook carefully in a drawer and went on deck to take the wheel.

3

BAD WEATHER

As soon as I had the *Curlew* swung round upon her course again I noticed something peculiar: we were not going as fast as we had been. Our favorable wind had almost entirely disappeared.

This, at first, we did not worry about, thinking that at any moment it might spring up again. But the whole day went by; then two days; then a week,—ten days, and the wind grew no stronger. The *Curlew* just dawdled along at the speed of a toddling babe.

I now saw that the Doctor was becoming uneasy. He kept getting out his sextant (an instrument which tells you what part of the ocean you are in) and making calculations. He was forever looking at his maps and measuring distances on them. The far edge of the sea, all around us, he examined with his telescope a hundred times a day.

"But Doctor," I said when I found him one afternoon mumbling to himself about the misty appearance of the sky, "it wouldn't matter so much, would it, if we did take a little longer over the trip? We've got plenty to eat on board now; and the Purple Bird-of-Paradise will know that we have been delayed by something that we couldn't help."

"Yes, I suppose so," he said thoughtfully. "But I hate to keep her waiting. At this season of the year she generally goes to the Peruvian mountains—for her health. And besides, the good weather she prophesied is likely to end any day now and delay us still further. If we could only keep moving at even a fair speed, I wouldn't mind. It's this hanging around, almost dead still, that gets me restless—Ah, here comes a wind—Not very strong—but maybe it'll grow."

A gentle breeze from the Northeast came singing through the ropes; and we smiled up hopefully at the *Curlew*'s leaning masts.

"We've only got another hundred and fifty miles to make, to sight the coast of Brazil," said the Doctor. "If that wind would just stay with us, steady, for a full day we'd see land."

But suddenly the wind changed, swung to the East, then back to the Northeast—then to the North. It came in fitful gusts, as though it hadn't made up its mind which way to blow; and I was kept busy at the wheel, swinging the *Curlew* this way and that to keep the right side of it.

Presently we heard Polynesia, who was in the rigging keeping a lookout for land or passing ships, screech down to us.

"Bad weather coming. That jumpy wind is an ugly sign. And look!—over there in the East—see that black line, low down? If that isn't a storm I'm a landlubber. The gales round here are fierce, when they do blow—tear your canvas out like paper. You take the wheel, Doctor: it'll need a strong arm if it's a real storm. I'll go wake Bumpo and Chee-Chee. This looks bad to me. We'd best get all the sail down right away, till we see how strong she's going to blow."

Indeed the whole sky was now beginning to take on a very threatening look. The black line to the eastward grew blacker as it came nearer and nearer. A low, rumbly, whispering noise went moaning over the sea. The water which had been so blue and smiling turned to a ruffled ugly gray. And across the darkening sky, shreds of cloud swept like tattered witches flying from the storm.

I must confess I was frightened. You see I had only so far seen the sea in friendly moods: sometimes quiet and lazy; sometimes laughing, venturesome and reckless; sometimes brooding and poetic, when moonbeams turned her ripples into silver threads and dreaming snowy night-clouds piled up fairy-castles in the sky. But as yet I had not known, or even guessed at, the terrible strength of the Sea's wild anger.

When that storm finally struck us we leaned right over flatly on our side, as though some invisible giant had slapped the poor *Curlew* on the cheek.

After that things happened so thick and so fast that what with the wind that stopped your breath, the driving, blinding water, the deafening noise and the rest, I haven't a very clear idea of how our shipwreck came about.

I remember seeing the sails, which we were now trying to roll up upon the deck, torn out of our hands by the wind and go overboard like a penny balloon—very nearly carrying Chee-Chee with them. And I have a dim recollection of Polynesia screeching somewhere for one of us to go downstairs and close the portholes.

In spite of our masts being bare of sail we were now scudding along to the southward at a great pace. But every once in a while huge gray-black waves would arise from under the ship's side like nightmare monsters, swell and climb, then crash down upon us, pressing us into the sea; and the poor *Curlew* would come to a standstill, half under water, like a gasping, drowning pig.

While I was clambering along towards the wheel to see the Doctor, clinging like a leech with hands and legs to the rails lest I be blown overboard, one of these tremendous waves tore loose my hold, filled my throat with water and swept me like a cork the full length of the deck. My head struck door with an awful bang. And then I fainted.

4

WRECKED!

When I awoke I was very hazy in my head. The sky was blue and the sea was calm. At first I thought that I must have fallen asleep in the sun on the deck of the *Curlew*. And thinking that I would be late for my turn at the wheel, I tried to rise to my feet. I found I couldn't; my arms were tied to something behind me with a piece of rope. By twisting my neck around I found this to be a mast, broken off short. Then I realized that I wasn't sitting on a ship at all; I was only sitting on a piece of one. I began to feel uncomfortably scared. Screwing up my eyes, I searched the rim of the sea North, East, South and West: no land; no ships; nothing was in sight. I was alone in the ocean!

At last, little by little, my bruised head began to remember what had happened: first, the coming of the storm; the sails going overboard; then the big wave which had banged me against the door. But what had become of the Doctor and the others? What day was this, tomorrow or the day after?— And why was I sitting on only part of a ship?

Working my hand into my pocket, I found my penknife and cut the rope that tied me. This reminded me of a shipwreck story which Joe had once told me, of a captain who had tied his son to a mast in order that he shouldn't be washed overboard by the gale. So of course it must have been the Doctor who had done the same to me.

But where was he?

The awful thought came to me that the doctor and the rest of them must be drowned since there was no other wreckage to be seen upon the waters. I got to my feet and stared around the sea again—Nothing—nothing but water and sky!

Presently a long way off I saw the small dark shape of a bird skimming low down over the swell.

When it came quite close I saw it was a Stormy Petrel. I tried to talk to it, to see if it could give me news. But unluckily I hadn't learned much seabird language and I couldn't even attract its attention, much less make it understand what I wanted.

Twice it circled round my raft, lazily, with hardly a flip of the wing. And I could not help wondering, in spite of the distress I was in, where it had spent last night—how it, or any other living thing, had weathered such a smashing storm. It made me realize the great big difference between different creatures; and that size and strength are not everything. To this petrel, a frail little thing of feathers, much smaller and weaker than I, the Sea could do anything she liked, it seemed; and his only answer was a lazy, saucy flip of the wing! *He* was the one who should be called the *able seaman*. For, come raging gale, come sunlit calm, this wilderness of water was his home.

After swooping over the sea around me (just looking for food, I supposed) he went off in the direction from which he had come. And I was alone once more.

I found I was somewhat hungry—and a little thirsty too. I began to think all sorts of miserable thoughts, the way one does when he is lonesome and has missed breakfast. What was going to become of me now, if the Doctor and the rest were drowned? I would starve to death or die of thirst. Then the sun went behind some clouds and I felt cold. How many hundreds or thousands of miles was I from any land? What if another storm should come and smash up even this poor raft on which I stood?

I went on like this for a while, growing gloomier and gloomier, when suddenly I thought of Polynesia. "You're always safe with the Doctor," she had said. "He gets there. Remember that."

I'm sure I wouldn't have minded so much if he had been here with me. It was this being alone that made me want to weep. And yet the petrel was alone!—What a baby I was, I told myself, to be scared to the verge of tears just by loneliness! I was quite safe where I was—for the present anyhow. John Dolittle wouldn't get scared by a little thing like this. He only got excited when he made a discovery, found a new bug or something. And if what Polynesia had said was true, he couldn't be drowned and things would come out all right in the end somehow.

I threw out my chest, buttoned up my collar and began walking up and down the short raft to keep warm. I would be like John Dolittle. I wouldn't cry—and I wouldn't get excited.

How long I paced back and forth I don't know. But it was a long time—for I had nothing else to do.

At last I got tired and lay down to rest. And in spite of all my troubles, I soon fell fast asleep.

This time when I woke up, stars were staring down at me out of a cloudless sky. The sea was still calm; and my strange craft was rocking gently under me on an easy swell. All my fine courage left me as I gazed up into the big silent night and felt the pains of hunger and thirst set to work in my stomach harder than ever.

"Are you awake?" said a high silvery voice at my elbow.

I sprang up as though someone had stuck a pin in me. And there perched at the very end of my raft, her beautiful golden tail glowing dimly in the starlight, sat Miranda, the Purple Bird-of-Paradise!

Never have I been so glad to see anyone in my life. I almost fell into the water as I leapt to hug her.

"I didn't want to wake you," said she. "I guessed you must be tired after all you've been through—Don't squash the life out of me, boy: I'm not a stuffed duck, you know."

"Oh, Miranda, you dear old thing," said I, "I'm so glad to see you. Tell me, where is the Doctor? Is he alive?"

"Of course he's alive—and it's my firm belief he will live for many years. He's over there, about forty miles to the westward."

"What's he doing there?"

"He's sitting on the other half of the *Curlew* shaving himself—or he was, when I left him."

"Well, thank Heaven he's alive!" said I—"And Bumpo—and the animals, are they all right?"

"Yes, they're with him. Your ship broke in half in the storm. The Doctor had tied you down when he found you stunned. And the part you were on got separated and floated away. Golly, it *was* a storm! One has to be a gull or an albatross to stand that sort of weather. I had been watching for the Doctor for three weeks, from a cliff-top; but last night I had to take refuge in a cave to keep my tail-feathers from blowing out. As soon as I found the Doctor, he sent me off with some porpoises to look for you. A Stormy Petrel volunteered to help us in our search. There had been quite a gathering of seabirds waiting to greet the Doctor; but the rough weather sort of broke up the arrangements that had been made to welcome him properly. It was the petrel that first gave us the tip where you were."

"Well, but how can I get to the Doctor, Miranda?—I haven't any oars."

"Get to him!—Why, you're going to him now. Look behind you."

Word Bank   stunned (STUND) *adj.*: made senseless or dizzy as if by a blow; shocked

I turned around. The moon was just rising on the sea's edge. And I now saw that my raft was moving through the water, but so gently that I had not noticed it before.

"What's moving us?" I asked.

"The porpoises," said Miranda.

I went to the back of the raft and looked down into the water. And just below the surface I could see the dim forms of four big porpoises, their sleek skins glinting in the moonlight, pushing at the raft with their noses.

"They're old friends of the Doctor's," said Miranda. "They'd do anything for John Dolittle. We should see his party soon now. We're pretty near the place I left them—Yes, there they are! See that dark shape?—No, more to the right of where you're looking. Can't you make out the figure of the man standing against the sky?—Now Chee-Chee spies us—he's waving. Don't you see them?"

I didn't—for my eyes were not as sharp as Miranda's. But presently from somewhere in the murky dusk I heard Bumpo singing his African comic songs with the full force of his enormous voice. And in a little, by peering and peering in the direction of the sound, I at last made out a dim mass of tattered, splintered wreckage—all that remained of the poor *Curlew*—floating low down upon the water.

A hulloa came through the night. And I answered it. We kept it up, calling to one another back and forth across the calm night sea. And a few minutes later the two halves of our brave little ruined ship bumped gently together again.

Now that I was nearer and the moon was higher I could see more plainly. Their half of the ship was much bigger than mine.

It lay partly upon its side; and most of them were perched upon the top munching ship's biscuit.

But close down to the edge of the water, using the sea's calm surface for a mirror and a piece of broken bottle for a razor, John Dolittle was shaving his face by the light of the moon.

5

LAND!

They all gave me a great greeting as I clambered off my half of the ship onto theirs. Bumpo brought me a wonderful drink of fresh water which he drew from a barrel; and Chee-Chee and Polynesia stood around me feeding me ship's biscuit.

But it was the sight of the Doctor's smiling face—just knowing that I was with him once again—that cheered me more than anything else. As I watched him carefully wipe his glass razor and put it away for future use, I could not help comparing him in my mind with the Stormy Petrel. Indeed the vast strange knowledge which he had gained from his speech and friendship with animals had brought him the power to do things which no other human being would dare to try. Like the petrel, he could apparently play with the sea in all her moods. And ridiculous though it was, I could quite understand what Miranda meant when she said she firmly believed that he would live a long time. Just to be with him gave you a wonderful feeling of comfort and safety.

Except for his appearance (his clothes were crumpled and damp and his battered high hat was stained with saltwater) that storm which had so terrified me had disturbed him no more than getting stuck on the mudbank in Puddleby River.

Politely thanking Miranda for getting me so quickly, he asked her if she would now go ahead of us and show us the way to Spidermonkey Island. Next, he gave orders to the porpoises to leave my old piece of the ship and push the bigger half wherever the Bird-of-Paradise should lead us.

How much he had lost in the wreck besides his razor I did not know—everything, most likely, together with all the money he had saved up to buy the ship with. And still he was smiling as though he wanted for nothing in the world. The only things he had saved, as far as I could see—beyond the barrel of water and bag of biscuit—were his precious notebooks. These, I saw when he stood up, he had strapped around his waist with yards and yards of twine. He was, as old Matthew Mugg used to say, a great man. He was unbelievable.

And now for three days we continued our journey slowly but steadily—southward.

The only inconvenience we suffered from was the cold. This seemed to increase as we went forward. The Doctor said that the island, disturbed from its usual paths by the great gale, had evidently drifted further South than it had ever been before.

On the third night poor Miranda came back to us nearly frozen. She told the Doctor that in the morning we would find the island quite close to us, though we couldn't see it now as it was a misty dark night. She said that she must hurry back at once to a warmer climate; and that she would visit the Doctor in Puddleby next August as usual.

"Don't forget, Miranda," said John Dolittle, "if you should hear anything of what happened to Long Arrow, to get word to me."

The Bird-of-Paradise assured him she would. And after the Doctor had thanked her again and again for all that she had done for us, she wished us good luck and disappeared into the night.

We were all awake early in the morning, long before it was light, waiting for our first glimpse of the country we had come so far to see. And as the rising sun turned the eastern sky to gray, of course it was old Polynesia who first shouted that she could see palm-trees and mountain tops.

With the growing light it became plain to all of us: a long island with high rocky mountains in the middle—and so near to us that you could almost throw your hat upon the shore.

The porpoises gave us one last push and our strange-looking craft bumped gently on a low beach. Then, thanking our lucky stars for a chance to stretch our cramped legs, we all bundled off onto the land—the first land, even though it was floating land, that we had trodden for six weeks. What a thrill I felt as I realized that Spidermonkey Island, the little spot in the atlas which my pencil had touched, lay at last beneath my feet!

When the light increased still further we noticed that the palms and grasses of the island seemed withered and almost dead. The Doctor said that it must be on account of the cold that the island was now suffering from in its new climate. These trees and grasses, he told us, were the kind that belonged to warm, tropical weather.

The porpoises asked if we wanted them any further. And the Doctor said that he didn't think so, not for the present—nor the raft either, he added; for it was already beginning to fall to pieces and could not float much longer.

As we were preparing to go inland and explore the island, we suddenly noticed a whole band of Red Indians watching us with great curiosity from among the trees. The Doctor went forward to talk to them. But he could not make them understand. He tried by signs to show them that he had come on a friendly visit. The Indians didn't seem to like us however. They had bows and arrows and long hunting spears, with stone points, in their hands; and they made signs back to the Doctor to tell him that if he came a step nearer they would kill us all. They evidently wanted us to leave the island at once. It was a very uncomfortable situation.

At last the Doctor made them understand that he only wanted to see the island all over and that then he would go away—though how he meant to do it, with no boat to sail in, was more than I could imagine.

While they were talking among themselves another Indian arrived—apparently with a message that they were wanted in some other part of the island, because presently, shaking their spears threateningly at us, they went off with the newcomer.

"What discourteous pagans!" said Bumpo. "Did you ever see such inhospitability?—Never even asked us if we'd had breakfast, the benighted bounders!"

"Sh! They're going off to their village," said Polynesia. "I'll bet there's a village on the other side of those mountains. If you take my advice, Doctor, you'll get away from this beach while their backs are turned. Let us go up into the higher land for the present—someplace where they won't know where we are. They may grow friendlier when they see we mean no harm. They have honest, open faces and look like a decent crowd to me. They're just ignorant—probably never saw white folks before."

So, feeling a little bit discouraged by our first reception, we moved off towards the mountains in the center of the island.

Studying THE SELECTION

Recalling

1. Why did the fidgit whistle English tunes?

2. How did the fidgit and Clippa escape from captivity?

3. Who was the Great Glass Sea Snail?

4. Where was Christopher Columbus' diary?

5. How could Polynesia tell that bad weather was coming?

Interpreting

6. What happened to Tommy during the storm? How was he reunited with Dr. Dolittle? Who helped Tommy?

7. How had Dr. Dolittle saved his notebooks during the storm? What does this tell you about Dr. Dolittle's character?

Concluding

8. What kind of welcome did Dr. Dolittle receive when he arrived on land? Why do you think he was received in this manner?

Examining the Novel

The reader is probably impatiently waiting to discover what happened to Long Arrow. Why do you think the author keeps delaying the search by including these chapters about the fidgit and the storm? Do these stories give us more information about Dr. Dolittle's character? Do they add more information about Tommy?

Thinking About the Novel

Tommy remarks that a Stormy Petrel, a frail-looking seabird, was a more able seaman than himself. Write a compare/contrast paragraph comparing Tommy to the petrel. What are each of their strengths, and what are each of their limitations?

Creating and Writing

The fidgit hated living in an aquarium. He hated people staring and gawking at him. Imagine you were the fidgit or his sister, Clippa, and you could talk to the people staring at your tank. A family of five walks by. What would you say to them?

Into • *The Voyages of Dr. Dolittle*
Part Four—Chapters 6-7

What is a story without suspense? One important element of suspense is a race against time. In this section, Dr. Dolittle and his small band of helpers race against time to save Long Arrow. Another element of suspense is conflict. In this case, the conflict is with a natural event. A rock has fallen down and trapped Long Arrow; Dr. Dolittle must find a way to free him from his prison inside the mountain.

Focus

One of the many ways Hugh Lofting delights readers is through his colorful transitions. A **transition** is something that connects two very different things, the way a bridge connects two pieces of land that are separated by water. Throughout the story, something happens at the end of one episode that links it to the next episode. Dr. Dolittle has landed on Spidermonkey Island. He must find Long Arrow. How will the author move the plot along? What transition will connect Dr. Dolittle's landing on the island with his discovery of Long Arrow?

6

THE JABIZRI

We found the woods at the feet of the hills thick and tangly and somewhat hard to get through. On Polynesia's advice, we kept away from all paths and trails, feeling it best to avoid meeting any Indians for the present.

But she and Chee-Chee were good guides and splendid jungle-hunters; and the two of them set to work at once looking for food for us. In a very short space of time they had found quite a number of different fruits and nuts which made excellent eating, though none of us knew the names of any of them. We discovered a nice clean stream of good water which came down from the mountains; so we were supplied with something to drink as well.

We followed the stream up towards the heights. And presently we came to parts where the woods were thinner and the ground rocky and steep. Here we could get glimpses of wonderful views all over the island, with the blue sea beyond.

While we were admiring one of these the Doctor suddenly said, "Sh!—A Jabizri!—Don't you hear it?"

We listened and heard, somewhere in the air about us, an extraordinarily musical hum—like a bee, but not just one note. This hum rose and fell, up and down—almost like someone singing.

"No other insect but the Jabizri beetle hums like that," said the Doctor. "I wonder where he is—quite near, by the sound—flying among the trees probably. Oh, if I only had my butterfly-net! Why didn't I think to strap that around my waist too. Confound the storm: I may miss the chance of a lifetime now of getting the rarest beetle in the world—Oh look! There he goes!"

A huge beetle, easily three inches long I should say, suddenly flew by our noses. The Doctor got frightfully excited. He took off his hat to use as a net, swooped at the beetle and caught it. He nearly fell down a precipice onto the rocks below in his wild hurry, but that didn't bother him in the least. He knelt down, chortling, upon the ground with the Jabizri safe under his hat. From his pocket he brought out a glass-topped box, and into this he very skillfully made the beetle walk from under the rim of the hat. Then he rose up, happy as a child, to examine his new treasure through the glass lid.

It certainly was a most beautiful insect. It was pale blue underneath; but its back was glossy black with huge red spots on it.

"There isn't an entymologist in the whole world who wouldn't give all he has to be in my shoes today," said the Doctor—"Hulloa! This Jabizri's got something on his leg—Doesn't look like mud. I wonder what it is."

He took the beetle carefully out of the box and held it by its back in his fingers, where it waved its six legs slowly in the air. We all crowded about him peering at it. Rolled around the middle section of its right foreleg was something that looked like a thin dried leaf. It was bound on very neatly with strong spiderweb.

It was marvelous to see how John Dolittle with his fat heavy fingers undid that cobweb cord and unrolled the leaf, whole, without tearing it or hurting the precious beetle. The Jabizri he put back into the box. Then he spread the leaf out flat and examined it.

You can imagine our surprise when we found that the inside of the leaf was covered with signs and pictures, drawn so tiny that you almost needed a magnifying-glass to tell what they were. Some of the signs we couldn't make out at all; but nearly all of the pictures were quite plain, figures of men and mountains mostly. The whole was done in a curious sort of brown ink.

For several moments there was a dead silence while we all stared at the leaf, fascinated and mystified.

"I think this is written in blood," said the Doctor at last. "It turns that

Word Bank	**swooped** (SWOOPT) *v.*: plunged suddenly; moved in a sweeping arc
	precipice (PREH sih PEECE) *n.*: an abrupt, downward slope
	chortling (CHORT ling) *v.*: uttering a chuckling laugh
	mystified (MISS tih FYD) *adj.*: puzzled; perplexed

color when it's dry. Somebody pricked his finger to make these pictures. It's an old dodge when you're short of ink—but highly unsanitary—What an extraordinary thing to find tied to a beetle's leg! I wish I could talk beetle language, and find out where the Jabizri got it from."

"But what is it?" I asked—"Rows of little pictures and signs. What do you make of it, Doctor?"

"It's a letter," he said—"a picture letter. All these little things put together mean a message—But why give a message to a beetle to carry—and to a Jabizri, the rarest beetle in the world?—What an extraordinary thing!"

Then he fell to muttering over the pictures.

"I wonder what it means: men walking up a mountain; men walking into a hole in a mountain; a mountain falling down—it's a good drawing, that; men pointing to their open mouths; bars—prison-bars, perhaps; men praying; men lying down—they look as though they might be sick; and last of all, just a mountain—a peculiar-shaped mountain."

All of a sudden the Doctor looked up sharply at me, a wonderful smile of delighted understanding spreading over his face.

"*Long Arrow*!" he cried, "don't you see, Stubbins?—Why, of course! Only a naturalist would think of doing a thing like this: giving his letter to a beetle—not to a common beetle, but to the rarest of all, one that other naturalists would try to catch—Well, well! Long Arrow!—A picture-letter from Long Arrow. For pictures are the only writing that he knows."

"Yes, but who is the letter to?" I asked.

"It's to me very likely. Miranda had told him, I know, years ago, that someday I meant to come here. But if not for me, then it's for anyone who caught the beetle and read it. It's a letter to the world."

"Well, but what does it say? It doesn't seem to me that it's much good to you now you've got it."

"Yes, it is," he said, "because, look, I can read it now. First picture: men walking up a mountain—that's Long Arrow and his party; men going into a hole in a mountain—they enter a cave looking for medicine-plants or mosses; a mountain falling down—some hanging rocks must have slipped and trapped them, imprisoned them in the cave. And this was the only living creature that could carry a message for them to the outside world—a beetle, who could *burrow* his way into the open air. Of course it was only a slim chance that the beetle would ever be caught and the letter read. But it *was* a chance; and when men are in great danger, they grab at any straw of hope...All right. Now look at the next picture: men pointing to their open mouths—they are hungry; men praying—begging anyone who finds this letter to come to their assistance; men lying down—they are sick, or starving. This letter, Stubbins, is their last

---

Word Bank   burrow (BURR oh) *v.*: digging by tunneling in the ground cry for help."

He sprang to his feet as he ended, snatched out a notebook and put the letter between the leaves. His hands were trembling with haste and agitation.

"Come on!" he cried—"up the mountain—all of you. There's not a moment to lose. Bumpo, bring the water and nuts with you. Heaven only knows how long they've been pining underground. Let's hope and pray we're not too late!"

"But where are you going to look?" I asked. "Miranda said the island was a hundred miles long and the mountains seem to run all the way down the center of it."

"Didn't you see the last picture?" he said, grabbing up his hat from the ground and cramming it on his head. "It was an oddly shaped mountain—looked like a hawk's head. Well, there's where he is—if he's still alive. First thing for us to do, is to get up on a high peak and look around the island for a mountain shaped like a hawk's head—Just to think of it! There's a chance of my meeting Long Arrow, the son of Golden Arrow, after all!—Come on! Hurry! To delay may mean death to the greatest naturalist ever born!"

7

HAWK'S-HEAD MOUNTAIN

We all agreed afterwards that none of us had ever worked so hard in our lives before as we did that day. For my part, I know I was often on the point of dropping exhausted with fatigue; but I just kept on going—like a machine—determined that, whatever happened, *I* would not be the first to give up.

When we had scrambled to the top of a high peak, almost instantly we saw the strange mountain pictured in the letter. In shape it was the perfect image of a hawk's head, and was, as far as we could see, the second highest summit in the island.

Although we were all out of breath from our climb, the Doctor didn't let us rest a second as soon as he had sighted it. With one look at the sun for direction, down he dashed again, breaking through thickets, splashing over brooks, taking all the shortcuts. For a fat man, he was certainly the swiftest cross-country runner I ever saw.

We floundered after him as fast as we could. When I say *we*, I mean Bumpo and myself; for the animals, Jip, Chee-Chee and Polynesia, were a long way ahead—even beyond the Doctor—enjoying the hunt like a paper-chase.

At length we arrived at the foot of the mountain we were making for; and we found its sides very steep. Said the Doctor, "Now we will

---

Word Bank **peak** (PEEK) *n.*: the top of a mountain or hill; highest point
fatigue (fuh TEEG) *adj.*: weariness from labor; exhaustion

separate and search for caves. This spot where we now are, will be our meeting place. If anyone finds anything like a cave or a hole where the earth and rocks have fallen in, he must shout and hulloa to the rest of us. If we find nothing we will all gather here in about an hour's time—Everybody understand?"

Then we all went off our different ways.

Each of us, you may be sure, was anxious to be the one to make a discovery. And never was a mountain searched so thoroughly. But alas! nothing could we find that looked in the least like a fallen-in cave. There were plenty of places where rocks had tumbled down to the foot of the slopes; but none of these appeared as though caves or passages could possibly lie behind them.

One by one, tired and disappointed, we straggled back to the meeting-place. The Doctor seemed gloomy and impatient but by no means inclined to give up.

"Jip," he said, "couldn't you *smell* anything like an Indian anywhere?"

"No," said Jip. "I sniffed at every crack on the mountainside. But I am afraid my nose will be of no use to you here, Doctor. The trouble is, the whole air is so saturated with the smell of spider monkeys that it drowns every other scent—And besides, it's too cold and dry for good smelling."

"It is certainly that," said the Doctor—"and getting colder all the time. I'm afraid the island is still drifting to the southward. Let's hope it stops before long, or we won't be able to get even nuts and fruit to eat—everything in the island will perish—Chee-Chee, what luck did you have?"

"None, Doctor. I climbed to every peak and pinnacle I could see. I searched every hollow and cleft. But not one place could I find where men might be hidden."

"And Polynesia," asked the Doctor, "did you see nothing that might put us on the right track?"

"Not a thing, Doctor—But I have a plan."

"Oh good!" cried John Dolittle, full of hope renewed. "What is it? Let's hear it."

"You still have that beetle with you," she asked—"the Biz-biz, or whatever it is you call the wretched insect?"

"Yes," said the Doctor, producing the glass-topped box from his pockct, "here it is."

"All right. Now listen," said she. "If what you have supposed is true—that is, that Long Arrow had been trapped inside the mountain by falling rock, he probably found that beetle inside the cave—perhaps many other different beetles too, eh? He wouldn't have been likely to take the Biz-biz in with him, would he?—He was hunting plants, you say, not beetles. Isn't that right?"

"Yes," said the Doctor, "that's probably so."

"Very well. It is fair to suppose then that the beetle's home, or his

---

Word Bank   saturated (SACH ur AYT id) *v.*: filled completely

hole, is in that place—the part of the mountain where Long Arrow and his party are imprisoned, isn't it?"

"Quite, quite."

"All right. Then the thing to do is to let the beetle go—and watch him; and sooner or later he'll return to his home in Long Arrow's cave. And there we will follow him—Or at all events," she added smoothing down her wing-feathers with a very superior air, "we will follow him till the miserable bug starts nosing under the earth. But at least he will show us what part of the mountain Long Arrow is hidden in."

"But he may fly, if I let him out," said the Doctor. "Then we shall just lose him and be no better off than we were before."

"*Let* him fly," snorted Polynesia scornfully. "A parrot can wing it as fast as a Biz-biz, I fancy. If he takes to the air, I'll guarantee not to let the little devil out of my sight. And if he just crawls along the ground you can follow him yourself."

"Splendid!" cried the Doctor. "Polynesia, you have a great brain. I'll set him to work at once and see what happens."

Again we all clustered round the Doctor as he carefully lifted off the glass lid and let the big beetle climb out upon his finger.

"Ladybug, Ladybug, fly away home!" crooned Bumpo. "Your house is on fire and your chil—"

"Oh, be quiet!" snapped Polynesia crossly. "Stop insulting him! Don't you suppose he has wits enough to go home without your telling him?"

"I thought perchance he might be of an adventurous nature," said Bumpo humbly. "It could be that he is tired of his home and needs to be encouraged. Shall I sing him 'Home Sweet Home,' think you?"

"No. Then he'd never go back. Your voice needs a rest. Don't sing to him: just watch him—Oh, and Doctor, why not tie another message to the creature's leg, telling Long Arrow that we're doing our best to reach him and that he mustn't give up hope?"

"I will," said the Doctor. And in a minute he had pulled a dry leaf from a bush nearby and was covering it with little pictures in pencil.

At last, neatly fixed up with his new mailbag, Mr. Jabizri crawled off the Doctor's finger to the ground and looked about him. He stretched his legs, polished his nose with his front feet and then moved off leisurely to the westward.

We had expected him to walk *up* the mountain; instead, he walked *around* it. Do you know how long it takes a beetle to walk round a mountain? Well, I assure you it takes an unbelievably long time. As the hours dragged by, we hoped and hoped that he would get up and fly the rest, and let Polynesia carry on the work of following him. But he never opened his wings once. I had not realized before how hard it is for a human being to walk slowly enough to keep up with a beetle. It was the most tedious thing I have ever gone through. And as we dawdled along behind, watching him like hawks lest we lose him under a leaf or something, we all got so cross and ill-tempered we were ready to bite one another's heads off. And when he stopped to look at the scenery or polish his nose some more, I could hear Polynesia behind me letting out the most dreadful seafaring words you ever heard.

After he had led us the whole way round the mountain he brought us to the exact spot where we started from and there he came to a dead stop.

"Well," said Bumpo to Polynesia, "what do you think of the beetle's sense now? You see he *doesn't* know enough to go home."

"Oh, be still," snapped Polynesia. "Wouldn't *you* want to stretch your legs for exercise if you'd been shut up in a box all day. Probably his home is near here, and that's why he's come back."

"But why," I asked, "did he go the whole way round the mountain first?"

Then the three of us got into a violent argument. But in the middle of it all the Doctor suddenly called out, "Look, look!"

We turned and found that he was pointing to the Jabizri, who was now walking up the mountain at a much faster and more businesslike gait.

"Well," said Bumpo sitting down wearily; "if he is going to walk *over* the mountain and back, for more exercise, I'll wait for him here. Chee-Chee and Polynesia can follow him."

Indeed it would have taken a monkey or a bird to climb the place which the beetle was now walking up. It was a smooth, flat part of the mountain's side, steep as a wall.

But presently, when the Jabizri was no more than ten feet above our heads, we all cried out together. For, even while we watched him, he had disappeared into the face of the rock like a raindrop soaking into sand.

"He's gone," cried Polynesia. "There must be a hole up there." And in a twinkling she had fluttered up the rock and was clinging to the face of it with her claws.

"Yes," she shouted down, "we've run him to earth at last. His hole is right here, behind a patch of lichen—big enough to get two fingers in."

"Ah," cried the Doctor, "this great slab of rock then must have slid down from the summit and shut off the mouth of the cave like a door. Poor fellows! What a dreadful time they must have spent in there!—Oh, if we only had some picks and shovels now!"

"Picks and shovels wouldn't do much good," said Polynesia. "Look at the size of the slab: a hundred feet high and as many broad. You would need an army for a week to make any impression on it."

"I wonder how thick it is," said the Doctor; and he picked up a big stone and banged it with all his might against the face of the rock. It made a hollow booming sound, like a giant drum. We all stood still listening while the echo of it died slowly away.

And then a cold shiver ran down my spine. For from within the mountain, back came three answering knocks: Boom!...Boom!... Boom!

Wide-eyed we looked at one another as though the earth itself had spoken. And the solemn little silence that followed was broken by the Doctor.

"Thank Heaven," he said in a hushed reverent voice, "some of them at least are alive!"

Recalling

1. Describe the Jabizri beetle.

2. What was attached to the Jabizri beetle's leg?

3. What was the importance of the last picture on the picture-letter?

Interpreting

4. Why was Dr. Dolittle excited when he saw the picture-letter?

5. Why was the island constantly getting colder?

Concluding

6. Give an example of Polynesia's intelligence.

7. Where exactly did the Jabizri beetle live?

Examining the Novel

Note how the element of suspense was introduced. The important message was drawn on a leaf which was attached to the leg of a humble bug, the Jabizri beetle. How is that incident in keeping with the theme of this book?

Thinking About the Novel

This novel is a combination of an adventure story and a character study of Dr. Dolittle. The search for Long Arrow is part of the larger plot, which is Dr. Dolittle's adventure. Draw a timeline recounting Dr. Dolittle's journey up to this point. Note how the author creates tension and suspense by inserting seemingly unrelated incidents that will make sense as we read on.

Creating and Writing

Years ago there were people who raised pigeons as messengers. Certain types of pigeons called carrier pigeons or homing pigeons were trained to fly home, no matter how far away they were. These pigeons were used to carry messages in times of war and danger.

Imagine you are trapped in a mountain cave and a pigeon flies in with a message attached to its leg. The pigeon lands on your shoulder. You can read the message and send one back. What do you think the first message would say? What would you write in your return message?

Into • *The Voyages of Dr. Dolittle* *Part Five—Chapters 1-4*

The reason Dr. Dolittle set off on his journey was, if you remember, to find Long Arrow. He has located him, but has not found him, for Long Arrow is imprisoned behind a mass of rock. Dr. Dolittle and the animals do what they can to free Long Arrow and his friends. The author then adds a subplot to the main story, the problem of Spidermonkey Island moving towards the South Pole.

In this small section, Hugh Lofting introduces a theme that was popular in other works of English fiction of his day—the relationship between modern man and primitive man. Because modern man has knowledge of science, he appears, to primitive man, to have superhuman powers. In this story, the natives are so extremely primitive, that they have never even learned to make a fire. We will find this theme developed later on in the story.

Focus

Hugh Lofting, like Lewis Carroll in *Alice and Wonderland*, enjoys silly-sounding names. You or I might laugh at names like Popsipetels and Bag-jagderags, but how could someone with a name like Bumpo Kahbooboo laugh at anyone else? Indeed, he does not! None of the characters seem to notice how outlandish each others' names are—that's all part of the fun.

PART V

1

A GREAT MOMENT

The next part of our problem was the hardest of all: how to roll aside, pull down or break open, that gigantic slab. As we gazed up at it towering above our heads, it looked indeed a hopeless task for our tiny strength.

But the sounds of life from inside the mountain had put new heart in us. And in a moment we were all scrambling around trying to find any opening or crevice which would give us something to work on. Chee-Chee scaled up the sheer wall of the slab and examined the top of it where it leaned against the mountain's side; I uprooted bushes and stripped off hanging creepers that might conceal a weak place; the Doctor got more leaves and composed new picture-letters for the Jabizri to take in if he should turn up again; whilst Polynesia carried up a handful of nuts and pushed them into the beetle's hole, one by one for the prisoners inside to eat.

"Nuts are so nourishing," she said.

But Jip it was who, scratching at the foot of the slab like a good ratter, made the discovery which led to our final success.

"Doctor," he cried, running up to John Dolittle with his nose all covered with black mud, "this slab is resting on nothing but a bed of soft earth. You never saw such easy digging. I guess the cave behind must be just too high up for the Indians to reach the earth with their hands, or they could have scraped a way out long ago. If we can only scratch the earth-bed away from under, the slab might drop a little. Then maybe the Indians can climb out over the top."

The doctor hurried to examine the place where Jip had dug.

"Why, yes," he said, "if we can get the earth away from under this front edge, the slab is standing up so straight, we might even make it fall right down in this direction. It's well worth trying. Let's get at it, quick."

We had no tools but the sticks and slivers of stone which we could find around. A strange sight we must have looked, the whole crew of us squatting down on our heels, scratching and burrowing at the foot of the mountain, like six badgers in a row.

After about an hour, during which in spite of the cold the sweat fell from our foreheads in all directions, the Doctor said, "Be ready to jump

Word	nourishing (NUR ish ing) *adj.*: nutritious; promoting growth; sustaining
Bank	slivers (SLIV urz) *n.*: long, slender pieces cut off of larger pieces; splinters

from under, clear out of the way, if she shows signs of moving. If this slab falls on anybody, it will squash him flatter than a pancake."

Presently there was a grating, grinding sound.

"Look out!" yelled John Dolittle, "here she comes!—Scatter!"

We ran for our lives, outwards, toward the sides. The big rock slid gently down, about a foot, into the trough which we had made beneath it. For a moment I was disappointed, for like that, it was as hopeless as before—no signs of a cave-mouth showing above it. But as I looked upward, I saw the top coming very slowly away from the mountainside. We had unbalanced it below. As it moved apart from the face of the mountain, sounds of human voices, crying gladly in a strange tongue, issued from behind. Faster and faster the top swung forward, downward. Then, with a roaring crash which shook the whole mountain-range beneath our feet, it struck the earth and cracked in halves.

How can I describe to anyone that first meeting between the two greatest naturalists the world ever knew, Long Arrow, the son of Golden Arrow and John Dolittle, M.D., of Puddleby-on-the-Marsh? The scene rises before me now, plain and clear in every detail, though it took place so many, many years ago. But when I come to write of it, words seem such poor things with which to tell you of that great occasion.

I know that the Doctor, whose life was surely full enough of big happenings, always counted the setting free of the Indian scientist as the greatest thing he ever did. For my part, knowing how much this meeting must mean to him, I was on pins and needles of expectation and curiosity as the great stone finally thundered down at our feet and we gazed across it to see what lay behind.

The gloomy black mouth of a tunnel, full twenty feet high, was revealed. In the center of this opening stood an enormous Red Indian, seven feet tall, handsome, muscular, slim and wearing beaded clothing and an eagle's feather in his hair. He held one hand across his face to shield his eyes from the blinding sun which he had not seen in many days.

"It is he!" I heard the Doctor whisper at my elbow. "I know him by his great height and the scar upon his chin."

And he stepped forward slowly across the fallen stone with his hand outstretched to the Red man.

Presently the Indian uncovered his eyes. And I saw that they had a curious piercing gleam in them—like the eyes of an eagle, but kinder and more gentle. He slowly raised his right arm, the rest of him still and motionless like a statue, and took the Doctor's hand in his. It was a great moment. Polynesia nodded to me in a knowing, satisfied kind of way. And I heard old Bumpo sniffle sentimentally.

Then the Doctor tried to speak to Long Arrow. But the Indian knew no English of course, and the Doctor knew no Indian. Presently, to my surprise, I heard the Doctor trying him in different animal languages.

"How do you do?" he said in dog-talk; "I am glad to see you," in horse-signs; "How long have you been buried?" in deer-language. Still the Indian made no move but stood there, straight and stiff, understanding not a word.

The Doctor tried again, in several other animal dialects. But with no result.

Till at last he came to the language of eagles.

"Great Red-Skin," he said in the fierce screams and short grunts that the big birds use, "never have I been so glad in all my life as I am today to find you still alive."

In a flash Long Arrow's stony face lit up with a smile of understanding; and back came the answer in eagle-tongue, "Mighty White Man, I owe my life to you. For the remainder of my days I am your servant to command."

Afterwards Long Arrow told us that this was the only bird or

animal language that he had ever been able to learn. But that he had not spoken it in a long time, for no eagles ever came to his island.

Then the Doctor signaled to Bumpo who came forward with the nuts and water. But Long Arrow neither ate nor drank. Taking the supplies with a nod of thanks, he turned and carried them into the inner dimness of the cave. We followed him.

Inside we found nine other Indians, men, women and boys, lying on the rock floor in a dreadful state of thinness and exhaustion.

Some had their eyes closed, as if dead. Quickly the Doctor went round them all and listened to their hearts. They were all alive; but one woman was too weak even to stand upon her feet.

At a word from the Doctor, Chee-Chee and Polynesia sped off into the jungles after more fruit and water.

While Long Arrow was handing round what food we had to his starving friends, we suddenly heard a sound outside the cave. Turning about we saw, clustered at the entrance, the band of Indians who had met us so inhospitably at the beach.

They peered into the dark cave cautiously at first. But as soon as they saw Long Arrow and the other Indians with us, they came rushing in, laughing, clapping their hands with joy and jabbering away at a tremendous rate.

Long Arrow explained to the Doctor that the nine Indians we had found in the cave with him were two families who had accompanied him into the mountains to help him gather medicine-plants. And while they had been searching for a kind of moss—good for indigestion—which grows only inside of damp caves, the great rock slab had slid down and shut them in. Then for two weeks they had lived on the medicine-moss and such fresh water as could be found dripping from the damp walls of the cave. The other Indians on the island had given them up for lost and mourned them as dead; and they were now very surprised and happy to find their relatives alive.

When Long Arrow turned to the newcomers and told them in their own language that it was the white man who had found and freed their relatives, they gathered round John Dolittle, all talking at once.

Long Arrow said they were apologizing and trying to tell the Doctor how sorry they were that they had seemed unfriendly to him at the beach. They had never seen a white man before and had really been afraid of him—especially when they saw him conversing with the porpoises.

Then they went outside and looked at the great stone we had thrown down, big as a meadow; and they walked round and round it, pointing to the break running through the middle and wondering how the trick of felling it was done.

Travelers who have since visited Spidermonkey Island tell me that that huge stone slab is now one of the regular sights of the island. And that the Indian guides, when showing it to visitors, always tell *their* story of how it came there. They say that when the Doctor found that the rocks had entrapped his friend, Long Arrow, he was so angry that he ripped the mountain in halves with his bare hands and let him out.

2

"The Men of the Moving Land"

From that time on the Indians' treatment of us was very different. We were invited to their village for a feast to celebrate the recovery of the lost families. And after we had made a litter from saplings to carry the sick woman in, we all started off down the mountain.

On the way the Indians told Long Arrow something which appeared to be sad news, for on hearing it, his face grew grave. The Doctor asked him what was wrong. And Long Arrow said he had just been informed that the chief of the tribe, an old man of eighty, had died early that morning.

"That," Polynesia whispered in my ear, "must have been what they went back to the village for, when the messenger fetched them from the beach.—Remember?"

"What did he die of?" asked the Doctor.

"He died of cold," said Long Arrow.

Indeed, now that the sun was setting, we were all shivering ourselves.

"This is a serious thing," said the Doctor to me. "The island is still in the grip of that wretched current flowing southward. We will have to look into this tomorrow. If nothing can be done about it, the Indians had better take to canoes and leave the island. The chance of being wrecked will be better, than getting frozen to death in the ice-floes of the Antarctic."

Presently we came over a saddle in the hills, and looking downward on the far side of the island, we saw a village—a large cluster of grass huts and gaily colored totem-poles close by the edge of the sea.

"How artistic!" said the Doctor—"Delightfully situated. What is the name of the village?"

"Popsipetel," said Long Arrow. "That is the name also of the tribe. The word signifies in Indian tongue, *The Men of the Moving Land*. There are two tribes of Indians on the island: the Popsipetels at this end and the Bag-jagderags at the other."

"Which is the larger of the two peoples?"

"The Bag-jagderags, by far. Their city covers two square leagues. But," added Long Arrow, a slight frown darkening his handsome face, "for me, I would rather have one Popsipetel than a hundred Bag-jagderags."

The news of the rescue we had made had evidently gone ahead of us. For as we drew nearer to the village we saw crowds of Indians streaming out to greet the friends and relatives whom they had never thought to see again.

These good people, when they too were told how the rescue had been the work of the strange white visitor to their shores, all gathered round the Doctor, shook him by the hands, patted him and hugged him. Then they lifted him up upon their strong shoulders and carried him down the hill into the village.

There the welcome we received was even more wonderful. In spite of the cold air of the coming night, the villagers, who had all been shivering within their houses, threw open their doors and came out in hundreds. I had no idea that the little village could hold so many. They thronged about us, smiling and nodding and waving their hands; and as the details of what we had done were recited by Long Arrow they kept shouting strange singing noises, which we supposed were words of gratitude or praise.

We were next escorted to a brand-new grass house, clean and sweet-smelling within, and informed that it was ours. Six strong Indian boys were told off to be our servants.

On our way through the village we noticed a house, larger than the rest, standing at the end of the main street. Long Arrow pointed to it and told us it was the Chief's house, but that it was now empty—no new chief having yet been elected to take the place of the old one who had died.

Inside our new home a feast of fish and fruit had been prepared. Most of the more important men of the tribe were already seating themselves at the long dining-table when we got there. Long Arrow invited us to sit down and eat.

This we were glad enough to do, as we were all hungry. But we were both surprised and disappointed when we found that the fish had not been cooked. The Indians did not seem to think this extraordinary in the least, but went ahead gobbling the fish with much relish the way it was, raw.

With many apologies, the Doctor explained to Long Arrow that if they had no objection we would prefer our fish cooked.

Imagine our astonishment when we found that the great Long Arrow, so learned in the natural sciences, did not know what the word *cooked* meant!

Polynesia who was sitting on the bench between John Dolittle and myself pulled the Doctor by the sleeve.

"I'll tell you what's wrong, Doctor," she whispered as he leant down to listen to her: "*these people have no fires*! They don't know how to make a fire. Look outside: It's almost dark, and there isn't a light showing in the whole village. This is a fireless people."

3

FIRE

Then the Doctor asked Long Arrow if he knew what fire was, explaining it to him by pictures drawn on the buckskin tablecloth. Long Arrow said he had seen such a thing—coming out of the tops of volcanoes; but that neither he nor any of the Popsipetels knew how it was made.

"Poor perishing heathens!" muttered Bumpo. "No wonder the old chief died of cold!"

At that moment we heard a crying sound at the door. And turning round, we saw a weeping Indian mother with a baby in her arms. She said something to the Indians which we could not understand; and Long Arrow told us the baby was sick and she wanted the white doctor to try and cure it.

"Oh L-rd!" groaned Polynesia in my ear—"Just like Puddleby: patients arriving in the middle of dinner. Well, one thing: the food's raw, so nothing can get cold anyway."

The Doctor examined the baby and found at once that it was thoroughly chilled.

"Fire—*fire*! That's what it needs," he said turning to Long Arrow—"That's what you all need. This child will have pneumonia if it isn't kept warm."

"Aye, truly. But how to make a fire," said Long Arrow—"where to get it: that is the difficulty. All the volcanoes in this land are dead."

Then we fell to hunting through our pockets to see if any matches had survived the shipwreck. The best we could muster were two whole ones and a half—all with the heads soaked off them by saltwater.

"Hark, Long Arrow," said the Doctor: "diverse ways there be of making fire without the aid of matches. One: with a strong glass and the rays of the sun. That however, since the sun has set, we cannot now employ. Another is by grinding a hard stick into a soft log—Is the daylight gone without?—Alas yes. Then I fear we must await the morrow; for besides the different woods, we need an old squirrel's nest for fuel—And that without lamps you could not find in your forests at this hour."

"Great are your cunning and your skill, oh White Man," Long Arrow replied. "But in this you do us an injustice. Know you not that all fireless peoples can see in the dark? Having no lamps we are forced to train ourselves to travel through the blackest night, lightless. I will dispatch a messenger and you shall have your squirrel's nest within the hour."

He gave an order to two of our boy-servants who promptly disappeared running. And sure enough, in a very short space of time a squirrel's nest, together with hard and soft woods, was brought to our door.

The moon had not yet risen and within the house it was practically pitch-black. I could feel and hear, however, that the Indians were moving about comfortably as though it were daylight. The task of making fire the Doctor had to perform almost entirely by the sense of touch, asking Long Arrow and the Indians to hand him his tools when he mislaid them in the dark. And then I made a curious discovery: now that I had to, I found that I was beginning to see a little in the dark myself. And for the first time I realized that of course there *is* no such thing as pitch-dark, so long as you have a door open or a sky above you.

Calling for the loan of a bow, the Doctor loosened the string, put the hard stick into a loop and began grinding this stick into the soft wood of the log. Soon I smelt that the log was smoking. Then he kept feeding the part that was smoking with the inside lining of the squirrel's nest, and he asked me to blow upon it with my breath. He made the stick drill faster and faster. More smoke filled the room. And at last the darkness about us was suddenly lit up. The squirrel's nest had burst into flame.

The Indians murmured and grunted with astonishment. They wanted to pick it up with their bare hands and play with it. We had to teach them how it was to be used; and they were quite fascinated when we laid our fish across it on sticks and cooked it. They sniffed the air with relish as, for the first time in history, the smell of fried fish passed through the village of Popsipetel.

Then we got them to bring us piles and stacks of dry wood; and we made an enormous bonfire in the middle of the main street. Round this, when they felt its warmth, the whole tribe gathered and smiled and wondered. It was a striking sight, one of the pictures from our voyages that I most frequently remember: that roaring jolly blaze beneath the black night sky, and all about it a vast ring of Indians, the firelight gleaming on bronze cheeks, white teeth and flashing eyes—a whole town trying to get warm, giggling and pushing like schoolchildren.

In a little, when we had got them more used to the handling of fire, the Doctor showed them how it could be taken into their houses if a hole were only made in the roof to let the smoke out. And before we turned in after that long, long, tiring day, we had fires going in every hut in the village.

The poor people were so glad to get really warm again that we thought they'd never go to bed. Well on into the early hours of the morning the little town fairly buzzed with a great low murmur: the Popsipetels sitting up talking of their wonderful pale-faced visitor and this strange good thing he had brought with him—*fire*!

4

WHAT MAKES AN ISLAND FLOAT

Very early in our experience of Popsipetel kindness we saw that if we were to get anything done at all, we would almost always have to do it secretly. The Doctor was so popular and loved by all that as soon as he showed his face at his door in the morning crowds of admirers, waiting patiently outside, flocked about him and followed him wherever he went. After his fire-making feat, this childlike people expected him, I think, to be continually doing magic; and they were determined not to miss a trick.

It was only with great difficulty that we escaped from the crowd the first morning and set out with Long Arrow to explore the island at our leisure.

In the interior we found that not only the plants and trees were suffering from the cold: the animal life was in even worse straits. Everywhere shivering birds were to be seen, their feathers all fluffed out, gathering together for flight to summer lands. And many lay dead upon the ground. Going down to the shore, we watched land-crabs in large numbers taking to the sea to find some better home. While away to the Southeast we could see many icebergs floating—a sign that we were now not far from the terrible region of the Antarctic.

As we were looking out to sea, we noticed our friends the porpoises jumping through the waves. The doctor hailed them and they came inshore.

He asked them how far we were from the South Polar Continent.

About a hundred miles, they told him. And then they asked why he wanted to know.

"Because this floating island we are on," said he, "is drifting southward all the time in a current. It's an island that ordinarily belongs somewhere in the tropic zone—real sultry weather, sunstrokes and all that. If it doesn't stop going southward pretty soon everything on it is going to perish."

"Well," said the porpoises, "then the thing to do is to get it back into a warmer climate, isn't it?"

"Yes, but how?" said the Doctor. "We can't *row* it back."

"No," said they, "but whales could push it—if you only got enough of them."

"What a splendid idea!—Whales, the very thing!" said the Doctor. "Do you think you could get me some?"

"Why, certainly," said the porpoises, "we passed one herd of them out there, sporting about among the icebergs. We'll ask them to come over. And if they aren't enough, we'll try and hunt up some more. Better have plenty."

"Thank you," said the Doctor. "You are very kind—By the way, do you happen to know how this island came to be a floating island? At least half of it, I notice, is made of stone. It is very odd that it floats at all, isn't it?"

"It is unusual," they said. "But the explanation is quite simple. It used to be a mountainous part of South America—an overhanging part—sort of an awkward corner, you might say. Way back, many years ago, it broke off from the mainland; and by some curious accident the inside of it, which is hollow, got filled with air as it fell into the ocean. You can only see less than half of the island: the bigger half is underwater. And in the middle of it, underneath, is a huge rock air-chamber, running right up inside the mountains. And that's what keeps it floating."

"What a pecurious phenometer!" said Bumpo.

"It is indeed," said the Doctor. "I must make a note of that." And out came the everlasting notebook.

The porpoises went bounding off towards the icebergs. And not long after, we saw the sea heaving and frothing as a big herd of whales came towards us at full speed.

They certainly were enormous creatures; and there must have been a good two hundred of them.

"Here they are," said the porpoises, poking their heads out of the water.

"Good!" said the Doctor. "Now just explain to them, will you please? That this is a very serious matter for all the living creatures in this land. And ask them if they will be so good as to go down to the far end of the island, put their noses against it and push it back near the coast of Southern Brazil."

The porpoises evidently succeeded in persuading the whales to do as the Doctor asked; for presently we saw them thrashing through the seas, going off towards the south end of the island.

Then we lay down upon the beach and waited.

After about an hour the Doctor got up and threw a stick into the water. For a while this floated motionless. But soon we saw it begin to move gently down the coast.

"Ah!" said the Doctor, "see that?—The island is going North at last. Thank goodness!"

Faster and faster we left the stick behind; and smaller and dimmer grew the icebergs on the skyline.

The Doctor took out his watch, threw more sticks into the water and made a rapid calculation.

"Humph!—Fourteen and a half knots an hour," he murmured—"A very nice speed. It should take us about five days to get back near Brazil. Well, that's that—Quite a load off my mind. I declare I feel warmer already. Let's go and get something to eat."

Recalling

1. What did Jip discover about the slab?

2. How did Dr. Dolittle free Long Arrow?

3. Why did Long Arrow and Dr. Dolittle have trouble communicating? In what language were they able to communicate?

4. How had the Indians become trapped in the cave? How long had they been trapped? What did they eat and drink while trapped?

5. What caused the eighty-year-old chief's death? Why did this worry Dr. Dolittle? What did he suggest?

6. What was unusual about the meal that the Indians served to Dr. Dolittle? Why didn't Long Arrow know what the word "cooked" meant?

Interpreting

7. Why did Dr. Dolittle consider saving Long Arrow the greatest accomplishment of his life?

8. How did Dr. Dolittle create fire? Why was this such an important accomplishment for everyone on the island?

Concluding

9. Give an example of the porpoises' cleverness.

Examining the Novel

Dr. Dolittle does not rescue Long Arrow and head back home. He remains and becomes involved in further adventures. What three problems does Dr. Dolittle solve in this section?

Thinking About the Novel

Dr. Dolittle is a humble person who speaks in an ordinary manner. Even when he speaks in simile-like language, he uses commonplace associations. For example, Dr. Dolittle claims the mountain's fall "will squash him flatter than a pancake." He compares Long Arrow's eyes to an eagle's. Write a paragraph in which you describe an event. Use at least two similes as part of your description.

Creating and Writing

Dr. Dolittle's world is one of interdependence. Dr. Dolittle helps the animals and the animals help him. Think of the animals in your neighborhood. Perhaps you'll think of squirrels, cats, or pigeons. If you live in a more suburban neighborhood, perhaps you'll think of chipmunks, raccoons, or skunks. How can one of these animals help you, and how can you learn to live with them? Write a story where a small animal helps a human. Make your story as farfetched and humorous as possible.

Blueprint FOR READING

Into • *The Voyages of Dr. Dolittle* *Part Five—Chapters 5-10*

How does a kind and reasonable man like Dr. Dolittle deal with unkind and unreasonable people? At first, he gives them the benefit of the doubt, and offers to negotiate and understand their point of view. When they prove to be just plain bad, he prepares to fight them. One of Dr. Dolittle's many virtues is courage. A second one is clarity. Clarity means knowing clearly what must be done and doing it. Once Dr. Dolittle has made up his mind to fight, he does not begin to reconsider, ask someone else to do the fighting, or pretend that the enemy is really not so bad after all. The author does not see Dr. Dolittle's willingness to take up arms as a contradiction to his gentle, caring nature. On the contrary, because Dr. Dolittle cares about the Popsipetels, he must defend them.

In this section we can see that the author, Hugh Lofting, is presenting his own ideas about when and how wars should be fought.

Focus

A second topic of this part of the story is "power." Many wars are fought because one nation or even one individual wants power. Dr. Dolittle does not want power—he actually despises the idea of having it. Do you think this is a positive or a negative—perhaps it would be better if good people took power? Do you think there are many people like Dr. Dolittle? Do you think that agreeing to rule will be good for him? Will he grow better or worse?

5

WAR!

On our way back to the village the Doctor began discussing natural history with Long Arrow. But their most interesting talk, mainly about plants, had hardly begun when an Indian runner came dashing up to us with a message.

Long Arrow listened gravely to the breathless, babbled words, then turned to the Doctor and said in eagle tongue, "Great White Man, an evil thing has befallen the Popsipetels. Our neighbors to the southward, the thievish Bag-jagderags, who for so long have cast envious eyes on our stores of ripe corn, have gone upon the warpath; and even now are advancing to attack us."

"Evil news indeed," said the Doctor. "Yet let us not judge harshly. Perhaps it is that they are desperate for food, having their own crops frost-killed before harvest. For are they not even nearer the cold South than you?"

"Make no excuses for any man of the tribe of the Bag-jagderags," said Long Arrow shaking his head. "They are an idle shiftless race. They do but see a chance to get corn without the labor of husbandry.[1] If it were not that they are a much bigger tribe and hope to defeat their neighbor by sheer force of numbers, they would not have dared to make open war upon the brave Popsipetels."

When we reached the village we found it in a great state of excitement. Everywhere men were seen putting their bows in order, sharpening spears, grinding battle-axes and making arrows by the hundred. Women were raising a high fence of bamboo poles all round the village. Scouts and messengers kept coming and going, bringing news of the movements of the enemy. While high up in the trees and hills about the village we could see lookouts watching the mountains to the southward.

Long Arrow brought another Indian, short but enormously broad, and introduced him to the Doctor as Big Teeth, the chief warrior of the Popsipetels.

The Doctor volunteered to go and see the enemy and try to argue the matter out peacefully with them instead of fighting; for war, he said, was at best a stupid wasteful business. But the two shook their heads. Such a plan was hopeless, they said. In the last war when they had sent a messenger to do peaceful arguing, the enemy had merely hit him with an ax.

---

1. *Husbandry* (HUZ bin dree) is the cultivation of plants.

Word Bank	**shiftless** (SHIFT liss) *adj.*: marked by a lack of ambition, energy, or purpose; lazy

While the Doctor was asking Big Teeth how he meant to defend the village against attack, a cry of alarm was raised by the lookouts.

"They're coming!—The Bag-jagderags—swarming down the mountains in thousands!"

"Well," said the Doctor, "it's all in the day's work, I suppose. I don't believe in war; but if the village is attacked we must help defend it."

And he picked up a club from the ground and tried the heft of it against a stone.

"This," he said, "seems like a pretty good tool to me." And he walked to the bamboo fence and took his place among the other waiting fighters.

Then we all got hold of some kind of weapon with which to help our friends, the gallant Popsipetels: I borrowed a bow and a quiver full of arrows; Jip was content to rely upon his old, but still strong teeth; Chee-Chee took a bag of rocks and climbed a palm where he could throw them down upon the enemies' heads; and Bumpo marched after the Doctor to the fence armed with a young tree in one hand and a doorpost in the other.

When the enemy drew near enough to be seen from where we stood we all gasped with astonishment. The hillsides were actually covered with them—thousands upon thousands. They made our small army within the village look like a mere handful.

"Oh my!" muttered Polynesia, "our little lot will stand no chance against that swarm. This will never do. I'm going off to get some help."

Where she was going and what kind of help she meant to get, I had no idea. She just disappeared from my side. But Jip, who had heard her, poked his nose between the bamboo bars of the fence to get a better view of the enemy and said, "Likely enough she's gone after the Black Parrots. Let's hope she finds them in time. Just look at those ugly ruffians climbing down the rocks—millions of 'em! This fight's going to keep us all hopping."

And Jip was right. Before a quarter of an hour had gone by our village was completely surrounded by one huge mob of yelling, raging Bag-jagderags.

I now come again to a part in the story of our voyages where things happened so quickly, one upon the other, that looking backwards I see the picture only in a confused kind of way. I know that if it had not been for the Terrible Three—as they came afterwards to be fondly called in Popsipetel history—Long Arrow, Bumpo and the Doctor, the war would have been soon over and the whole island would have belonged to the worthless Bag-jagderags. But the Englishman, the African and the Indian were a regiment in themselves; and between them they made that village a dangerous place for any man to try to enter.

The bamboo fencing which had been hastily set up around the town was not a very strong affair; and right from the start it gave way in one

---

Word Bank hastily (HAYS tih lee) *adv.*: rapidly and often with little attention to detail; hurriedly place after another as the enemy thronged and crowded against it. Then the Doctor, Long Arrow and Bumpo would hurry to the weak spot, a terrific hand-to-hand fight would take place and the enemy be thrown out. But almost instantly a cry of alarm would come from some other part of the village-wall; and the Three would have to rush off and do the same thing all over again.

The Popsipetels were themselves no mean fighters; but the strength and weight of those three men of different lands and colors, standing close together, swinging their enormous war-clubs, was really a sight for the wonder and admiration of anyone.

Many weeks later when I was passing an Indian campfire at night I heard this song being sung. It has since become one of the traditional folk-songs of the Popsipetels.

The Song of the Terrible Three

Oh hear ye the Song of the Terrible Three
And the fight that they fought by the edge of the sea.
Down from the mountains, the rocks and the crags,
Swarming like wasps, came the Bag-jagderags.

Surrounding our village, our walls they broke down.
Oh, sad was the plight of our men and our town!
But Heaven determined our land to set free
And sent us the help of the Terrible Three.

One was a Black—he was dark as the night;
One was a Red-skin, a mountain of height;
But the chief was a White Man, round like a bee;
And all in a row stood the Terrible Three.

Shoulder to shoulder, they hammered and hit.
Like demons of fury they kicked and they bit.
Like a wall of destruction they stood in a row,
Flattening enemies, six at a blow.

Oh, strong was the Red-skin fierce was the Black.
Bag-jagderags trembled and tried to turn back.
But 'twas of the White Man they shouted, "Beware!
He throws men in handfuls, straight up in the air!"

Long shall they frighten bad children at night
With tales of the Red and the Black and the White.
And long shall we sing of the Terrible Three
And the fight that they fought by the edge of the sea.

6

GENERAL POLYNESIA

But alas! even the Three, mighty though they were, could not last forever against an army which seemed to have no end. In one of the hottest scrimmages, when the enemy had broken a particularly wide hole through the fence, I saw Long Arrow's great figure topple and come down with a spear sticking in his broad chest.

For another half-hour Bumpo and the Doctor fought on side by side. How their strength held out so long I cannot tell, for never a second were they given to get their breath or rest their arms.

The Doctor—the quiet, kindly, peaceable, little Doctor!—well, you wouldn't have known him if you had seen him that day dealing out whacks you could hear a mile off, walloping and swatting in all directions.

As for Bumpo, with staring eyeballs and grim set teeth, he was a veritable monster. None dared come within yards of that wicked, wide-circling doorpost. But a stone, skillfully thrown, struck him at last in the center of the forehead. And down went the second of the Three. John Dolittle, the last of the Terribles, was left fighting alone.

Jip and I rushed to his side and tried to take the places of the fallen ones. But, far too light and too small, we made but a poor exchange. Another length of the fence crashed down, and through the widened gap the Bag-jagderags poured in on us like a flood.

"To the canoes!—To the sea!" shouted the Popsipetels. "Fly for your lives!—All is over!—The war is lost!"

But the Doctor and I never got a chance to fly for our lives. We were swept off our feet and knocked down flat by the sheer weight of the mob. And once down, we were unable to get up again. I thought we would surely be trampled to death.

But at that moment, above the din and racket of the battle, we heard the most terrifying noise that ever assaulted human ears: the sound of millions and millions of parrots all screeching with fury together.

The army, which in the nick of time Polynesia had brought to our rescue, darkened the whole sky to the westward. I asked her afterwards how many birds there were; and she said she didn't know exactly but that they certainly numbered somewhere between sixty and seventy millions. In that extraordinarily short space of time she had brought them from the mainland of South America.

If you have ever heard a parrot screech with anger you will know that it makes a truly frightful sound; and if you have ever been bitten by one, you will know that its bite can be a nasty and a painful thing.

Word Bank	**topple** (TAHP il) *v.*: to fall or tumble from top-heaviness
	assaulted (us SALT id) *v.*: attacked violently

The Black Parrots (coal-black all over, they were—except for a scarlet beak and a streak of red in wing and tail) on the word of command from Polynesia set to work upon the Bag-jagderags who were now pouring through the village looking for plunder.

And the Black Parrots' method of fighting was peculiar. This is what they did: on the head of each Bag-jagderag three or four parrots settled and took a good foothold in his hair with their claws; then they leant down over the sides of his head and began clipping snips out of his ears, for all the world as though they were punching tickets. That is all they did. They never bit them anywhere else except the ears. But it won the war for us.

With howls pitiful to hear, the Bag-jagderags fell over one another in their haste to get out of that accursed village. It was no use their trying to pull the parrots off their heads; because for each head there were always four more parrots waiting impatiently to get on.

Some of the enemy were lucky; and with only a snip or two managed to get outside the fence—where the parrots immediately left them alone. But with most, before the black birds had done with them, the ears presented a very singular appearance—like the edge of a postage-stamp. This treatment, very painful at the time, did not however do them any permanent harm beyond the change in looks. And it later got to be the tribal mark of the Bag-jagderags. And that (though it is not generally known to scientists) is how this people came to be called by the other Indian nations, the *Ragged-Eared Bag-jagderags*.

As soon as the village was cleared of the enemy the Doctor turned his attention to the wounded.

In spite of the length and fierceness of the struggle, there were surprisingly few serious injuries. Poor Long Arrow was the worst off. However, after the Doctor had washed his wound and got him to bed, he opened his eyes and said he already felt better. Bumpo was only badly stunned. With this part of the business over, the Doctor called to Polynesia to have the Black Parrots drive the enemy right back into their own country and to wait there, guarding them all night.

Polynesia gave the short word of command; and like one bird those millions of parrots opened their red beaks and let out once more their terrifying battle-scream.

The Bag-jagderags didn't wait to be bitten a second time, but fled helter-skelter over the mountains from which they had come; whilst Polynesia and her victorious army followed watchfully behind like a great, threatening, black cloud.

The Doctor picked up his high hat which had been knocked off in the fight, dusted it carefully and put it on.

"Tomorrow," he said, shaking his fist towards the hills, "we will arrange the terms of peace—and we will arrange them—in the City of Bag-jagderag!"

His words were greeted with cheers of triumph from the admiring Popsipetels. The war was over.

7

THE PEACE OF THE PARROTS

The next day we set out for the far end of the island, and reaching it in canoes (for we went by sea) after a journey of twenty-five hours, we remained no longer than was necessary in in the City of Bag-jagderag.

When he threw himself into that fight at Popsipetel, I saw the Doctor really angry for the first time in my life. But his anger, once aroused, was slow to die. All the way down the coast of the island he never ceased to rail against this cowardly people who had attacked his friends, the Popsipetels, for no other reason but to rob them of their corn, because they were too idle to till the land themselves. And he was still angry when he reached the City of Bag-jagderag.

Long Arrow had not come with us for he was as yet weak from his wound. But the Doctor—always clever at languages—was already getting familiar with the Indian tongue. Besides, among the half-dozen Popsipetels who accompanied us to paddle the canoes, was one boy to whom we had taught a little English. He and the Doctor between them managed to make themselves understood to the Bag-jagderags. This people, with the terrible parrots still blackening the hills about their stone town, waiting for the word to descend and attack, were, we found, in a very humble mood.

Leaving our canoes we passed up the main street to the palace of the chief. Bumpo and I couldn't help smiling with satisfaction as we saw how the waiting crowds which lined the roadway bowed their heads in shame, as the little, round, angry figure of the Doctor strutted ahead of us with his chin in the air.

At the foot of the palace-steps the chief and all the more important personages of the tribe were waiting to meet him, smiling humbly and holding out their hands in friendliness. The Doctor took not the slightest notice. He marched right by them, up the steps to the door of the palace. There he turned around and at once began to address the people in a firm voice.

I never heard such a speech in my life—and I am quite sure that they never did either. First he called them a long string of names: cowards, loafers, thieves, vagabonds, good-for-nothings, bullies and whatnot. Then he said he was still seriously thinking of allowing the parrots to drive them on into the sea, in order that this pleasant land might be rid, once and for all, of their worthless carcasses.

At this a great cry for mercy went up, and the chief and all of them called out that they would submit to any conditions of peace he wished.

Then the Doctor called for one of their scribes—that is, a man who did picture-writing. And on the stone walls of the palace of Bag-jagderag he bade him write down the terms of the peace as he dictated it. This peace is known as *The Peace of the Parrots*, and—unlike most peaces— was, and is, strictly kept—even to this day.

It was quite long in words. The half of the palace-front was covered with picture-writing, and fifty pots of paint were used, before the weary scribe had done. But the main part of it all was that there should be no more fighting; and that the two tribes should give solemn promise to help one another whenever there was corn-famine or other distress in the lands belonging to either.

This greatly surprised the Bag-jagderags. They had expected from the Doctor's angry face that he would at least chop a couple of hundred heads off—and probably make the rest of them slaves for life.

But when they saw that he only meant kindly by them, their great fear of him changed to a tremendous admiration. And as he ended his long speech and walked briskly down the steps again on his way back to the canoes, the group of chieftains threw themselves at his feet and cried, "Do but stay with us Great Man, and all the riches of Bag-jagderags shall be poured into your lap. Gold-mines we know of in the mountains and pearl-beds beneath the sea. Only stay with us, that your all-powerful wisdom may lead our Council and our people in prosperity and peace."

The Doctor held up his hand for silence.

"No man," said he, "would wish to be the guest of the Bag-jagderags till they had proved by their deeds that they are an honest race. Be true to the terms of the Peace and from yourselves shall come good government and prosperity—Farewell!"

Then he turned and followed by Bumpo, the Popsipetels and myself, walked rapidly down to the canoes.

8

THE HANGING STONE

But the change of heart in the Bag-jagderags was really sincere. The Doctor had made a great impression on them—a deeper one than even he himself realized at the time. In fact I sometimes think that that speech of his from the palace-steps had more effect upon the Indians of Spidermonkey Island than had any of his great deeds which, great though they were, were always magnified and exaggerated when the news of them was passed from mouth to mouth.

A sick girl was brought to him as he reached the place where the boats lay. She turned out to have some quite simple ailment which he quickly gave the remedy for. But this increased his popularity still more. And when he stepped into his canoe, the people all around us actually burst into tears. It seems (I learned this afterwards) that they thought he was going away across the sea, for good, to the mysterious foreign lands from which he had come.

Some of the chieftains spoke to the Popsipetels as we pushed off. What they said I did not understand; but we noticed that several canoes filled with Bag-jagderags followed us at a respectful distance all the way to Popsipetel.

The Doctor had determined to return by the other shore, so that we should be thus able to make a complete trip round the island's shores.

Shortly after we started, while still off the lower end of the island, we sighted a steep point on the coast where the sea was in a great state of turmoil, white with soapy froth. On going nearer, we found that this was caused by our friendly whales who were still faithfully working away with their noses against the end of the island, driving us northward. We had been kept so busy with the war that we had forgotten all about them. But as we paused and

watched their mighty tails lashing and churning the sea, we suddenly realized that we had not felt cold in quite a long while. Speeding up our boat lest the island be carried away from us altogether, we passed on up the coast; and here and there we noticed that the trees on the shore already looked greener and more healthy. Spidermonkey Island was getting back into her home climates.

About halfway to Popsipetel we went ashore and spent two or three days exploring the central part of the island. Our Indian paddlers took us up into the mountains, very steep and high in this region, overhanging the sea. And they showed us what they called the Whispering Rocks.

This was a very peculiar and striking piece of scenery. It was like a great vast basin,[2] or circus,[3] in the mountains, and out of the center of it there rose a table of rock with an ivory chair upon it. All around this the mountains went up like stairs, or theater-seats, to a great height—except at one narrow end which was open to a view of the sea. You could imagine it a council-place or concert-hall for giants, and the rock table in the center the stage for performers or the stand for the speaker.

We asked our guides why it was called the Whispering Rocks; and they said, "Go down into it and we will show you."

The great bowl was miles deep and miles wide. We scrambled down the rocks and they showed us how, even when you stood far, far apart

---

2. Here, a *basin* (BAY sin) is a depression in the land.
3. A *circus* (SIR kus) is an arena where rows of seats are placed on three of four sides.

from one another, you merely had to whisper in that great place and everyone in the theater could hear you. This was, the Doctor said, on account of the echoes which played backwards and forwards between the high walls of rock.

Our guides told us that it was here, in days long gone by when the Popsipetels owned the whole of Spidermonkey Island, that the kings were crowned. The ivory chair upon the table was the throne in which they sat. And so great was the big theater that all the Indians in the island were able to get seats in it to see the ceremony.

They showed us also an enormous hanging stone perched on the edge of a volcano's crater—the highest summit in the whole island. Although it was very far below us, we could see it quite plainly; and it looked wobbly enough to be pushed off its perch with the hand. There was a legend among the people, they said, that when the greatest of all Popsipetel kings should be crowned in the ivory chair, this hanging stone would tumble into the volcano's mouth and go straight down to the center of the earth.

The Doctor said he would like to go and examine it closer.

And when we were come to the lip of the volcano (it took us half a day to get up to it) we found the stone was unbelievably large. Underneath it we could look right down into a black hole which seemed to have no bottom. The Doctor explained to us that volcanoes sometimes spurted up fire from the holes in their tops; but that those on floating islands were always cold and dead.

"Stubbins," he said, looking up at the great stone towering above us, "do you know what would most likely happen if that boulder should fall in?"

"No," said I, "what?"

"You remember the air-chamber which the porpoises told us lies under the center of the island?"

"Yes."

"Well, this stone is heavy enough, if it fell into the volcano, to break through into that air-chamber from above. And once it did, the air would escape and the floating island would float no more. It would sink."

"But then everybody on it would be drowned, wouldn't they?" said Bumpo.

"Oh no, not necessarily. That would depend on the depth of the sea where the sinking took place. The island might touch bottom when it had only gone down, say, a hundred feet. But there would be lots of it still sticking up above the water then, wouldn't there?"

"Yes," said Bumpo, "I suppose there would. Well, let us hope that the ponderous fragment does *not* lose its equilibriosity, for I don't believe it would stop at the center of the earth—more likely it would fall right through the world and come out the other side."

Many other wonders there were which these men showed us in the central regions of their island. But I have not time or space to tell you of them now.

Descending towards the shore again, we noticed that we were still being watched, even here among the highlands, by the Bag-jagderags who had followed us. And when we put to sea once more a boatload of them proceeded to go ahead of us in the direction of Popsipetel. Having lighter canoes, they traveled faster than our party; and we judged that they should reach the village—if that was where they were going—many hours before we could.

The Doctor was now becoming anxious to see how Long Arrow was getting on, so we all took turns at the paddles and went on traveling by moonlight through the whole night.

We reached Popsipetel just as the dawn was breaking.

To our great surprise we found that not only we, but the whole village also, had been up all night. A great crowd was gathered about the dead chief's house. And as we landed our canoes upon the beach we saw a large number of old men, the seniors of the tribe, coming out at the main door.

We inquired what was the meaning of all this; and were told that the election of a new chief had been going on all through the whole night. Bumpo asked the name of the new chief; but this, it seemed, had not yet been given out. It would be announced at midday.

As soon as the Doctor had paid a visit to Long Arrow and seen that he was doing nicely, we proceeded to our own house at the far end of the village. Here we ate some breakfast and then lay down to take a good rest.

Rest, indeed, we needed; for life had been strenuous and busy for us ever since we had landed on the island. And it wasn't many minutes after our weary heads struck the pillows that the whole crew of us were sound asleep.

9

The Election

We were awakened by music. The glaring noonday sunlight was streaming in at our door, outside of which some kind of a band appeared to be playing. We got up and looked out. Our house was surrounded by the whole population of Popsipetel. We were used to having quite a number of curious and admiring Indians waiting at our door at all hours; but this was quite different. The vast crowd was dressed in its best clothes. Bright beads, gawdy feathers and gay blankets gave cheerful color to the scene. Everyone seemed in very good humor, singing or playing on musical instruments—mostly painted wooden whistles or drums made from skins.

We found Polynesia—who while we slept had arrived back from Bag-jagderag—sitting on our doorpost watching the show. We asked her what all the holiday-making was about.

"The result of the election has just been announced," said she. "The name of the new chief was given out at noon."

"And who is the new chief?" asked the Doctor.

"You are," said Polynesia quietly.

"*I!*" gasped the Doctor—"Well, of all things!"

"Yes," said she. "You're the one—And what's more, they've changed your surname for you. They didn't think that Dolittle was a proper or respectful name for a man who had done so much. So you are now to be known as Jong Thinkalot. How do you like it?"

"But I don't *want* to be a chief," said the Doctor in an irritable voice.

"I'm afraid you'll have hard work to get out of it now," said she— "unless you're willing to put to sea again in one of their rickety canoes. You see you've been elected not merely the Chief of the Popsipetels; you're to be a king—the King of the whole of Spidermonkey Island. The Bag-jagderags, who were so anxious to have you govern them, sent spies and messengers ahead of you; and when they found that you had been elected Chief of the Popsipetels overnight they were bitterly disappointed. However, rather than lose you altogether, the Bag-jagderags were willing to give up their independence, and insisted that they and their lands be united to the Popsipetels in order that you could be made king of both. So now you're in for it."

"Oh my!" groaned the Doctor, "I do wish they wouldn't be so enthusiastic! Bother it, I don't *want* to be a king!"

"I should think, Doctor," said I, "you'd feel rather proud and glad. I wish *I* had a chance to be a king."

"Oh I know it sounds grand," said he, pulling on his boots miserably. "But the trouble is, you can't take up responsibilities and then just drop them again when you feel like it. I have my own work to do. Scarcely one moment have I had to give to natural history since I landed on this island. I've been doing someone else's business all the time. And now they want me to go on doing it! Why, once I'm made King of the Popsipetels, that's the end of me as a useful naturalist. I'd be too busy for anything. All I'd be then is just a er—er—just a king."

"Well, that's something!" said Bumpo. "My father is a king and has a wonderful life."

"I have my work to do. I don't want to be a king," said the Doctor.

"Look," said Polynesia, "here come the head men to announce your election. Hurry up and get your boots laced."

The throng before our door had suddenly parted asunder, making a long lane; and down this we now saw a group of personages coming towards us. The man in front, a handsome old Indian with a wrinkled face, carried in his hands a wooden crown—a truly beautiful and gorgeous crown, even though of wood. Wonderfully carved and painted, it had two lovely blue feathers springing from the front of it. Behind the old man came eight strong Indians bearing a litter, a sort of chair with long handles underneath to carry it by.

Kneeling down on one knee, bending his head almost to the ground, the old man addressed the Doctor who now stood in the doorway putting on his collar and tie.

"Oh, Mighty One," said he, "we bring you word from the Popsipetel people. Great are your deeds beyond belief, kind is your heart and your wisdom, deeper than the sea. Our chief is dead. The people clamor for a worthy leader. Our old enemies, the Bag-jagderags, are become, through you, our brothers and good friends. They too desire to bask beneath the sunshine of your smile. Behold then, I bring to you the Sacred Crown of Popsipetel which, since ancient days when this island and its people were one, beneath one monarch, has rested on no kingly brow. Oh Kindly One, we are bidden by the united voices of the peoples of this land to carry you to the Whispering Rocks, that there, with all respect and majesty, you may be crowned our king—King of all the Moving Land."

The good Indians did not seem to have even considered the possibility of John Dolittle's refusing. As for the poor Doctor, I never saw him so upset by anything. It was in fact the only time I have known him to get thoroughly fussed.

"Oh dear!" I heard him murmur, looking around wildly for some escape. "What *shall* I do?—Did any of you see where I laid that stud of mine?—How on earth can I get this collar on without a stud? What a day this is, to be sure!—Maybe it rolled under the bed, Bumpo—I do think they might have given me a day or so to think it over in. Who ever heard of waking a man right out of his sleep, and telling him he's got to be a king, before he has even washed his face? Can't any of you find it? Maybe you're standing on it, Bumpo. Move your feet."

"Oh don't bother about your stud," said Polynesia. "You will have to be crowned without a collar. They won't know the difference."

"I tell you I'm not going to be crowned," cried the Doctor—"not if I can help it. I'll make them a speech. Perhaps that will satisfy them."

He turned back to the Indians at the door.

"My friends," he said, "I am not worthy of this great honor you would do to me. Little or no skill have I in the arts of kingcraft. Assuredly among your own brave men you will find many better fitted to lead you. For this compliment, this confidence and trust, I thank you. But, I pray you, do not think of me for such high duties which I could not possibly fulfill."

The old man repeated his words to the people behind him in a louder voice. Stolidly they shook their heads, moving not an inch. The old man turned back to the Doctor.

"You are the chosen one," said he. "They will have none but you."

Into the Doctor's perplexed face suddenly there came a flash of hope.

"I'll go and see Long Arrow," he whispered to me. "Perhaps he will know of some way to get me out of this."

And asking the personages to excuse him a moment, he left them there, standing at his door, and hurried off in the direction of Long Arrow's house. I followed him.

Word Bank	**perplexed** (pur PLEXT) *adj.*: filled with doubt, uncertainty, or confusion; puzzled

We found our big friend lying on a grass bed outside his home, where he had been moved that he might witness the holiday-making.

"Long Arrow," said the Doctor speaking quickly in eagle tongue so that the bystanders should not overhear, "in dire peril I come to you for help. These men would make me their king. If such a thing befall me, all the great work I hoped to do must go undone, for who is there unfreer than a king? I pray you speak with them and persuade their kind well-meaning hearts that what they plan to do would be unwise."

Long Arrow raised himself upon his elbow.

"Oh Kindly One," said he (this seemed now to have become the usual manner of address when speaking to the Doctor), "sorely it grieves me that the first wish you ask of me I should be unable to grant. Alas! I can do nothing. These people have so set their hearts on keeping you for king that if I tried to interfere they would drive me from their land and likely crown you in the end in any case. A king you must be, if only for a while. We must so arrange the business of governing that you may have time to give to Nature's secrets. Later we may be able to hit upon some plan to relieve you of the burden of the crown. But for now you must be king. These people are a headstrong tribe and they will have their way. There is no other course."

Sadly the Doctor turned away from the bed and faced about. And there behind him stood the old man again, the crown still held in his wrinkled hands and the royal litter waiting at his elbow. With a deep reverence the bearers motioned towards the seat of the chair, inviting the white man to get in.

Once more the poor Doctor looked wildly, hopelessly about him for some means of escape. For a moment I thought he was going to take to his heels and run for it. But the crowd around us was far too thick and densely packed for anyone to break through it. A band of whistles and drums nearby suddenly started the music of a solemn processional march. He turned back pleadingly again to Long Arrow in a last appeal for help. But the big Indian merely shook his head and pointed, like the bearers, to the waiting chair.

At last, almost in tears, John Dolittle stepped slowly into the litter and sat down. As he was hoisted onto the broad shoulders of the bearers I heard him still feebly muttering beneath his breath, "Botheration take it!—I don't *want* to be a king!"

"Farewell!" called Long Arrow from his bed, "and may good fortune ever stand within the shadow of your throne!"

"He comes!—He comes!" murmured the crowd. "Away! Away!—To the Whispering Rocks!"

And as the procession formed up to leave the village, the crowd about us began hurrying off in the direction of the mountains to make sure of good seats in the giant theater where the crowning ceremony would take place.

10

THE CORONATION OF KING JONG

In my long lifetime I have seen many grand and inspiring things, but never anything that impressed me half as much as the sight of the Whispering Rocks as they looked on the day King Jong was crowned. As Bumpo, Chee-Chee, Polynesia, Jip and I finally reached the dizzy edge of the great bowl and looked down inside it, it was like gazing over a never-ending ocean of copper-colored faces; for every seat in the theater was filled, every man, woman and child in the island—including Long Arrow who had been carried up on his sick bed—was there to see the show.

Yet not a sound, not a pin-drop, disturbed the solemn silence of the Whispering Rocks. It was quite creepy and sent chills running up and down your spine. Bumpo told me afterwards that it took his breath away too much for him to speak, but that he hadn't known before that there were that many people in the world.

Away down by the Table of the Throne stood a brand-new, brightly colored totem-pole. All the Indian families had totem-poles and kept them set up before the doors of their houses. The idea of a totem-pole is something like a doorplate or a visiting card. It represents in its carvings the deeds and qualities of the family to which it belongs. This one, beautifully decorated and much higher than any other, was the Dolittle or, as it was to be henceforth called, the Royal Thinkalot totem. It had nothing but animals on it, to signify the Doctor's great knowledge of creatures. And the animals chosen to be shown were those which to the Indians were supposed to represent good qualities of character, such as, the deer for speed; the ox for perseverance; the fish for discretion, and so on. But at the top of the totem is always placed the sign or animal by which the family is most proud to be known. This, on the Thinkalot pole, was an enormous parrot, in memory of the famous Peace of the Parrots.

The Ivory Throne had been all polished with scented oil and it glistened whitely in the strong sunlight. At the foot of it there had been strewn great quantities of branches of flowering trees, which with the new warmth of milder climates were now blossoming in the valleys of the island.

Soon we saw the royal litter, with the Doctor seated in it, slowly ascending the winding steps of the Table. Reaching the flat top at last, it halted and the Doctor stepped out upon the flowery carpet. So still and perfect was the silence that even at that distance above I distinctly heard a twig snap beneath his tread.

Walking to the throne accompanied by the old man, the Doctor got up upon the stand and sat down. How tiny his little round figure looked when seen from that tremendous height! The throne had been made for longer-legged kings; and when he was seated, his feet did not reach the ground but dangled six inches from the top step.

Then the old man turned round and looking up at the people began to speak in a quiet even voice; but every word he said was easily heard in the furthest corner of the Whispering Rocks.

First he recited the names of all the great Popsipetel kings who in days long ago had been crowned in this ivory chair. He spoke of the greatness of the Popsipetel people, of their triumphs, of their hardships. Then waving his hand towards the Doctor he began recounting the things which this king-to-be had done. And I am bound to say that they easily outmatched the deeds of those who had gone before him.

As soon as he started to speak of what the Doctor had achieved for the tribe, the people, still strictly silent, all began waving their right hands towards the throne. This gave to the vast theater a very singular appearance: acres and acres of something moving—with never a sound.

At last the old man finished his speech and stepping up to the chair, very respectfully removed the Doctor's battered high hat. He was about to put it upon the ground; but the Doctor took it from him hastily and kept it on his lap. Then taking up the Sacred Crown he placed it upon John Dolittle's head. It did not fit very well (for it had been made for smaller-headed kings), and when the wind blew in freshly from the sunlit sea the Doctor had some difficulty in keeping it on. But it looked very splendid.

Turning once more to the people, the old man said, "Men of Popsipetel, behold your elected king!—Are you content?"

And then at last the voice of the people broke loose.

"JONG! JONG!" they shouted, "LONG LIVE KING JONG!"

The sound burst upon the solemn silence with the crash of a hundred cannon. There, where even a whisper carried miles, the shock of it was like a blow in the face. Back and forth the mountains threw it to one another. I thought the echoes of it would never die away as it passed rumbling through the whole island, jangling among the lower valleys, booming in the distant sea-caves.

Suddenly I saw the old man point upward, to the highest mountain in the island; and looking over my shoulder, I was just in time to see the Hanging Stone topple slowly out of sight—down into the heart of the volcano.

"See ye, Men of the Moving Land!" the old man cried: "The stone has fallen. Our legend has come true: the greatest of Popsipetel kings is crowned this day!"

The Doctor too had seen the stone fall and he was now standing up looking at the sea expectantly.

"He's thinking of the air-chamber," said Bumpo in my ear. "Let us hope that the sea isn't very deep in these parts."

After a full minute (so long did it take the stone to fall that depth) we heard a muffled, distant, crunching thud—and then immediately after, a great hissing of escaping air. The Doctor, his face tense with anxiety, sat down in the throne again still watching the blue water of the ocean with staring eyes.

Soon we felt the island slowly sinking beneath us. We saw the sea creep inland over the beaches as the shores went down—one foot, three feet, ten feet, twenty, fifty, a hundred. And then, thank goodness, gently as a butterfly alighting on a rose, it stopped! Spidermonkey Island had come to rest on the sandy bottom of the Atlantic, and earth was joined to earth once more.

Of course many of the houses near the shores were now under water. Popsipetel Village itself had entirely disappeared. But it didn't matter. No one was drowned; for every soul in the island was high up in the hills watching the coronation of King Jong.

The Indians themselves did not realize at the time what was taking place, though of course they had felt the land sinking beneath them. The Doctor told us afterwards that it must have been the shock of that tremendous shout, coming from a million throats at once, which had toppled the Hanging Stone off its perch. But in Popsipetel history the story was handed down (and it is firmly believed to this day) that when King Jong sat upon the throne, so great was his mighty weight, that the very island itself sank down to do him honor and never moved again.

Recalling

1. Why was the battle between the Popsipetels and the Bag-jagderags fought? What was Dr. Dolittle's opinion of war?

2. Who were the Terrible Three? What did they do to fight off the Bag-jagderags?

3. What were the attack methods that the Black Parrots employed? What was the reaction of the Bag-jagderags to Dr. Dolittle's terms of peace? What does this tell you about Dr. Dolittle?

4. Describe the Whispering Rocks. Why was this place given that name?

5. What was pictured on the Royal Thinkalot totem pole? Why were these objects placed on this totem pole?

Interpreting

6. Why did the Hanging Stone fall, according to Popsipetel history?

Concluding

7. Why didn't the island sink when the Hanging Stone toppled over?

Examining the Novel

Consider the setting of Spidermonkey Island. What is the mood as the Popsipetels prepare to battle the Bag-jagderags? Does the location of the fighting help or hinder the Popsipetels? Does location or climate have any relation to the cause of the battle? Answer each of these questions in full sentences.

Thinking About the Novel

Whispering Rocks is a theater where two live shows take place: (1) Dr. Dolittle's coronation and (2) the Hanging Stone falls. The natives interpret the fall of the Hanging Stone as a sign that Dr. Dolittle is the greatest of all Popsipetel kings. What does Dr. Dolittle think of the natives' interpretation, and how does Dr. Dolittle explain the stone's fall? Is Dr. Dolittle's interpretation consistent with his view of the respect that man owes nature? Write a paragraph explaining your viewpoint.

Creating and Writing

The Popsipetels wrote a song celebrating the three men who fought together against the Bag-jagderags. Write a poem celebrating Dr. Dolittle's coronation and the fall of the Hanging Stone. Remember that it does not have to rhyme, but should include some elements of poetry like alliteration, similes, rhythm, and metaphors.

Into • *The Voyages of Dr. Dolittle*
Part Six—Chapters 1-3

Dr. Dolittle is finding that being king is just as difficult as he had thought it would be. This is because Dr. Dolittle takes no joy in pomp and ceremony and does not wish to be honored. He would prefer to do his work among equals in a quiet, efficient way. Ruling, to him, is a huge responsibility. He finds himself working at all hours of the day and night, his animal studies put aside, possibly forever. Is he happy? Is he fulfilled? If honor and glory are not what he wants, does the job of king hold any reward for him at all?

Focus

Long Arrow returns with a load of herbs that can cure many illnesses and difficulties. It is interesting to compare these herbs to today's medicines. Pills for sleeplessness, snakebite, and seasickness were the stuff of storybooks in those days—not the real world. Today, medicines for those very problems are readily available. If you were writing a story today, what cures would you describe, which might be considered ordinary one hundred years from now?

PART VI

1

NEW POPSIPETEL

Jong Thinkalot had not ruled over his new kingdom for more than a couple of days before my notions about kings and the kind of lives they led changed very considerably. I had thought that all that kings had to do was to sit on a throne and have people bow down before them several times a day. I now saw that a king can be the hardest-working man in the world—if he attends properly to his business.

From the moment that he got up, early in the morning, till the time he went to bed, late at night—seven days in the week—John Dolittle was busy, busy, busy. First of all there was the new town to be built. The village of Popsipetel had disappeared: the City of New Popsipetel must be made. With great care a place was chosen for it—and a very beautiful position it was, at the mouth of a large river. The shores of the island at this point formed a lovely wide bay where canoes—and ships too, if they should ever come—could lie peacefully at anchor without danger from storms.

In building this town the Doctor gave the Indians a lot of new ideas. He showed them what town-sewers were, and how garbage should be collected each day and burnt. High up in the hills he made a large lake by damming a stream. This was the water-supply for the town. None of these things had the Indians ever seen; and many of the sicknesses which they had suffered from before were now entirely prevented by proper drainage and pure drinking-water.

Peoples who don't use fire do not of course have metal either; because without fire it is almost impossible to shape iron and steel. One of the first things that John Dolittle did was to search the mountains till he found iron and copper mines. Then he set to work to teach the Indians how these metals could be melted and made into knives and plows and water-pipes and all manner of things.

In his kingdom the Doctor tried his hardest to do away with most of the old-fashioned pomp and grandeur of a royal court. As he said to Bumpo and me, if he must be a king he meant to be a thoroughly democratic one, that is a king who is chummy and friendly with his subjects and doesn't put on airs. And when he drew up the plans for the City of New Popsipetel he had no palace shown of any kind. A little cottage in a back street was all that he had provided for himself.

But this the Indians would not permit on any account. They had been used to having their kings rule in a truly grand and kingly manner; and they insisted that he have built for himself the most magnificent palace ever seen. In all else they let him have his own way absolutely; but they wouldn't allow him to wriggle out of any ceremony or show that goes with being a king. A thousand servants he had to keep in his palace, night and day, to wait on him. The Royal Canoe had to be kept up—a gorgeous, polished mahogany boat, seventy feet long, inlaid with mother-o'-pearl and paddled by the hundred strongest men in the island. The palace-gardens covered a square mile and employed a hundred and sixty gardeners.

Even in his dress the poor man was compelled always to be grand and elegant and uncomfortable. The beloved and battered high hat was put away in a closet and only looked at secretly. State robes had to be worn on all occasions. And when the Doctor did once in a while manage to sneak off for a short, natural-history expedition he never dared to wear his old clothes, but had to chase his butterflies with a crown upon his head and a scarlet cloak flying behind him in the wind.

There was no end to the kinds of duties the Doctor had to perform and the questions he had to decide upon—everything, from settling disputes about lands and boundaries, to making peace between men who had been throwing shoes at one another. In the east wing of the Royal Palace was the Hall of Justice. And here King Jong sat every morning from nine to eleven passing judgment on all cases that were brought before him.

Then in the afternoon he taught school. The sort of things he taught were not always those you find in ordinary schools. Grown-ups as well as children came to learn. You see, these Indians were ignorant of many of the things that quite small white children know—though it is also true that they knew a lot that white grown-ups never dreamed of.

Bumpo and I helped with the teaching as far as we could—simple arithmetic, and easy things like that. But the classes in astronomy, farming science, the proper care of babies, with a host of other subjects, the Doctor had to teach himself. The Indians were tremendously keen about the schooling and they came in droves and crowds; so that even with the open-air classes (a schoolhouse was impossible of course) the Doctor had to take them in rclays and batches of five or six thousand at a time and used a big megaphone or trumpet to make himself heard.

The rest of his day was more than filled with road-making, building water-mills, attending the sick and a million other things.

In spite of his being so unwilling to become a king, John Dolittle made a very good one—once he got started. He may not have been as dignified as many kings in history who were always running off to war and getting themselves into exciting situations; but since I have grown up and seen something of foreign lands and governments I have often thought that Popsipetel under the reign of Jong Thinkalot was perhaps the best ruled state in the history of the world.

The Doctor's birthday came round after we had been on the island six months and a half. The people made a great public holiday of it and there was much feasting, dancing, fireworks, speechmaking and jollification.

Towards the close of the day the chief men of the two tribes formed a procession and passed through the streets of the town, carrying a very gorgeously painted tablet of ebony wood, ten feet high. This was a picture-history, such as they preserved for each of the ancient kings of Popsipetel to record their deeds.

With great and solemn ceremony it was set up over the door of the new palace; and everybody then clustered round to look at it. It had six pictures on it commemorating the six great events in the life of King Jong and beneath were written the verses that explained them. They were composed by the Court Poet; and this is a translation:

I

(His Landing On The Island)
Heaven-sent,
In his dolphin-drawn canoe
From worlds unknown
He landed on our shores.
The very palms
Bowed down their heads
In welcome to the coming King.

II

(His Meeting With The Beetle)
By moonlight in the mountains
He communed with beasts.
The shy Jabizri brings him picture-words
Of great distress.

III

(He Liberates The Lost Families)
Big was his heart with pity;
Big were his hands with strength.
See how he tears the mountain like a yam!
See how the lost ones
Dance forth to greet the day!

Word Bank	**dignified** (DIG nih fyd) *adj.*: noble; showing or expressing dignity; honored or esteemed

IV
(He Makes Fire)
Our land was cold and dying.
He waved his hand and lo!
Lightning leapt from cloudless skies;
The sun leant down;
And Fire was born!
Then while we crowded round
The grateful glow, pushed he
Our wayward, floating land
Back to peaceful anchorage
In sunny seas.

V
(He Leads The People To Victory In War)
Once only
Was his kindly countenance
Darkened by a deadly frown.
Woe to the wicked enemy
That dares attack
The tribe with Thinkalot for Chief!

VI
(He Is Crowned King)
The birds of the air rejoiced;
The Sea laughed and gambolled with her shores;
All Red-skins wept for joy
The day we crowned him King.
He is the Builder, the Healer, the Teacher and the Prince;
He is the greatest of them all.
May he live a thousand thousand years,
Happy in his heart,
To bless our land with Peace.

2

THOUGHTS OF HOME

In the Royal Palace Bumpo and I had a beautiful suite of rooms of our very own—which Polynesia, Jip and Chee-Chee shared with us. Officially Bumpo was Minister of the Interior; while I was First Lord of the Treasury. Long Arrow also had quarters there; but at present he was absent, traveling abroad.

One night after supper when the Doctor was away in the town somewhere visiting a newborn baby, we were all sitting round the big table in Bumpo's reception-room. This we did every evening, to talk over the plans for the following day and various affairs of state. It was a kind of Cabinet Meeting.

Tonight however we were talking about England—and also about things to eat. We had got a little tired of Indian food. You see, none of the natives knew how to cook; and we had the most discouraging time training a chef for the Royal Kitchen. Most of them were champions at spoiling good food. Often we got so hungry that the Doctor would sneak downstairs with us into the palace basement, after all the cooks were safe in bed, and fry pancakes secretly over the dying embers of the fire. The Doctor himself was the finest cook that ever lived. But he used to make a terrible mess of the kitchen; and of course we had to be awfully careful that we didn't get caught.

Well, as I was saying, tonight food was the subject of discussion at the Cabinet Meeting; and I had just been reminding Bumpo of the nice dishes we had had at the bed-maker's house in Monteverde.

"I tell you what I would like now," said Bumpo: "a large cup of cocoa with whipped cream on the top of it. In Oxford we used to be able to get the most wonderful cocoa. It is really too bad they haven't any cocoa-trees in this island, or cows to give cream."

"When do you suppose," asked Jip, "the Doctor intends to move on from here?"

"I was talking to him about that only yesterday," said Polynesia. "But I couldn't get any satisfactory answer out of him. He didn't seem to want to speak about it."

There was a pause in the conversation.

"Do you know what I believe?" she added presently. "I believe the Doctor has given up even thinking of going home."

"Good L-rd!" cried Bumpo. "You don't say!"

"Sh!" said Polynesia. "What's that noise?"

We listened; and away off in the distant corridors of the palace we heard the sentries crying, "The King!—Make way! —The King!"

"It's he—at last," whispered Polynesia—"late, as usual. Poor man, how he does work!—Chee-Chee, get the pipe and tobacco out of the cupboard and lay the dressing-gown ready on his chair."

When the Doctor came into the room he looked serious and thoughtful. Wearily he took off his crown and hung it on a peg behind the door. Then he exchanged the royal cloak for the dressing-gown, dropped into his chair at the head of the table with a deep sigh and started to fill his pipe.

"Well," asked Polynesia quietly, "how did you find the baby?"

"The baby?" he murmured—his thoughts still seemed to be very far away—"Ah yes. The baby was much better, thank you—It has cut its second tooth."

Word Bank   embers (EM burz) *n.*: glowing fragments from a fire

Then he was silent again, staring dreamily at the ceiling through a cloud of tobacco-smoke; while we all sat round quite still, waiting.

"We were wondering, Doctor," said I at last,—"just before you came in—when you would be starting home again. We will have been on this island seven months tomorrow."

The Doctor sat forward in his chair looking rather uncomfortable.

"Well, as a matter of fact," said he after a moment, "I meant to speak to you myself this evening on that very subject. But it's—er—a little hard to make anyone exactly understand the situation. I am afraid that it would be impossible for me to leave the work I am now engaged in…You remember, when they first insisted on making me king, I told you it was not easy to shake off responsibilities, once you had taken them up. These people have come to rely on me for a great number of things. We found them ignorant of much that white people enjoy. And we have, one might say, changed the current of their lives considerably. Now it is a very ticklish business, to change the lives of other people. And whether the changes we have made will be, in the end, for good or for bad, is our lookout."

He thought a moment—then went on in a quieter, sadder voice: "I would like to continue my voyages and my natural history work; and I would like to go back to Puddleby—as much as any of you. This is March, and the crocuses will be showing in the lawn…But that which I feared has come true: I cannot close my eyes to what might happen if I should leave these people and run away. They would probably go back to their old habits and customs: wars, superstitions, and whatnot; and many of the new things we have taught them might be put to improper use and make their condition, then, worse by far than that in which we found them…They like me; they trust me; they have come to look to me for help in all their problems and troubles. And no man wants to do unfair things to them who trust him…And then again, *I* like *them*. They are, as it were, my children—I never had any children of my own—and I am terribly interested in how they will grow up. Don't you see what I mean?—How can I possibly run away and leave them in the lurch?…No. I have thought it over a good deal and tried to decide what was best. And I am afraid that the work I took up when I assumed the crown I must stick to. I'm afraid—I've got to stay."

"For good—for your whole life?" asked Bumpo in a low voice.

For some moments the Doctor, frowning, made no answer.

"I don't know," he said at last—"Anyhow for the present there is certainly no hope of my leaving. It wouldn't be right."

The sad silence that followed was broken finally by a knock upon the door.

With a patient sigh the Doctor got up and put on his crown and cloak again.

"Come in," he called, sitting down in his chair once more.

The door opened and a footman—one of the hundred and forty-three who were always on night duty—stood bowing in the entrance.

"Oh Kindly One," said he, "there is a traveler at the palace-gate who would have speech with Your Majesty."

"Another baby's been born, I'll bet a shilling," muttered Polynesia.

"Did you ask the traveler's name?" inquired the Doctor.

"Yes, Your Majesty," said the footman. "It is Long Arrow, the son of Golden Arrow."

3

THE RED MAN'S SCIENCE

"Long Arrow!" cried the Doctor. "How splendid! Show him in—show him in at once."

"I'm so glad," he continued, turning to us as soon as the footman had gone. "I've missed Long Arrow terribly. He's an awfully good man to have around—even if he doesn't talk much. Let me see: it's five months now since he went off to Brazil. I'm so glad he's back safe. He does take such tremendous chances with that canoe of his—clever as he is. It's no joke, crossing a hundred miles of open sea in a twelve-foot canoe. I wouldn't care to try it."

Another knock; and when the door swung open in answer to the Doctor's call, there stood our big friend on the threshold, a smile upon his strong, bronzed face. Behind him appeared two porters carrying loads done up in Indian palm-matting. These, when the first salutations were over, Long Arrow ordered to lay their burdens down.

"Behold, oh Kindly One," said he, "I bring you, as I promised, my collection of plants which I had hidden in a cave in the Andes. These treasures represent the labors of my life."

The packages were opened; and inside were many smaller packages and bundles. Carefully they were laid out in rows upon the table.

It appeared at first a large but disappointing display. There were plants, flowers, fruits, leaves, roots, nuts, beans, honeys, gums, bark, seeds, bees and a few kinds of insects.

The study of plants—or botany, as it is called—was a kind of natural history which had never interested me very much. I had considered it, compared with the study of animals, a dull science. But as Long Arrow began taking up the various things in his collection and explaining their qualities to us, I became more and more fascinated. And before he had done I was completely absorbed by the wonders of the Vegetable Kingdom which he had brought so far.

"These," said he, taking up a little packet of big seeds, "are what I have called 'laughing beans.'"

"What are they for?" asked Bumpo.

"To cause mirth,"[1] said the Indian.

Bumpo, while Long Arrow's back was turned, took three of the beans and swallowed them.

---

1. *Mirth* is joyous laughter.

"Alas!" said the Indian when he discovered what Bumpo had done. "If he wished to try the powers of these seeds he should have eaten no more than a quarter of a one. Let us hope that he does not die of laughter."

The beans' effect upon Bumpo was most extraordinary. First he broke into a broad smile; then he began to giggle; finally he burst into such prolonged roars of hearty laughter that we had to carry him into the next room and put him to bed. The Doctor said afterwards that he probably would have died laughing if he had not had such a strong constitution. All through the night he gurgled happily in his sleep. And even when we woke him up the next morning he rolled out of bed still chuckling.

Returning to the Reception Room, we were shown some red roots which Long Arrow told us had the property, when made into a soup with sugar and salt, of causing people to dance with extraordinary speed and endurance. He asked us to try them; but we refused, thanking him. After Bumpo's exhibition we were a little afraid of any more experiments for the present.

There was no end to the curious and useful things that Long Arrow had collected: an oil from a vine which would make hair grow in one night; an orange as big as a pumpkin which he had raised in his own mountain-garden in Peru; a black honey (he had brought the bees that made it too and the seeds of the flowers they fed on) which would put you to sleep, just with a teaspoonful, and make you wake up fresh in the morning; a nut that made the voice beautiful for singing; a water-weed that stopped cuts from bleeding; a moss that cured snakebite; a lichen that prevented seasickness.

The Doctor of course was tremendously interested. Well into the early hours of the morning he was busy going over the articles on the table one by one, listing their names and writing their properties and descriptions into a notebook as Long Arrow dictated.

"There are things here, Stubbins," he said as he ended, "which in the hands of skilled druggists will make a vast difference to the medicine and chemistry of the world. I suspect that this sleeping-honey by itself will take the place of half the bad drugs we have had to use so far. Long Arrow has discovered a pharmacopoeia of his own. Miranda was right: he is a great naturalist. His name deserves to be placed beside Linnaeus.[2] Someday I must get all these things to England—But when," he added sadly—"Yes, that's the problem: when?"

---

2. Carl *Linnaeus* (lih NEE us) (1707-1778) was a great botanist, renowned for his system of naming plants and other organisms.

Word Bank	**prolonged** (PRO longd) *adj.*: lengthened in extent, scope, or range; extended **endurance** (in DUR intz) *n.*: the ability to sustain a prolonged stressful effort or activity

Recalling

1. How had the city of Popsipetel disappeared?

2. Describe the king's palace. How large was the garden? How many servants worked there? Were the palace and its grounds in keeping with Dr. Dolittle's wishes?

3. What were Dr. Dolittle's duties as king? What were some of the things he taught the Popsipetels?

4. List the six incidents illustrated on Dr. Dolittle's birthday tablet.

Interpreting

5. After seven months as king, why did Dr. Dolittle feel he could not leave the island? Do you think his reasons are logical? Do you agree with him? Explain.

Concluding

6. Long Arrow brought back at least eight wonderful plants from Brazil. List five of these plants and their amazing properties. Do you think it is possible for natural substances to have medicinal qualities? If so, can you give any examples?

Examining the Novel

Dr. Dolittle feels a sense of responsibility and emotional attachment toward the Popsipetels. He feels like a father guiding young children, and he wants to stay until the children are grown and able to manage on their own. What could Dr. Dolittle learn from the Popsipetels? Consider abstract ideas like loyalty, gratitude, respect, openness to change, lack of prejudice, poetic expression, devotion, and optimism after disasters. Which of these abstract concepts could Dr. Dolittle bring back to England?

Thinking About the Novel

Dr. Dolittle has taught the natives many Western skills like building fire and welding metals. He has introduced them to the ideas of urban construction, medicine, and child care. He views the natives as children whom he has enlightened with modern ideas. Yet a seed of doubt creeps into Dr. Dolittle's thinking, and he fears that if he leaves, the natives will revert to their old customs. They would then be left with powerful weapons and equipment they could not quite understand. Should Dr. Dolittle have taught modern skills to the Popsipetels? Were they just as happy with their lives before Dr. Dolittle arrived? Should Dr. Dolittle have left immediately after he moved the island to the Atlantic? Write a paragraph stating your opinion.

Creating and Writing

It is 1900. An esteemed American doctor of medicine walks into Dr. Dolittle's house. Dr. Dolittle hands him samples of the medicines that he has received from Long Arrow. The American doctor leaves Dr. Dolittle's house with a smile on his face. Write a story describing what happens next.

Blueprint FOR READING

Into • *The Voyages of Dr. Dolittle Part Six—Chapters 4-7*

Finally, the Great Glass Sea Snail appears! This snail was described by the fidgit as the one possible way Dr. Dolittle could get close enough to the shellfish to learn their language. If you recall, that was why Dr. Dolittle set out on his journey in the first place! As the story draws to a close, Hugh Lofting ties all the "loose strings" together in a most satisfying way.

Focus

The idea that every person has a mission in life is expressed in this section. One must be true to one's mission and use one's gifts to fulfill it. Dr. Dolittle, helpful as he has been to the Popsipetels, has lost sight of his true calling: to be the world's greatest naturalist. The voice of reason in the story, Polynesia, sees clearly that she must steer Dr. Dolittle back on course, or his talents will be lost to the world. She takes steps to see that he returns to his studies of animals, and, so the story ends, having come full circle.

Two of the story's themes, exploration and love of learning, are developed here, at the conclusion of the book. The description of the view from the ocean-floor is thrilling. It makes the reader want to take an underwater voyage to see these wonderful sights. For Hugh Lofting, the world is a huge adventure, to be savored, experienced, and enjoyed!

4

The Sea-Serpent

For a long time after that Cabinet Meeting of which I have just told you we did not ask the Doctor anything further about going home. Life in Spidermonkey Island went forward, month in and month out, busily and pleasantly. The Winter came and went, and Summer was with us once again before we knew it.

As time passed the Doctor became more and more taken up with the care of his big family; and the hours he could spare for his natural history work grew fewer and fewer. I knew that he often still thought of his house and garden in Puddleby and of his old plans and ambitions; because once in a while we would notice his face grow thoughtful and a little sad, when something reminded him of England or his old life. But he never spoke of these things. And I truly believe he would have spent the remainder of his days on Spidermonkey Island if it hadn't been for an accident—and for Polynesia.

The old parrot had grown very tired of the Indians and she made no secret of it.

"The very idea," she said to me one day as we were walking on the seashore—"the idea of the famous John Dolittle spending his valuable life waiting on these Indians!—Why, it's preposterous!"

All that morning we had been watching the Doctor superintend the building of the new theater in Popsipetel—there was already an opera-house and a concert-hall; and finally she had got so grouchy and annoyed at the sight that I had suggested her taking a walk with me.

"Do you really think," I asked as we sat down on the sands, "that he will never go back to Puddleby again?"

"I don't know," said she. "At one time I felt sure that the thought of the pets he had left behind at the house would take him home soon. But since Miranda brought him word last August that everything was all right there, that hope's gone. For months and months I've been racking my brains to think up a plan. If we could only hit upon something that would turn his thoughts back to natural history again—I mean something big enough to get him really excited—we might manage it. But how?"—she shrugged her shoulders in disgust—"How?—when all he thinks of now is paving streets and teaching children that twice one are two!"

It was a perfect Popsipetel day, bright and hot, blue and yellow. Drowsily I looked out to sea thinking of my mother and father. I wondered if they were getting anxious over my long absence. Beside me

---

Word Bank   **preposterous** (prih PAHS tur us) *adj.*: contrary to nature, reason, or common sense; absurd

old Polynesia went on grumbling away in low steady tones; and her words began to mingle and mix with the gentle lapping of the waves upon the shore. It may have been the even murmur of her voice, helped by the soft and balmy air, that lulled me to sleep. I don't know. Anyhow I presently dreamed that the island had moved again—not floatingly as before, but suddenly, jerkily, as though something enormously powerful had heaved it up from its bed just once and let it down.

How long I slept after that I have no idea. I was awakened by a gentle pecking on the nose.

"Tommy!—Tommy!" (it was Polynesia's voice) "Wake up!—Gosh, what a boy, to sleep through an earthquake and never notice it!—Tommy, listen: here's our chance now. Wake *up*, for goodness' sake!"

"What's the matter?" I asked sitting up with a yawn.

"Sh!—Look!" whispered Polynesia pointing out to sea.

Still only half awake, I stared before me with bleary, sleep-laden eyes. And in the shallow water, not more than thirty yards from shore I saw an enormous pale pink shell. Dome-shaped, it towered up in a graceful rainbow curve to a tremendous height; and round its base the surf broke gently in little waves of white. It could have belonged to the wildest dream.

"What in the world is it?" I asked.

"That," whispered Polynesia, "is what sailors for hundreds of years have called the *Sea-serpent*. I've seen it myself more than once from the decks of ships, at long range, curving in and out of the water. But now that I have seen it close and still, I very strongly suspect that the Sea-serpent of history is no other than the Great Glass Sea Snail that the fidgit told us of. If that isn't the only fish of its kind in the seven seas, call me a carrion-crow—Tommy, we're in luck. Our job is to get the Doctor down here to look at that prize specimen before it moves off to the Deep Hole. If we can, then trust me, we may leave this blessed island yet. You stay here and keep an eye on it while I go after the Doctor. Don't move or speak—don't even breathe heavy: he might get scared—awful timid things, snails. Just watch him; and I'll be back in two shakes."

Stealthily creeping up the sands till she could get behind the cover of some bushes before she took to her wings, Polynesia went off in the direction of the town; while I remained alone upon the shore fascinatedly watching this unbelievable monster wallowing in the shallow sea.

It moved very little. From time to time it lifted its head out of the water showing its enormously long neck and horns. Occasionally it would try and draw itself up, the way a snail does when he goes to move, but almost at once it would sink down again as if exhausted. It seemed

---

Word Bank
jerkily (JURK ih lee) *adv.*: moving along marked by fits and starts
stealthily (STEL thih lee) *adv.*: secretly; in a sneaky manner

to me to act as though it were hurt underneath; but the lower part of it, which was below the level of the water, I could not see.

I was still absorbed in watching the great beast when Polynesia returned with the Doctor. They approached so silently and so cautiously that I neither saw nor heard them coming till I found them crouching beside me on the sand.

One sight of the snail changed the Doctor completely. His eyes just sparkled with delight. I had not seen him so thrilled and happy since the time we caught the Jabizri beetle when we first landed on the island.

"It is he!" he whispered—"the Great Glass Sea Snail himself—not a doubt of it. Polynesia, go down the shore a way and see if you can find any of the porpoises for me. Perhaps they can tell us what the snail is doing here—It's very unusual for him to be in shallow water like this. And Stubbins, you go over to the harbor and bring me a small canoe. But be most careful how you paddle it round into this bay. If the snail should take fright and go out into the deeper water, we may never get a chance to see him again."

"And don't tell any of the Indians," Polynesia added in a whisper as I moved to go. "We must keep this a secret or we'll have a crowd of sightseers round here in five minutes. It's mighty lucky we found the snail in a quiet bay."

Reaching the harbor, I picked out a small light canoe from among the number that were lying there and without telling anyone what I wanted it for, got in and started off to paddle it down the shore.

I was mortally afraid that the snail might have left before I got back. And you can imagine how delighted I was, when I rounded a rocky cape and came in sight of the bay, to find he was still there.

Polynesia, I saw, had got her errand done and returned ahead of me, bringing with her a pair of porpoises. These were already conversing in low tones with John Dolittle. I beached the canoe and went up to listen.

"What I want to know," the Doctor was saying, "is how the snail comes to be here. I was given to understand that he usually stayed in the Deep Hole; and that when he did come to the surface it was always in mid-ocean."

"Oh, didn't you know?—Haven't you heard?" the porpoises replied: "you covered up the Deep Hole when you sank the island. Why yes: you let it down right on top of the mouth of the Hole—sort of put the lid on, as it were. The fishes that were in it at the time have been trying to get out ever since. The Great Snail had the worst luck of all: the island nipped him by the tail just as he was leaving the Hole for a quiet evening stroll. And he was held there for six months trying to wriggle himself free. Finally he had to heave the whole island up at one end to get his tail loose. Didn't you feel a sort of an earthquake shock about an hour ago?"

Word Bank	**mortally** (MORT uh lee) *adv.*: in a deadly or fatal manner; to an extreme degree

"Yes I did," said the Doctor, "it shook down part of the theater I was building."

"Well, that was the snail heaving up the island to get out of the Hole," they said. "All the other fishes saw their chance and escaped when he raised the lid. It was lucky for them he's so big and strong. But the strain of that terrific heave told on him: he sprained a muscle in his tail and it started swelling rather badly. He wanted some quiet place to rest up; and seeing this soft beach handy he crawled in here."

"Dear me!" said the Doctor. "I'm terribly sorry. I suppose I should have given some sort of notice that the island was going to be let down. But, to tell the truth, we didn't know it ourselves; it happened by a kind of an accident. Do you imagine the poor fellow is hurt very badly?"

"We're not sure," said the porpoises; "because none of us can speak his language. But we swam right around him on our way in here, and he did not seem to be really seriously injured."

"Can't any of your people speak shellfish?" the Doctor asked.

"Not a word," said they. "It's a most frightfully difficult language."

"Do you think that you might be able to find me some kind of a fish that could?"

"We don't know," said the porpoises. "We might try."

"I should be extremely grateful to you if you would," said the Doctor. "There are many important questions I want to ask this snail—And besides, I would like to do my best to cure his tail for him. It's the least I can do. After all, it was my fault, indirectly, that he got hurt."

"Well, if you wait here," said the porpoises, "we'll see what can be done."

5

THE SHELLFISH RIDDLE SOLVED AT LAST

So Doctor Dolittle with a crown on his head sat down upon the shore like King Knut, and waited. And for a whole hour the porpoises kept going and coming, bringing up different kinds of sea-beasts from the deep to see if they could help him.

Many and curious were the creatures they produced. It would seem however that there were very few things that spoke shellfish except the shellfish themselves. Still, the porpoises grew a little more hopeful when they discovered a very old sea-urchin (a funny, ball-like, little fellow with long whiskers all over him) who said he could not speak pure shellfish, but he used to understand starfish—enough to get along— when he was young. This was coming nearer, even if it wasn't anything to go crazy about. Leaving the urchin with us, the porpoises went off once more to hunt up a starfish.

They were not long getting one, for they were quite common in those parts. Then, using the sea-urchin as an interpreter, they questioned the starfish. He was a rather stupid sort of creature; but he tried his best to be helpful. And after a little patient examination we found to our delight that he could speak shellfish moderately well.

Feeling quite encouraged, the Doctor and I now got into the canoe; and, with the porpoises, the urchin and the starfish swimming alongside, we paddled very gently out till we were close under the towering shell of the Great Snail.

And then began the most curious conversation I have ever witnessed. First the starfish would ask the snail something; and whatever answer the snail gave, the starfish would tell it to the sea-urchin, the urchin would tell it to the porpoises and the porpoises would tell it to the Doctor.

In this way we obtained considerable information, mostly about the very ancient history of the Animal Kingdom; but we missed a good many of the finer points in the snail's longer speeches on account of the stupidity of the starfish and all this translating from one language to another.

While the snail was speaking, the Doctor and I put our ears against the wall of his shell and found that we could in this way hear the sound of his voice quite plainly. It was, as the fidgit had described, deep and bell-like. But of course we could not understand a single word he said. However the Doctor was by this time terrifically excited about getting near to learning the language he had sought so long. And presently by making the other fishes repeat over and over again short phrases which the snail used, he began to put words together for himself. You see, he was already familiar with one or two fish languages; and that helped him quite a little. After he had practiced for a while like this he leant over the side of the canoe and putting his face below the water, tried speaking to the snail direct.

It was hard and difficult work; and hours went by before he got any results. But presently I could tell by the happy look on his face that little by little he was succeeding.

The sun was low in the West and the cool evening breeze was beginning to rustle softly through the bamboo-groves when the Doctor finally turned from his work and said to me, "Stubbins, I have persuaded the snail to come in onto the dry part of the beach and let me examine his tail. Will you please go back to the town and tell the workmen to stop working on the theater for today? Then go on to the palace and get my medicine-bag. I think I left it under the throne in the Audience Chamber."

"And remember," Polynesia whispered as I turned away, "not a word to a soul. If you get asked questions, keep your mouth shut. Pretend you have a toothache or something."

This time when I got back to the shore—with the medicine-bag—I found the snail high and dry on the beach. Seeing him in his full length like this, it was easy to understand how old-time, superstitious sailors had called him the Sea-serpent. He certainly was a most gigantic, and in his way, a graceful, beautiful creature. John Dolittle was examining a swelling on his tail.

From the bag which I had brought the Doctor took a large bottle of embrocation[3] and began rubbing the sprain. Next he took all the bandages he had in the bag and fastened them end to end. But even like that, they were not long enough to go more than halfway round the enormous tail. The Doctor insisted that he must get the swelling strapped tight somehow. So he sent me off to the palace once more to get all the sheets from the Royal Linen-closet. These Polynesia and I tore into bandages for him. And at last, after terrific exertions, we got the sprain strapped to his satisfaction.

The snail really seemed to be quite pleased with the attention he had received; and he stretched himself in lazy comfort when the Doctor was done. In this position, when the shell on his back was empty, you could look right through it and see the palm-trees on the other side.

"I think one of us had better sit up with him all night," said the Doctor. "We might put Bumpo on that duty; he's been napping all day, I know—in the summerhouse. It's a pretty bad sprain, that; and if the snail shouldn't be able to sleep, he'll be happier with someone with him for company. He'll get all right though—in a few days I should judge. If I wasn't so confoundedly busy I'd sit up with him myself. I wish I could, because I still have a lot of things to talk over with him."

"But Doctor," said Polynesia as we prepared to go back to the town, "you ought to take a holiday. All kings take holidays once in the while— every one of them. King Charles, for instance—of course Charles was before your time—but he!—why, he was *always* holiday-making. Not that he was ever what you would call a model king. But just the same, he was frightfully popular. Everybody liked him—even the golden-carp in the fishpond at Hampton Court. As a king, the only thing I had against him was his inventing those stupid, little, snappy dogs they call King Charles Spaniels. There are lots of stories told about poor Charles; but that, in my opinion, is the worst thing he did. However, all this is beside the point. As I was saying, kings have to take holidays the same as anybody else. And you haven't taken one since you were crowned, have you now?"

"No," said the Doctor, "I suppose that's true."

"Well now I tell you what you do," said she: "as soon as you get back to the palace you publish a royal proclamation that you are going away for a week into the country for your health. And you're going *without any servants*, you understand—just like a plain person. It's called traveling incognito, when kings go off like that. They all do it—It's the only way they can ever have a good time. Then the week you're away you can spend lolling on the beach back there with the snail. How's that?"

---

3. *Embrocation* (EM bro KAY shun) is a thin ointment.

| **Word Bank** | incognito (IN kahg NEE toe) *adj.*: with one's identity concealed |

"I'd like to," said the Doctor. "It sounds most attractive. But there's the new theater to be built; none of our carpenters would know how to get those rafters on without me to show them—And then there are the babies: these native mothers are so frightfully ignorant."

"Oh bother the theater—and the babies too," snapped Polynesia. "The theater can wait a week. And as for babies, they never have anything more than colic. How do you suppose babies got along before you came here, for heaven's sake?—Take a holiday…You need it."

6

THE LAST CABINET MEETING

From the way Polynesia talked, I guessed that this idea of a holiday was part of her plan.

The Doctor made no reply; and we walked on silently towards the town. I could see, nevertheless, that her words had made an impression on him.

After supper he disappeared from the palace without saying where he was going—a thing he had never done before. Of course we all knew where he had gone: back to the beach to sit up with the snail. We were sure of it because he had said nothing to Bumpo about attending to the matter.

As soon as the doors were closed upon the Cabinet Meeting that night, Polynesia addressed the Ministry: "Look here, you fellows," said she: "we've simply got to get the Doctor to take this holiday somehow—unless we're willing to stay in this blessed island for the rest of our lives."

"But what difference," Bumpo asked, "is his taking a holiday going to make?"

Impatiently Polynesia turned upon the Minister of the Interior.

"Don't you see? If he has a clear week to get thoroughly interested in his natural history again—marine stuff, his dream of seeing the floor of the ocean and all that—there may be some chance of his consenting to leave this pesky place. But while he is here on duty as king he never gets a moment to think of anything outside of the business of government."

"Yes, that's true. He's far too consententious," Bumpo agreed.

"And besides," Polynesia went on, "his only hope of ever getting away from here would be to escape secretly. He's got to leave while he is holiday-making, incognito—when no one knows where he is or what he's doing, but us. If he built a ship big enough to cross the sea in, all the Indians would see it, and hear it, being built; and they'd ask what it was for. They would interfere. They'd sooner have anything happen than lose the Doctor. Why, I believe if they thought he had any idea of escaping they would put chains on him."

"Yes, I really think they would," I agreed. "Yet without a ship of some kind I don't see how the Doctor is going to get away, even secretly."

"Well, I'll tell you," said Polynesia. "If we do succeed in making him take this holiday, our next step will be to get the sea-snail to promise to take us all in his shell and carry us to the mouth of Puddleby River. If we can once get the snail willing, the temptation will be too much for John Dolittle and he'll come, I know—especially as he'll be able to take those new plants and drugs of Long Arrow's to the English doctors, as well as see the floor of the ocean on the way."

"How thrilling!" I cried. "Do you mean the snail could take us under the sea all the way back to Puddleby?"

"Certainly," said Polynesia, "a little trip like that is nothing to him. He would crawl along the floor of the ocean and the Doctor could see all the sights. Perfectly simple. Oh, John Dolittle will come all right, if we can only get him to take that holiday—*and* if the snail will consent to give us the ride."

"Golly, I hope he does!" sighed Jip. "I'm sick of these beastly tropics—they make you feel so lazy and good-for-nothing. And there are no rats or anything here—not that a fellow would have the energy to chase 'em even if there were. My, wouldn't I be glad to see old Puddleby and the garden again! And won't Dab-Dab be glad to have us back!"

"By the end of next month," said I, "it will be two whole years since we left England—since we pulled up the anchor at Kingsbridge and bumped our way out into the river."

"And got stuck on the mudbank," added Chee-Chee in a dreamy, far-away voice.

"Do you remember how all the people waved to us from the river-wall?" I asked.

"Yes. And I suppose they've often talked about us in the town since," said Jip—"wondering whether we're dead or alive."

"Cease," said Bumpo, "I feel I am about to weep from sediment."

7

THE DOCTOR'S DECISION

Well, you can guess how glad we were when next morning the Doctor, after his all-night conversation with the snail, told us that he had made up his mind to take the holiday. A proclamation was published right away by the Town Crier that His Majesty was going into the country for a seven-day rest, but that during his absence the palace and the government offices would be kept open as usual.

Polynesia was immensely pleased. She at once set quietly to work making arrangements for our departure—taking good care the while that no one should get an inkling of where we were going, what we were taking with us, the hour of our leaving or which of the palace-gates we would go out by.

Cunning, old schemer that she was, she forgot nothing. And not even we, who were of the Doctor's party, could imagine what reasons she had for some of her preparations. She took me inside and told me that the one thing I must remember to bring with me was *all* of the Doctor's notebooks. Long Arrow, who was the only Indian let into the secret of our destination, said he would like to come with us as far as the beach to see the Great Snail; and him Polynesia told to be sure and bring his collection of plants. Bumpo she ordered to carry the Doctor's high hat—carefully hidden under his coat. She sent off nearly all the footmen who were on night duty to do errands in the town, so that there should be as few servants as possible to see us leave. And midnight, the hour when most of the townspeople would be asleep, she finally chose for our departure.

We had to take a week's food-supply with us for the royal holiday. So, with our other packages, we were heavy laden when on the stroke of twelve we opened the west door of the palace and stepped cautiously and quietly into the moonlit garden.

"Tiptoe incognito," whispered Bumpo as we gently closed the heavy doors behind us.

No one had seen us leave.

At the foot of the stone steps leading from the Peacock Terrace to the Sunken Rose, something made me pause and look back at the magnificent palace which we had built in this strange, far-off land where no white men but ourselves had ever come. Somehow I felt it in my bones that we were leaving it tonight never to return again. And I wondered what other kings and ministers would dwell in its splendid halls when we were gone. The air was hot; and everything was deadly still but for the gentle splashing of the tame flamingoes paddling in the lily-pond. Suddenly the twinkling lantern of a night watchman appeared round the corner of a cypress hedge. Polynesia plucked at my stocking and, in an impatient whisper, bade me hurry before our flight be discovered.

On our arrival at the beach we found the snail already feeling much better and now able to move his tail without pain.

The porpoises (who are by nature inquisitive creatures) were still hanging about in the offing to see if anything of interest was going to

Word Bank	**inquisitive** (in KWIZ ih tiv) *adj.*: inclined to ask questions; curious

happen. Polynesia, the plotter, while the Doctor was occupied with his new patient, signaled to them and drew them aside for a little private chat.

"Now see here, my friends," said she speaking low: "you know how much John Dolittle had done for the animals—given his whole life up to them, one might say. Well, here is your chance to do something for him. Listen: he got made king of this island against his will, see? And now that he has taken the job on, he feels that he can't leave it—thinks the Indians won't be able to get along without him and all that—which is nonsense, as you and I very well know. All right. Then here's the point: if this snail were only willing to take him and us—and a little baggage—not very much, thirty or forty pieces, say—inside his shell and carry us to England, we feel sure that the Doctor would go; because he's just crazy to mess about on the floor of the ocean. What's more this would be his one and only chance of escape from the island. Now it is highly important that the Doctor return to his own country to carry on his proper work which means such a lot to the animals of the world. So what we want you to do is to tell the sea-urchin to tell the starfish to tell the snail to take us in his shell and carry us to Puddleby River. Is that plain?"

"Quite, quite," said the porpoises. "And we will willingly do our very best to persuade him—for it is, as you say, a perfect shame for the great man to be wasting his time here when he is so much needed by the animals."

"And don't let the Doctor know what you're about," said Polynesia as they started to move off. "He might balk if he thought we had any hand in it. Get the snail to offer on his own account to take us. See?"

John Dolittle, unaware of anything save the work he was engaged in, was standing knee-deep in the shallow water, helping the snail try out his mended tail to see if it were well enough to travel on. Bumpo and Long Arrow, with Chee-Chee and Jip, were lolling at the foot of a palm a little way up the beach. Polynesia and I now went and joined them.

Half an hour passed.

What success the porpoises had met with, we did not know, till suddenly the Doctor left the snail's side and came splashing out to us, quite breathless.

"What *do* you think?" he cried, "while I was talking to the snail just now he offered, of his own accord, to take us all back to England inside his shell. He says he has got to go on a voyage of discovery anyway, to hunt up a new home, now that the Deep Hole is closed. Said it wouldn't be much out of his way to drop us at Puddleby River, if we cared to come along—Goodness, what a chance! I'd love to go. To examine the floor of the ocean all the way from Brazil to Europe! No man ever did it before. What a glorious trip!—Oh that I had never allowed myself to be made king! Now I must see the chance of a lifetime slip by."

He turned from us and moved down the sands again to the middle beach, gazing wistfully, longingly out at the snail. There was something peculiarly sad and forlorn about him as he stood there on the lonely, moonlit shore, the crown upon his head, his figure showing sharply black against the glittering sea behind.

Out of the darkness at my elbow Polynesia rose and quietly moved down to his side.

"Now Doctor," said she in a soft persuasive voice as though she were talking to a wayward child, "you know this king business is not your real work in life. These natives will be able to get along without you—not so well as they do with you of course—but they'll manage—the same as they did before you came. Nobody can say you haven't done your duty by them. It was their fault: they made you king. Why not accept the snail's offer; and just drop everything now, and go? The work you'll do, the information you'll carry home, will be of far more value than what you're doing here."

"Good friend," said the Doctor turning to her sadly, "I cannot. They would go back to their old unsanitary ways: bad water, uncooked fish, no drainage, enteric fever and the rest…No. I must think of their health, their welfare. I began life as a people's doctor: I seem to have come back to it in the end. I cannot desert them. Later perhaps something will turn up. But I cannot leave them now."

"That's where you're wrong, Doctor," said she. "Now is when you should go. Nothing will 'turn up.' The longer you stay, the harder it will be to leave—Go now. Go tonight."

"What, steal away without even saying good-bye to them! Why, Polynesia, what a thing to suggest!"

"A fat chance they would give you to say good-bye!" snorted Polynesia growing impatient at last. "I tell you, Doctor, if you go back to that palace tonight, for good-byes or anything else, you will stay there. Now—this moment—is the time for you to go."

The truth of the old parrot's words seemed to be striking home; for the Doctor stood silent a minute, thinking.

"But there are the notebooks," he said presently: "I would have to go back to fetch them."

"I have them here, Doctor," said I, speaking up—"all of them."

Again he pondered.

"And Long Arrow's collection," he said. "I would have to take that also with me."

"It is here, Oh Kindly One," came the Indian's deep voice from the shadow beneath the palm.

"But what about provisions," asked the Doctor—"food for the journey?"

"We have a week's supply with us, for our holiday," said Polynesia—"that's more than we will need."

For a third time the Doctor was silent and thoughtful.

Word Bank pondered (PAHN durd) *v.*: contemplated; thought; reflected on

"And then there's my hat," he said fretfully at last. "That settles it: I'll *have* to go back to the palace. I can't leave without my hat. How could I appear in Puddleby with this crown on my head?"

"Here it is, Doctor," said Bumpo producing the hat, old, battered and beloved, from under his coat.

Polynesia had indeed thought of everything.

Yet even now we could see the Doctor was still trying to think up further excuses.

"Oh Kindly One," said Long Arrow, "why tempt ill fortune? Your way is clear. Your future and your work beckon you back to your foreign home beyond the sea. With you will go also what lore I too have gathered for mankind—to lands where it will be of wider use than it can ever here. I see the glimmerings of dawn in the eastern heaven. Day is at hand. Go before your subjects are abroad. Go before your project is discovered. For truly I believe that if you go not now you will linger the remainder of your days a captive king in Popsipetel."

Great decisions often take no more than a moment in the making. Against the now paling sky I saw the Doctor's figure suddenly stiffen. Slowly he lifted the Sacred Crown from off his head and laid it on the sands.

And when he spoke his voice was choked with tears.

"They will find it here," he murmured, "when they come to search for me. And they will know that I have gone...My children, my poor children!—I wonder will they ever understand why it was I left them...I wonder will they ever understand—and forgive."

He took his old hat from Bumpo; then facing Long Arrow, gripped his outstretched hand in silence.

"You decide aright, oh Kindly One," said the Indian—"though none will miss and mourn you more than Long Arrow, the son of Golden Arrow—Farewell, and may good fortune ever lead you by the hand!"

It was the first and only time I ever saw the Doctor weep. Without a word to any of us, he turned and moved down the beach into the shallow water of the sea.

The snail humped up its back and made an opening between its shoulders and the edge of its shell. The Doctor clambered up and passed within. We followed him, after handing up the baggage. The opening shut tight with a whistling suction noise.

Then turning in the direction of the East, the great creature began moving smoothly forward, down the slope into the deeper waters.

Just as the swirling dark green surf was closing in above our heads, the big morning sun popped his rim up over the edge of the ocean. And through our transparent walls of pearl we saw the watery world about us suddenly light up with that most wondrously colorful of visions, a daybreak beneath the sea.

The rest of the story of our homeward voyage is soon told.

Our new quarters we found very satisfactory. Inside the spacious shell, the snail's wide back was extremely comfortable to sit and lounge on—better than a sofa, when you once got accustomed to the damp and clammy feeling of it. He asked us, shortly after we started, if we wouldn't mind taking off our boots, as the hobnails in them hurt his back as we ran excitedly from one side to another to see the different sights.

The motion was not unpleasant, very smooth and even; in fact, but for the landscape passing outside, you would not know, on the level going, that you were moving at all.

I had always thought for some reason or other that the bottom of the sea was flat. I found that it was just as irregular and changeful as the surface of the dry land. We climbed over great mountain-ranges, with peaks towering above peaks. We threaded our way through dense forests of tall sea-plants. We crossed wide empty stretches of sandy mud, like deserts—so vast that you went on for a whole day with nothing ahead of you but a dim horizon. Sometimes the scene was moss-covered, rolling country, green and restful to the eyes like rich pastures; so that you almost looked to see sheep cropping on these underwater downs. And sometimes the snail would roll us forward inside him like peas, when he suddenly dipped downward to descend into some deep secluded valley with steeply sloping sides.

In these lower levels we often came upon the shadowy shapes of dead ships, wrecked and sunk Heaven only knows how many years ago; and passing them we would speak in hushed whispers like children seeing famous monuments.

Here too, in the deeper, darker waters, monstrous fishes, feeding quietly in caves and hollows would suddenly spring up, alarmed at our approach, and flash away into the gloom with the speed of an arrow. While other bolder ones, all sorts of unearthly shapes and colors, would come right up and peer in at us through the shell.

"I suppose they think we are a sort of sanaquarium,"[4] said Bumpo— "I'd hate to be a fish."

It was a thrilling and ever-changing show. The Doctor wrote or sketched incessantly. Before long we had filled all the blank notebooks we had left. Then we searched our pockets for any odd scraps of paper on which to jot down still more observations. We even went through the used books a second time, writing in between the lines, scribbling all over the covers, back and front.

Our greatest difficulty was getting enough light to see by. In the lower waters it was very dim. On the third day we passed a band of fire-eels, a sort of large, marine glowworm; and the Doctor asked the snail to get them to come with us for a way. This they did, swimming alongside; and their light was very helpful, though not brilliant.

How our giant shellfish found his way across that vast and gloomy world was a great puzzle to us. John Dolittle asked him by what means he navigated—how he knew he was on the right road to Puddleby River.

---

4. *Sanaquarium* (SAN uh KWAIR ee um) is a made-up combination of "sanatorium" and "aquarium," a place to rest and relax in a watery atmosphere.

And what the snail said in reply got the Doctor so excited, that having no paper left, he tore out the lining of his precious hat and covered it with notes.

By night of course it was impossible to see anything; and during the hours of darkness the snail used to swim instead of crawl. When he did so he could travel at a terrific speed, just by waggling that long tail of his. This was the reason why we completed the trip in so short a time—five and a half days.

The air of our chamber, not having a change in the whole voyage, got very close and stuffy; and for the first two days we all had headaches. But after that we got used to it and didn't mind it in the least.

Early in the afternoon of the sixth day, we noticed we were climbing a long gentle slope. As we went upward it grew lighter. Finally we saw that the snail had crawled right out of the water altogether and had now come to a dead stop on a long strip of gray sand.

Behind us we saw the surface of the sea rippled by the wind. On our left was the mouth of a river with the tide running out. While in front, the low flat land stretched away into the mist—which prevented one from seeing very far in any direction. A pair of wild ducks with craning necks and whirring wings passed over us and disappeared like shadows, seaward.

As a landscape, it was a great change from the hot brilliant sunshine of Popsipetel.

With the same whistling suction sound, the snail made the opening for us to crawl out by. As we stepped down upon the marshy land we noticed that a fine, drizzling autumn rain was falling.

"Can this be Merrie England?" asked Bumpo, peering into the fog—"doesn't look like any place in particular. Maybe the snail hasn't brought us right after all."

"Yes," sighed Polynesia, shaking the rain off her feathers, "this is England all right—You can tell it by the beastly climate."

"Oh, but fellows," cried Jip, as he sniffed up the air in great gulps, "it has a *smell*—a good and glorious smell!—Excuse me a minute: I see a water-rat."

"Sh!—Listen!" said Chee-Chee through teeth that chattered with the cold. "There's Puddleby Tower-clock striking four. Why don't we divide up the baggage and get moving. We've got a long way to foot it home across the marshes."

"Let's hope," I put in, "that Dab-Dab has a nice fire burning in the kitchen."

"I'm sure she will," said the Doctor as he picked out his old handbag from among the bundles—"With this wind from the East she'll need it to keep the animals in the house warm. Come on. Let's hug the river-bank so we don't miss our way in the fog. You know, there's something rather attractive in the bad weather of England—when you've got a kitchen-fire to look forward to…Four o'clock! Come along—we'll just be in nice time for tea."

Studying THE SELECTION

Recalling

1. Why had the Great Glass Sea Snail come to the quiet beach on Spidermonkey Island?

2. How did Dr. Dolittle communicate with the Great Glass Sea Snail? What information did the Doctor obtain from the sea snail?

3. How did Dr. Dolittle treat the Great Glass Sea Snail's sprained tail?

4. What did Polynesia suggest to Dr. Dolittle? What motivated her to make this suggestion?

Interpreting

5. What final argument convinced Dr. Dolittle that he should return to England?

6. What geographical and natural wonders did Dr. Dolittle see when they traveled underwater? What did Dr. Dolittle do while they were seeing these sights? How long did this voyage take?

Concluding

7. What was the general feeling of the group when they finally landed near Puddleby? What was Dr. Dolittle's comment on the bad weather of England, and what was he looking forward to?

Examining the Novel

Dr. Dolittle is an example of the good in the human world; Polynesia's character portrays the good in the animal world; the Great Glass Sea Snail represents the good in the natural world. The reader's acquaintance with these characters adds depth and understanding to the theme of this book. Think about these three characters. List at least two special qualities that each of them possess. Explain how these qualities make each of them well-suited to help each other.

Thinking About the Novel

The main storyline of this novel is Dr. Dolittle's journey. The novel has several subplots like the search for Long Arrow, the rebuilding of Popsipetel, and the Great Glass Sea Snail's arrival. Do you think any of the subplots were unnecessary and boring? Would you have liked the author to include more subplots? Write a paragraph explaining your point of view.

Creating and Writing

Dr. Dolittle accomplished what he set out to do. He met with Long Arrow and shared his wisdom. He spoke with the Great Glass Sea Snail and viewed the deepest regions of the ocean. What do you think Dr. Dolittle will do next? What further adventures await him? Who will accompany him on his future adventures? Will Tommy come along or will Polynesia, Chee-Chee, Bumpo, Jip, or Miranda accompany him? Will Long Arrow and the Doctor meet again? Grab your pen and write the first chapter of a new book called *The Voyages of Dr. Dolittle, Part II*. Good luck and good writing!

Enrichment

Organizing a Critique of This Novel

We read a book. We enjoy the characters. We follow the plot. Tension rises and suspense increases. Finally, we come to the climax of the story: How will the plot be resolved? What will the characters do to get out of their predicament? The author answers these questions in the resolution. We are left with the final chapter: Characters return home or move on to new challenges, usually wiser and more mature than they were at the beginning of the book. We, the readers, feel satisfied, because we have grown wiser, too.

In the novel, *The Voyages of Dr. Dolittle*, we start off in Puddleby-on-the-Marsh, expecting a great man to teach us something about the wonders of the world. Tommy Stubbins, a little boy, is our guide. He introduces us to Dr. Dolittle and explains how the animals in the Doctor's home live in a protected environment, where they are cared for with loving-kindness. Through Tommy's reminiscences, we learn of the adventures of Dr. Dolittle, the animals, and other members of the Dolittle group.

Among those Tommy describes are Polynesia, a shrewd parrot with both intelligence and common sense, and Chee-Chee, a monkey who escaped from the jungle. Tommy tells how he became Dr. Dolittle's assistant; how Luke, a hermit, was declared innocent of a violent crime, because Dr. Dolittle translated the testimony of Luke's dog; how Bumpo, an African man, joined the troupe; and how Matthew Mugg, Luke, his wife, and Ben Butcher tried to stow away aboard the Dolittle boat, the *Curlew*.

As the story moves forward, the Dolittle group defends the bulls of Monteverde. Wiff-Waff, a tiny shellfish, fights valiantly for his freedom. Then, we are told of the wreck of the *Curlew*; the Jabizri beetle that leads the troupe to Long Arrow; Dr. Dolittle's rescue of Long Arrow; and his persuading the whales to move Spidermonkey Island to a warmer climate. Dr. Dolittle teaches the islanders about fire, metal, child care, and peace. He is crowned king, and the Hanging Stone falls. Finally, the group returns home through the Great Glass Sea Snail's educational and convenient mode of transportation.

We really learn about a book when we write about it. When journalists do this, it is called a "book review." In order to write a good review, we consider the following points:

1. Think about the main plot and the subplots of the book. Does each episode contribute to the broader theme? Are all of the subplots needed? Do they each add information about the characters or add color to the story?

2. Think of each of the characters that were part of the world of Dr. Dolittle. Does each character play an important part in the story? Is each of the characters realistically portrayed? Does each character have unique and interesting traits? Are the actions of each character consistent with the character's personality? For instance, is Polynesia shrewd and intelligent throughout the story, or does her character change without reason, at some point in the novel?

3. Think of the various settings in the novel, for example, Puddleby-on-the-Marsh and Spidermonkey Island. Are they well-described? Are you able to visualize them?

Write a review of *The Voyages of Dr. Dolittle*. Begin with an incident from the book that you enjoyed reading. Finish your report with your evaluation of the book. What makes the book unique and special? Is it worth reading? Who would enjoy reading this book? Write your review in one or two pages. Then share your work with the rest of your class.

glossary

A

abruptly (uh BRUPT lee) *adv.*: change without preparation or warning; unexpectedly

accumulated (uh KYOOM yoo layt id) *v.*: gathered or piled up little by little; amassed

acrid (AK rid) *adj.*: bitter

adroitly (uh DROYT lee) *adv.*: expertly

ailerons (AY ler onz) *n.*: movable surfaces near the trailing edges of aircraft wings, used for banking

alley (AL lee) *n.*: a path in a park or garden

aloof (uh LOOF) *adj.*: reserved; withdrawn

anchorage (AYNG ker ij) *n.*: something that serves to hold a person or object firmly and securely

animosity (AN ih MAHS ih tee) *n.*: ill will; dislike

annoyance (uh NOY intz) *n.*: a source of irritation

antics (AN tiks) *n.*: attention-drawing, often wildly playful or funny acts or actions

anxious (ANK shuss) *adj.*: *here*, eager; *generally*, extremely worried and uneasy

apprehensive (APP re HEN siv) *adj.*: uneasy; concerned; viewing the future with anxiety or alarm

arid (AIR id) *adj.*: excessively dry

armadillo (ARM uh DILL oh) *n.*: a small insect-eating mammal with an armor-like shell

articulating (AR tick yoo LAYT ing) *v.*: pronouncing clearly

assaulted (us SALT id) *v.*: attacked violently

assented (uh SENT id) *v.*: agreed

attaché (AT uh SHAY) *n.*: a person who is on the staff of an ambassador or diplomat

augmented (awg MEN tid) *v.*: expanded; enlarged

awe (AW) *n.*: overwhelming feeling of admiration, fear, or wonder

B

bank (BAYNK) *n.*: a controlled tilt made by a turning plane

barren (BAHR in) *adj.*: not bearing fruit or seed; desolate

battered (BAT terd) *adj.*: worn or damaged by hard usage or by blows

bellowed (BELL ode) *v.*: roared like a bull; cried out in a deep, blaring voice

benevolent (ben EV uh lint) *adj.*: kind and generous; inclined to doing good

berated (bee RAYT id) *v.*: scolded; expressed sharp, stern disapproval of

biased (BY ust) *adj.*: prejudiced

bigots (BIG its) *n.*: people who treat other people or groups of people with prejudice and intolerance

bland (BLAND) *adj.*: mild; expressionless

breed (BREED) *n.*: lineage; stock; strain; sort; kind; group

briers (BRY ers) *n.*: thorns; thistles

brutal (BROO til) *adj.*: cruel; harsh

bulged (BUHLJD) *v.*: swelled outward

burrow (BURR oh) *v.*: digging by tunneling in the ground

C

camouflaged (KAM ih flahjd) *v.*: concealed by means of disguise

canine (KAY nyn) *n.*: dog

captivity (kap TIV ih tee) *n.*: confinement; imprisonment; the state of being held captive

carp (KARP) *n.*: large freshwater fish

cataract (KAT UH RAKT) *n.*: a condition of the eye in which the lens becomes cloudy and vision is impaired

cauterizing (KAUT er IYZ ing) *v.*: burning, with a hot iron

cautiously (KAW shis lee) *adv.*: behaving carefully because of fear of danger

chaos (KAY ahss) *n.*: a state of utter confusion

chattered (CHAT urd) *v.*: uttered rapidly repeated, unclear sounds

chivalrous (SHIV ihl rihs) *adj.*: gallant; courteous

chortling (CHORT ling) *v.*: uttering a chuckling laugh

clouted (CLOW tid) *v.*: struck forcefully, especially with the hand or fist

clustered (KLUS terd) *v.*: gathered into a group or bunch

clutching (KLUCH ing) *v.*: holding tightly with the hands

cobbler (KAHB lur) *n.*: repairer or maker of shoes

colossal (kuh LAHS il) *adj.*: of very great size; gigantic

commenced (cum MENST) *v.*: began

conjectured (kun JEK cherd) *v.*: guessed

consented (kun SEN tid) *v.*: gave approval; agreed

consternation (KAHN ster NAY shin) *n.*: amazement or dismay that hinders or throws into confusion

contempt (kun TEMPT) *n.*: scorn

contraption (kun TRAP shin) *n.*: device; gadget

converse (kahn VERS) *v.*: exchange thoughts and opinions in speech; talk with

cordial (KOR jil) *adj.*: friendly and warm

corridor (KOR ih DOOR) *n.*: a long passageway or hallway in a building, often with doors opening to rooms off of it

covey (CUV ee) *n.*: a small group of game birds, especially partridges or quail

cowardly (COW urd lee) *adv.*: in a weak manner; not bravely

crevasse (kruh VASS) *n.*: a very deep and wide break or opening

cul-de-sac (KUL DUH SAK) *n.*: a passage or street that is closed at one end

cunningly (KUN ing lee) *adv.*: cleverly or craftily

currency (KUHR uhn see) *n.*: money

D

deflating (dee FLAYT ing) *v.*: releasing air or gas from

delineate (dih LIN ee ayt) *v.*: to describe with accuracy or in detail

demeanor (dih MEEN ur) *n.*: conduct; behavior; facial appearance

derelicts (DEHR uh LIKTS) *n.*: persons abandoned or forgotten

descent (dih SENT) *n.*: the act of proceeding from a higher place to a lower one

desolate (DEZ uh lit) *adj.*: empty; having no inhabitants or visitors

despise (dih SPYZ) *v.*: to regard with contempt

detected (dee TEK tid) *v.*: discovered or determined the existence or presence of

devoid (dih VOYD) *adj.*: empty; not the usual or expected

dignified (DIG nih fyd) *adj.*: noble; showing or expressing dignity; honored or esteemed

diminishing (dih MIN ish ing) *adj.*: decreasing; becoming gradually less

discourse (DISS korce) *v.*: converse; talk

dismal (DIZ mul) *adj.*: gloomy or depressing; particularly bad

dismally (DIZ muh lee) *adv.*: threateningly; miserably

distinguish (diss TIN gwish) *v.*: to see as being separate or different; to recognize a difference in

dunes (DOONZ) *n.*: a sand hill or sand ridge formed by the wind, usually in desert regions or near the ocean

E

efficiency (eh FISH ihn see) *n.*: effectiveness; productivity

egotism (EE go TIZ um) *n.*: an exaggerated sense of self-importance

elation (ee LAY shun) *n.*: delight

emaciated (ih MAY shee AYT id) *adj.*: wasted away physically; malnourished

embers (EM burz) *n.*: glowing fragments from a fire

eminent (EM in ent) *adj.*: outstanding; prominent

emphatic (em FAT ik) *adj.*: definite; accented

endurance (in DUR intz) *n.*: the ability to sustain a prolonged stressful effort or activity

engineered (EN jin eared) *v.*: planned; designed or produced

epic (EH pick) *adj.*: heroic; extending beyond the usual in size or scope

excursions (ex CER zhuns) *n.*: brief, pleasure trips

F

fatigue (fih TEEG) *n.*: weariness or exhaustion from labor, exertion, or stress

filed (FY uhld) *v.*: marched in a line, one after the other

flinched (FLINCHT) *v.*: drew back or away, as if from something dangerous; winced

flushed (FLUSHT) *v.*: drove out of hiding

forage (FOR idj) *v.*: search for provisions or food

formidable (FOR mid ih bul) *adj.*: threatening; causing fear, dread, and apprehension

frenzied (FREN zeed) *adj.*: desperately agitated

freshet (FRESH it) *n.*: a sudden rise in the level of a stream; flooding caused by heavy rain or rapidly melting snow or ice

frowned (FROUND) *v.*: contracted the brow in displeasure; looked displeased

furiously (FYOOR ee us lee) *adv.*: a stormy or turbulent appearance

G

gabardine (GAB er DEEN) *n.*: a durable fabric used in making suits and dresses

gait (GAYT) *n.*: a manner of walking, stepping, or running

galvanized (GAL vuh nyzd) *v.*: plated with zinc to resist rust; motivated

gamboling (GAM buh ling) *v.*: skipping; dancing; frolicking

gash (GASH) *n.*: cut or wound

gasp (GASP) *v.*: to catch one's breath with shock

gazelles (guh ZELZ) *n.*: small, graceful African antelopes

gesturing (JEST cher ing) *v.*: motioning with the body or the limbs to express an idea, a feeling, or an attitude

glacier (GLAY sher) *n.*: a large mass of ice and snow

gleaned (GLEEND) *v.*: gathered information bit by bit

gradually (GRAJ oo lee) *adv.*: slowly

gravely (GRAYV lee) *adv.*: with serious bearing or manner

H

hamper (HAM pur) *v.*: interfere with; restrict the movement of

hastily (HAYS tih lee) *adv.*: rapidly and often with little attention to detail; hurriedly

heaps (HEEPS) *n.*: piles

hillocks (HILL ahks) *n.*: small hills

hitch (HICH) *v.*: tie; to fasten

horizon (hor I zun) *n.*: a line or circle that forms the apparent boundary between earth and sky

hospitable (hahs PIT uh bul) *adj.*: giving a generous and friendly welcome

hurl (HERL) *v.*: throw forcefully; fling

I

imbecile (IM buh sil) *n.*: a simple-minded person

immobility (IM oh BILL ih tee) *n.*: the state of being motionless

impatiently (im PAYSH int lee) *adv.*: restlessly; in a manner that is without patience

impertinent (im PUR tih nint) *adj.*: rude

implored (im PLORD) *v.*: begged; asked for earnestly

impudence (IMP yoo duntz) *n.*: bold and shameless rudeness

incessantly (in SESS int lee) *adv.*: in an unceasing manner; without intermission; continually

incognito (IN kahg NEE toe) *adj.*: with one's identity concealed

incomprehensible (IN com pree HEN sih bul) *adj.*: not possible to understand

indefinitely (in DEF in it lee) *adv.*: having no fixed or specific limit

inevitable (in EV it uh bul) *adj.*: unavoidable

inexorable (in EX ser uh bul) *adj.*: unyielding; relentless

inflammatory rheumatism (in FLAM uh TOR ee ROOM uh TIZ im) *n.*: a disease characterized by painful swelling and stiffness in the joints or muscles

inherent (in HIR int) *adj.*: inborn

innovations (IN oh VAY shunz) *n.*: new ideas, methods, or devices

inoculation (in OCK yoo LAY shun) *n.*: vaccination

inquisitive (in KWIZ ih tiv) *adj.*: inclined to ask questions; curious

interplanetary (IN ter PLAN uh tehr ee) *adj.*: occurring between planets or between planets and the sun

irritable (EAR it uh bul) *adj.*: cranky; upset and impatient

J

jagged (JAG id) *adj.*: raggedly notched; sharply irregular on the surface or borders

jerked (JURKT) *v.*: pushed, pulled, or twisted suddenly

jerkily (JURK ih lee) *adv.*: moving along marked by fits and starts

juncture (JUNK cher) *n.*: point of time

jutting (JUT ting) *v.*: projecting outward

K

keener (KEEN er) *adj.*: quicker; sharper

L

lariat (LAIR ee ut) *n.*: a long rope that is used with a noose to catch livestock

laths (LATHZ) *n.*: thin, narrow strips of wood used to make a backing for plaster or stucco

launching (LAWN ching) *n.*: to send forth with force; to release

limber (LIM ber) *v.*: make flexible; loosen up

limply (LIMP lee) *adv.*: lacking in strength, vigor, or firmness

lingered (LING urd) *v.*: was slow in parting from

loam (LOAM) *n.*: fertile soil consisting of clay, silt, and sand

M

majestic (muh JES tuk) *adj.*: regal; grand

maneuvered (mun OOV erd) *v.*: to manage or move into or out of a position

marina (muh REEN uh) *n.*: landing pier for docking small boats

martial (MAR shuhl) *adj.*: warlike; military

Mayday (MAY DAY) *n.*: an international radiotelephone distress signal used by ships and aircraft

melancholy (MEL in KAHL ee) *n.*: a feeling of sadness

mellow (MEL oh) *adj.*: made gentle by age or experience; pleasant; agreeable; laid-back

metamorphosis (MET uh mor FO siss) *n.*: a profound change

meticulously (meh TICK yoo lus lee) *adv.*: extremely careful in the treatment of details

microbes (MY krohbz) *n.*: very small disease-causing bacteria or organisms

miscellaneous (miss uh LAY nee us) *adj.*: consisting of various things, traits, or members

monitoring (MAHN ih ter ing) *v.*: watching; keeping track of; checking

mortally (MORT uh lee) *adv.*: in a deadly or fatal manner; to an extreme degree

mourning (MORN ing) *n.*: the state of grieving over a death

mutely (MYOOT lee) *adv.*: silently

mystified (MISS tih FYD) *adj.*: puzzled; perplexed

N

naturalist (NAT chur uh list) *n.*: one who studies natural science

nonplused (nahn PLUST) *v.*: puzzled; unsure; at a loss of what to say, think, or do

notion (NO shun) *n.*: idea

nourishing (NUR ish ing) *adj.*: nutritious; promoting growth; sustaining

O

obliging (uh BLY jing) *adj.*: ready to do favors

obscure (ub SKYOOR) *adj.*: remote and secluded; not prominent or famous

obstinate (AHB stin it) *adj.*: stubborn

ominous (AHM in us) *adj.*: threatening; foreshadows evil or disaster

ordeal (oar dee UHL) *n.*: a severe trial or experience

P

pace (PAYS) *n.*: the rate of movement in stepping and walking

pathetic (puh THET ik) *adj.*: extremely pitiful; bringing to mind pity, sympathy, or sorrow

pathos (PATH ose) *n.*: feelings of pity

peak (PEEK) *n.*: the top of a mountain or hill; highest point

pedestal (PED ih stuhl) *n.*: the base of an upright structure

peeved (PEEVD) *adj.*: annoyed

pension (PEN shun) *n.*: a payment received periodically by a retired person

perched (PERCHT) *v.*: to settle or rest on a usually high place

perilous (PEHR ih lus) *adj.*: dangerous

perished (PEHR isht) *v.*: ceased to exist; died

perplexed (pur PLEXT) *adj.*: filled with doubt, uncertainty, or confusion; puzzled

persistently (per SIS tint lee) *adv.*: continuing without change; relentlessly; stubbornly

pestilence (PES tih lintz) *n.*: a natural population suddenly and greatly enlarged; epidemic

philosopher (fil AHSS uh fer) *n.*: one who studies ideas and seeks wisdom

phobia (FO bee yuh) *n.*: an exaggerated, illogical fear

phosphorescent (FAHS fer ESS int) *adj.*: glowing that is caused by the absorption of light

pippins (PIP inz) *n.*: a variety of apple

pliant (PLY uhnt) *adj.*: easily bent; flexible

ploy (PLOY) *n.*: a playful game; a plan or tactic that is different from ordinary contact

poised (POYZD) *v.*: balanced

pondered (PAHN durd) *v.*: contemplated; thought; reflected on

portable (POR tih bul) *adj.*: capable of being carried or moved about

precipice (PREH sih PEECE) *n.*: an abrupt, downward slope

premium (PREE mee um) *n.*: an extra amount charged in addition to the usual price

preposterous (prih PAHS tur us) *adj.*: contrary to nature, reason, or common sense; absurd

prerogative (prih RAHG ih tiv) *n.*: an exclusive or special right, power, or privilege; option

procession (pro SESH un) *n.*: a group of individuals moving along in an orderly way

prodigious (prah DIDJ iss) *adj.*: immense; extraordinary size

profusion (pro FYOO zhun) *n.*: a great supply; superabundance

prolonged (PRO longd) *adj.*: lengthened in extent, scope, or range; extended

prominent (PRAHM in int) *adj.*: widely and popularly known; standing out

prone (PROAN) *adj.*: lying face down

provisions (pruh VIZH unz) *n.*: a stock of needed materials and supplies

prowling (PROW ling) *v.*: to move about in a slow, secret way, intended to escape observation

pruning (PROON ing) *v.*: trimming; cutting back

pummeled (PUM meld) *v.*: thump and pound; to strike repeatedly

punctured (PUNK churd) *v.*: pierced with a pointed instrument or object

purgative (PUR guh tiv) *n.*: a medicine that cleanses the intestines

R

racket (RAK it) *n.*: confused, loud noise

radiant (RAY dee int) *adj.*: shining; marked by an expression of love, confidence, or happiness

rafters (RAFT erz) *n.*: beams of a ceiling

ratified (RAD ih fyd) *v.*: approved; upheld

rattle (RAT il) *v.*: to make or cause a rapid succession of short, sharp noises; clatter

reconnoiter (REE cun oy ter) *v.*: to make an exploratory or preliminary survey, inspection, or examination

reflecting (rih FLECKT ing) *v.*: thinking about calmly or quietly

refraction (ree FRAK shun) *n.*: the bending of a ray of light as it passes from the air through water or glass

refuge (REF yooj) *n.*: a safe haven or sanctuary; a place of shelter

register (REJ ih stur) *n.*: a written record containing regular entries of items, details, events, or names

resented (ree ZEN tid) *v.*: felt annoyed with

resilient (ree ZIL yint) *adj.*: flexible and elastic; able to return to its original shape after being pressed out of shape by some force

revelation (REV ih lay shun) *n.*: the discovery of something previously unknown; something unexpected that creates surprise

roan (ROAN) *n.*: a brownish-red colored horse

rupees (ROO peez) *n.*: Indian currency; at the time of the story, one rupee was worth about ten cents

S

saturated (SACH ur AYT id) *v.*: filled completely

savoring (SAY vohr ing) *v.*: relishing; enjoying

scattered (SKAT erd) *v.*: to separate and go in various directions

scrambled (SKRAM buld) *v.*: hurried; climbed up by moving quickly

seasoned (SEE zuhnd) *adj.*: experienced

sedative (SED uh TIV) *adj.*: tending to calm or soothe

sentimental (SENT im EN tul) *adj.*: having or showing tender feelings

sequestered (sih KWES terd) *v.*: secluded; set off; set apart

shaft (SHAFT) *n.*: beam or beacon of light; a sharply defined beam that shines through an opening

sheen (SHEEN) *n.*: luster; glimmer

shiftless (SHIFT liss) *adj.*: marked by a lack of ambition, energy, or purpose; lazy

simultaneous (sy mul TAY nee us) *adj.*: occurring at the same time

sinews (SIN yooz) *n.*: tendons that connect the muscles with other parts of the body; tendons that have been dressed for use as cords or thread

skeptics (SKEHP ticks) *n.*: doubters

sketch (SKECH) *n.*: a rough drawing

slithered (SLITH erd) *v.*: moved or walked with a sliding motion, as a snake; slid unsteadily down a surface, from side to side

slivers (SLIV urz) *n.*: long, slender pieces cut off of larger pieces; splinters

solace (SAHL uss) *n.*: comfort

solemn (SAHL um) *adj.*: serious; grave

solitary (SAHL ih TAIR ee) *adj.*: being, living, or going alone or without companions

sorghum molasses (SORE gum muh LASS iss) *n.*: sweet syrup made from the juicy stalks of a cereal grass

specimen (SPESS ih mihn) *n.*: a portion of material for use in testing, examination, or study; a sample

spectator (SPEK tay ter) *n.*: one who looks or watches

spore (SPOR) *n.*: a simple one-celled organism produced by plants, fungi, and other microorganisms

staggering (STAG er ing) *v.*: having difficulty standing; reeling from side to side

stalk (STAWK) *v.*: walk in a slow, stiff manner

stalwart (STAHL wert) *adj.*: marked by outstanding strength and vigor of body, mind, or spirit

stealthily (STEL thih lee) *adv.*: secretly; in a sneaky manner

stern (STURN) *adj.*: strict; forbidding

strep (STREP) *n.*: an abbreviation of streptococcus, a disease-causing bacteria

stunned (STUND) *adj.*: made senseless or dizzy as if by a blow; shocked

sturdy (STER dee) *adj.*: firmly built and strong; hardy

sufficient (suh FISH int) *adj.*: enough to meet the needs of a situation

sulking (SUL king) *v.*: being moodily silent

superfluous (suh PER floo uss) *adj.*: being more than is sufficient; unnecessary; needless

superior (suh PEER ee ur) *adj.*: of higher grade or quality; greater in quality, amount

surgeon (SUR jun) *n.*: a medical specialist who performs surgery

surplus (SIR plus) *n.*: superabundance

suspending (sus PEN ding) *v.*: hanging from above

swagger (SWAG er) *n.*: a walk with an air of overbearing self-confidence

swathed (SWAWTHD) *v.*: wrapped

swell (SWELL) *n.*: a long, often huge wave or waves coming one after the other

swindle (SWIN dul) *n.*: an act of deceit; a trick

swooped (SWOOPT) *v.*: plunged suddenly; moved in a sweeping arc

synchronize (SIN kruh NYZ) *v.*: to set to the same time, as with watches; to operate, move, or work at the same rate and exactly together

T

tarpaulin (TAR pihl in) *n.*: a piece of waterproof material used for protecting exposed objects or areas

taut (TAWT) *adj.*: tense; tightly stretched

teeming (TEEM ing) *v.*: swarming, as with people or animals; falling in torrents, as with rain

tenacity (tih NASS ih tee) *n.*: perseverance; persistence in seeking something valued or desired

tiresome (TY ehr sum) *adj.*: possessing a quality that tires, bores, or annoys

topple (TAHP il) *v.*: to fall or tumble from top-heaviness

tragically (TRAJ ick lee) *adv.*: sadly; having a disastrous conclusion; regrettably

translucent (tranz LOO sint) *adj.*: allowing light to pass through

turmoil (TUR moy il) *n.*: an extremely disturbed state or condition

U

uncanny (un CAN ee) *adj.*: mysterious; weird

uncomprehendingly (un CAHM pre HEND ing lee) *adv.*: without understanding

undercurrent (UN der KUHR int) *n.*: a force which is not readily visible

uniform (YOO nih form) *adj.*: having the same form; alike

V

vague (VAYG) *adj.*: unclear

valiant (VAL yint) *adj.*: brave

vanished (VAN isht) *v.*: passed quickly from sight; disappeared

vapor (VAY per) *adj.*: steam

varnished (VAR nisht) *v.*: coated with varnish; gave a glossy appearance to

venturesome (VEN chur SUM) *adj.*: taking a bold, daring risk; adventurous

veranda (ver AND uh) *n.*: an open porch extending along one or more sides of a building, at the ground level

vibrations (vy BRAY shins) *n.*: shaking to and fro movements; a quivering or trembling motion

vicinity (vih SIN ih tee) *n.*: a surrounding area or district; neighborhood

virtually (VER choo uh lee) *adv.*: almost entirely; nearly; for all practical purposes

vitality (vy TAL ih tee) *n.*: full of energy, strength, and vigor

voyages (VOY ij iz) *n.*: act or instances of traveling; journeys by water

vulnerable (VUL nur uh bul) *adj.*: capable of being physically or emotionally wounded

W

wistfully (WHIST fuh lee) *adv.*: showing longings; wishfully

wonderment (WUN der mint) *n.*: amazement

wretched (RECH id) *adj.*: appearing mean or miserable; suffering

writhes (RYTHES) *v.*: twists and turns, as in pain